APPLIED
GROUP-THEORETIC AND
MATRIX METHODS

APPLIED
GROUP-THEORETIC AND
MATRIX METHODS

BY

BRYAN HIGMAN, B.Sc., M.A.

FORMERLY LECTURER IN CHEMISTRY
UNIVERSITY COLLEGE OF THE GOLD COAST

OXFORD
AT THE CLARENDON PRESS
1955

Oxford University Press, Amen House, London E.C.4

GLASGOW NEW YORK TORONTO MELBOURNE WELLINGTON
BOMBAY CALCUTTA MADRAS KARACHI CAPE TOWN IBADAN

Geoffrey Cumberlege, Publisher to the University

PREFACE

THIS book arose out of a course of lectures delivered in the academic year 1950–1 to honours students in Physics and Chemistry in the University College of the Gold Coast. During the preparation of those lectures it became apparent that although the mathematical student has now a liberal choice of introductions to group and matrix theory, and the engineering student to the latter, there is no book which deals with this work in a manner designed primarily for physical scientists and which covers systematically the various fields for its application. I therefore approached the Oxford University Press with the suggestion that these lectures should be amplified in book form, and the present work is the result of their courteous reaction to that suggestion. The amplification has been more than I expected; the design of the original course will be found in Chapters I–VI, VIII, X, and parts of XI, XII, XVI, and XVII. One reason for this is that applied group theory is something of a push-button affair which works very smoothly and simply but has a surprising mass of cross connexions behind the button panel.

The elementary theory of finite groups is a beautiful toy which can hardly fail to fascinate a mathematically-minded person who is introduced to it. It becomes serious only when one studies the representations and the characters—hence the title of Chapter V. It enters on a third phase in continuous groups and the study of the symmetric groups through the full linear groups. But the freshness of this phase is concerned with proofs, especially rigorous proofs, rather than with concepts and results. Anyone completely familiar with the representation theory of finite groups could, if given character tables of the continuous groups and their decomposition formulae, understand what they were about and use them intelligently, though his equipment hardly permitted him to follow their derivation. As many of these proofs are available only in works of somewhat forbidding character, I have thought it right to include them here. It will be seen, therefore, that the book may be read on several different levels.

Originally the word 'elementary' was included in the title, and though honesty rather compels its omission, it would not be without justification of a sort if it were retained. (1) The early stages are taken as gently as possible; no one should be frightened at the start, and Chapter VI has been designed as a synopsis and revision combined. (2) In the later applications I have tried as far as possible to avoid 'clever' proofs, and to ensure that any reader for whom Chapter XIII, for example, seems impossible, should be shown the easiest route to the establishment of the physical results he is interested in. He may be referred to Chapter XIII for mathematical results, and if he is, he must take them on trust, but I hope he will not find it necessary to consult that chapter to fill in details of the argument. If he sees the significance of the formula

$$\frac{\sin(k+\frac{1}{2})\theta}{\sin\frac{1}{2}\theta} = 2\cos k\theta + 2\cos(k-1)\theta + \ldots + 2\cos\theta + 1$$

but can neither prove it nor prove that the left-hand side is a simple character of the rotation group, he is in no worse position than many who use the formula $\frac{4}{3}\pi r^3$ for the volume of a sphere and cannot prove it. The note at the beginning of Chapter XVII provides an explicit representation of this principle in the place where it seems most likely to be needed. (3) I have kept the argument in terms of concrete illustrations wherever possible, in a form suitable for generalization by the reader if he wishes. But the book is about methods, and one detailed example, even in the applications, has usually been preferred to anything in the nature of a survey of all that has been done. This explains my preoccupation with ozone! (4) I have not set examples as such, but have directed the student from time to time to check statements made in the text.

The attitude to mathematical rigour has been that of the scientist. It is desirable, but an understanding of what is going on is more important, especially when the physical application seems to guarantee the fulfilment of the necessary conditions of continuity, convergence, etc. I am sure that the work is not above criticism, but I hope that the mathematician will try to get inside the head of the scientist before criticizing. It is also probable that most of my readers will know more than I do about one or other of the subjects touched upon. I expect many readers will start with Part I and then turn to see how it works out in their particular field. I invite their criticism, but crave their indulgence that they will remember that this is not a book addressed solely to workers in their subject.

In a few chapters, notably those on relativity theory, it has been necessary to condense arguments which are available in the standard texts, to a point at which they must be obscure to anyone who is not already acquainted with the theory. But the purpose of these sections is rather (1) to obtain the advantages of presenting a familiar theory from a new angle, and (2) to establish results required later in the book in the correct notation for the general scheme of the book. In these circumstances greater prolixity would have defeated its purpose. I have, however, again mainly in Chapters XIV and XV, expanded a few points on which, speaking as one who was in the first instance a chemist, I have felt that the standard texts might have been clearer.

I apologize for solving the question of which of the various notations for vectors to adopt by inventing a new one. But there may be some virtue in neutrality as between the conventions of the various applications. For the mathematician who wishes to go straight to the applications I have summarized the notation immediately after the contents pages. (Incidentally, as I have been taken to task for using the word 'invent' here, on the ground that crystallographers have long used the star notation, I had better say (1) that an a, a^* notation is not the same as an a^*, $^*a$ notation, since much of the virtue of the latter rests in the ready apprehension of the two products $^*aa^*$ and $a^{**}a$, and (2) that in fact the notation was designed as an improvement on the one used momentarily by Eddington in *Fundamental Theory*, p. 145, at a time when I had only met the a, $\bar{a}$ notation in crystallography.) More difficult is the question of Schönflies $v.$ Hermann and Mauguin. The real trouble here is that, great though the advantages of the latter are in a limited field, they have no way of writing what the former writes $3C_2$—meaning three (equivalent?) twofold axes—since 32 means something quite different. A satisfactory notation to cover more than mere space-group theory has still to be designed—here I have merely achieved a regrettable hybrid. At several points I have considered that a bird's-eye view of several subjects, such as this book contains, is a useful place in which to undertake a certain amount of reviewing of nomenclature.

As regards choice of subject-matter, the most serious omissions are the applications in nuclear physics, but to have included them would have meant a considerable delay in publication. The space-group theory is said to be a dead subject. It is—so dead that even my crystallographic friends say that they find it hard to dig up when they want it, and they have assured me that its presentation in a modern mathematical technique should be welcome. I hope it is, because a lot of the symmetry concepts required later drop out of it *passim*, and it is irreplaceable as an exercise before passing on to the continuous groups.

Chapter XI is more debatable, but it is a technique which I think ought to be introduced to chemists, and I hope that the example I give —its first application in this direction so far as I know—will be a recommendation. The other debatable inclusion is Chapter XVIII, and I refer the reader to the final paragraph of that chapter for my views here.

My debt to the authors of the works listed in the bibliography must be very obvious to those who know the works. Such a debt is unavoidable, and I hope this acknowledgement may be sufficient; if this book leads readers on to those, the debt may be to some extent repaid. I must also thank Dr. N. B. Slater, for valuable criticism on parts of Chapter XVIII, and those colleagues who have always been ready to discuss points which were not clear to me, particularly Mr. R. Hulme, my only physico-chemical colleague, on the crystallography, and Mr. D. M. Burns and Fr. J. R. Koster, of the physics department of this college, the former of whom has read much of the manuscript, and the latter (with whose name must be coupled that of the students) who sat through the original lectures and gave me the tip when I was being unduly obscure. My thanks are also due to Professor Graham, the head of my department, first for permitting so essentially experimental a course of lectures in the first instance, and also because, while maintaining in other respects an incorrigibly organic chemist's attitude towards a mathematical subject, he never failed to encourage me to get this work into print at the earliest possible moment.

B. H.

43 St. John's Rd., Watford
1954

CONTENTS

SUMMARY OF NOTATION
USED IN THIS BOOK FOR VECTORS

A vector is an ordered set of n numbers. (Vectors in Hilbert space are also used.)

Vectors are denoted by capitals, e.g. P, X, taken as far as possible from the later letters in the alphabet.

The same letter followed by a star or dagger represents the vector as a column matrix.

The same letter preceded by a dagger represents the vector as a row matrix—i.e. $\dagger X$ is the transpose of $X^\dagger$.

The same letter preceded by a star represents the conjugate of the vector as a row matrix—i.e. $*X$ is the associate of X^*.

Except when this notation suffices, $\sim$ denotes a transpose, $^-$ a conjugate, and $\simeq$ or $=$ an associate. When the components of the vector are real I have, for purely typographical reasons, preferred the star to the dagger.

Thus $*XY^*$ is the scalar product of X and Y in an orthonormal unitary space; $\dagger XY^\dagger$ is their scalar product in an orthonormal orthogonal space; $X^{\dagger\dagger}X$ is a symmetrical matrix and $X^{**}X$ is a Hermitian matrix.

Vectors as above are assumed defined in an orthonormal space—one whose metric is the identity. No distinction is therefore required between co- and contravariant forms (except in so far as X^* and $*X$ are 'ket' and 'bra' vectors —see § 14.7). When a non-orthonormal coordinate system is introduced. . . .

The same letter followed by a $^+$ sign represents the contravariant components of the vector in this system, arranged as a column matrix;

The same letter preceded by a $^\circ$ sign represents the covariant components of the vector in this system, arranged as a row matrix;

The same letter preceded by the $^+$ or followed by the $^\circ$ represents either the transpose or the associate of the foregoing according to the context.

A capital letter without an attached sign may refer to a vector conceived apart from any carrier space, but if from the early part of the alphabet or used in conjunction with capital letters carrying any of the above-mentioned signs, it represents an $n \times n$ matrix, or, in some contexts, an $n \times m$ matrix.

PART I
FINITE GROUPS

CHAPTER I

ABSTRACT FINITE GROUPS

IF we consider the operations which are initiated by the orders (1) 'right about turn', (2) 'take the reciprocal of the given number', and (3) 'press the switch button on the table lamp', we see that they have this in common, that a single repetition of the operation reverses its effect and restores the *status quo*, whatever that may have been. In this they contrast with, for example, pressing the button of a stop-watch, or with 'right turn', which require two or three repetitions respectively of the original operation to restore the *status quo*. Just as in arithmetic we abstract from two hats, two books, two tables, etc., to the number 'two', and in algebra from $2+4 = 4+2$, $5+7 = 7+5$, etc., to $a+b = b+a$, so in the Theory of Groups we abstract from these first three examples 'the cyclic group of order 2', that is, a group of two operations, the first of which is to leave things alone, and the other of which just undoes itself if it is repeated, so that the second repeated is equivalent to the first.

The operation 'right turn' if repeated gives rise to the operation 'about turn' and then to 'left turn' before ultimately restoring the original state of affairs. It thus gives rise to a group of four elements in all, known as 'the cyclic group of order 4'. The reason for this name will be explained presently. We notice that 'Left turn! About turn!' is equivalent to 'Right turn!', and we are thus led to the idea that any two elements of the group combine to give a third. It is perhaps not obvious that this is always so, but we shall dispose of this doubt by requiring it to be so when we define a group formally. The process of combination we shall refer to as multiplication, since in all but the rarest cases we shall find that this helps rather than confuses thought. Further, if A and B are elements of the group of operations, the product AB will be the result of doing first B and then A—a somewhat awkward procedure which is, however, dictated by current usage in expressions

B

such as logsin x, in which we first take the sine of x and then the logarithm of that. Logsin x is not the same thing as sinlog x, of course, although 'left turn—about turn' and 'about turn—left turn' produce exactly the same result, and we are thus led to realize that AB and BA may or may not be the same. In these two cases multiplication is described as commutative or non-commutative respectively.

When multiplication is non-commutative, care has to be taken in a number of small matters, one of which we mention here as it will be needed later in this chapter:

THEOREM 1.1.1. *The inverse,* $(ST)^{-1}$, *of a product* ST, *is the product of the inverses of the factors* **taken in reverse order**, *viz.* $T^{-1}S^{-1}$.

The proof is simply that $STT^{-1}S^{-1} = SS^{-1} = I$ (the 'leave it alone' or 'identical' operation), without any questions of order being raised. The inverse of 'logsin' is not 'antilog arcsin' but 'arcsin antilog'.

We might pursue a search for other groups either by abstraction from real groups of operations or by experimenting with combinations of abstract relations. However, we shall soon prove a theorem (Theorem 1.6.5) which will make these two methods practically equivalent, and therefore we start with the former method, as being more readily comprehensible at first.

1.2. The cyclic group of order n

It is obvious that our cyclic group of order 4 consists of rotations about a certain axis through angles of $\frac{1}{2}\pi$, π, $\frac{3}{2}\pi$, and 2π, the last being equivalent to doing nothing. It is clear that this can be generalized, and that for any n, rotations through

$$2\pi/n,\ 4\pi/n,...,\ 2k\pi/n,...,\ 2(n-1)\pi/n,\ 2\pi\ (\equiv 0)$$

form a group. This group is often referred to as the group of proper rotations of a regular n-gon (n-sided polygon), since apart from any labels we may attach to the corners, such a polygon rotated through any of these angles is indistinguishable from its former self. From this we abstract 'the cyclic group of order n', which consists of an element A, its powers A^2, A^3,..., A^{n-1}, and the leave-it-alone, or identical element, which we shall always denote by I (except in a few applications where E is conventionally used), and to which A^n is equal. Whenever a set of elements has this structure it will constitute a *realization* of the cyclic group of order n, which will be referred to briefly as $\mathfrak{c}_n$. Throughout this book gothic small letters will be used to denote complete abstract groups.

1.3. The dihedral groups

In addition to their proper rotations, regular polygons are indistinguishable from their former selves if given an 'improper rotation'. This is a rotation which turns the polygon so that vertices which formerly followed each other clockwise around the perimeter now follow in the same sequence but anticlockwise. A little trial will show that they are rotations about axes *in* the paper and not (as is the main axis)

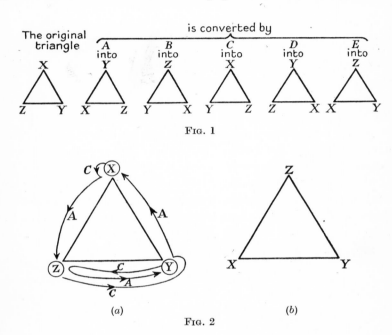

Fig. 1

Fig. 2

perpendicular to it. Alternatively, and this description generalizes better to higher spaces, they are rotations combined with a reflection of each point across some axis. The inclusion of the improper rotations leads to a group twice the size of the cyclic one.

The proper and improper rotations of an equilateral triangle are shown in Fig. 1. With the aid of this figure we can work out the various products of one element with another. Thus AC is the result of applying first the rotation C and then A. These movements are shown in Fig. 2 a, and the result in Fig. 2 b, whence it is clear that $AC = E$. The product CA is similarly worked out in Figs. 3 a and 3 b, from which $CA = D$. The remaining products can be worked out in similar fashion

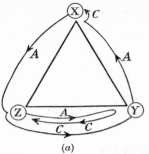
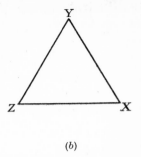

(a)   (b)

Fig. 3

and collected in a multiplication table thus:

$$
\begin{array}{cccccc}
I & A & B & C & D & E \\
A & B & I & E & C & D \\
B & I & A & D & E & C \\
C & D & E & I & A & B \\
D & E & C & B & I & A \\
E & C & D & A & B & I
\end{array}
$$

in which we adopt the convention that the product PQ is found in the row beginning with P and the column headed by Q, and not vice versa. This group is clearly different from c_6 since it is non-commutative. For comparison, here is the multiplication table of c_6:

$$
\begin{array}{cccccc}
I & A & B & C & D & E \\
A & B & C & D & E & I \\
B & C & D & E & I & A \\
C & D & E & I & A & B \\
D & E & I & A & B & C \\
E & I & A & B & C & D
\end{array}
$$

The student should investigate similarly the proper and improper rotations of other polygons. He will find that the rotations of a regular n-gon form a group of $2n$ elements; the proper rotations form a 'subgroup' c_n; any improper rotation with the identity forms a subgroup with structure c_2; the multiplication table can be laid out in four quadrants as with the rotations of the triangle, proper rotations top left and bottom right with a characteristic left and right diagonal distribution of the I's, improper rotations in the other two quadrants; analytically the table can be expressed as follows—if A is a proper rotation and B an improper rotation, then $A^k B = BA^{n-k} =$ another improper rotation. Such a group of $2n$ elements is called the dihedral group $\mathfrak{d}_n$.

1.4. S-groups

Suppose we have an m-gon and an n-gon. Then a possible operation is the simultaneous rotation of the former through $2p\pi/m$ and of the latter through $2q\pi/n$. We may call this element $A_{p,q}$. The total number of such operations is mn. The multiplication table is summarized by

$$A_{p,q} A_{r,s} = A_{r,s} A_{p,q} = A_{p+r,q+s}.$$

We shall find it convenient to call such a group $\mathfrak{s}_{m \times n}$. The student should construct the full table for a few of these groups, and satisfy himself if possible (a proof will be given later) that if m and n are prime to each other, $\mathfrak{s}_{m \times n}$ is simply $\mathfrak{c}_{mn}$, but that in other cases a new group may result. Thus $\mathfrak{s}_{2 \times 2}$ is not $\mathfrak{c}_4$ as may be seen from the multiplication tables:

$\mathfrak{c}_4$	I	A	B	C
	A	B	C	I
	B	C	I	A
	C	I	A	B

$\mathfrak{s}_{2 \times 2}$	I	A	B	C
	A	I	C	B
	B	C	I	A
	C	B	A	I

A realization of this S-group can be obtained in terms of *two* press-button switches, the interpretation being $I =$ leave alone, $A =$ press A, $B =$ press B, $C =$ press both.

1.5. Permutation groups

What appears at first to be a new source of operations from which to discover new abstract groups is the process of permutation, or re-arrangement. It is obvious enough that two permutations performed in succession result in a new permutation, and that as there are $n!$ permutations of n objects, we are on the track of a new series of groups. We define the group $\boldsymbol{\pi}_n$ as the group whose $n!$ members are obtained by abstraction from the $n!$ possible permutations of n objects, and we call it the symmetric group on n objects to distinguish it from other permutation groups which may contain less elements than the symmetric group itself.

It is necessary to have a notation for stating a particular permutation, and the usual one is most easily stated by means of an example. Consider the permutation which converts GHENT KID into KNIGHTED. The G from the first place goes to the fourth, replacing the N which goes to the second, where it replaces the H which goes to the fifth, this in its turn replacing the T which goes to the sixth, and replaces the K which goes to the empty space in the first place. The E and I in the third and seventh places merely change places, and the final D remains unmoved. We denote this permutation by the expression (14256)(37)(8). (It should be added that some books use the same symbols with a 'passive' meaning, viz. (142...) means that after the change the first place is occupied by what was in the fourth, the fourth by what was in the second, and so on. In this convention each symbol represents that permutation which is the inverse of the one which we take it to mean.)

Every permutation is either odd or even. One cycle, such as $(ABCD)$, can be resolved into exchanges—(AB) followed by (AC) (B now being in place A) followed by (AD) (C now being in place A), and so on, so that, remembering the convention of order in multiplication, $(ABCD) = (AD)(AC)(AB)$, etc. It is possible, of course, to effect the permutation by a roundabout route, but it can be shown that the number of exchanges remains odd or even for a given permutation. A permutation consisting of p cycles of a objects each, q of b objects each, and so on, is therefore odd or even according as

$$p(a-1)+q(b-1)+...$$

is odd or even.

Two odd permutations combine to give an even permutation, but two even permutations also give an even permutation. The even permutations taken alone thus form a group; it is known as the alternating group on n objects, $\mathfrak{a}_n$, and is a subgroup of π_n.

That the rotation and dihedral groups are subgroups of the symmetric groups as well, we realize as soon as we see that the rotations, proper and improper, may just as well be expressed as permutations of the labels attached to the vertices of the n-gon. In Fig. 1, for example, instead of regarding the triangle as rotating we can regard the operators as permuting the X, Y, and Z, thus:

$$I = (X)(Y)(Z) \qquad\qquad C = (X)(YZ)$$

$$A = (XZY) \qquad\qquad D = (XY)(Z)$$

$$B = (XYZ) \qquad\qquad E = (XZ)(Y)$$

Since this is all the 3! permutations of X, Y, and Z, we see that π_3 and $\mathfrak{d}_3$ are abstractly the same group; likewise $\mathfrak{c}_3$ and $\mathfrak{a}_3$. Another group of operations with the same structure as the former pair is the group of transformations:

$$I: \quad x \to x \qquad\qquad C: \quad x \to 1/x$$
$$A: \quad x \to 1/(1-x) \qquad D: \quad x \to 1-x$$
$$B: \quad x \to 1-1/x \qquad E: \quad x \to x/(x-1)$$

(Note that, for example, $DAx = D(1/(1-x)) = 1-1/(1-x)$ which by elementary algebra simplifies to $x/(x-1) = Ex$.)

Groups which are the same in the above sense are said to be *simply isomorphic*; any distinction between simply isomorphic abstract groups lies somewhere in their background—either they have been derived by different processes (as we have derived them here), or they may be different subgroups of a larger group.

1.6. Basic definitions and theorems

In the foregoing sections we have introduced a number of ideas by example and by the use of terms whose meanings have been sufficiently obvious for introductory purposes. We must now define some of them more precisely. These definitions should be scrutinized carefully as certain of their details have been passed over without mention earlier.

A *group* is a set of elements and a method of combination of them satisfying the following conditions:

(a) If S and T are members, so also are ST and TS (which may or may not be the same).

(b) $(RS)T = R(ST)$. (This is the associative law, and the necessity for it to be obeyed was one of the points omitted above. When the method of combination is successive performance its validity is guaranteed.)

(c) There is an element I such that $SI = IS = S$, and for each S there is an S^{-1} such that $SS^{-1} = S^{-1}S = I$. (Not all of these statements are independent, but there seems no good reason for us to single out certain ones as definitions and prove the rest here.)

A *subgroup* is any subset of elements from among those of a group which itself satisfies the definition of a group. (It is sometimes convenient to regard the whole group, on the one hand, and the element I, on the other, as extreme cases of the concept of a subgroup. These are distinguished as IMPROPER SUBGROUPS. In using them as such we shall depart from the convention of small gothics for groups, and write them as $\mathfrak{G}$ and $\mathfrak{I}$, respectively.)

The *order* of a group is the number of elements in it. (Thus the orders of $\mathfrak{c}_n$, $\mathfrak{d}_n$, and π_n are n, $2n$, and $n!$ respectively.)

A (*right*- or *left-hand*) *coset* of a subgroup $\mathfrak{g}$ of a group $\mathfrak{G}$ is the set of elements of $\mathfrak{G}$ obtained by multiplying each of the elements of $\mathfrak{g}$ in turn (on the right- or left-hand) by some element of $\mathfrak{G}$ not in $\mathfrak{g}$.

An *invariant subgroup* is one whose right and left cosets are identical.

The last two definitions introduce something new. We can illustrate from π_3. This has four subgroups (a) IAB, (b) IC, (c) ID, (d) IE. Considering the first, it does not contain C and we can therefore form the left coset $CI\ CA\ CB = C\ D\ E$ and the right coset $IC\ AC\ BC = C\ E\ D$. Both cosets contain the same elements, though in a different order, and IAB is thus an invariant subgroup. On the other hand, IC gives rise (using A) to $AI\ AC = A\ E$ and to $IA\ CA = A\ D$. Since these are not the same, the subgroup IC is not invariant.

We conclude this chapter with some theorems which are either obvious or very simply proved, and which will be needed later.

THEOREM 1.6.1. *Each element of a group gives rise to a cyclic subgroup.*

For successive powers of the element must all be members of the group, and it is not difficult to show that no repetition is possible ($A^m \neq A^n$) unless some lower power is the identity ($A^k = I$, where $k = |m-n|$). By the order of an element we mean the order of this cyclic subgroup— it is the power to which the element must be raised to produce the identity.

THEOREM 1.6.2. *Given a group $\mathfrak{G}$ and a subgroup $\mathfrak{g}$ the cosets of $\mathfrak{g}$ are unique.*

For if A is not in $\mathfrak{g}$, then $A\mathfrak{g}$ is a coset. If B is in $\mathfrak{g}$, let $AB = C$, then using the fact that $\mathfrak{g}$ is a group, we can show that $C\mathfrak{g}$ is the coset $A\mathfrak{g}$ reproduced with the elements in a different order. Thus nothing new is obtained by multiplying $\mathfrak{g}$ by any member of $A\mathfrak{g}$, but if the group $\mathfrak{G}$ is not exhausted by $\mathfrak{g}$ and $A\mathfrak{g}$, we can go on to the formation of a new coset $D\mathfrak{g}$ with the aid of any element D which is neither in $\mathfrak{g}$ nor $A\mathfrak{g}$. This procedure can be carried out equally with right-multiplication. We write these results formally

$$\mathfrak{G} = \mathfrak{g} + A\mathfrak{g} + D\mathfrak{g} + \ldots$$
$$= \mathfrak{g} + \mathfrak{g}A + \mathfrak{g}E + \ldots.$$

(We can only be sure of using the same sequence A, D,... in right-multiplication if the subgroup $\mathfrak{g}$ is invariant.)

THEOREM 1.6.3. *The order of a subgroup is a factor of the order of the group.*

THEOREM 1.6.4. *The order of every element in a group is a factor of the order of the group.*

These follow from the above argument, the second by taking as $\mathfrak{g}$ the cyclic subgroup generated by the element.

The converse process to abstraction is realization, and we may ask whether any abstract group we may devise can be realized in a group of real operations. That the answer is 'yes', is shown by the next theorem, which asserts that there is always a permutation realization.

THEOREM 1.6.5. *Every abstract group has a faithful realization in the operations obtained by associating with the element S the permutation $\mathfrak{G} \to \mathfrak{G}S$.*

The permutation in question is the permutation which converts the first column of the multiplication table into the column headed by S. To prove the theorem we notice that the result of following this operation by the permutation T will be to produce the permutation TS, since in these two operations an element A goes to AS^{-1} and $AS^{-1}T^{-1} = A(TS)^{-1}$, successively. (The reason for the word 'faithful' is explained in § 5.2. Note that the *row* permutation $S\mathfrak{G}$ realizes S^{-1}, not S.) From this result we can go one step further:

THEOREM 1.6.6. *Every group of order n is a subgroup of π_n.*

CHAPTER II

MATRIX ALGEBRA

IN this chapter we again discuss operations but with a different approach, in a sense more specifically geometrical, though in view of the possibilities of graphical representation of non-geometrical relations, this restricted approach is not as narrow as at first sight it might appear.

In elementary usage a vector is a directed magnitude and may often be conveniently represented by its two or three components (or coordinates—for most purposes these words are equivalent, but see § 3.10) along perpendicular directions in the plane or in space. Here we shall reverse this procedure, and regard a vector as an ordered set of two, or three, or n numbers, its components, and we shall regard the directed magnitude concept as merely a method of assisting the imagination when necessary. (It also assists the vocabulary, especially through the concept of the 'carrier space'.) By the phrase 'ordered set' we merely mean that the vectors $(2, 3)$ and $(3, 2)$, for example, are different. In many of the elementary applications a vector is regarded also as having a point of application, but for the moment, at least, this idea will not be necessary, and usually it will be most convenient to regard all vectors as lines starting from the origin of coordinates. From the start we shall, for the sake of generality, work in n dimensions, a vector, that is, being an ordered n-tuple of numbers, but for the sake of simplicity our illustrative examples will mostly be worked in two dimensions.

2.2. Linear operators

Any geometrical figure may, of course, be specified by the coordinates of its significant points; that is, it may be regarded as composed of the vectors joining these points to the origin. We may classify possible operations on such a figure as follows:

A. Operations which move the origin of coordinates.
B. Operations which leave the origin unchanged.
    B1. Operations which leave size and shape unchanged.
    B2. Operations which leave shape but not size unchanged.
    B3. Distortions.

For the present we confine ourselves to classes B1, B2, and certain of B3. We omit A so that our transformed vectors, like the original ones, shall all start from the origin. Operations of type B1 are rotations: a vector $X = (X_1 X_2)$ in two dimensions becomes $X' = (X'_1 X'_2)$ where

$$X'_1 = \quad\cos\theta\, X_1 + \sin\theta\, X_2$$
$$X'_2 = -\sin\theta\, X_1 + \cos\theta\, X_2.$$

Operations of type B2, not involving a rotation, transform a vector thus

$$X''_1 = aX_1$$
$$X''_2 = \qquad\quad aX_2.$$

And a particularly simple form of distortion, which changes a square into a rectangle or a circle into an ellipse, would be unequal magnification along the two axes:

$$X'''_1 = aX_1$$
$$X'''_2 = \qquad\quad bX_2.$$

All these operations are particular cases of a general type of operation in which the vector X (which we may now think of in n dimensions) is transformed into the vector X' by the rule

$$X'_1 = a_{11} X_1 + a_{12} X_2 + a_{13} X_3 + \ldots$$
$$X'_2 = a_{21} X_1 + a_{22} X_2 + a_{23} X_3 + \ldots, \text{ etc.,}$$

which we may write more concisely in the form

$$X' = AX,$$

$$A = \begin{bmatrix} a_{11} & a_{12} & a_{13} & \cdot & \cdot \\ a_{21} & a_{22} & a_{23} & \cdot & \cdot \\ \cdot & \cdot & \cdot & \cdot & \cdot & \cdot \end{bmatrix}.$$

The array of n^2 numbers which we have expressed concisely as A is called a matrix, or, in its present context, a matrix operator. Alternatively, for a reason shortly to be explained, it may be called a linear operator.

Two vectors are added by adding their corresponding components:

$$(X_1 \ X_2 \ldots) + (Y_1 \ Y_2 \ldots) = (X_1 + Y_1 \ X_2 + Y_2 \ldots)$$

this being the natural generalization of the 'parallelogram law' of elementary theory, as well as the simplest and most natural addition process analytically. It follows that an integral scalar multiple of a vector is obtained by multiplying each component:

$$k(X_1 \ X_2 \ X_3 \ldots) = (kX_1 \ kX_2 \ kX_3 \ldots)$$

or by operating on it by the operator

$$K = \begin{bmatrix} k & 0 & 0 & . & . \\ 0 & k & 0 & . & . \\ 0 & 0 & k & . & . \\ . & . & . & . & . \end{bmatrix}$$

This relation can be extended by the usual methods to allow k any value in the complex field. When $k = 1$, K becomes the leave-it-alone operator, I. But it is sometimes necessary to distinguish the identity operators in different spaces, in which case we may write this operator (in n dimensions) as $I^{(n)}$.

It is now a straightforward matter to prove that

$$A(X+Y) = AX + AY$$
$$A(kX) = k(AX)$$

and it is in virtue of these relations that the matrix operators are referred to as linear.

2.3. Combinations of operators

We now proceed to natural definitions of sums, multiples, and products of linear operators or matrices. We define

$$A + B = C \qquad \text{if} \qquad CX = AX + BX$$
$$kA = D \qquad \text{if} \qquad DX = kAX$$
$$AB = E \qquad \text{if} \qquad EX = A(BX).$$

These definitions are equivalent to the relations

$$(A+B)X = AX + BX$$
$$(kA)X = k(AX)$$
$$(AB)X = A(BX)$$

and guarantee that we may use operators in a fashion similar to our manipulation of ordinary algebraic quantities except that multiplication is non-commutative. They lead to the following explicit expressions:

$$A+B = \begin{bmatrix} A_{11}+B_{11} & A_{12}+B_{12} & . & . \\ A_{21}+B_{21} & A_{22}+B_{22} & . & . \\ . & . & . & . \end{bmatrix}$$

$$AB = \begin{bmatrix} A_{11}B_{11}+A_{12}B_{21}+\ldots & A_{11}B_{12}+A_{12}B_{22}+\ldots & . & . \\ A_{21}B_{11}+A_{22}B_{21}+\ldots & A_{21}B_{12}+A_{22}B_{22}+\ldots & . & . \\ . & . & . & . & . & . & . \end{bmatrix}$$

Writing out this equation in detail,

$$aX_1 + bY_1 + \ldots = 0$$

$$aX_2 + bY_2 + \ldots = 0, \text{ etc.,}$$

we see that we have n equations for the m unknowns a, b,... when the vectors themselves are given. Consequently, if $m > n$, the vectors cannot be independent. If $m = n$, they are independent provided that the determinant

$$\begin{vmatrix} X_1 & Y_1 & . & . \\ X_2 & Y_2 & . & . \\ & . & . & . \end{vmatrix} \neq 0.$$

If $m < n$, the vectors will again be independent provided that no one of the determinants obtained by choosing any m rows from the matrix

$$\begin{bmatrix} X_1 & Y_1 & . & . \\ X_2 & Y_2 & . & . \\ & . & . & . \end{bmatrix} \tag{2.6.2}$$

is zero.

Geometrically, of course, the interpretation of these results is as follows. The equation (2.6.1) means that any one of the vectors can be expressed in terms of the rest, e.g.

$$X = -\frac{b}{a} Y - \ldots .$$

Now two vectors determine a plane through the origin, provided that they are not in the same direction, in which case one is a multiple of the other. Three vectors determine a three-dimensional space (or *3-space*) provided they do not all lie in a plane; if they do, any one may be expressed in terms of the other two. But if the vectors are only two-dimensional they *must* lie in a plane. And similarly for larger values of m and n.

Consequently we define the *rank, r*, of the $m \times n$ matrix (2.6.2), formed from m n-dimensional vectors, as the largest order of any non-vanishing determinant which can be made by selecting from its rows and columns. If this is less than m the vectors are not independent, but it is possible to choose r of them which are independent, and to express the rest in terms of these r.

It is important to distinguish linear from algebraic dependence. Thus, for example, it is a result that will be important later that the vectors $(1, 1,\ldots, 1)$, $(x_1, x_2,\ldots, x_p)$, $(x_1^2, x_2^2,\ldots, x_p^2),\ldots, (x_1^{p-1}, x_2^{p-1},\ldots, x_p^{p-1})$ are linearly independent, provided that $x_1,..., x_p$ are all different. For no equation

$$c_0+c_1x+c_2x^2+...+c_{p-1}x^{p-1} = 0 \qquad (2.6.3)$$

can be satisfied by more than $p-1$ values of x. Similarly the vectors $(x_1,...,x_p),..., (x_1^p,...,x_p^p)$ are linearly independent provided $x_1,..., x_p$ are all different and none equal to zero. The determinant

$$\begin{vmatrix} x_1^{p-1} & x_2^{p-1} & . & . & x_p^{p-1} \\ . & . & . & . & . \\ x_1^2 & x_2^2 & . & . & x_p^2 \\ x_1 & x_2 & . & . & x_p \\ 1 & 1 & . & . & 1 \end{vmatrix} \qquad (2.6.4)$$

is zero if any two x_r and x_s are equal, and therefore contains (x_r-x_s) as a factor. But the product

$$(x_1-x_2)(x_1-x_3)...(x_2-x_3)...(x_{p-1}-x_p)$$

is of degree $p-1$ in each variable and gives the term $x_1^{p-1}x_2^{p-2}...$ with coefficient $+1$ and is therefore equal to the determinant.

2.7. Eigenvectors and eigenvalues

An *eigenvector* of a matrix operator is a vector which is not altered in direction by the operator, though in general it will be altered in magnitude. It is therefore a solution of the equation

$$AX = kX$$

or

$$(A-k)X = 0.$$

In the latter expression k must be given the operator form already discussed in § 2.2. Written in full, this equation is

$$\left.\begin{aligned} (A_{11}-k)X_1+ \quad A_{12}X_2 \quad +...+ \quad A_{1n}X_n &= 0 \\ A_{21}X_1 \quad +(A_{22}-k)X_2+...+ \quad A_{2n}X_n &= 0 \\ . \quad . \quad . \quad . \quad . \quad . \quad . \quad . \quad . \\ A_{n1}X_1 \quad + \quad A_{n2}X_2 \quad +...+(A_{nn}-k)X_n &= 0 \end{aligned}\right\}, \qquad (2.7.1)$$

which is a system of n homogeneous equations for the n unknowns $X_1,..., X_n$. By the general theory of such systems of equations, a solution is only possible if the determinant formed from the coefficients is zero, that is, if

$$\begin{vmatrix} A_{11}-k & A_{12} & . & . & A_{1n} \\ A_{21} & A_{22}-k & . & . & A_{2n} \\ . & . & . & . & . \\ A_{n1} & A_{n2} & . & . & A_{nn}-k \end{vmatrix} = k^n+\alpha_1 k^{n-1}+\alpha_2 k^{n-2}+...+\alpha_n = 0$$

$$(2.7.2)$$

where $\qquad \alpha_n = $ determinant of $A \times (-1)^n$,

$\qquad\qquad \alpha_1 = $ sum of diagonal elements (or *trace*) of A,

and the other coefficients are more complex symmetric functions of the elements of the matrix A. This equation has n roots, so that there are n possible values of k. If these are all distinct, then by substituting these into equation (2.7.1) in turn, we get n sets of values for the ratios $X_1 : X_2 : \ldots : X_n$; in other words we have found n eigenvectors of A each with its *eigenvalue*, as the corresponding value of k is called.

As this process is so important, we illustrate with a numerical example; the student should make up others for himself. To find the eigenvectors of the matrix $\begin{bmatrix} 4 & -1 \\ 2 & 1 \end{bmatrix}$, we solve the equation

$$\begin{vmatrix} 4-k & -1 \\ 2 & 1-k \end{vmatrix} = 0, \quad \text{i.e.} \quad 0 = (4-k)(1-k)+2 = k^2 - 5k + 6.$$

The roots are $+2$ and $+3$, and we find the vectors in turn. First,

$$\begin{aligned} 4x - y &= 2x \\ 2x + y &= 2y \end{aligned} \quad \text{give} \quad \frac{x}{y} = \frac{1}{2}$$

and then

$$\begin{aligned} 4x - y &= 3x \\ 2x + y &= 3y \end{aligned} \quad \text{give} \quad \frac{x}{y} = 1$$

so that the vector $(1, 2)$ is an eigenvector with eigenvalue 2, and the vector $(1, 1)$ is an eigenvector with eigenvalue 3.

Eigenvectors belonging to different eigenvalues must be independent. For suppose that $X, Y, \ldots$ were eigenvectors of A belonging to different eigenvalues $\xi, \eta, \ldots$, and that they satisfied equation (2.6.1). Operating on this equation repeatedly with A we should have

$$aX + bY + \ldots = 0$$
$$a\xi X + b\eta Y + \ldots = 0$$
$$a\xi^2 X + b\eta^2 Y + \ldots = 0, \text{ etc.,}$$

and we should have enough equations to establish that $X, Y, \ldots$ were all identically zero.

The position is more tricky when the equation (2.7.2) has some of its roots equal. By making a suitable infinitesimal change in the matrix we can cause these roots to separate infinitesimally, and they will then certainly belong to independent eigenvectors. It is possible that if we now let the infinitesimal tend to zero the eigenvectors may become dependent. This behaviour is definitely pathological, however, and is discussed briefly in § 7.2. In all the cases most important to us (as we shall see in the next chapter) the eigenvectors belonging to different eigenvalues are not merely independent but perpendicular, and thus in general p equal roots will correspond to p independent vectors. But if two of these are U and V, then

$$A(uU+vV) = AuU+AvV = k_1 uU+k_1 vV$$
$$= k_1(uU+vV)$$

so that all vectors in the p-dimensional subspace spanned by these independent vectors are also eigenvectors. In the case of a p times repeated root of equation (2.7.2), therefore, we may speak of a p-dimensional eigen-subspace.

Equation (2.7.2) is known as the *characteristic equation* of the operator A. We may summarize these results in the following theorem:

THEOREM 2.7.3. *A linear operator in an n-space has in general n independent eigenvectors, with eigenvalues which are the roots of an equation formed from its elements, known as its characteristic equation.*

The following is also obvious.

THEOREM 2.7.4. *A **diagonal** operator (i.e. one whose only non-zero elements are those, A_{rr}, on the main diagonal) has its eigenvectors along the coordinate axes, that along the rth axis having the eigenvalue A_{rr}.*

It should be noted that an eigenvector is defined in direction only, and, as we shall see in more detail in the next chapter, even if required to be of unit length, it is still arbitrary to within a factor of modulus unity. If, for example, $(1, i)$ is an eigenvector of a given matrix, then so are $(2, 2i)$ and $(i, -1)$.

2.8. Functions of a diagonal operator

By direct application of the detailed multiplication rule for matrices, we find that the nth power of a diagonal matrix is obtained by raising each diagonal element to the nth power. And by applying in addition the rule for addition of matrices, we see that any polynomial function of a diagonal matrix is a diagonal matrix whose elements are that polynomial function of the original diagonal elements. Symbolically,

$$f\left(\begin{bmatrix} a & 0 & 0 & . & . \\ 0 & b & 0 & . & . \\ 0 & 0 & c & . & . \\ . & . & . & . & . \end{bmatrix}\right) = \begin{bmatrix} f(a) & 0 & 0 & . & . \\ 0 & f(b) & 0 & . & . \\ 0 & 0 & f(c) & . & . \\ . & . & . & . & . \end{bmatrix}.$$

And since most of the non-polynomial functions can be expressed as power series, we could, provided these series converge for every eigenvalue, remove even the restriction to polynomial functions in this way. The process is unnecessary with matrices of finite order, however, since a suitable equivalent polynomial of degree not higher than the order of the matrix can always be found which will agree with the desired function for each eigenvalue as argument, and its behaviour for other values does not matter.

It follows that if A is diagonal, with eigenvalues $k_1,...$, the eigenvalues of $f(A)$ are $f(k_1),...$, with the same eigenvectors. Actually this conclusion is not confined to diagonal matrices, and the student should be able to show directly that if

$$AX = kX,$$

then
$$f(A)X = f(k)X,$$

where f is any polynomial function.

Both methods may be applied to functions of two or more operators, and if the student will carry them through he will arrive at the important conclusion:

THEOREM 2.8.1. *The eigenvalues of a function of several operators are that function of the eigenvalues of the said operators, provided that the operators have the same eigenvectors.*

We shall show in § 4.8 that the proviso may be given the alternative form that the operators must be commuting ones, and develop the whole question somewhat further there.

CHAPTER III

COMPLEX AND HYPERCOMPLEX NUMBERS

In most mathematical expositions of the theory of matrix operators in vector space it is assumed early on that the components of a vector may be not only real, but also complex numbers. For clarity's sake we have said nothing of this so far. But at this stage we are forced to choose between admitting complex numbers into our scheme or abandoning the whole symmetry of the subject which arises from the fact that the characteristic equation of an operator has exactly n roots. In fact, if we apply the procedure for calculating eigenvalues and eigenvectors to the simple rotation operator in the plane

$$\begin{bmatrix} \cos\theta & \sin\theta \\ -\sin\theta & \cos\theta \end{bmatrix}$$

we find that this operator has eigenvalues $e^{i\theta}$ and $e^{-i\theta}$ belonging to the eigenvectors $(1, i)$ and $(1, -i)$ respectively. But if we admit complex values for the components of our vectors, we shall have to examine certain elementary ideas more closely.

3.2. Scalar products and vector duals

The length of a real vector is given by the Pythagorean expression $(X_1^2 + X_2^2 + ...)^{\frac{1}{2}}$. A second expression of importance in elementary theory is the scalar product of two vectors X and Y given by $X_1 Y_1 + X_2 Y_2 + ...$. For example, when an object which is acted on by a force F moves a distance S, the work done is the scalar product of F and S. By analogy with the scalar product we shall occasionally find it convenient to describe the square of the length of a vector as its 'scalar square'.

Now even in dealing with a single complex number $a + bi$ we frequently write it as $r(\cos\theta + i\sin\theta)$ or as $re^{i\theta}$ and refer to r as its absolute magnitude. It is very desirable that the absolute magnitude of any vector shall be a real quantity, and we attain this if we make its scalar square the sum of the squares of the absolute magnitudes of its components—or, what comes to the same thing, to $\bar{X}_1 X_1 + \bar{X}_2 X_2 + ...$, where the bar over a quantity denotes its complex conjugate. To do this does no violence to more elementary ideas, since if X is real this is exactly the same as the original definition. The same convention can be applied to a scalar product, with the slight complication that the multiplication is now non-commutative to the extent that XY and YX are conjugate quantities— $\sum\limits_r \overline{X}_r Y_r$ and $\sum\limits_r X_r \overline{Y}_r$ respectively. The choice is, in the abstract, a free one; the difference between the unmodified and the modified Pythagorean expression may be regarded as one of the geometry of the space in which the vectors occur, since it shows itself in a difference in the form of the 'metric' (§§ 14.2 and 14.7) and the carrier spaces are described as 'orthogonal' and 'unitary' respectively. But we may say at once that in practically all applications either the components of a vector are real or it is the unitary system that we shall want.

Whichever system we adopt, however, the rules of matrix multiplication demand that in the formation of a scalar product (or square) the first factor shall be a one-*row* and the second a one-*column* matrix. Given a vector X we are thus forced to consider two different forms of it. We shall therefore denote the vector X in an orthogonal space by $X^\dagger$ when in column form and by $^\dagger X$ when in row form. In a unitary space we shall denote by X^* the vector in column form, and by $^*X$ the row-vector whose components are the conjugates of those of X^*. Thus

$$X^\dagger = \begin{bmatrix} X_1 \\ X_2 \\ \cdot \end{bmatrix} \qquad {}^\dagger X = [X_1 \, X_2 \ldots] \qquad {}^\dagger X X^\dagger = X_1^2 + X_2^2 + \ldots$$

$$X^* = \begin{bmatrix} X_1 \\ X_2 \\ \cdot \end{bmatrix} \qquad {}^*X = [\overline{X}_1 \, \overline{X}_2 \ldots] \qquad {}^*X X^* = \overline{X}_1 X_1 + \overline{X}_2 X_2 + \ldots.$$

When all the components are real, the distinction between stars and daggers disappears, and we shall normally use stars. Since most proofs carry over with merely formal changes from one system to the other, we shall make no more reference to the dagger system except where its behaviour is sufficiently different to warrant comment.

The student should be warned that this notation is the author's own, but that there is no very general agreement in the literature, especially as between one application and another. In these circumstances there would seem even to be some advantage in a new notation which can be related in turn to the notations which are more or less standard in each application. There is also superficial disagreement as to whether X^* and $^*X$ are to be called vectors in different spaces, different kinds of vectors, or different forms of the same vector. This question is examined in more detail in § 14.7. For the present it will do no harm if we regard the choice as one of imaginative preference, the root of the trouble being that the calculus has outstripped our powers of geometrical intuition. Dirac, in his *Quantum Mechanics*, uses the symbols $\langle X|$ and $|X\rangle$ for $*X$ and $X*$, calling them 'bra' and 'ket' vectors, the scalar product being a complete bra(c)ket (in earlier editions they were ψ_X and ϕ_X, respectively), but the use of these terms is subject to a restriction explained in § 14.7. Other writers, including Weyl, have a tendency to use corresponding Greek and Roman capitals for the two forms. Whatever the notation, the two forms are known as *duals* of each other. (The relation between them is clearly a reciprocal one.)

3.3. Related matrices: (i) the adjoint and reciprocal

The reciprocal, A^{-1}, of a matrix A is best approached by way of the *adjoint* matrix $\hat{A}$. This is defined by

$$\hat{A}_{st} = \text{co-factor of } A_{ts} \text{ in } |A|$$

(the co-factor being $(-1)^{s+t}$ times the minor, which is the determinant $|A|$ with the column and row containing A_{ts} omitted). With this definition, the product $A\hat{A} = B$ is given by

$$B_{rt} = \sum_s A_{rs} \hat{A}_{st}$$

$$= \sum_s A_{rs} \cdot \text{co-factor of } A_{ts}$$

$$= \begin{cases} |A| & \text{if } r = t \\ 0 & \text{if } r \neq t \end{cases}$$

since $r = t$ corresponds to a well-known rule for evaluating the determinant, and $r \neq t$ evaluates a determinant similar to A but with the tth column the same as the rth. Thus

$$A\hat{A} = |A|I,$$

and similarly
$$\hat{A}A = |A|I,$$

whence
$$A^{-1} = \frac{\hat{A}}{|A|},$$

provided $|A| \neq 0$. If $|A| = 0$, the adjoint still exists, but not the reciprocal.

3.4. Related matrices: (ii) the transpose and associate

The *transpose*, $\tilde{A}$, of a matrix A, is the matrix obtained by inter-changing rows and columns. Thus $\tilde{A}_{rs} = A_{sr}$. The *conjugate*, $\bar{A}$, is the matrix obtained by taking the conjugate of each element, $\bar{A}_{rs} = \overline{(A_{rs})}$. The *associate*, properly $\tilde{\bar{A}}$, but more conveniently $\bar{\tilde{A}}$, is the matrix obtained by performing both operations, so that $\bar{\tilde{A}}_{rs} = \bar{A}_{sr}$.

The products $A*X$ and $X*A$ have no meaning, according to the rules for matrix multiplication, and attempts to give them one by supplementing X with zeros to make a square matrix out of it lead to no useful result. On the other hand, $*XA$ and $^\dagger XA$ are new vectors, $*Y$ and $^\dagger Z$. The latter is the dual of $Z^\dagger = \tilde{A}X^\dagger$, and is the dual of AX only if $\tilde{A} = A$. A matrix which is equal to its transpose, i.e. for which $A_{pq} = A_{qp}$, is called a *symmetric* matrix. Similarly, $*Y$ is the dual of $Y* = \bar{A}X*$, and is the dual of $AX*$ only if $A = \bar{A}$; such a matrix, equal to its associate, or $A_{pq} = \bar{A}_{qp}$, is called a *Hermitian* matrix.

If all components are real, the transpose and the associate are the same thing, and symmetric matrices are Hermitian, and vice versa.

3.5. Related matrices: (iii) orthogonal and unitary matrices

If the transpose of a matrix equals its reciprocal, the matrix is described as *orthogonal*. In this case

$$^\dagger(AX)(AX)^\dagger = (^\dagger X\tilde{A})(AX^\dagger)$$

$$= {}^\dagger XA^{-1}AX^\dagger$$

$$= {}^\dagger XX^\dagger.$$

If, on the other hand, the associate of a matrix equals its reciprocal, the matrix is described as *unitary*. In this case, by a similar argument,

$$*(AX)(AX)* = *XX*.$$

According to their conventions, therefore, these two types of operator preserve the length of a vector. If all the components of the operator are real, orthogonal and unitary mean the same thing, and the operator is a *rotation*. (Some of the earlier writers on quantum mechanics have used orthogonal as including unitary.) In two dimensions, the most general real orthogonal matrix has the familiar form

$$\begin{bmatrix} \cos\theta & \sin\theta \\ -\sin\theta & \cos\theta \end{bmatrix}$$

and the general unitary matrix is

$$e^{i\alpha}\begin{bmatrix} \cos\theta\,.\,e^{i\phi} & \sin\theta\,.\,e^{i\psi} \\ -\sin\theta\,.\,e^{-i\psi} & \cos\theta\,.\,e^{-i\phi} \end{bmatrix},$$

though frequently no generality is lost by putting $\alpha = 0$. In these expressions α, θ, ϕ, and ψ are assumed real. In general, in n dimensions, a unitary matrix obeys

$$\sum_s \bar{A}_{ps} A_{qs} = \sum_s \bar{A}_{sp} A_{sq} = \delta_{pq}$$

(i.e. is 1 or 0 according as p is or is not equal to q) and its determinant is unity. Similar relations hold for orthogonal matrices.

Unitary matrices form a group, so do the orthogonal matrices, and so do the rotation matrices common to both. The proof, which consists in showing (a) that the product of two matrices of the given type is another of the same type, and (b) that every matrix of the type has a reciprocal of the same type, is left to the student.

3.6. Eigenvalues of special matrices

The eigenvalues of a matrix are the roots of its characteristic equation, and thus a property of the matrix itself, but eigenvectors are properly only right- or left-eigenvectors. A vector is only an eigenvector both on the right and the left of an operator if the operator is symmetric or Hermitian, and then only with the appropriate convention of the 'same' vector in each case.

If X is an eigenvector on either side of A, then the expression *XAX*/*XX* obviously gives the eigenvalue associated with it. Hermitian matrices have real eigenvalues, and, in the orthogonal coordinates we are using, conversely. We prove the former by expanding *XAX* as $\sum_i \sum_k A_{ik} \bar{X}_i X_k$ and noting that in this expansion the terms occur in conjugate pairs. The converse is established with the aid of the results of § 4.6, where non-orthogonal coordinates are discussed.

Two vectors are described as orthogonal or perpendicular if their scalar product is zero. (But see § 4.6 for a warning here.) A right-eigenvector of a matrix and a left-eigenvector of the same matrix belonging to different eigenvalues are orthogonal. For

$$*YAX* = (*YA)X* = k_y *YX*,$$

but also

$$*YAX* = *Y(AX*) = k_x *YX*,$$

and if $k_y \neq k_x$, these can only be equal if *YX* = 0. In the case of symmetric or Hermitian matrices we can drop the prefixes right- and left-, and we have the very important result:

THEOREM 3.6.1. *Eigenvectors belonging to different eigenvalues of symmetrical or Hermitian matrices are orthogonal (in their respective ways).*

The eigenvalues of A^{-1} are, of course, the reciprocals of those of A, though the student may notice that our polynomial proof hardly covers this case, and may prefer to establish this result directly. The eigenvalues of a square or higher even root are subject to an ambiguity of sign, of course, and corresponding ambiguities occur in all fractional powers. The ambiguities in respect of different eigenvalues are independent, so that there are p^n pth roots of an $n \times n$ matrix. If nothing is said to the contrary, $A^{\frac{1}{2}}$ is understood to mean that matrix whose eigenvalues are the positive square roots of those of A for the same eigenvectors.

The eigenvalues of a unitary matrix are of modulus unity. This is obvious when the matrix is in diagonal form. When it is not, the results of the next chapter must be used. A similar argument shows that if H is Hermitian, $\exp iH$ is unitary; this formulation is sometimes useful.

3.7. Reciprocal vectors

This is perhaps the moment to point out that a matrix can be regarded in several ways. We have already regarded it (1) as a single quantity, the operator, and (2) as an ordered n-tuple of column vectors (§ 2.5). In the light of the preceding sections we now see that the matrix may equally well be regarded (3) as an ordered n-tuple (m-tuple if not square) of row vectors. In this case, in the product AB, the operator B operates on the right of each row of A independently. This concept will be very valuable in Chapter XI. On the other hand, in § 7.6 and elsewhere, we shall find it convenient to regard the n^2 components of a square matrix as (4) the n^2 components of a vector in a space of n^2 dimensions.

Concepts (2) and (3) together give rise to the idea of reciprocal vectors, invaluable whenever oblique coordinates are used. Any n independent vectors $A_1, \ldots, A_n$ may be used to set up a coordinate system in n-space. These vectors may be regarded as the successive columns of a matrix A. (In this case we are regarding them as $A_1^*, \ldots, A_n^*$. We shall also accept the implications of this notation by assuming in all further work that the addition of a suffix n and a star to the symbol of an operator implies the selection of the nth row or column (according to the position of the star) for consideration as a vector.) Since the vectors $A_1,..., A_n$ are independent, $|A| \neq 0$. Then the successive rows $*B_1,..., *B_n$ of the matrix $B = A^{-1}$ are called the reciprocal vectors of the set $A_1^*,..., A_n^*$. We note that

$$*B_r A_r^* = \sum_s B_{rs} A_{sr}$$
$$= \sum_s \text{co-factor of } A_{sr} . A_{sr} / |A|$$
$$= 1,$$

and similarly $\qquad\qquad *B_s A_r^* = 0.$

Thus B_r is perpendicular to all the A_s $(s \neq r)$, and is of such a length that its scalar product with A_r is 1. (Its length is therefore $1/\cos\theta$ of the reciprocal of the length of A_r, θ being the obliqueness of A_r to the space defined by the other A's.) The result $*B_r A_s^* = \delta_{rs}$ is sometimes made the definition of the reciprocal set. It is important to realize that we do not define the reciprocal of a vector in isolation, but only of a vector in a complete coordinate system—though actually only the directions of the other vectors need be known. (Note: the student who is already acquainted with crystallography should observe that the crystallographers' a and a^* are, in our notation, a^* and $*a$, or sometimes P_a^* and $*R_a$.)

From the argument preceding Theorem 3.6.1, we see that the right- and left-eigenvectors of *any* matrix, if adjusted to suitable lengths, are reciprocal sets.

3.8. Dyads and dyadics

Stars and daggers are, we have seen, a warning not to multiply on that side of a vector. But the rules of matrix multiplication give a meaning to $X**Y$ and $Y^{\dagger\dagger}Y$—bringing *two* stars or daggers together. The result is a new operator,

$$X**Y = \begin{bmatrix} X_1\overline{Y}_1 & X_1\overline{Y}_2 & X_1\overline{Y}_3 & . & . \\ X_2\overline{Y}_1 & X_2\overline{Y}_2 & X_2\overline{Y}_3 & . & . \\ . & . & . & . & . \end{bmatrix}$$

This operator is called a dyad (or sometimes the outer product of the two vectors, in which case the scalar product is called the inner product) and it has some remarkable properties. Thus

$$(X**Y)^2 = (X**Y)(X**Y)$$
$$= X*(*YX*)*Y$$
$$= K.X**Y,$$

since $K = *YX*$ is a scalar, and therefore commutes with the other factors. Therefore if $A = K^{-\frac{1}{2}}X**Y$, $A^2 = A$. Such a matrix is called idempotent, since repeated application of it yields no further change after the original effect of its first application. In certain contexts it may be thought of as a type-selection operator, or sieve. Geometrically it is a projection operator, as we shall see in a moment. The eigenvectors and eigenvalues of $X**Y$ are easily found, for

$$(X**Y)X* = X*(*YX*) = KX*,$$

and

$$*Y(X**Y) = (*YX*)*Y = K*Y,$$

while

$$(X**Y)Z* = X*(*YZ*) = 0,$$

if $Z*$ is *any* vector orthogonal to $*Y$, and

$$*Z(X**Y) = (*ZX*)*Y = 0,$$

if $*Z$ is any vector orthogonal to $X*$. Thus the eigenvalues of $X**Y$ are $*YX*$ (once) and 0 ($n-1$ times), and applied to an arbitrary vector, $X**Y$ multiplies the component parallel to $X*$ (or to $*Y$) by $*YX*$, and annuls all components perpendicular to this. When $*YX* = 1$, this is projection.

Let P_1*, P_2*,..., be any set of n independent vectors, and $*R_1$, $*R_2$,..., be the reciprocal set. Then

$$P_1**R_1 + P_2**R_2 + ... = I.$$

Before proving this, let us first try to see its significance intuitively by considering a special case. If P_1*, P_2*,... are the basic vectors I_1*, I_2*,..., of the coordinate system, viz. $(1,0,...)$, $(0,1,0,...)$, $(0,0,1,...)$,..., then $R_s = P_s$. The single term P_s**R_s has every element zero except $(P_s**R_s)_{ss}$ which is unity. It operates on the right of an arbitrary matrix A to select its sth column (or on the left to select its sth row), whence it is clear that the left-hand side of the above identity selects all the columns in turn and puts them together again! To prove the relation in general, consider the operator

$$B = P_1**R_1A + P_2**R_2A + ...$$

If $*V$ is any one of the vectors $*R_s$, we see that $*VB = *VA$. But if two operators produce the same result on every one of n independent vectors, they must be identical, $B = A$. Since A is arbitrary, the theorem is proved.

We thus see that

$$A = P_1^*(^*R_1 A) + P_2^*(^*R_2 A) + \dots$$
$$= (AP_1^*)^*R_1 + (AP_2^*)^*R_2 + \dots$$

are two ways of expanding the arbitrary operator A as a sum of not more than n dyads. Willard Gibbs developed the whole theory of operators from this basis, calling a sum of dyads a dyadic, and a few writers still follow this usage.

An expansion of particular importance is the one in which the vectors P^* and $^*R$ are the eigenvectors of A. In this case we have

$$A = \alpha_1 P_1^* \, {}^*R_1 + \alpha_2 P_2^* \, {}^*R_2 + \dots + \alpha_n P_n^* \, {}^*R_n,$$

where $\alpha_1, \alpha_2, \dots$ are the eigenvalues of A. We shall be mainly concerned with A Hermitian (or symmetric and real), and when this is so, if p_s is a vector of unit length in the direction of P_s, then $r_s = p_s$, and we can write the expansion of A in the alternative forms

$$A = \alpha_1 p_1^* \, {}^*p_1 + \alpha_2 p_2^* \, {}^*p_2 + \dots$$
$$= (\alpha_1^{\frac{1}{2}} p_1)^* \, {}^*(p_1 \alpha_1^{\frac{1}{2}}) + (\alpha_2^{\frac{1}{2}} p_2)^* \, {}^*(p_2 \alpha_2^{\frac{1}{2}}) + \dots.$$

We shall call this the 'proper expansion' of A. It contains as many terms, say f, as there are non-zero eigenvalues of A.

Combining the vectors $^*p_s$ into a matrix p of f rows and n columns the vectors p_s^* combine into the transposed matrix $\tilde{p}$ of f columns and n rows, and we can write, in a self-explanatory notation which the student should expand for himself

$$p\tilde{p} = \begin{bmatrix} ^*p_1 \\ ^*p_2 \\ \cdot \\ ^*p_f \end{bmatrix} \begin{bmatrix} p_1^* & p_2^* & \cdot & \cdot & p_f^* \end{bmatrix} = \begin{bmatrix} ^*p_1 p_1^* & ^*p_1 p_2^* & \cdot & \cdot & ^*p_1 p_f^* \\ ^*p_2 p_1^* & ^*p_2 p_2^* & \cdot & \cdot & ^*p_2 p_f^* \\ \cdot & \cdot & \cdot & \cdot & \cdot \\ ^*p_f p_1^* & ^*p_f p_2^* & \cdot & \cdot & ^*p_f p_f^* \end{bmatrix}$$

$$= \text{the } f \times f \text{ identical matrix, } I^{(f)}.$$

Also

$$\tilde{p}p = \begin{bmatrix} p_1^* & p_2^* & \cdot & \cdot & p_f^* \end{bmatrix} \begin{bmatrix} ^*p_1 \\ ^*p_2 \\ \cdot \\ ^*p_f \end{bmatrix} = p_1^* \, {}^*p_1 + p_2^* \, {}^*p_2 + \dots + p_f^* \, {}^*p_f,$$

which is the identical matrix in the subspace spanned by the p_s and the zero matrix outside it—i.e. it projects on to this subspace. Finally, if we define the matrix

$$\alpha = \begin{bmatrix} \alpha_1 & 0 & 0 & . & . & 0 \\ 0 & \alpha_2 & 0 & . & . & 0 \\ 0 & 0 & \alpha_3 & . & . & 0 \\ & & . & . & . & . \\ 0 & 0 & 0 & . & . & \alpha_f \end{bmatrix}$$

we can verify that $\alpha p = [(\alpha_1 p_1)^* \ (\alpha_2 p_2)^* \ ... \ (\alpha_f p_f)^*]$ and thence that

$$A = \tilde{p}\alpha p = (\tilde{p}\alpha^{\frac{1}{2}})(\alpha^{\frac{1}{2}}p),$$

the latter form being sometimes more convenient than the former.

We could, of course, supplement the vectors p_s by $n-f$ other vectors orthogonal to them and to one another, giving us a complete set in the n-space. Of this extended matrix, p_+, we can write $p_+ \tilde{p}_+ = \tilde{p}_+ p_+ = I$ without reservations or restrictions to subspaces, thereby showing, incidentally, that a square matrix made up of normalized orthogonal vectors is orthogonal. We can also define, if we like, the matrix

$$p\alpha^{-1}p = \sum_{\phi=1}^{f} \alpha_\phi^{-1} p_\phi^* \, ^*p_\phi$$

as the pseudo-reciprocal of the singular matrix A, since *within the f-space* it is the reciprocal of A. But while these devices may help an investigation, neither finds much place in formal presentation.

To return to Gibbs. He uses one concept familiar in the elementary vector of three dimensions, but confusing in a more general treatment, namely, the vector product. We have

$$X^* {}^*Y - Y^* {}^*X = \begin{bmatrix} 0 & x_1 y_2 - x_2 y_1 & . & . \\ x_2 y_1 - x_1 y_2 & 0 & . & . \\ . & . & . & . \end{bmatrix},$$

an antisymmetric matrix with $n(n-1)/2$ essentially distinct components. In three dimensions this is conveniently written as

$$\begin{bmatrix} 0 & Z_3 & -Z_2 \\ -Z_3 & 0 & Z_1 \\ Z_2 & -Z_1 & 0 \end{bmatrix}$$

where Z_1, Z_2, and Z_3 are the components of a vector Z known as the vector product $X \times Y$ of X and Y. That this can be done is an accident due to the fact that $n = 3$ is a solution of $^nC_2 = n$, and as far as possible we shall, for this reason, avoid using the concept of a vector product.

It is easily verified that

$$\begin{bmatrix} * & Y_1 & Z_1 \\ * & Y_2 & Z_2 \\ * & Y_3 & Z_3 \end{bmatrix} \begin{bmatrix} 1 \\ 0 \\ 0 \end{bmatrix},$$

which is independent of the quantities in the first column of the first factor, is an alternative formulation, and that this can be generalized into a 'vector product' of $n-1$ vectors in n dimensions (which is permissible since $^nC_{n-1} = n$ identically), but further analysis along these lines must be postponed until Chapter XIV.

The vector product in conjunction with dyadic theory is used, notably by Zachariasen, in discussing rotations in three dimensions. Introducing the notation

$$\left(\sum_n X_n^* {}^*Y_n \right) \times Z = \sum_n X_n^* {}^*(Y_n \times Z)$$

as the definition of the vector product of a dyadic with a vector, he represents a rotation through θ about an axis defined by the unit vector U, as

$$R = \pm\{U^* {}^*U + (I - U^* {}^*U)\cos\theta + I \times U \sin\theta\}.$$

If U is directed along the X-axis, this equation, transcribed term by term into the notation we have become accustomed to, becomes

$$\begin{bmatrix} 1 & 0 & 0 \\ 0 & \cos\theta & \sin\theta \\ 0 & -\sin\theta & \cos\theta \end{bmatrix} = \begin{bmatrix} 1 & 0 & 0 \\ 0 & 0 & 0 \\ 0 & 0 & 0 \end{bmatrix} + \begin{bmatrix} 0 & 0 & 0 \\ 0 & \cos\theta & 0 \\ 0 & 0 & \cos\theta \end{bmatrix} + \begin{bmatrix} 0 & 0 & 0 \\ 0 & 0 & \sin\theta \\ 0 & -\sin\theta & 0 \end{bmatrix}.$$

This decomposition is along the lines of the quaternion notation discussed in the next section, and it has the advantage of avoiding imaginaries, but it is not in the form of a dyadic, for the second and third terms both have *two* non-zero eigenvalues. The decomposition of this matrix into dyads is

$$\begin{bmatrix} 1 & 0 & 0 \\ 0 & \cos\theta & \sin\theta \\ 0 & -\sin\theta & \cos\theta \end{bmatrix} = \begin{bmatrix} 1 & 0 & 0 \\ 0 & 0 & 0 \\ 0 & 0 & 0 \end{bmatrix} + \tfrac{1}{2}e^{i\theta}\begin{bmatrix} 0 & 0 & 0 \\ 0 & 1 & -i \\ 0 & i & 1 \end{bmatrix} + \tfrac{1}{2}e^{-i\theta}\begin{bmatrix} 0 & 0 & 0 \\ 0 & 1 & i \\ 0 & -i & 1 \end{bmatrix}.$$

3.9. Linear algebras

Since an $n \times n$ matrix has n^2 components, it may be expressed as a linear combination of n^2 more or less arbitrarily chosen matrices. Further, the products of these basic matrices among themselves may be expressed as similar linear combinations. For $n = 2$, for example, two possibilities are (i) the 'simple' system,

$$\begin{bmatrix} a & b \\ c & d \end{bmatrix} = a\begin{bmatrix} 1 & 0 \\ 0 & 0 \end{bmatrix} + b\begin{bmatrix} 0 & 1 \\ 0 & 0 \end{bmatrix} + c\begin{bmatrix} 0 & 0 \\ 1 & 0 \end{bmatrix} + d\begin{bmatrix} 0 & 0 \\ 0 & 1 \end{bmatrix}$$

$$= a\epsilon_{11} + b\epsilon_{12} + c\epsilon_{21} + d\epsilon_{22},$$

and (ii) the 'quaternion' system,

$$\begin{bmatrix} a & b \\ c & d \end{bmatrix} = \frac{d+a}{2}\begin{bmatrix} 1 & 0 \\ 0 & 1 \end{bmatrix} + \frac{i(d-a)}{2}\begin{bmatrix} i & 0 \\ 0 & -i \end{bmatrix} + \frac{c+b}{2}\begin{bmatrix} 0 & 1 \\ -1 & 0 \end{bmatrix} + \frac{i(c-b)}{2}\begin{bmatrix} 0 & i \\ i & 0 \end{bmatrix}$$

$$= \tfrac{1}{2}(d+a)\eta_1 + \tfrac{1}{2}i(d-a)\eta_2 + \tfrac{1}{2}(c+b)\eta_3 + \tfrac{1}{2}i(c-b)\eta_4,$$

with the multiplication tables

	ϵ_{11}	ϵ_{12}	ϵ_{21}	ϵ_{22}
ϵ_{11}	ϵ_{11}	ϵ_{12}	0	0
ϵ_{12}	0	0	ϵ_{11}	ϵ_{12}
ϵ_{21}	ϵ_{21}	ϵ_{22}	0	0
ϵ_{22}	0	0	ϵ_{21}	ϵ_{22}

and

	η_1	η_2	η_3	η_4
η_1	η_1	η_2	η_3	η_4
η_2	η_2	$-\eta_1$	η_4	$-\eta_3$
η_3	η_3	$-\eta_4$	$-\eta_1$	η_2
η_4	η_4	η_3	$-\eta_2$	$-\eta_1$

and, of course, other systems could easily be designed. Quantities expressed in this form were formerly known as hypercomplex numbers, but this term is no longer in use except for its aesthetic value in chapter headings. Their study is the study of linear algebras, which are defined thus:

A *linear algebra* of order n is a set of entities $\xi_1,..., \xi_n$ such that every product $\xi_r\xi_s$ is a sum of multiples of the $\xi_1,..., \xi_n$.

A matrix algebra needs no further explanation. A *simple* matrix algebra is one which corresponds (for matrices of arbitrary size) to the 'simple' system described above for the 2×2 matrices. A *group* or *Frobenius* algebra is one in which the $\xi_1,..., \xi_n$ follow the same multiplication table as the elements $X_1,..., X_n$ of a group. It can be shown (the proof is based on Burnside's theorem, § 7.6) that a group algebra can be expressed as the sum of simple matrix algebras.

For many purposes the concept of linear algebras enables us to avoid the clumsy matrix notation without the extreme abstraction of writing single letters for matrices. For example, if we put the 2×2 matrix A in terms of the $\eta_1,..., \eta_4$, then

$$A = p_1\eta_1 + p_2\eta_2 + p_3\eta_3 + p_4\eta_4,$$
$$A^2 = (p_1^2 - p_2^2 - p_3^2 - p_4^2)\eta_1 + 2p_1p_2\eta_2 + 2p_1p_3\eta_3 + 2p_1p_4\eta_4$$

by straightforward squaring (taking care, if necessary, of the order of the factors) and then use of the multiplication table. Hence A is idempotent if $p_1 = p_1^2 - p_2^2 - p_3^2 - p_4^2$, etc., whence we can find $\frac{1}{2}(\eta_1 \pm \eta_s)$ ($s = 2, 3,$ or 4), as examples of idempotent operators. A neat analysis by these methods is Dirac's theory of electron spin, in § 16.5.

3.10. Nomenclature

To conclude this chapter we summarize for convenience certain points of nomenclature, which, because they developed when different parts of the subject were still separate studies, are apt to be confusing.

An element of a group is any one of the operations within it. It is equivalent to a basis element of the corresponding algebra (ξ_1, ξ_2, etc.). An element of an algebra is any linear combination of its basis elements (e.g. $a\xi_1 + b\xi_2$), and, as an ordered set of numbers, the coefficients thereof are effectively a vector. (Multiplication of vectors as such, however, is not defined; though multiplication of elements of an algebra is.) The elements of a matrix are the same as its components.

The order of a group or subgroup is the number of elements in it. The order of an element in a group is the order of the cyclic subgroup it generates (the power of it which is needed to generate the identity). The order of an algebra is the number of basis elements in it. The order of a matrix is the number of its components ($m \times n$), and in the case of a square matrix it is the square of its *degree*. The *rank* of a matrix is the degree of the largest square matrix which can be made from it by deleting rows and columns whose determinant is not zero. If a group is of order n, the regular matrix representation of it (permuting the axes) is of degree n and order n^2.

The element I of a group such that $IX = XI = X$ for every X is called the *identical element*. But the element m of an algebra such that $mx = xm = x$ for every x is called the *modulus* of the algebra.

A *coordinate system* and a *basis* are the alternative names for the same thing when ordered sets of numbers are alternatively considered as vectors or as elements of an algebra. Generally speaking, *components* and *coordinates* of a vector are the same thing, though it may be convenient, given a vector $(a, b, c, ...)$, to distinguish its coordinates, a, b, c, ..., from its components $(a, 0, 0, ...)$, $(0, b, 0, ...)$, $(0, 0, c, ...)$... .

For later reference:

A *tensor of order 2 in n dimensions* is a matrix of order $n \times n$; a realization of a group is any set of operations which, with successive performance as the method of combination, has the same multiplication table as the group; a realization in terms of matrices is a *representation*; the representation formed by the method of § 2.4 is known as the *regular representation*.

CHAPTER IV

CONJUGATION AND EQUIVALENCE

WE begin this chapter by inquiring into the effects of changing our coordinate system. Possible changes are rotations of the axes, changes of scale, and so on. And so far as a vector is concerned, the answer appears as soon as we see that in its effects on the components of a vector, a rotation of the coordinate axes clockwise is equivalent to a rotation of the vector anticlockwise; an increase in scale is equivalent to a reduction in magnitude of the vector; and in general, a change in coordinate system has the same effect as a linear operator on the components of a vector.

This conclusion can be reached by a somewhat more analytical process. If K, M, N,... are n independent vectors, any vector X can be expressed as a linear combination of them; that is, they can be used as a basis for a new coordinate system. Let

$$X = kK + mM + nN + ...,$$

which, in the old coordinate system, amounts to

$$X_1 = kK_1 + mM_1 + nN_1 + ...,$$
$$X_2 = kK_2 + mM_2 + nN_2 + ..., \quad \text{etc.,}$$

then these are n simultaneous equations to determine the coefficients k, m, n,... which are the coordinates of X in the new system. The standard solution of these equations is

$$k = \frac{\text{determinant } \sum \pm X_a M_b N_c ...}{\text{determinant } \sum \pm K_a M_b N_c ...}, \quad \text{etc.,}$$

which inspection shows to be equivalent to the statement that the vector $(k, m, n, ...)$ is exactly $A^{-1}X$, where A is the matrix made up (by columns) of the new basis vectors expressed in the old coordinates.

The effect of a change of coordinate system on an operator is slightly more complicated. Let us suppose that X on the old basis becomes $X' = BX$ in the new one, and let us suppose that $CX = Y$. Then

$$Y' = BY = BCX = BCB^{-1}X'$$

so that the operator which was C in the old coordinates has become BCB^{-1} in the new ones.

　　　　　　　　　D

4.2. Conjugation

The transformation by which each operator C becomes BCB^{-1} is of considerable importance in abstract group theory, although it does not arise by any such obvious process; it is called conjugation, and BCB^{-1} is called a conjugate element to C, B being the conjugating or transforming element.

A single element conjugates into itself if it commutes with the conjugating element. If, but only if, it commutes with all the elements of the group, it has no conjugate different from itself. It is then known as invariant, or self-conjugate. An element may be self-conjugate as a member of a subgroup but not in the complete group if it commutes with all the members of the subgroup but not with other members of the complete group.

A subgroup conjugates into a subgroup. For

$$(BCB^{-1})(BDB^{-1}) = B(CD)B^{-1},$$

or, in words, there is the same multiplication table between elements after transformation as there was before. Seen from the 'change of coordinate' point of view, of course it is obvious that this must be so. An invariant subgroup, as already defined in Chapter I, always conjugates into itself, and is described as self-conjugate, though separate elements of the subgroup need not be invariant—it is sufficient that any member of the subgroup always transforms into some member of the subgroup. Two types of subgroup may be recognized at once as invariant (a) subgroups of order $\frac{1}{2}n$ (because their right and left cosets cannot be different), and (b) subgroups which are the only subgroup of their order.

4.3. Factor groups

A self-conjugate subgroup defines what is known as a factor group, whereas a subgroup that is not self-conjugate does not. We may illustrate this from π_3, where we already know that the subgroup $I\,A\,B$ is self-conjugate whereas the subgroup $I\,C$ is not. We can arrange the table for the whole group by starting with the invariant subgroup in one corner, thus:

$$
\begin{array}{ccc\,ccc}
I\,A\,B & C\,D\,E \\
A\,B\,I & E\,C\,D \\
B\,I\,A & D\,E\,C \\
\\
C\,D\,E & I\,A\,B \\
D\,E\,C & B\,I\,A \\
E\,C\,D & A\,B\,I \\
\end{array}
$$

and we see that each 3×3 square is occupied either by the subgroup or by the elements of its coset, so that we have two sorts of square arranged, as it were, in the form of a c_2 multiplication table. But if we try to do the same thing with the non-invariant subgroup we run into difficulties:

$$I\ C \quad A\ D$$
$$C\ I \quad D\ A$$
$$A\ E,$$

for whereas A pairs up with D in one square, it pairs with E in another owing to the right and left cosets not being identical. It is the c_2 which is the factor group in the former case. The factor group is often identical with another subgroup, as in this example, where $I\ C$ displays the c_2 structure, but not necessarily so, for example in the quaternion group

I	i	A	a	B	b	C	c				
i	I	a	A	b	B	c	C				

I	A	B	C

A	a	i	I	c	C	B	b
a	A	I	i	C	c	b	B

there is no subgroup with the structure $\mathfrak{s}_{2 \times 2}$:

A	I	C	B

B	b	C	c	i	I	a	A
b	B	c	C	I	i	A	a

B	C	I	A

C	c	b	B	A	a	i	I
c	C	B	b	a	A	I	i

C	B	A	I

What then is a factor group? It is the group which arises when, for any reason, it becomes unnecessary to distinguish between the members of a subgroup.

An illustration may be taken from the process of 'addition to a modulus'. We define $a + b = c \pmod{n}$ if when a and b are added and the result divided by n, the remainder is the same as when c is divided by n. It can easily be verified that the integers $1, \ldots, n$ form the group c_n under addition $\pmod{n}$ as the method of combination, n (which $= 0$ $\pmod{n}$) playing the part of the identity. Under addition the set of all integers, positive, negative, and zero, form a group. The numbers $0, \pm n, \pm 2n, \ldots$ form an invariant subgroup (since the group is commutative, and therefore any subgroup is invariant), and the numbers $a, a \pm n, a \pm 2n, \ldots$ (where a is not a multiple of n) are a coset of this subgroup. The process of addition $\pmod{n}$ appears when we do not distinguish between the members of this coset, and refer to them all indifferently as a, and the group $\mathfrak{c}_n$ is the factor group resulting from this process. It appears in a concrete form in counting round the vertices of an n-gon, when a, $a+n$,... are literally indistinguishable from each other. Another example is discussed in some detail in § 8.2.

There is a fairly thorough analogy which can be traced between factors of a number and factor groups of a group. In particular, there is a theorem that if $\mathfrak{g}_1$ and $\mathfrak{g}_2$ are both invariant subgroups of $\mathfrak{G}$, and $\mathfrak{h}$ is the set of elements common to $\mathfrak{g}_1$ and $\mathfrak{g}_2$, then (a) $\mathfrak{h}$ is a group, and (b) the factor groups $\mathfrak{G}/\mathfrak{g}_1$ and $\mathfrak{g}_2/\mathfrak{h}$ are isomorphic. This corresponds to the theorem that if p and q are two numbers, and h and k their h.c.f. and l.c.m., then $h/p = q/k$. A second theorem, the Jordan–Hölder theorem, states that if we form a series $\mathfrak{G}$, $\mathfrak{g}_1$, $\mathfrak{g}_2$,..., $\mathfrak{J}$, such that each member of the series is an invariant subgroup of the preceding one, and so large that no other subgroup of $\mathfrak{G}$ satisfying this condition can be squeezed into the series, then the factor groups $\mathfrak{G}/\mathfrak{g}_1$, $\mathfrak{g}_1/\mathfrak{g}_2$,..., are uniquely determined except for the order in which they appear. This corresponds to the theorem that the prime factors of a number are uniquely determined by the number itself except for order, e.g.

$$\begin{array}{cccccc} 60 & 30 & 15 & 3 & 1 \\ & 2 & 2 & 5 & 3 \end{array} \quad \text{or} \quad \begin{array}{cccccc} 60 & 20 & 10 & 2 & 1 \\ & 3 & 2 & 5 & 2 \end{array}.$$

For proofs of these theorems the student is referred to any of the standard works on group theory.

4.4. The implications of equivalence

Elements which are conjugate are often described as equivalent, and sets of equivalent elements are called classes. To see just how justified the word equivalent is, we may return to the matrix approach, in which conjugate elements can be regarded as the same element in different coordinate systems.

It is thus obvious by geometrical intuition that equivalent elements in a matrix group—and we remember that every group can be given a matrix realization—have the same eigenvalues, and therefore the same characteristic equation. But this means that they have the same determinant and the same trace, since these two properties of a matrix are coefficients in the characteristic equation. In view of the very great importance of these results they ought perhaps to be proved analytically, but rather than break the thread of the present treatment we defer this to Chapter VII.

It does not follow that because two elements are 'as good as one another'—equivalent in a non-technical sense—that they are equivalent in the technical sense. The necessary conjugating element may not be available. In $\mathfrak{d}_4$, for example, the improper elements are all of order two, and are all equivalent. There is another element, one of the proper rotations, also a rotation through 180° and therefore of order 2, but it is not equivalent to the others, because the elements of the group itself do not provide a coordinate change which will convert it into any of the others. In this connexion we recollect that conjugate elements in a group may cease to be conjugate in a subgroup; thus one class of elements may split into several classes in going from a group to a subgroup. The class is then said to be *refined*.

4.5. The algebra of classes

There is an algebra associated with any group which is obtained by taking as basis elements the classes of the group. In π_3, for example, we may write the classes as

$$\mathcal{I} = I, \qquad \mathcal{A} = A+B, \qquad \mathcal{C} = C+D+E.$$

In so doing, the plus signs are merely a formal notation, though they can take on their normal meaning as soon as we replace the group elements by appropriate matrices. Arranging the multiplication table in classes, we have

I	$A\ B$	$C\ D\ E$		$\mathcal{I}$	$\mathcal{A}$	$\mathcal{C}$	
A	$B\ I$	$E\ C\ D$					
B	$I\ A$	$D\ E\ C$	or	$\mathcal{A}$	$\mathcal{A}+2\mathcal{I}$	$2\mathcal{C}$	
C	$D\ E$	$I\ A\ B$					
D	$E\ C$	$B\ I\ A$		$\mathcal{C}$	$2\mathcal{C}$	$3\mathcal{A}+3\mathcal{I}$	
E	$C\ D$	$A\ B\ I$					

This algebra is commutative, and is needed to prove certain theorems in the next chapter.

4.6. Oblique axis theory

We must return to the subject of change of coordinates which we allowed to be side-tracked in § 4.2. In doing so, we shall recapitulate some results already obtained, but this is very necessary as in some cases we shall be rediscovering abstract relations but putting entirely new interpretations on them. We had one example of this in the first section of this chapter when we saw that in the relation $X' = BX$, X' could be either a different vector from X, or it could be X re-expressed in different coordinates.

When we developed the dagger and star notations, we assumed that the length of a vector was derived from its components by a Pythagorean (or quasi-pythagorean) law—the square root of the sum of the squares of the components (or of their absolute values). Geometrically, this implies that the basic reference vectors $(1, 0, 0, ...)$, $(0, 1, 0, ...)$, $(0, 0, 1, ...)$, ... are equal in length and at right angles to each other. Such a coordinate system is called 'ortho-normal'. We shall use the term 'oblique' to cover all systems of basic vectors which are not ortho-normal—i.e. we shall let the term include, for convenience, systems based on perpendicular but unequal basic vectors.

The original basic vectors, $(1, 0, 0, ...)$, $(0, 1, 0, ...)$, ... may be conveniently denoted by $I_1{}^*$, $I_2{}^*$, ..., since they are successive columns of the identical matrix. (Compare § 3.7.) Since $I = I^{-1}$, the same vectors in row form, $*I_1$, $*I_2$, ... are their own reciprocal set. Let us also assume that we are given a set of n independent vectors $P_1{}^*$, $P_2{}^*$, ..., and that $P^{-1} = R$, so that the set reciprocal to the P^* is the set $*R_1$, $*R_2$, ... It will be convenient, if we choose to express the vector X in terms of the P^* as basic vectors, that it should still be denoted by the symbol X, but since the actual set of numbers representing it will now be different, some new symbol is essential when we are thinking of the vector in terms of its components. We can do this by using X^+ to denote that column matrix whose numbers are the components of X in the system using the P^* as basic vectors. Then ^+X will denote the corresponding row matrix. (In most of our applications X will be real; if it is not, the context will usually show that the components of ^+X must be the conjugates of those of X^+, but in any case of real ambiguity it will be necessary to state which geometry, orthogonal or unitary, we are using. Such cases are far too rare to warrant further complication of the notation.) We can summarize our intentions in this notation by writing

$$X^* = X_1{}^* I_1{}^* + X_2{}^* I_2{}^* + ... \qquad (4.6.1\,\text{a})$$

$$= X_1{}^+ P_1{}^* + X_2{}^+ P_2{}^* + ... \qquad (4.6.1\,\text{b})$$

(In these expressions, note that as X^* and X^+ are vectors, so $X_r{}^*$ and $X_r{}^+$ are numbers; normally we should drop the star, but the necessity of distinguishing $*$ and $^+$ components forces us to retain them here, and the rule about single stars in multiplication is not really broken. I, on the other hand, is a matrix, and so is P, so that I_r^* and P_r^* are vectors.) From these two expressions follow immediately the very important formulae

$$(X^*)_r = {}^*I_r X^*, \qquad (X^+)_r = {}^*R_r X^*. \qquad (4.6.2)$$

By combining the results for $r = 1,..., n$ implied by the second of these relations, we can write them in the form

$$X^+ = RX^* = P^{-1}X^*, \qquad (4.6.3)$$

which is the relation we deduced algebraically in § 4.1.

As basis vectors for a coordinate system, the P^* have rivals in the $^*R$, so let us define the row vector $^{\circ}X$ as the set of numbers which are such that
$$^{\circ}X_1 {}^*R_1 + {}^{\circ}X_2 {}^*R_2 + ... = {}^*X,$$

and, of course, X° will be the corresponding column vector. We call X^+ and ^+X the contravariant form of the vector X in the coordinate system P, and X° and $^{\circ}X$ the covariant forms of the same vector.

It is now very simple to verify the following relations, which are all transforms of (4.6.3), or direct consequences of it (in the unitary convention the transpose sign must be replaced by the associate sign):

$$\left. \begin{array}{ll} X^+ = RX^* = P^{-1}X^* & {}^+X = {}^*X\tilde{R} = {}^*X\tilde{P}^{-1} \\ X^{\circ} = \tilde{P}X^* = \tilde{R}^{-1}X^* & {}^{\circ}X = {}^*XP = {}^*XR^{-1} \\ {}^*XY^* = {}^+X\tilde{P}PY^+ = {}^{\circ}XR\tilde{R}Y^{\circ} = {}^{\circ}XY^+ = {}^+XY^{\circ} \end{array} \right\} . \quad (4.6.4)$$

The equations in the third row may also be expressed verbally in the following theorems:

THEOREM 4.6.5 a.   *The scalar product of two vectors X^+ and Y^+ which are specified by their components in oblique coordinates based on the vectors P_r^*, is given by the expression $^+XGY^+$ where G is the symmetric matrix $\tilde{P}P$ ($G_{rs} =$ the scalar product of P_r and P_s).*

THEOREM 4.6.5 b.   *The expression $\sum_r X_r Y_r$ will always represent the scalar product of two vectors if one of the vectors is referred to the direct and one to the reciprocal coordinate system (i.e. if one is co- and the other contravariant), even if these are oblique.*

In Chapter XIV we shall re-word this in the tensor language by saying that the scalar product of a contravariant vector with a covariant vector is an invariant. We may call G the *metrical* operator of the coordinate system. By putting it in the form $(g\gamma^{\frac{1}{2}})(\gamma^{\frac{1}{2}}g)$ of § 3.8 (and see the next section) a set of axes with any given metrical operator may be found.

Readers who prefer to think in more specifically geometrical terms may find an analysis in two dimensions illuminating. Let the lines OX and OY of Fig. 4 be the axes of an oblique coordinate system, the basic

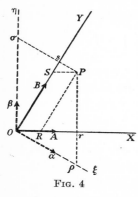

vectors being OA and OB. The components of OP in this system are OR and OS, or numerically (i.e. the coordinates) OR/OA and OS/OB. The point is that PS and PR are parallel to OA and OB respectively. If, as an alternative, we drop Ps and Pr perpendicular to OB and OA respectively, then while Ps and Pr are PS and PR (i.e. OR and OS) multiplied by $\sin XOY$, Os and Or are something different. The reciprocal system has axes $O\xi$ and $O\eta$, perpendicular to OY and OX respectively, and Or and Os are the components $O\rho$ and $O\sigma$ of OP in the reciprocal system, multiplied by

FIG. 4

$$\sin XOY \ (= \sin \xi O\eta = \cos XO\xi = \cos YO\eta).$$

Now

$$OP^2 = OR^2 + OS^2 + 2OR.OS\cos XOY$$

$$= OR(OR + OS\cos XOY) + OS(OS + OR\cos XOY)$$

$$= OR.Or + OS.Os$$

$$= (OR.O\rho + OS.O\sigma)\sin XOY.$$

In the reciprocal system, however, the basic vectors $O\alpha$ and $O\beta$ are of such lengths that the factor $\sin XOY$ is incorporated into the numerical values of the components, viz. $O\rho/O\alpha$ and $O\sigma/O\beta$.

Analysis along these lines is incomplete and misleading, however, unless it is clearly realized that the basic reciprocal vectors $O\alpha$ and $O\beta$ *are not defined unless* in addition to the direct basic vectors OA and OB *a unit of length is also given,* and that if, in the mechanical sense, the dimensions of OA and OB are L, those of $O\alpha$ and $O\beta$ are L^{-1}. The student should amplify this statement by considering a change of coordinate system from an ordinary rectangular one into one with the same unit of length, but basic vectors which are varying multiples of, though in the same directions as, the original ones. He should also refer to § 15.8.

It is useful to have formulae for proceeding from an operator to its components and vice versa. The formulae are, in rectangular coordinates,

$$A_{ij} = {}^*I_i A I_j{}^*, \qquad A = \sum_i \sum_j A_{ij} I_i^* {}^*I_j,$$

and the proof trivial. In oblique coordinates they generalize to

$$A_{ij} = {}^*R_i A P_j{}^*, \qquad A = \sum_i \sum_j A_{ij} P_i^* {}^*R_j,$$

and the proof is left as an exercise to the student.

4.7. Reduction of a matrix to diagonal form

A very important change of coordinates is that in which a matrix M is transformed so that its own eigenvectors become the axes. We assume, of course, that the matrix is not of the pathological type which has insufficient eigenvectors. When the change has been made, the matrix will be in diagonal form. The procedure is somewhat lengthy but straightforward. The eigenvalues are first found by setting up and solving the characteristic equation, then the eigenvectors corresponding to each root are found. If the right-eigenvectors have been found, they are put together in successive columns to form the matrix P of the previous section, and by the first section of this chapter, the transform of M will be $P^{-1}MP$. (Finding the left-eigenvectors leads alternatively to RMR^{-1}, which is the same thing, since the right- and left-eigenvectors are reciprocal sets.) If M is symmetric or Hermitian, the eigenvectors are orthogonal or unitary-orthogonal, and by normalizing them to unit length the matrix A can be made orthogonal or unitary.

THEOREM 4.7.1. *A symmetric (or Hermitian) matrix can be reduced to diagonal form by transformation with an orthogonal (or unitary) matrix.*

Two matrices can be simultaneously reduced to diagonal form (i.e. reduced by the same transformation) if and only if they commute. This is obviously a necessary condition, since in diagonal form they do commute, and we have seen that if they commute after transformation they must do so before it, since transformation does not alter the multiplication table. That it is a sufficient condition is not quite so obvious, since a transformation which makes M diagonal need not make L diagonal even if they commute. We have, if $ML = LM$,

$$\sum_s M_{rs} L_{st} = \sum_s L_{rs} M_{st},$$

or, when M is already diagonal, and only one term in each sum is different from zero,

$$M_{rr} L_{rt} = L_{rt} M_{tt},$$

so that $L_{rt} = 0$ when $M_{rr} \neq M_{tt}$. When the characteristic equation of M has repeated roots, therefore, the transformation of L need only reduce it to a semi-diagonal form in which we have zeros everywhere except in certain squares on the diagonal, thus:

$$M = \begin{bmatrix} a & 0 & 0 & 0 & 0 & 0 & 0 & . & . \\ 0 & a & 0 & 0 & 0 & 0 & 0 & . & . \\ 0 & 0 & b & 0 & 0 & 0 & 0 & . & . \\ 0 & 0 & 0 & c & 0 & 0 & 0 & . & . \\ 0 & 0 & 0 & 0 & c & 0 & 0 & . & . \\ 0 & 0 & 0 & 0 & 0 & c & 0 & . & . \\ 0 & 0 & 0 & 0 & 0 & 0 & d & . & . \\ . & . & . & . & . & . & . & . \end{bmatrix} \quad L = \begin{bmatrix} * & * & 0 & 0 & 0 & 0 & 0 & . & . \\ * & * & 0 & 0 & 0 & 0 & 0 & . & . \\ 0 & 0 & * & 0 & 0 & 0 & 0 & . & . \\ 0 & 0 & 0 & * & * & * & 0 & . & . \\ 0 & 0 & 0 & * & * & * & 0 & . & . \\ 0 & 0 & 0 & * & * & * & 0 & . & . \\ 0 & 0 & 0 & 0 & 0 & 0 & * & . & . \\ . & . & . & . & . & . & . & . \end{bmatrix}.$$

But in this case the eigenvectors of M are not unique; the repeated roots give rise to eigen-subspaces, and a further transformation within these spaces, while not affecting the diagonal form of M, can be so made as to make L completely diagonal. This argument can be extended to three or more matrices.

4.8. Functions of an arbitrary operator

Everything that was said in § 2.8 about functions of a single operator in diagonal form can now be asserted of a general operator, since nothing that was said there is invalidated by transformation to diagonal form first. A polynomial function of an operator is another operator with the same eigenvectors and with eigenvalues which are that function of the eigenvalues of the original operator. Two functions which agree in value for each eigenvalue of the original operator as argument cannot be distinguished, and therefore for matrices of finite order, any definable function always exists provided it converges for all values of the argument represented in these eigenvalues. An example of one which does not is the reciprocal of a singular matrix. The matrix

$$A = \begin{bmatrix} \frac{1}{4}\pi & -\frac{1}{4}\pi \\ -\frac{1}{4}\pi & \frac{1}{4}\pi \end{bmatrix}$$

has eigenvectors $(1, -1)$ and $(1, 1)$ with eigenvalues $\frac{1}{2}\pi$ and 0 respectively. Accordingly $\cos A$ is definable as a matrix with the same eigenvectors and eigenvalues 0 and 1 respectively, viz. $\begin{bmatrix} \frac{1}{2} & \frac{1}{2} \\ \frac{1}{2} & \frac{1}{2} \end{bmatrix}$, but $\tan A$ presents difficulties. The matrix for $\cos A$ could also be obtained from the cosine series; the tangent series would be found to diverge for A as argument. It is necessary to appreciate these points if we are to pass, later on, to continuous groups of matrices or to matrices with an infinite number of rows and columns.

In the last section we showed that commuting operators are simultaneously reducible to diagonal form, and thus have redeemed the promise made in § 2.8 that we would show that this theory also applies to functions of several operators provided that they commute, or, which is the same thing, have a complete set of eigenvectors in common. We can apply ordinary algebraic theory to commuting operators, and any algebraic relation involving them holds also of their eigenvalues.

The requirement that the operator M of the previous section be diagonal does not define the coordinate system uniquely, owing to the ambiguity in the eigen-subspaces. A requirement that L be also diagonal may remove some of this ambiguity—it will do so if the sub-matrices of L have unequal eigenvalues. If it does not do so completely, a third matrix K which commutes with both M and L may do so. Proceeding in this way we obtain eventually a set of commuting operators which completely defines the coordinate system in which it is diagonal. Such a set is called a *complete set of commuting operators*. Any further matrix which may be found which commutes with all the members of the complete set can be expressed as a function of them. For such a matrix will be diagonal in the coordinate system defined by the others, and thus a set of eigenvalues of the others defines a particular eigenvalue of this operator, and this, in general, is all that can be meant by saying it is a function of the others.

Functions of non-commuting operators need more careful handling. An elementary point is that, for example,

$$(A+B)^2 = A^2 + AB + BA + B^2,$$

and cannot be simplified further. The quantity $*XAX*/*XX*$, which gives the eigenvalue of A when $X*$ is an eigenvector is known, if $X*$ is a general vector, as the expectation of A for $X*$. When $X*$ is not an eigenvector, expectations are additive, but not multiplicative, since

$$*X(A+B)X* = *XAX* + *XBX*,$$

but there is no such relation for $*XABX*$. As a vector is probably not a simultaneous eigenvector of A and B, expectations are the best we can do in getting a pure number out of A, B, and X. Formulae are usually obtained by evading the non-commutation in some way.

For example, we can find the product of the expectations of A and B for $X*$ as follows. Let them be a and b; then

$$ab = \left(\frac{a+b}{2}\right)^2 - \left(\frac{a-b}{2}\right)^2$$

$$= *X\left[\left(\frac{A+B}{2}\right)^2 - \left(\frac{A-B}{2}\right)^2\right]X*/*XX*$$

$$= *X\left(\frac{AB+BA}{2}\right)X*/*XX*,$$

so that when A and B do not commute, the product of their expectations is the expectation of $\frac{1}{2}(AB+BA)$.

CHAPTER V

REPRESENTATIONS—THE HEART OF THE MATTER

WE have used the expression 'a realization of a group' to mean any group of concretely performable operations which has the same structure as a given abstract group. Some of these have been geometrical and expressible in matrix form. But the matrix realizations of a group are of such paramount importance that they are known by a distinct name—representations. We may legitimately ask how many representations there are of a given abstract group. This chapter will be mainly concerned with answering that question, but in order that the student may know where he is going, we may give a brief answer at once. There are an infinite number of representations of a given group, but they are all built up from a relatively small number of so-called 'irreducible' ones, and the number of these for any group is the number of classes in it. It will also help the student to find his way around this fundamental part of the subject if we look first at the building up process.

5.2. Reducibility

It is not necessary in a representation that different elements of the group are associated with different matrices, though in a way those representations in which this is so are better ones, and we describe them as *faithful*. But all that is really necessary is that if $AB = C$, then the matrix associated with A multiplied on the right by the matrix associated with B shall give the matrix associated with C.

Nor is there any ban on one-dimensional matrices. Hence the simplest representation of any group is the one which associates the number 1 with every element, for in this case every $AB = C$ is represented by $1 \times 1 = 1$. Next in simplicity comes the representation of the generating member of a cyclic group c_n by any one of the nth roots of unity. This applies to more groups than cyclic ones, for if any group has a factor group, then any representation of the factor group is also an unfaithful representation of the main group, in which all members of a given coset are associated with the same matrix. Hence this representation of c_n is a representation of any group which has c_n as a factor group.

Let us take c_6 as an example. There are 6 sixth roots of unity and association of each of them with the generating element leads to six representations of the group which we denote by $\Gamma_1,..., \Gamma_6$. These are

	I	A	A^2	A^3	A^4	A^5
Γ_1	1	1	1	1	1	1
Γ_2	1	-1	1	-1	1	-1
Γ_3	1	ω	ω^2	1	ω	ω^2
Γ_4	1	ω^2	ω	1	ω^2	ω
Γ_5	1	$-\omega$	ω^2	-1	ω	$-\omega^2$
Γ_6	1	$-\omega^2$	ω	-1	ω^2	$-\omega$

Of these only the last two associate a different number with each element of the group, and only these two are faithful representations. If the group operates in a two-space, it could operate independently with any two of these on the two components of the vector. Thus a seventh representation could be

$$\Gamma_7 \quad \begin{bmatrix} 1 & 0 \\ 0 & 1 \end{bmatrix} \begin{bmatrix} -1 & 0 \\ 0 & \omega \end{bmatrix} \begin{bmatrix} 1 & 0 \\ 0 & \omega^2 \end{bmatrix} \begin{bmatrix} -1 & 0 \\ 0 & 1 \end{bmatrix} \begin{bmatrix} 1 & 0 \\ 0 & \omega \end{bmatrix} \begin{bmatrix} -1 & 0 \\ 0 & \omega^2 \end{bmatrix},$$
$$\quad I \qquad\qquad A \qquad\qquad A^2 \qquad\qquad A^3 \qquad\qquad A^4 \qquad\qquad A^5$$

but inasmuch as Γ_7 can be broken down into Γ_2 and Γ_3 it is spoken of as *reducible*. We write $\Gamma_7 = \Gamma_2 \dotplus \Gamma_3$, and we shall also occasionally use the symbol $\sum$. Notice that although Γ_2 and Γ_3 are neither of them faithful, Γ_7 is faithful.

Γ_7 is not only reducible, it is 'reduced', that is, it is in a coordinate system in which the components transform separately according to the two irreducible representations of which it is composed. If we rotate through an angle θ, then according to the BCB^{-1} rule,

$$\begin{bmatrix} a & 0 \\ 0 & b \end{bmatrix} \text{ becomes } \begin{bmatrix} a\cos^2\theta + b\sin^2\theta & (a-b)\sin\theta\cos\theta \\ (a-b)\sin\theta\cos\theta & a\sin^2\theta + b\cos^2\theta \end{bmatrix},$$

whence by substituting for a and b we can transform each of the matrices of Γ_7. The resulting representation is still described as reducible, though it is no longer reduced. Representations that can be transformed into each other in this way are described as equivalent, a word we have already used in practically the same sense in Chapter IV. (Note how the trace of the matrix is unaltered by the transformation.)

As a further example, we may consider the representation of c_3 which consists in permuting the axes. The matrices are

$$I = \begin{bmatrix} 1 & 0 & 0 \\ 0 & 1 & 0 \\ 0 & 0 & 1 \end{bmatrix}, \quad A = \begin{bmatrix} 0 & 1 & 0 \\ 0 & 0 & 1 \\ 1 & 0 & 0 \end{bmatrix}, \quad B = \begin{bmatrix} 0 & 0 & 1 \\ 1 & 0 & 0 \\ 0 & 1 & 0 \end{bmatrix}.$$

Whichever of these matrices we operate with on the vector $(1, 1, 1)$, the result is $(1, 1, 1)$, and thus so far as this vector is concerned the representation is the identical one, in which each element is associated with the number 1. We say that this vector is invariant under the group. The situation is simple enough here to picture geometrically; the operation consists of a rotation through 0 or $2\pi/3$ (clockwise or anticlockwise) about this vector as axis. Consequently, without analysis, we can say that by a suitable change of coordinates this group of matrices can be transformed into

$$I = \begin{bmatrix} 1 & 0 & 0 \\ 0 & 1 & 0 \\ 0 & 0 & 1 \end{bmatrix}, \quad A = \begin{bmatrix} 1 & 0 & 0 \\ 0 & -\frac{1}{2} & \frac{1}{2}\sqrt{3} \\ 0 & -\frac{1}{2}\sqrt{3} & -\frac{1}{2} \end{bmatrix}, \quad B = \begin{bmatrix} 1 & 0 & 0 \\ 0 & -\frac{1}{2} & -\frac{1}{2}\sqrt{3} \\ 0 & \frac{1}{2}\sqrt{3} & -\frac{1}{2} \end{bmatrix},$$

in which form it is partly reduced. We shall see later that it is reduced as far as is possible in real terms, the fully reduced form being

$$I = \begin{bmatrix} 1 & 0 & 0 \\ 0 & 1 & 0 \\ 0 & 0 & 1 \end{bmatrix}, \quad A = \begin{bmatrix} 1 & 0 & 0 \\ 0 & \omega & 0 \\ 0 & 0 & \omega^2 \end{bmatrix}, \quad B = \begin{bmatrix} 1 & 0 & 0 \\ 0 & \omega^2 & 0 \\ 0 & 0 & \omega \end{bmatrix},$$

where ω and ω^2 are the complex cube roots of unity.

The student would do well to pause at this point and examine his own reaction to this last example. Comparing the permutation of the axes with the rotation about the vector $(1, 1, 1)$ he will see that the resolution of a group of operators into their irreducible representations constitutes a considerable mental as well as mathematical simplification, and he will be more prepared to find how much of the pure theory of groups is concerned with discovering what are the irreducible representations of a given group and how a given representation can be analysed.

It must not be thought from the above examples that every representation of a group of matrices can be reduced to one-dimensional ones. § 4.7 showed that a faithful representation of a non-commutating group cannot be as completely reducible as that. Had we considered

π_3 instead of c_3 above, we should still have found $(1, 1, 1)$ to be invariant, but the first stage of reduction would have been the last. A useful result easily proved by the method of § 4.7 is the following

THEOREM 5.2.1. *If a matrix M commutes with all the matrices of a group, then either* (1) *the representation is reducible or* (2) *M is a scalar multiple of the identity.*

The proof is left to the student.

In the next section we prove that the number of irreducible representations of a group is equal to the number of its classes, and that the sum of their orders is equal to the order of the group. § 5.4 discusses some simple corollaries of this, and in § 5.5 we introduce group characters. These are the traces of the matrices in a representation, and we prove certain relations between them which allow us to analyse a reducible representation whose characters are known, so far as saying which of the irreducible representations they are built out of. § 5.6 discusses further ways of building new representations when some are given. The results of these considerations are applied in Chapter VI, and the student who, on first reading, prefers to omit the proofs, should proceed straight from this point to § 6.1.

5.3. The fundamental theorems

The first of the theorems to be proved in this section has already been stated:

THEOREM 5.3.1. *The number of irreducible representations of an abstract group is equal to the number of its classes.*

Let the group $\mathfrak{G}$ consist of N elements in p classes. Let the element A_i be in the class C_r which contains h_r members.   Consider the elements $A_j A_i A_j^{-1}$ $(j = 1,..., N)$; they will be A_i for each A_j that commutes with A_i, and one of the conjugates of A_i in every other case. It is not difficult to show that all the elements of $\mathfrak{G}$ which commute with A_i form a subgroup of $\mathfrak{G}$ (known as the normalizer of A_i), that elements in the same coset of this subgroup give rise to the same conjugate of A_i, and elements in different cosets give rise to different conjugates of A_i. Hence the elements $A_j A_i A_j^{-1}$ are the h_r members of the class C_r each repeated N/h_r times. Thus in the group algebra we can write

$$\sum_{j=1}^{N} A_j A_i A_j^{-1} = \frac{N}{h_r} C_r.$$

With the aid of this result we can prove the following lemma:

LEMMA. *A linear function of the classes commutes with every element of the group, and conversely, if an element of the group algebra commutes with every element of the group it is a linear function of the classes.*

For if (abandoning systematic notation for the moment) the class C_r consists of the elements c_{rs}, A is any group element, and $S = \sum p_r C_r$ is the linear function of the classes, then

$$AS = \sum_r \sum_s p_r A c_{rs} = \sum_r \sum_s p_r A A^{-1} c_{rs} A = SA,$$

since $\sum_s A^{-1} c_{rs} A$ is the same as the elements $\sum_s c_{rs}$ in a different order; and if S' commutes with every A, then

$$S' = \frac{1}{N} \sum A_j S' A_j^{-1} = \text{a linear function of the classes.}$$

Now any matrix representation of the group at once provides basis elements for a representation both of the group and of the class algebra. Since the class algebra is commutative, every basis element, and therefore every element in it, can be simultaneously presented in diagonal form; we shall assume a coordinate system to be chosen so that this is so. If the representation is irreducible, then by Theorem 5.2.1 any class function must be a scalar multiple of the identity. If it is reducible, then it will be reduced in the coordinate system we have chosen, class functions being of the form of M of § 4.7 and group elements therefore of the form of L. As the class function S is built up linearly (by additive processes only) from the group elements, an irreducible representation occurring several times will necessarily give rise to the same diagonal terms of S each time it occurs (remembering that equivalent representations have the same traces) and therefore different diagonal terms of S correspond to inequivalent representations. But the class algebra is of order p and a class function is therefore, in general, dependent on p parameters, though in a given case some may be missing. Hence the group must have p inequivalent representations.

The second fundamental theorem concerns the dimensionality of these irreducible representations, and is

THEOREM 5.3.2. *If the p irreducible representations of a group $\mathfrak{G}$ of order N are of degrees $m_1,..., m_p$, then $\sum m_r^2 = N$.*

We consider again, not the group, but the group algebra, and in a representation which includes each irreducible representation exactly once. It is of order N, and there must therefore be N independent parameters in the typical matrix. But the number of asterisks in the matrix L of § 4.7 is just $\sum m_r^2$, which must therefore equal N, the order of the group. (It might be argued that $\sum m_r^2$ might be greater than N, not all matrices of the form of L being included in the group algebra, but this possibility is excluded by Burnside's theorem. We shall put this discussion on a more rigid basis in § 7.7, where Burnside's theorem is discussed.)

5.4. Some simple corollaries

The theorems of the preceding section immediately yield enlightening information when applied to groups which are completely commutative. (Such groups are often called Abelian groups.) In such a group every element is self-conjugate, and therefore constitutes a class by itself; $p = N$, and the equation $\sum m_r^2 = N$ is only to be satisfied by every $m_r = 1$. Thus an Abelian group of order N has N one-dimensional irreducible representations. The six representations of c_6 given earlier are therefore all the irreducible representations it has, and the association of the n nth roots of unity with a generating element of c_n gives us all the irreducible representations of a cyclic group. S-groups are dealt with in the next chapter.

Where a representation involves complex numbers, it can often be interpreted physically by the following device: the complex number $a+bi$ and the matrix $\begin{bmatrix} a & b \\ -b & a \end{bmatrix}$ have identical properties mathematically, and a complex representation can in this way be interpreted as a real one in a larger number of dimensions. This is effectively the technique of the Argand diagram; if in a problem we find that there should exist a complex representation of a group in a physical situation, we may be able to combine two coordinates, say x and y, in the form of a single complex one $x+iy$, which transforms in the way required. For example, the representation Γ_7 of c_6 in § 5.2, with the two coordinates put equal to Z and $X+iY$ respectively, gives the rotations of structure 1 of Fig. 5 into itself. The rotations of structure 2 into itself are also a group of structure c_6, but whereas Z still transforms by Γ_2, $X+iY$ now transforms by Γ_5 and not Γ_3. (The student should make sure that he fully understands this point, as it is introduced here so as not to be a completely new idea in Chapters VIII–X.)

Since there is always one one-dimensional representation of any group, the identical one, every irreducible representation must be of lower order than $\sqrt{N}$. Thus the regular representation must always be reducible.

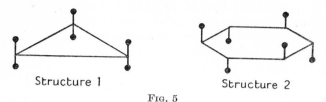

Structure 1   Structure 2

Fig. 5

5.5. Group characters

The characters of a group are the traces of the matrices in the representations of the group. We remember that the trace of a matrix is the sum of the diagonal elements of the matrix, and as it is unchanged by conjugation of the matrix it must be the same for all the matrices of the same class in a given representation. A character is described as simple if the representation is irreducible, and compound if the representation is reducible. A compound character is thus a linear combination of simple characters with positive integral coefficients. A linear function of the simple characters with unrestricted coefficients is sometimes called a generalized character, but it cannot, unless the coefficients are positive integral, be the character of a representation. As the number of irreducible representations is equal to the number of classes, the simple characters can be set out in a square table thus:

Classes Representations	$I = C_0$	C_1	C_2	...	C_{p-1}
Γ_1	1	1	1	...	1
Γ_2	m_2	$\chi_{1,2}$	$\chi_{2,2}$	...	$\chi_{p-1,2}$
.	.	.	.	.	.

in which the characters of the identical representation and of the identity (which in each representation is a diagonal line of 1's) have been included explicitly. The use of the symbol χ for group characters is conventional. The character of any one-dimensional representation is, of course, the same as the representation itself.

These simple characters are subject to certain important relations which enable a reducible representation to be analysed if its compound character is known. These are known as the orthogonality relations, from their form, and are as follows:

1. Sum of squares‡ in column C_r multiplied by number of elements in class C_r $= N.$
2. Sum of products‡ of corresponding numbers in columns C_r and C_s $= 0.$
3. Sum of squares‡ in row Γ_r, counting elements, not classes $= N.$
4. Sum of products‡ of corresponding numbers in rows Γ_r and Γ_s, counting elements, not classes $= 0.$

‡ Squares or products if real, but if complex, one factor is to be replaced by its conjugate.

As these relations are very important, but the proof somewhat abstract and difficult, we shall first illustrate them here for the group π_3, and then give a proof which is not entirely satisfactory, deferring a complete proof to Chapter VII.

In π_3, as we have seen, $N = 6$, and there are three classes, $\mathscr{I} = I$, $\mathscr{A} = A + B$, and $\mathscr{C} = C + D + E$. The only possible solution of $\sum m_r^2 = N$ is $1^2 + 1^2 + 2^2 = 6$. The group $\mathfrak{c}_2$ is a factor group, and its representations provide the two first-degree representations; the geometrical interpretation of π_3 as $\mathfrak{d}_3$ provides the second-degree representation. (This representation is irreducible because it will be found that no transformation can reduce *all six* matrices *simultaneously* to diagonal form.) Accordingly the irreducible representations are:

	I	A	B	C	D	E
Γ_1	1	1	1	1	1	1
Γ_2	1	1	1	-1	-1	-1
Γ_3	$\begin{pmatrix} 1 & 0 \\ 0 & 1 \end{pmatrix}$	$\begin{pmatrix} c & -s \\ s & c \end{pmatrix}$	$\begin{pmatrix} c & s \\ -s & c \end{pmatrix}$	$\begin{pmatrix} 1 & 0 \\ 0 & -1 \end{pmatrix}$	$\begin{pmatrix} c & s \\ s & -c \end{pmatrix}$	$\begin{pmatrix} c & -s \\ -s & -c \end{pmatrix}$

in which c and s stand for $\cos \frac{2}{3}\pi = -\frac{1}{2}$ and $\sin \frac{2}{3}\pi = \frac{1}{2}\sqrt{3}$ respectively, and the characters of the third representation are

$$2 \qquad -1 \qquad -1 \qquad 0 \qquad 0 \qquad 0$$

by adding the diagonal elements. It is easily verified that (1) no two elements have all three characters the same except such as belong to the same class, (2) the sum of the squares of the numbers in any one row, or in all the columns of any one class, is 6, and (3) the sums of the products of corresponding numbers in any two rows, or in any two columns belonging to different classes, is zero.

To prove that these relations must of necessity hold, we combine the representations, for convenience, into one of the fourth degree, its first row and column exhibiting Γ_1, its second Γ_2, and its third and fourth Γ_3, and we then form the matrices of the classes by adding those of the group elements.   We obtain

$$
\mathscr{I} \qquad\qquad \mathscr{A} \qquad\qquad \mathscr{C}
$$

$$
\begin{bmatrix} 1 & 0 & 0 & 0 \\ 0 & 1 & 0 & 0 \\ 0 & 0 & 1 & 0 \\ 0 & 0 & 0 & 1 \end{bmatrix}
\begin{bmatrix} 2 & 0 & 0 & 0 \\ 0 & 2 & 0 & 0 \\ 0 & 0 & -1 & 0 \\ 0 & 0 & 0 & -1 \end{bmatrix}
\begin{bmatrix} 3 & 0 & 0 & 0 \\ 0 & -3 & 0 & 0 \\ 0 & 0 & 0 & 0 \\ 0 & 0 & 0 & 0 \end{bmatrix}.
$$

In each representation the result is, as we saw in the previous section it must be, a scalar multiple of the identity in each representation, the multiple, except in the first class, being different in different representations.   Let us denote by M_1, M_2, and M_3 the matrices

$$
\begin{bmatrix} 1 & 0 & 0 & 0 \\ 0 & 0 & 0 & 0 \\ 0 & 0 & 0 & 0 \\ 0 & 0 & 0 & 0 \end{bmatrix}
\begin{bmatrix} 0 & 0 & 0 & 0 \\ 0 & 1 & 0 & 0 \\ 0 & 0 & 0 & 0 \\ 0 & 0 & 0 & 0 \end{bmatrix}
\begin{bmatrix} 0 & 0 & 0 & 0 \\ 0 & 0 & 0 & 0 \\ 0 & 0 & 1 & 0 \\ 0 & 0 & 0 & 1 \end{bmatrix}.
$$

They are an alternative basis for the algebra of classes, idempotent elements of this algebra; their products with one another are zero and their sum is I, the modulus of the algebra. They are called the primitive idempotents of the algebra. By inspection of the matrices for the classes we see that

$$
\mathscr{I} = M_1 + M_2 + M_3,
$$

$$
\mathscr{A} = 2M_1 + 2M_2 - M_3,
$$

$$
\mathscr{C} = 3M_1 - 3M_2,
$$

and by solving these equations we can obtain the inverse set

$$
M_1 = \tfrac{1}{6}(\mathscr{I} + \mathscr{A} + \mathscr{C}),
$$

$$
M_2 = \tfrac{1}{6}(\mathscr{I} + \mathscr{A} - \mathscr{C}),
$$

$$
M_3 = \tfrac{1}{3}(2\mathscr{I} - \mathscr{A}).
$$

Algebras in general may or may not possess primitive idempotents, but the non-possession is related to the existence of elements which are nil-potent (see § 7.2) and a group algebra always has the full number. We may therefore write, in the algebra of classes, the two sets of equations

$$
C_r = \sum_s \psi_{rs} M_s, \tag{5.5.1}
$$

$$
M_s = \sum_r \phi_{sr} C_r. \tag{5.5.2}
$$

Now by inspection of the process detailed above for π_3, we can write at once

$$\psi_{rs} = \frac{h_r \chi_{rs}}{m_s}. \tag{5.5.3}$$

In order to evaluate the ϕ's similarly, we consider the product

$$M_i C_r = \sum_s \phi_{is} C_s C_r,$$

in the regular representation. In this representation the trace of $C_s C_r$ is zero unless $C_s C_r$ contains the identity, in which case it is $N h_r$, since $C_{r'} C_r$ (where $C_{r'}$ is the class containing the inverses of the elements in C_r) will contain the identity, with trace N, h_r times. Thus by this method $M_i C_r$ has as trace $N h_f \phi_{ir'}$. But M_i as an operator selects from a matrix representation of C_r that part of it which reduces to Γ_i, and thus the trace of $M_i C_r$ is $n_i h_r \chi_{ri}$, where n_i is the number of times Γ_i is contained in the representation. Assuming that in the regular representation $n_i = m_i$, which is reasonable, since we know that the equations $\sum n_i m_i = N$ and $\sum m_i^2 = N$ must both be satisfied (but this is the weak point in this proof, and we shall return to it in Chapter VII), we have

$$\phi_{is} = \frac{m_i \chi_{is'}}{N} \quad \text{or} \quad \phi_{sr} = \frac{m_s \chi_{sr'}}{N}. \tag{5.5.4}$$

The orthogonality relations now become the detailed expression of the fact that the matrices ψ and ϕ are mutually reciprocal, provided we also show, as is obvious when the elements are in diagonal form, that $\chi_{ir} = \bar{\chi}_{ir'}$.

The orthogonality relations enable us to express any character (including a generalized character) as a linear function of the simple ones, and so to analyse a reducible representation. Illustrations will occur in the next chapter and elsewhere in the rest of this book.

5.6. Induced and Kronecker product representations

We have shown how representations may be built up from simpler ones, but two processes of some importance are rather different from anything we have yet done.

If (x, y) undergoes the transformation to $A(x, y) = (x', y')$, then the $(p+1)$-dimensional vector

$$(x^p, \; x^{p-1}y, \; x^{p-2}y^2, ..., \; xy^{p-1}, \; y^p)$$

also undergoes a linear transformation. For, for example,

$$(x')^{p-1}(y') = (a_{11}x + a_{12}y)^{p-1}(a_{21}x + a_{22}y)$$
$$= a_{11}^{p-1}a_{21}x^p + \{(p-1)a_{11}^{p-2}a_{12}a_{21} + a_{11}^{p-1}a_{22}\}x^{p-1}y + ..., \quad (5.6.1)$$

which is a linear transformation which we call A_p, the pth induced transformation. If the transformations A, B,... realize a group, then it is clear that the transformations A_p, B_p,... realize the same group. If the original transformations form an irreducible representation of the group, it does not follow without a special investigation that the induced transformations form an irreducible representation—indeed, although in one important case they do, in general they will not.

When the original vector is of more than two dimensions, the pth induced matrix has to take into account all the homogeneous products of degree p, i.e. it includes such components as $x_1 x_2 x_3$..., and therefore the transformation is in a space of $^{n+p-1}C_p$ dimensions (see § 13.2), n being the dimensionality of the original space.

A second important derived type of representation is that known as the Kronecker product of two already given representations. If the transformations (x, y) to $A(x, y) = (x', y')$ and (ξ, η, ζ) to

$$\alpha(\xi, \eta, \zeta) = (\xi', \eta', \zeta')$$

are separately under consideration, then the vector $(x\xi, x\eta, x\zeta, y\xi, y\eta, y\zeta)$ transforms to the vector $(x'\xi', x'\eta', x'\zeta', y'\xi', y'\eta', y'\zeta')$ by a linear transformation. This transformation is the Kronecker product of the transformations A and α. It is denoted by $A \times \alpha$.

The most obvious application of the Kronecker product is that in which quantities which are actually the products of vectors are transformed; we shall deal with these in more detail in Chapter XIV. But by way of illustration here we may consider the transformation of a dyad, or, since of course it is identical, a dyadic. If $A = X**Y$, then it must transform by the Kronecker product of the transformations of $X*$ and $*Y$—the latter being the transpose of the transformation of $Y*$. Thus under a rotation about the Z-axis, an arbitrary operator A is transformed into A' given by

$$\begin{bmatrix} c & -s & 0 \\ s & c & 0 \\ 0 & 0 & 1 \end{bmatrix} \begin{bmatrix} a_{11} & a_{12} & a_{13} \\ a_{21} & a_{22} & a_{23} \\ a_{31} & a_{32} & a_{33} \end{bmatrix} \begin{bmatrix} c & s & 0 \\ -s & c & 0 \\ 0 & 0 & 1 \end{bmatrix}$$
$$= \begin{bmatrix} c^2 a_{11} - csa_{12} - csa_{21} + s^2 a_{22} & \cdot & \cdot \\ csa_{11} - s^2 a_{12} + c^2 a_{21} - csa_{22} & \cdot & \cdot \\ ca_{13} - sa_{23} & \cdot & \cdot \end{bmatrix} \quad (5.6.2)$$

as may be verified in full by multiplying out. But this transformation may be expressed in the form

$$
\begin{bmatrix} a'_{11} \\ a'_{12} \\ a'_{13} \\ a'_{21} \\ a'_{22} \\ a'_{23} \\ a'_{31} \\ a'_{32} \\ a'_{33} \end{bmatrix} = \begin{bmatrix} c^2 & -cs & 0 & -cs & s^2 & 0 & 0 & 0 & 0 \\ cs & c^2 & 0 & -s^2 & -cs & 0 & 0 & 0 & 0 \\ 0 & 0 & c & 0 & 0 & -s & 0 & 0 & 0 \\ cs & -s^2 & 0 & c^2 & -cs & 0 & 0 & 0 & 0 \\ s^2 & cs & 0 & cs & c^2 & 0 & 0 & 0 & 0 \\ 0 & 0 & s & 0 & 0 & c & 0 & 0 & 0 \\ 0 & 0 & 0 & 0 & 0 & 0 & c & -s & 0 \\ 0 & 0 & 0 & 0 & 0 & 0 & s & c & 0 \\ 0 & 0 & 0 & 0 & 0 & 0 & 0 & 0 & 1 \end{bmatrix} \begin{bmatrix} a_{11} \\ a_{12} \\ a_{13} \\ a_{21} \\ a_{22} \\ a_{23} \\ a_{31} \\ a_{32} \\ a_{33} \end{bmatrix}
$$

$$(5.6.3)$$

and an examination of this matrix will show that each 3×3 square in it consists of the first of the matrices of the original triple product multiplied by the element of the transposed third matrix appropriate to the position of the square.

For one subsequent application we shall have to be more general and consider the product $*XAY*$, where $*X$ and $Y*$ are of dimensions m and n respectively, A being rectangular. Making two independent coordinate changes, $*X$ to $°X = *XR^{-1}$ and $Y*$ to $Y^+ = S^{-1}Y*$, the invariance of $*XAY* = (*XR^{-1})(RAS)(S^{-1}Y*)$ shows that the transform of A is $RAS = B$. Here R and S are $m \times m$ and $n \times n$ square matrices, and B, like A, is rectangular. But A and B are ordered sets of mn numbers, and can be regarded as vectors in an mn-space. We have $B_{rs} = \sum_{i,j} R_{ri} A_{ij} S_{js}$, summed over all the mn pairs (i,j), which can also be written

$$ B_{rs} = \sum_{i,j} T_{rs,ij} A_{ij}, \qquad T_{rs,ij} = R_{ri} S_{js} = R_{ri} \tilde{S}_{sj}, \qquad (5.6.4) $$

whence again T is the Kronecker product, $R \times \tilde{S}$. Using the sign $\sim$ to connect identical statements in different notation we can thus write

$$ RAS = B \sim (R \times \tilde{S})A* = B*. \qquad (5.6.4\,\text{a}) $$

It should be noted that Kronecker multiplication is in a sense non-commutative—but only in that transposing the order of the factors alters the conventional order of the components. We assume the components of $A*$ or $A^\dagger$ to be in the numerical order of their two-digit suffixes, viz. 11, 12,..., 21, 22,..., and define $^\dagger A$ as the same components in the same order in column form. Then $^\dagger A = (\widetilde{A^\dagger})$. But $(\tilde{A})^\dagger$ and $^\dagger(\tilde{A})$ have their components in the order 11, 21,..., 12, 22,.... As we never need to use the transpose sign on a vector we can reserve the notation $\tilde{A}^\dagger$ and $^\dagger\tilde{A}$ for the latter. Then (5.6.4 a) can be extended to

$$\left.\begin{array}{l} RAS = B \ \sim \ (R\times\tilde{S})A^\dagger = B^\dagger \ \sim \ ^\dagger A(\tilde{R}\times S) = {}^\dagger B \\ \sim \ \tilde{S}\tilde{A}\tilde{R} = \tilde{B} \ \sim \ (\tilde{S}\times R)\tilde{A}^\dagger = \tilde{B}^\dagger \ \sim \ ^\dagger\tilde{A}(S\times\tilde{R}) = {}^\dagger\tilde{B} \end{array}\right\}. \quad (5.6.5)$$

Since $\qquad\qquad (AB)C(DE) = A(BCD)E,$

we have $\qquad\qquad (AB\times\widetilde{DE})C^* = (A\times\tilde{E})(B\times\tilde{D})C^*,$

or, since C is arbitrary, and $\widetilde{DE} = \tilde{E}\tilde{D}$,

$$(A\times\tilde{E})(B\times\tilde{D}) = AB\times\tilde{E}\tilde{D}. \qquad (5.6.6)$$

Applying this in the form

$$(A_1\times\alpha_1)(A_2\times\alpha_2) = A_1 A_2\times\alpha_1\alpha_2 \qquad (5.6.7)$$

we see that, as with induced representations, if A_1, A_2,... and α_1, α_2,... are representations of the same group, then the Kronecker products of A_1 and α_1, A_2 and α_2,... are also a representation of the group. Here too, the product of two irreducible representations is not itself usually irreducible. Reversing the order of the Kronecker multiplication, since it merely permutes the components, produces an equivalent representation. This also follows from the conclusion of the next paragraph.

In the mn diagonal elements of the Kronecker product of two matrices of orders m and n, each diagonal element of the first occurs once combined with each diagonal element of the second. Consequently,

$$\mathrm{Tr}(A\times B) = \mathrm{Tr}\,A\,.\,\mathrm{Tr}\,B. \qquad (5.6.8)$$

If the matrices are matrices from a representation of a group, these traces are the characters of the representations $A\times B$, A and B.

CHAPTER VI

REVIEW OF GROUPS TO ORDER 24

IT is probably clear to the student that the number of groups of any given low order is quite limited. As we have now covered all the essential points in the theory we shall require, and as the groups we shall meet in applications are mostly of order 24 or less, it would seem a useful consolidation process to review these groups. We shall work upwards, but certain classes of groups will be dealt with *in toto* on the first example we meet.

6.2. Cyclic groups

One limitation on the number of groups of a given order is contained in the following theorem:

THEOREM 6.2.1. *The only group of a prime order is the cyclic one.*

For the order of each element of the group must be a factor of the order of the group. Such a group differs from other cyclic groups in that all its representations are faithful ones, with the exception of the identical representation.

Concerning cyclic groups in general we may say that they are commutative, and all their irreducible representations are therefore one-dimensional. If n is prime, every element of c_n except I is of order n, but when n is composite, some elements are of lower order. Any one of the elements of order n may be selected as generating element; the order of its pth power is the denominator of p/n in its lowest terms. As generating elements, elements of order less than n lead to sub-groups. The n irreducible representations are obtained by associating with the generating element each of the n nth roots of unity. When the resulting number is complex, a more imaginable set of representations is obtained (as in the Argand diagram) by associating the generating element with a rotation through $2k\pi/n$, k being given the values $1,...,n$. The identical representation results from $k = n$.

6.3. S-groups

We have defined the group $s_{p \times q}$ as the group obtained by combining each element of c_p with each element of c_q; the combination is effectively one of commutative multiplication, and we sometimes write

$$s_{p \times q} = c_p \times c_q.$$

This group has pq elements, and both c_p and c_q are both sub- and factor groups of $s_{p \times q}$. When p is prime to q, $s_{p \times q}$ is the same as c_{pq}; this follows from the fact that if P is an element of c_p and Q is an element of c_q, $(PQ)^r = P^r Q^r$ and is not equal to I unless p and q are both factors of r. Thus the highest order of an element in $s_{p \times q}$ is the l.c.m. of p and q.

The group is commutative; its pq irreducible representations are obtained by associating any of its p representations with c_p and any of its q representations with c_q. Thus $s_{2 \times 2}$ has four elements, each (except I) of order 2; I, A, B, and AB. Its irreducible representations are

	I	A	B	AB
Γ_1	1	1	1	1
Γ_2	1	1	-1	-1
Γ_3	1	-1	1	-1
Γ_4	1	-1	-1	1

The restriction to two factors is unnecessary. It can be shown that all completely commutative groups (Abelian groups) are S-groups (including, for this purpose, c_n under S-groups) once the restriction is removed. Such a group of order $N = p^a q^b r^c ...$, where p, q, r,... are primes, must contain at least one element (and subgroup) of order pqr.... With this key we can determine the number of Abelian groups of any order; the method is best illustrated by an example, and we shall consider $N = 360$. In prime factors, $360 = 2^3 3^2 5$, and we have to consider the partition of these six factors between the orders of the cyclic groups of which any s_{360} must be a product.

The 3 factors 2 can be partitioned in 3 ways: 111, 21, 3
„ 2 „ 3 „ „ 2 „ : 11, 2
„ 1 factor 5 „ „ 1 way: 1

Each of the 3.2.1 ways of partitioning gives rise to a different S-group, and there are accordingly six Abelian groups of order 360. If we choose the partitions underlined—which is equivalent to writing $360 = (2^2 . 2)(3 . 3)(5)$—and then rearrange the factors by grouping together the first factor in each bracket, then the second, and so on, $360 = (2^2 . 3 . 5)(2 . 3) = 60.6$, we obtain the description $c_{60} \times c_6$, of the S-group corresponding to this partition. The other possible S-groups are $s_{30 \times 6 \times 2}$, $s_{120 \times 3}$, $s_{90 \times 2 \times 2}$, $s_{180 \times 2}$, and c_{360}. Any other method of factorizing 360, owing to the rule that '$c_p \times c_q = c_{pq}$ when p and q are prime to each other', merely yields one of the groups we have already found.

6.4. Groups up to order 6

The only commutative groups up to order 6 are c_1, c_2, c_3, c_4, $s_{2\times2}$, c_5, and c_6 ($= s_{3\times2}$). And a non-commutative group cannot be of order lower than six, for it must contain I, A, B, AB, and BA, all different, and it cannot be of order 5.

The smallest non-commutative group is, of course, the group $\pi_3 = \mathfrak{d}_3$, which we have used so much in illustrations, mainly because illustrations become so much more complex if larger groups are used. We shall use it once more in illustration, this time to show all the features of importance in a non-commutative group set out systematically with references to earlier sections at each stage. Its only disadvantage for this purpose is at the start, where either π_3 or $\mathfrak{d}_3$ can be taken as its definition.

As π_3 it consists of all the possible permutations of three objects X, Y, Z. These can be stated in the permutation notation of § 1.5. We then construct the multiplication table. An alternative permutation notation showing the elements as permutations of six objects is then furnished by Theorem 1.6.5.

$(X)(Y)(Z)$	I	A	B	C	D	E	$(I)(A)(B)(C)(D)(E)$
(XYZ)	A	B	I	E	C	D	$(IAB)(CDE)$
(XZY)	B	I	A	D	E	C	$(IBA)(CED)$
$(X)(YZ)$	C	D	E	I	A	B	$(IC)(AE)(BD)$
$(Y)(XZ)$	D	E	C	B	I	A	$(ID)(AC)(BE)$
$(Z)(XY)$	E	C	D	A	B	I	$(IE)(AD)(BC)$

There are four subgroups, $I\,C$, $I\,D$, and $I\,E$, all with structure c_2 and $I\,A\,B$ which has structure c_3. We must next examine the conjugation process, which we can do explicitly as follows (§ 4.2):

conjugated with

I A B C D E

produces

		I	A	B	C	D	E
The element	A	A	A	A	B	B	B
	B	B	B	B	A	A	A
	C	C	D	E	C	E	D
	D	D	E	C	E	D	C
	E	E	C	D	D	C	E

Or we may use the method of § 5.3; this has hardly any advantage here but is much faster with larger groups. The *normalizer* of A (the subgroup of all elements commuting with A) is $I\,A\,B$, of order 3, whence the class to which A belongs contains $\frac{6}{3} = 2$ elements, and conjugation with either C, D, or E shows that the other element of its class is B; similarly the normalizer of C is $I\,C$, of order 2, whence the class to which C belongs contains $\frac{6}{2} = 3$ members, the cosets of $I\,C$ are $AI\,AC = A\,E$ and $BI\,BC = B\,D$, and conjugation of C with either A or E gives D, conjugation with B or D gives E. By either method the classes are (1) I, (2) $A\,B$, (3) $C\,D\,E$. The multiplication table of the algebra of classes as in § 4.5 (where the table is given) follows at once.

Of the subgroups, only $I\,A\,B$ is invariant, and the factor group (§ 4.3) has the structure c_2. The degrees of the irreducible representations are the only solution of the equation $\sum m_r^2 = N$, viz. $1^2 + 1^2 + 2^2 = 6$. (Theorem 5.3.2. With larger groups there may be several solutions to this equation, but knowledge of these, and that all irreducible representations of any factor groups are among the representations sought, narrows the field very considerably.) These representations are given in § 5.5, together with their characters. Two other representations are of importance, the two permutation representations already quoted, each put into matrix form as permutations of the axes. The first is

$$I = \begin{bmatrix} 1 & 0 & 0 \\ 0 & 1 & 0 \\ 0 & 0 & 1 \end{bmatrix} \quad A = \begin{bmatrix} 0 & 1 & 0 \\ 0 & 0 & 1 \\ 1 & 0 & 0 \end{bmatrix} \quad B = \begin{bmatrix} 0 & 0 & 1 \\ 1 & 0 & 0 \\ 0 & 1 & 0 \end{bmatrix} \quad C = \begin{bmatrix} 1 & 0 & 0 \\ 0 & 0 & 1 \\ 0 & 1 & 0 \end{bmatrix} \quad D = \begin{bmatrix} 0 & 0 & 1 \\ 0 & 1 & 0 \\ 1 & 0 & 0 \end{bmatrix} \quad E = \begin{bmatrix} 0 & 1 & 0 \\ 1 & 0 & 0 \\ 0 & 0 & 1 \end{bmatrix}$$

with characters

$$3 \qquad\qquad 0 \qquad\qquad 0 \qquad\qquad 1 \qquad\qquad 1 \qquad\qquad 1$$

and the second, similarly obtained from the second permutation representation, is the regular representation, with characters

$$6 \qquad\qquad 0 \qquad\qquad 0 \qquad\qquad 0 \qquad\qquad 0 \qquad\qquad 0$$

By means of the orthogonality relations we can analyse these, or any other representation of this group, into the irreducible ones. The work is set out as follows:

Classes:		I	AB	CDE	R	P
Irreducible	Γ_1	1	1	1	$6+0+0 = 6$ (once)	$3+0+3 = 6$ (once)
representations	Γ_2	1	1	-1	$6+0+0 = 6$ (once)	$3+0-3 = 0$ (not)
	Γ_3	2	-1	0	$12+0+0 = 12$ (twice)	$6+0+0 = 6$ (once)
Other	Γ_R	6	0	0		
representations	Γ_P	3	0	1		

The procedure, stated in general terms, is as follows. Suppose that $\Gamma_Q = a_1\,\Gamma_1 \dotplus a_2\,\Gamma_2 \dotplus \dots$. Then if we multiply each of the numbers in the row Γ_Q by the (conjugate of the) corresponding number in the row Γ_i and by the number of elements in the class and add them all, then by the orthogonality relations, the result will be $a_i N$. This has been done in the two wide columns on the right for Γ_R and Γ_P, showing that Γ_R contains Γ_1 once, Γ_2 once, and Γ_3 twice—thereby showing that our assumption in § 5.5 that each irreducible representation of degree m occurs in the regular representation m times is self-consistent—and that Γ_P contains Γ_1 once and Γ_3 once (as we found them for the elements A and B only in § 5.2) and Γ_2 not at all.

In the remainder of this chapter we shall not treat groups in such detail; the student is recommended to use this section as a model by which to set out the study of at least one other non-commutating group, the results of which he may check by the statements later in this chapter.

6.5. Groups of orders 7 and 8

The only group of order 7 is, of course, c_7. It is with order 8 that the first abundance of choice appears, there being five groups of this order, but of these, the Abelian groups s_8, $s_{4\times2}$, and $s_{2\times2\times2}$ need no further comment (except as below on the orders of the elements).

The first non-commutating group is $\mathfrak{d}_4$, and we may here give an account of $\mathfrak{d}$ groups in general. Apart from their geometrical realization they may be defined abstractly by the relations

$$A^n = I, \qquad B_0^2 = I, \qquad B_0 A = A^{-1}B_0,$$

and each element may be given a separate symbol by writing

$$A^r = A_r, \qquad B_0 A^r = A^{-r}B_0 = B_r.$$

It is easily verified that the second of these equations is a consequence of the defining equations. The cyclic group of order n is invariant, and the multiplication table assumes the form

I	A_1	A_2	.	.	A_{n-1}	B_0	B_1	B_2	.	.	B_{n-1}
A_1	A_2	A_3	.	.	I	B_{n-1}	B_0	B_1	.	.	B_{n-2}
A_2	A_3	A_4	.	.	A_1	B_{n-2}	B_{n-1}	B_0	.	.	B_{n-3}
.	.	.	.	.	.	.	.	.	.	.	.
A_{n-2}	A_{n-1}	I	.	.	A_{n-3}	B_2	B_3	B_4	.	.	B_1
A_{n-1}	I	A_1	.	.	A_{n-2}	B_1	B_2	B_3	.	.	B_0
B_0	B_1	B_2	.	.	B_{n-1}	I	A_1	A_2	.	.	A_{n-1}
B_1	B_2	B_3	.	.	B_0	A_{n-1}	I	A_1	.	.	A_{n-2}
.	.	.	.	.	.	.	.	.	.	.	.
B_{n-1}	B_0	B_1	.	.	B_{n-2}	A_1	A_2	A_3	.	.	I

Examination of the conjugation properties shows that it is necessary to distinguish n odd from n even, since $B_r B_k B_r^{-1} = B_{2r-k}$ or, if k is greater than $2r$, B_{n+2r-k}. Thus if n is even, the B_r form two classes, r odd and r even, but if n is odd, all the B_r are in the same class. The classes and their representations and characters are

TABLE 6.5.1

n even

	I	A_k, A_{n-k} ($\frac{1}{2}n-1$ classes, each of two members)	$A_{\frac{1}{2}n}$ (invariant)	All B_{2k} (1 class of $\frac{1}{2}n$ members)	All B_{2k-1} (1 class of $\frac{1}{2}n$ members)
Γ_1	1	1	1	1	1
Γ_2	1	1	1	-1	-1
Γ_3	1	$(-1)^k$	$(-1)^{\frac{1}{2}n}$	1	-1
Γ_4	1	$(-1)^k$	$(-1)^{\frac{1}{2}n}$	-1	1
Γ_5	2	$2 \cos 2k\pi/n$	-2	0	0
.	.	.	.	.	.
Γ_{4+p}	2	$2 \cos 2kp\pi/n$	-2	0	0

There are $(\frac{1}{2}n-1)+4 = \frac{1}{2}n+3$ classes, and the same number of representations, p running from 1 to $\frac{1}{2}n-1$. The matrices in the two dimensional representations are, as would be supposed from the geometrical interpretation of $\mathfrak{d}_n$,

$$A_k = \begin{bmatrix} \cos 2kp\pi/n & \sin 2kp\pi/n \\ -\sin 2kp\pi/n & \cos 2kp\pi/n \end{bmatrix} \qquad B_k = \begin{bmatrix} \cos 2kp\pi/n & \sin 2kp\pi/n \\ \sin 2kp\pi/n & -\cos 2kp\pi/n \end{bmatrix}$$

n odd

As above except that as there are $\frac{1}{2}(n-1)$ classes among the A's and only one among the B's, there are $\frac{1}{2}(n+3)$ classes in all. Γ_3 and Γ_4 drop out, and p runs from $1 \ldots \frac{1}{2}(n-1)$.

The student can verify that in each case the relation $\sum m_r^2 = N$ holds.

Important realizations of the $\mathfrak{d}$ groups are the groups C_{nv}, D_n, and S_{nv} of crystals discussed in the next chapter. We shall find that C_{nv} is a $\Gamma_1 \dotplus \Gamma_5$ realization, D_n a $\Gamma_2 \dotplus \Gamma_5$ realization, and S_{nv} a $\Gamma_3 \dotplus \Gamma_5$ realization, occurring only when n is even.

The second non-commutating group of order 8 is the quaternion group, which we shall call q_4. We have given the multiplication table of this group in § 4.3, where we used it as an example of a group with a factor group of structure different from that of any subgroup. It will be found that its structure in respect of classes and characters is identical with that of $\mathfrak{d}_4$, thereby incidentally disposing of the impression given by some books that the character table of a group is unique to that group. We have called it q_4 because it is the first member of a series of groups q_{2n} which can be defined by

$$A^{2n} = I, \qquad B_0^2 = A^n, \qquad B_0 A = A^{-1} B_0;$$

they have the same classes and character tables as $\mathfrak{d}_{2n}$, but in the second degree representations the matrices for the B's are those of $\mathfrak{d}_{2n}$ multiplied by $i = \sqrt{(-1)}$.

With $A^2 = -1$, the quaternion group multiplication table is identical with that of the η-bases for the second degree matrix algebra discussed in § 3.9. The name derives from Hamilton's quaternion algebra, which was a three-dimensional vector calculus. In the product

$$(a_2\,\eta_2 + a_3\,\eta_3 + a_4\,\eta_4)(b_2\,\eta_2 + b_3\,\eta_3 + b_4\,\eta_4),$$

the coefficient of η_1 is the scalar product of the vectors (a_2, a_3, a_4) and (b_2, b_3, b_4), and the remaining terms give the vector product, a result which held greater promise when it was discovered than its subsequent development has justified.

It is interesting to compare the five groups of order 8 in the following way:

Group	No. of elements of order			
	1	2	4	8
$\mathfrak{c}_8$	1	1	2	4
$\mathfrak{s}_{4\times2}$	1	3	4	
$\mathfrak{s}_{2\times2\times2}$	1	7		
$\mathfrak{d}_4$	1	5	2	
$\mathfrak{q}_4$	1	1	6	

This table shows that no two of them are alike when examined in this way, and suggests that such a table, extended to groups of other order, may be a useful method for the rapid identification of the structure of a group presented in some realized form. A table is given at the end of this chapter for this purpose, and shows that the only groups up to order 24 which cannot be distinguished in this way are $\mathfrak{q}_4 \times \mathfrak{c}_2$ and $\mathfrak{s}_{6\times2\times2}$, both of which have seven elements of order 2 and eight each of orders 3 and 6 besides the identity.

6.6. Direct product and generalized dihedral groups

The process by which S-groups were derived from cyclic groups can be applied in general. If we have two groups $\mathfrak{G}_1$ and $\mathfrak{G}_2$ of operations which are entirely independent, of orders N_1 and N_2, then a group of order $N_1 N_2$ may be formed consisting of all possible pairs of operation one from each group. Even if the two sets of operations are not independent, we may denote by $\mathfrak{G}_1 \mathfrak{G}_2$ the set of $N_1 N_2$ operations obtained by performing any one operation from $\mathfrak{G}_2$ first and following it by any one operation from $\mathfrak{G}_1$. This set is a group only if it contains the same operations as the set $\mathfrak{G}_2 \mathfrak{G}_1$. An example where this is not so is that of the two subgroups $\mathfrak{G}_1 = I, C$ and $\mathfrak{G}_2 = I, D$ of π_3. $\mathfrak{G}_1 \mathfrak{G}_2$ is I, C, D, CD which is not a group. It is not necessary for each element of $\mathfrak{G}_1$ to commute with each element of $\mathfrak{G}_2$, all that is necessary is that $\mathfrak{G}_1 \mathfrak{G}_2$ and $\mathfrak{G}_2 \mathfrak{G}_1$ be the same set of elements, possibly in a different order.

The case when every element of $\mathfrak{G}_1$ commutes with every element of $\mathfrak{G}_2$ is specially important, however, and the resulting group is known as the direct product, $\mathfrak{G}_1 \times \mathfrak{G}_2$, of $\mathfrak{G}_1$ and $\mathfrak{G}_2$. If $\mathfrak{G}_1 \mathfrak{G}_2$ is a group, but the separate members of $\mathfrak{G}_1$ and $\mathfrak{G}_2$ do not commute, $\mathfrak{G}_1 \mathfrak{G}_2$ may conveniently be called a non-direct product. The rule that the order of the product of two elements of orders p and q is the l.c.m. of p and q holds for the new members in the direct product of groups which are themselves non-commuting, but does not necessarily hold for non-direct products.

If Y and G_1 are in $\mathfrak{G}_1$ and X and G_2 are in $\mathfrak{G}_2$, then

$$YXG_1 G_2(YX)^{-1} = YG_1 Y^{-1}XG_2 X^{-1} \qquad (6.6.1)$$

without transposing any elements which may not commute; thus the classes and class algebra of a direct product group are direct products of those of the simple groups. Hence if $\mathfrak{G}_1$ and $\mathfrak{G}_2$ contain p_1 and p_2 classes respectively, then $\mathfrak{G}_1 \times \mathfrak{G}_2$ contains $p_1 p_2$ classes.

Consequently it has $p_1 p_2$ irreducible representations. These are the $p_1 p_2$ Kronecker products of one of the p_1 irreducible representations of $\mathfrak{G}_1$ with one of the p_2 irreducible representations of $\mathfrak{G}_2$. To prove this—they are clearly representations, and it is only necessary to prove that they are irreducible. But if the characters of the elements a, b,... in a representation of $\mathfrak{G}_1$ are χ_{1a}, χ_{1b},..., while those of α, β,... in a representation of $\mathfrak{G}_2$ are $\chi_{2\alpha}$, $\chi_{2\beta}$,..., then if these representations are irreducible, we have

$$\sum_{ab...} \chi_{1a} \bar{\chi}_{1a} = N_1, \qquad \sum_{\alpha\beta...} \chi_{2\alpha} \bar{\chi}_{2\alpha} = N_2,$$

and these equations imply

$$\sum_{ab...} \sum_{\alpha\beta...} (\chi_{1a} \chi_{2a})(\bar{\chi}_{1a} \bar{\chi}_{2\alpha}) = \sum_{\substack{\text{all elements} \\ \text{of } \mathfrak{G}_1 \times \mathfrak{G}_2}} (\chi)_{a\alpha}(\bar{\chi})_{a\alpha} = N_1 N_2, \qquad (6.6.2)$$

which expresses the irreducibility of the representation of $\mathfrak{G}_1 \mathfrak{G}_2$.

One possible source of confusion may be cleared up at once. If $\mathfrak{G}_1$ and $\mathfrak{G}_2$ are the *same* group $\mathfrak{G}$, structurally, *and we confine our attention to those elements obtained by combining corresponding elements in $\mathfrak{G}_1$ and $\mathfrak{G}_2$*, then the result is also isomorphic with $\mathfrak{G}$, and the representation obtained is a representation of $\mathfrak{G}$. It is the one which in § 5.6 we called a Kronecker product representation. We have not proved the irreducibility of this representation of $\mathfrak{G}$, and in fact, as stated there, it is generally reducible.

The lowest order direct product of two non-commutating groups is $\mathfrak{d}_3 \times \mathfrak{d}_3$ which has thirty-six elements, concisely expressible as $1^1 2^{15} 3^8 6^{12}$ (i.e. one element of order 1, fifteen elements of order 2, and so on); this can be exhibited as the simultaneous rotations, proper and improper, of two equilateral triangles, or as the permutations of six objects in two sets of three which do not exchange objects between the sets. The next such groups are $\mathfrak{d}_3 \times \mathfrak{d}_4$ (order $1^1 2^{23} 3^2 4^8 6^{10} 12^4 = 48$), $\mathfrak{d}_3 \times \mathfrak{d}_5$ (order $1^1 2^{23} 3^2 5^4 6^{10} 10^{12} 15^8 = 60$), and $\mathfrak{d}_4 \times \mathfrak{d}_4$ (order $1^1 2^{35} 4^{28} = 64$).

The abstract rule for forming dihedral groups can be extended to

$$I \quad A_1,..., A_n \text{ is a group; } B_0 A_n = A_n^{-1} B_0 = B_n$$

provided that the A-group is a commutative one, for

$$B_0 A_m A_n = A_m^{-1} B_0 A_n = A_m^{-1} A_n^{-1} B_0 = (A_n A_m)^{-1} B_0,$$

which is satisfactory provided A_m and A_n commute. As every commutating group is an S-group, it will be convenient to describe the group thus formed from $\mathfrak{s}_{p \times q}$ as $\mathfrak{d}_{p \times q}$.

If $B_0 A_m = A_n B_0$, A_m and A_n are in the same class and must be of the same order. If A is of prime order, all its powers are of the same order, and a group defined by

$$A^n = I, \qquad B_0 A^m = A^{2m} B_0,$$

becomes possible. We meet one in the next section. But these are, for our needs, unprofitable excursions.

We may note that $\mathfrak{d}_n \times \mathfrak{c}_2$ is $\mathfrak{d}_{2n}$ if n is odd, but not if it is even. Such relations illustrate the difficulties faced by anyone who attempts a systematic summary of possible groups.

6.7. Groups of orders 9 to 24; symmetric groups

The groups $\mathfrak{c}_9$ and $\mathfrak{s}_{3 \times 3}$, $\mathfrak{c}_{10}$ and $\mathfrak{d}_5$, and $\mathfrak{c}_{11}$ need no further comment. Nor do the groups $\mathfrak{c}_{12}$, $\mathfrak{s}_{6 \times 2}$, $\mathfrak{d}_6$, and $\mathfrak{q}_6$. But there is a fifth group of order 12 which is crystallographically very important, namely, $\mathfrak{a}_4$. The groups $\mathfrak{a}_n$ are defined as the groups abstracted from the 'even' permutations of n objects, and are of order $\frac{1}{2} n!$ It will be convenient to discuss $\mathfrak{a}_4$ and π_4 together.

Consider the regular matrix representation of π_n. Since we are dealing with the *complete* permutation group, a change of coordinates corresponding to *any* permutation of the axes is possible. Consequently, by conjugation, a permutation $(A)(B)(CDE)...$ can be converted into *any* other permutation in which the number of the elements in the several brackets is the same. Thus all permutations of which the numbers of elements in the several brackets form the same partition of n are in the same class. A partition such as $(A)(B)(CDE)...$ is given the symbol $(1,1,3,...)$ or more briefly $(1^2 3...)$. An element of π_n of the form $(1^{n-r} r)$ is of order r. An element of the form $(a^p b^q c^r...)$ is the product of p elements of form $(1^{n-a} a)$, q elements $(1^{n-b} b)$, and so on, these elements involving permutations on different objects from among the n, and thus commuting; hence the order of the original element is the l.c.m. of $a, b, c,....$ The number of elements in the class $(\rho) = (a^p b^q c^r...)$ can be seen to be

$$h_\rho = \frac{n!}{a^p b^q ... p!\, q!...} \tag{6.7.1}$$

by the following argument. If the brackets are inserted into each of the $n!$ arrangements of the objects, permutations are repeated for two reasons, (1) it is immaterial with which of the objects within a given bracket we begin the bracket, and (2) if there are several brackets of the same size it is immaterial in what order they are written. For example, $(123)(456)$ is the same as $(231)(456)$ and as $(456)(123)$. With the aid of these formulae we can construct the following table for π_4.

Class	Partition	No. in class	Order of class	Type
$\mathcal{I}$	1^4	1	1	even
$\mathcal{A}$	21^2	6	2	odd
$\mathcal{B}$	2^2	3	2	even
$\mathcal{C}$	31	8	3	even
$\mathcal{D}$	4	6	4	odd
		$\overline{24}$		

The theory of the symmetric groups π_n is much more difficult than that of the simpler groups, and in this chapter we shall quote without proof some of the simpler results, since the more elaborate theory which we consider in Chapter XIII may well be omitted by many readers. The alternating group $\mathfrak{a}_n$ is a self-conjugate subgroup (as any subgroup of order $\frac{1}{2}N$ must be) and has the factor group $\mathfrak{c}_2$. The symmetric group has the two one-dimensional irreducible representations predictable from this factor group, namely, (*a*) the identical one, and (*b*) the alternating one which is 1 for members of $\mathfrak{a}_n$ and -1 for members of the coset, but it has no others. It has also two irreducible representations of degree $n-1$ and the rest are all of higher degree, except in π_3 (degrees 1, 1, 2) and π_4 (degrees 1, 1, 2, 3, 3). The representations are grouped in pairs known as conjugate pairs, each of which is the Kronecker product of the alternating representation with the other, and they differ in their characters only in the sign of the characters of those classes not in the alternating group. (For this use of the word 'conjugate' see § 13.6.) In certain symmetric groups some representations, usually those of highest degree, are self-conjugate, and their characters are zero for all classes not in the alternating group. The characters of $\mathfrak{a}_n$ are the same as those of π_n, except that classes of π_n belonging to partitions into unrepeated odd numbers split into two in the alternating group, their characters in the self-conjugate representations splitting into two conjugate complex or irrational numbers and in all other representations being halved. Apart from this feature all the characters of these groups are real. The group $\mathfrak{a}_n$ for $n > 4$ has no factor groups and is therefore, but rather ironically, described as simple; this fact is important in the theory of equations (the connexion being that the coefficients in algebraic equations are sums of permutations of products of its roots) and is the reason why no general solution can be obtained to equations of degree higher than the fourth.

The multiplication table of $\mathfrak{a}_4$ can only be obtained by patient application of the process of following one permutation by another and noting the result. There are four classes, $\mathscr{I}$ and $\mathscr{B}$ of π_4 and two halves of $\mathscr{C}$. The degrees of the representations are given by

$$12 = 1^2 + 1^2 + 1^2 + 3^2.$$

Three subgroups of order 2 are generated by the members of the class $\mathscr{B}$, and there are four subgroups of order 3 consisting of the identity and one member from each half of $\mathscr{C}$. The identity and all three members of $\mathscr{B}$ gives a subgroup of order 4 which is invariant with factor group $\mathfrak{c}_3$. This at once gives us the three first degree representations. The fourth irreducible representation can be obtained by the following procedure, which the student is strongly recommended to carry through as an exercise. He should first show that the proper rotations of a tetrahedron into itself are a realization of $\mathfrak{a}_4$, by considering how they permute the vertices. The corresponding matrices are then easily set up for the tetrahedron whose vertices are $(1, 1, 1)$, $(1, -1, -1)$, $(-1, 1, -1)$, and $(-1, -1, 1)$. With the aid of the orthogonality relations and the characters already known, he should then show that the character of this representation does not contain any of the first-degree characters, and must therefore be the missing one. The complete character table for reference is:

Class	$\mathscr{I}$	$\mathscr{B}$	$\mathscr{C}_a$	$\mathscr{C}_b$
No. in class	1	3	4	4
Γ_1	1	1	1	1
Γ_2	1	1	ω	ω^2
Γ_3	1	1	ω^2	ω
Γ_4	3	-1	0	0

Even more patience is required for constructing the multiplication table of π_4 in full! The classes have already been given; the degrees of the irreducible representations are given by $24 = 3^2+3^2+2^2+1^2+1^2$. Apart from the cyclic subgroups, there are four subgroups $\mathfrak{s}_{2\times 2}$, three are composed of the identity, two elements from $\mathscr{A}$, and one from $\mathscr{B}$, and conjugate into each other, and the fourth is composed of the identity with all three members of $\mathscr{B}$, and is self-conjugate with factor group π_3. There are four conjugate subgroups of order 6, structure π_3, three of order 8, structure $\mathfrak{d}_4$, and there is the invariant alternating subgroup of order 12. Thus the factor groups are π_3 and $\mathfrak{c}_2$ and these define the one- and two-dimensional irreducible representations. There are two geometrical interpretations in three dimensions, the complete rotation group, proper and improper, of a tetrahedron, and the proper rotations of a cube or octahedron. (Note: the rotations of a cube are the same as those of the octahedron whose corners are the centres of the cube faces.) By methods similar to those used for $\mathfrak{a}_4$, we can show that these two are the irreducible third-degree representations. The complete character table is, including certain information for reference back from Chapter XIII,

Class	$\mathscr{I}$	$\mathscr{A}$	$\mathscr{B}$	$\mathscr{C}$	$\mathscr{D}$	
Partition	1^4	21^2	2^2	31	4	
No. in class	1	6	3	8	6	
Representation						
Γ_1 {4}	1	1	1	1	1	
Γ_2 {31}	3	1	-1	0	-1	P and I rotations of tetrahedron
Γ_3 {22}	2	0	2	-1	0	
Γ_4 {211}	3	-1	-1	0	1	P rotations of cube
Γ_5 {1⁴}	1	-1	1	1	-1	

After this there are no surprises in the groups of order up to 24, the list of which is given in the table, page 70, except two unimportant groups of orders 20 and 21. The former is generated by $A = (12345)$

TABLE OF FINITE GROUPS TO ORDER 24

Columns 1–12 and ">12" give the *Number of elements of order* indicated (the figure in brackets after the ">12" entry is the order of those elements). The last five columns give the *No. of irreducible representations of order* 1, 4, 9, 16, 25.

Order	Symbol	1	2	3	4	5	6	7	8	9	10	11	12	>12	Number of classes	1	4	9	16	25
2	c_2	1	1												2	2				
3	c_3 a_3	1		2											3	3				
4	c_4	1	1		2										4	4				
	$s_{2×2}$	1	3												4	4				
5	c_5	1				4									5	5				
6	c_6 $s_{3×2}$	1	1	2			2								6	6				
	d_3 π_3	1	3	2											3	2	1			
7	c_7	1						6							7	7				
8	c_8	1	1		2				4						8	8				
	$s_{2×2×2}$	1	7												8	8				
	$s_{4×2}$	1	3		4										8	8				
	d_4	1	5		2										5	4	1			
	q_4	1	1		6										5	4	1			
9	c_9	1		2						6					9	9				
	$s_{3×3}$	1		8											9	9				
10	c_{10}	1	1			4					4				10	10				
	d_5	1	5			4									4	2	2			
11	c_{11}	1										10			11	11				
12	c_{12}	1	1	2	2		2						4		12	12				
	$s_{6×2}$	1	3	2			6								12	12				
	d_6	1	7	2			2								6	4	2			
	q_6	1	1	2	6		2								6	4	2			
	a_4	1	3	8											4	3		1		
13	c_{13}	1												12 (13)	13	13				
14	c_{14} $s_{7×2}$	1	1					6						6 (14)	14	14				
	d_7	1	7					6							5	2	3			
15	c_{15} $s_{3×5}$	1		2		4								8 (15)	15	15				
16	c_{16}	1	1		2				4					8 (16)	16	16				
	$s_{4×4}$	1	3		12										16	16				
	$s_{8×2}$	1	3		4				8						16	16				
	$s_{4×2×2}$	1	7		8										16	16				
	$s_{2×2×2×2}$	1	15												16	16				
	d_8	1	9		2				4						7	4	3			
	q_8	1	1		10				4						7	4	3			
	$d_{4×2}$	1	11		4										10	8	2			
	$q_{4×2}$	1	3		12										10	8	2			
17	c_{17}	1												16 (17)	17	17				
18	c_{18}	1	1	2			2			6				6 (18)	18	18				
	$s_{6×3}$	1	1	8			8								18	18				
	d_9	1	9	2						6					6	2	4			
	$d_{3×3}$	1	9	8											6	2	4			
	$d_3×c_3$	1	3	8			6								9	6	3			
19	c_{19}	1												18 (19)	19	19				
20	c_{20}	1	1		2	4					4			8 (20)	20	20				
	$s_{10×2}$	1	3			4					12				20	20				
	d_{10}	1	11			4					4				8	4	4			
	q_{10}	1	1		10	4					4				8	4	4			
	..	1	5		10	4									5	4			1	
21	c_{21}	1		2				6						12 (21)	21	21				
	..	1		14				6							5	3		2		
22	c_{22}	1	1									10		10 (22)	22	22				
	d_{11}	1	11									10			7	2	5			
23	c_{23}	1												22 (23)	23	23				
24	c_{24}	1	1	2	2		2		4				4	8 (24)	24	24				
	$s_{12×2}$	1	3	2	4		6						8		24	24				
	$s_{6×2×2}$	1	7	2			14								24	24				
	d_{12}	1	13	2	2		2						4		9	4	5			
	q_{12}	1	1	2	14		2						4		9	4	5			
	$d_{6×2}$	1	15	2			6								12	8	4			
	$q_{6×2}$	1	3	2	12		6								12	8	4			
	$d_4×c_3$	1	5	2	2		10						4		15	12	3			
	$q_4×c_3$	1	1	2	6		2						12		15	12	3			
	$d_3×c_4$	1	7	2	8		2						4		12	8	4			
	π_4	1	9	8	6										5	2	1	2		
	$a_4×c_2$	1	7	8			8								8	6		2		
48	$\pi_4×c_2$	1	19	8	12		8								10	4	2	4		
60	a_5	1	15	20		24									5	1		2	1	1

and $B = (1)(2345)$, or abstractly by

$$A^5 = I, \qquad B^4 = I, \qquad BA^n = A^{2n}B,$$

and there are similar groups of order $p(p-1)$ for every prime p. The next group of this type is of order $7.6 = 42$, and the new group of order 21 is a subgroup of it. This information should be sufficient for the inquisitive student, who will find these groups not as uninteresting as they are unimportant.

The group $\pi_4 \times \mathfrak{c}_2$ of order 48 is the only crystallographic group of order higher than 24, and in most other applications it is a group like π_n with n unspecified that needs to be considered. The group of rotations of the icosahedron and dodecahedron is $\mathfrak{a}_5$, but these solids are not crystallographically possible ones. For reference, the character table of π_5 is

Class	1^5	21^3	2^21	31^2	32	41	5
No. in class	1	10	15	20	20	30	24
Type of class	even	odd	even	even	odd	odd	even
Representation							
$\{5\}$	1	1	1	1	1	1	1
$\{41\}$	4	2	0	1	-1	0	-1
$\{32\}$	5	1	1	-1	1	-1	0
$*\{31^2\}$	6	0	-2	0	0	0	1
$\{2^21\}$	5	-1	1	-1	-1	1	0
$\{21^3\}$	4	-2	0	1	1	0	-1
$\{1^5\}$	1	-1	1	1	-1	-1	1

For that of $\mathfrak{a}_5$ delete the odd classes; the representations then become identical in pairs except for the one marked * which splits into two, the characters being halved in the first three classes. The class (5) also splits into two with identical characters except that in the * representations the characters are $\frac{1}{2}(1+\sqrt{5})$ and $\frac{1}{2}(1-\sqrt{5})$ in the two classes in one representation and conversely in the other.

CHAPTER VII

MISCELLANEOUS ADDENDA AND NUMERICAL METHODS

In this chapter we gather together a number of matters which have not been touched upon, or have been inadequately dealt with, in the foregoing chapters. Several of the points are included not so much because they are needed in the applications in this book as because some acquaintance with them will assist the student in further reading.

7.2. Matrices not reducible to diagonal form

For a reason which will appear later, matrices which cannot be reduced to diagonal form play no part in the theory of finite groups. Some little acquaintance with them will save the student unnecessary mystification in further reading, however, as well as preserving him from being puzzled by an accidentally made-up one.

We first consider the $n \times n$ matrix

$$U = \begin{bmatrix} 0 & 1 & 0 & . & . & 0 & 0 \\ 0 & 0 & 1 & . & . & 0 & 0 \\ . & . & . & . & . & . \\ 0 & 0 & 0 & . & . & 0 & 1 \\ 0 & 0 & 0 & . & . & 0 & 0 \end{bmatrix}$$

which has zeros everywhere except on the 'first super-diagonal' where it has 1's. By direct multiplication we find that U^r has zeros everywhere except for 1's on the rth super-diagonal, and that U^n and all higher powers of U are identically zero. A matrix such as U, all of whose powers higher than a certain one are zero, is described as nilpotent. The determinant of U is zero; its characteristic equation is $\lambda^n = 0$, and thus its eigenvalues are all zero. But it has only one eigenvector, namely, $(0, 0,..., 0, a)$, and it cannot be transformed to diagonal form.

A matrix of the form $aI + bU$ has powers

$$(aI+bU)^r = a^r I + ra^{r-1}bU + ... + {}^pC_r a^{r-p}b^p U^p + ...,$$

and this polynomial terminates at the term in U^r or U^{n-1}, whichever comes first. Its characteristic equation is simply $(a-\lambda)^n = 0$ and it has n eigenvalues all equal to a, but again it has only one eigenvector. Its effect may be contrasted with that of an ordinary matrix in the two diagrams of Fig. 5A. By eliminating U, U^2,..., U^{n-1} from the equations for $(aI+bU)^r$, $r = 1,..., n$, we obtain an equation of degree n satisfied by $aI+bU$.

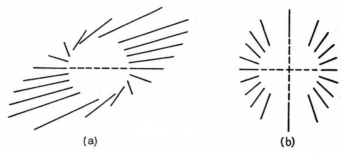

(a)   (b)

Fig. 5A. Showing effect on points on the unit circle of (a) $\begin{bmatrix} 2 & 2 \\ 0 & 2 \end{bmatrix}$, (b) $\begin{bmatrix} 1\cdot5 & 0 \\ 0 & 2 \end{bmatrix}$.

An examination of the remarks we have made about U and $aI+bU$ will show that they all express facts about the operators which are independent of the coordinate system. Any transform of any matrix of this type will therefore be equally pathological. Further, we must include under this head matrices such as

$$\begin{bmatrix} 3 & 1 & 0 \\ 0 & 3 & 0 \\ 0 & 0 & 3 \end{bmatrix} \quad \text{and} \quad \begin{bmatrix} 3 & 1 & 0 \\ 0 & 3 & 0 \\ 0 & 0 & 2 \end{bmatrix}$$

in which the matrix is of the type $aI+bU$ in any subspace.

It is clear that none of these matrices can give I by being raised to any finite power. Consequently no such matrix can ever occur in any representation of a finite group, which is why, on the whole, we have been able to ignore them. But we shall see in § 13.9 a representation of an infinite group which involves such matrices.

A diagonal matrix with all the diagonal terms equal to a, though its characteristic equation is $(\lambda-a)^n = 0$, not only satisfies this equation but also the simpler equation $M-aI = 0$. We have seen, however, that this is not true of a pathological matrix. Similarly a diagonal matrix with terms a (p times), b (q times),... satisfies not only the characteristic equation, which is $(\lambda-a)^p(\lambda-b)^q... = 0$, but also the simpler equation $(M-aI)(M-bI)... = 0$, which is known as the reduced characteristic equation, and once again the pathological type of matrix fails to do this. This conclusion is still valid if the matrices are transformed out of diagonal form. We thus have two methods of investigating a matrix in respect of this property: one is to attempt to transform it to diagonal form, and the other is to obtain the characteristic equation and its roots, and discover whether the matrix satisfies the fully reduced characteristic equation. The reduced characteristic equation of a pathological equation is defined as the equation of lowest order which it satisfies, and it can be obtained most easily by operating on an arbitrary vector with successive powers of the matrix until not all the vectors obtained are independent—taking suitable precautions against starting with a vector perpendicular to any of the eigenvectors. If the equation so obtained contains repeated roots, the matrix is pathological.

7.3. Numerical evaluation of determinants

The standard method for the evaluation of a determinant is that known as pivotal condensation; this method also determines the rank of a matrix. An alternative method, not very different, is described in the next section.

The method of pivotal condensation replaces a determinant or matrix of order $n \times n$ (or $n \times m$) by one of order $(n-1) \times (n-1)$ (or $(n-1) \times (m-1)$), and by repetition of this process the determinant is reduced to a number in at most $n-1$ stages. We may think of each stage in four steps. (1) Divide the elements of each row by the first* element in the row, and prefix that element as a factor. (2) Subtract the resulting first[†] row from every other row. (3) Clear of fractions by taking out as a factor the lowest common denominator in each row. (4) Expand by minors of the first* column. The result, at stage (3), is to show that

$$\begin{vmatrix} a_{11} & a_{12} & a_{13} & \cdot & \cdot \\ a_{21} & a_{22} & a_{23} & \cdot & \cdot \\ a_{31} & a_{32} & a_{33} & \cdot & \cdot \\ \cdot & \cdot & \cdot & \cdot & \cdot & \cdot \end{vmatrix} = \frac{1}{a_{11}^{n-2}} \begin{vmatrix} 1 & a_{12}/a_{11} & a_{13}/a_{11} & \cdot & \cdot \\ 0 & a_{11}a_{22}-a_{12}a_{21} & a_{11}a_{23}-a_{13}a_{21} & \cdot & \cdot \\ 0 & a_{11}a_{32}-a_{12}a_{31} & a_{11}a_{33}-a_{13}a_{31} & \cdot & \cdot \\ \cdot & \cdot & \cdot & \cdot & \cdot & \cdot & \cdot \end{vmatrix}$$

and the final stage, owing to the zeros, simply consists in omitting the first row and column of the right-hand side. The element a_{11} is known as the pivot element, but the element a_{rs} can be used as pivot element by replacing the asterisked 'first' in the above instructions by 'sth', and the daggered 'first' by 'rth', and including the factor $(-1)^{r+s}$ at the expansion stage. In practice, pivotal condensation is a much simpler process than the above outline would suggest, amounting to the following rule:

Omit the row and column containing the pivot element; replace every other element by the 2×2 minor which contains it and the pivot; prefix the factor $(-1)^{r+s} (a_{rs})^{n-2}$, where a_{rs} is the pivot element and n the order of the determinant. The sign of each minor is affixed as though the pivot were the leading element.

The leading element, a_{11}, should be used as pivot for preference, but a 1 anywhere on the principal diagonal is equally advantageous, and a 1 elsewhere almost equally so. We shall give an example after the next paragraph.

The first product of pivotal condensation consists of a determinant of all the minors of order 2 in the original determinant which contain a_{11}. A study of the second stage will show that the product obtained consists of all the 3×3 minors which contain a_{11} and a_{22} (assuming that leading pivots were used). Suppose that after p stages all the elements of the $(n-p) \times (n-p)$ determinant are zero—this shows that all $(p+1) \times (p+1)$ minors of the original determinant which contain $a_{11}, \ldots, a_{pp}$ are zero. This means the existence of linear relations

$$F_1(A_1^{**}, A_2^{**}, \ldots, A_p^{**}, A_{p+1}^{**}) = 0,$$
$$F_2(A_1^{**}, A_2^{**}, \ldots, A_p^{**}, A_{p+2}^{**}) = 0, \text{ etc.,}$$

where the double star is used to indicate that the vectors in question are from the columns of A indicated by the subscript, but consist only of the first p components and one other. But we could eliminate A_1^{**} from these two equations, or any other of the vectors $A_2^{**}, \ldots, A_p^{**}$, and by an extension of this process we could obtain linear relations between *any* p of the vectors $A_1^{**}, \ldots, A_n^{**}$. Alternatively or subsequently, we could apply this argument in row form, and thus in time prove equal to zero *any* $(p+1) \times (p+1)$ minor of A. Hence in the vanishing of all the minors of a given order actually calculated in pivotal condensation, we have all the data for asserting the vanishing of all minors of that order, and thus for asserting the rank of the matrix. If the matrix obtained after p stages is identically zero, then the original matrix was of rank p.

The following example will serve to illustrate the process:

$$\begin{vmatrix} 2 & 1 & 4 & 5 & 0 \\ 1 & 2 & 2 & 3 & 2 \\ 2 & 0 & 3 & 4 & 4 \\ 3 & 0 & 6 & 7 & -2 \\ 3 & 2 & 5 & 7 & 6 \end{vmatrix} = \frac{1}{2^3} \begin{vmatrix} 3 & 0 & 1 & 4 \\ -2 & -2 & -2 & 8 \\ -3 & 0 & -1 & -4 \\ 1 & -2 & -1 & 12 \end{vmatrix} = \frac{1}{2^3 3^2} \begin{vmatrix} -6 & -4 & 32 \\ 0 & 0 & 0 \\ -6 & -4 & 32 \end{vmatrix} = \begin{vmatrix} 0 & 0 \\ 0 & 0 \end{vmatrix}$$

The rank of the original 5×5 array is therefore 3. We add a recalculation using pivots which are not leading elements; the pivot element in each stage is starred.

$$
\begin{vmatrix}
2 & 1^* & 4 & 5 & 0 \\
1 & 2 & 2 & 3 & 2 \\
2 & 0 & 3 & 4 & 4 \\
3 & 0 & 6 & 7 & -2 \\
3 & 2 & 5 & 7 & 6
\end{vmatrix}
=
\begin{vmatrix}
-3 & -6 & -7 & 2 \\
2 & 3 & 4 & 4 \\
3 & 6 & 7 & -2 \\
-1^* & -3 & -3 & 6
\end{vmatrix}
=
\begin{vmatrix}
-3 & -2 & 16 \\
3 & 2 & -16 \\
3 & 2 & -16
\end{vmatrix}
=
\begin{vmatrix}
0 & 0 \\
0 & 0
\end{vmatrix}
$$

The method of pivotal condensation as used to determine rank may be applied to matrices which are not square. The final stage, if zeros are not reached earlier, is then a single row or column.

7.4. The reciprocal of a matrix

A second method of evaluating determinants is to subtract rows or columns from one another in a systematic manner so as to reduce the determinant to triangular form. Thus by subtracting suitable multiples of the first row from each of the others, then suitable multiples of the second row from the third,..., nth, and so on, we may go through the following stages

$$
\begin{vmatrix}
* & * & * & * & . & . \\
* & * & * & * & . & . \\
* & * & * & * & . & . \\
* & * & * & * & . & . \\
. & & & & . & .
\end{vmatrix}
=
\begin{vmatrix}
* & * & * & * & . & . \\
0 & * & * & * & . & . \\
0 & * & * & * & . & . \\
0 & * & * & * & . & . \\
. & & & & . & .
\end{vmatrix}
$$

$$
=
\begin{vmatrix}
* & * & * & * & . & . \\
0 & * & * & * & . & . \\
0 & 0 & * & * & . & . \\
0 & 0 & * & * & . & . \\
. & & & & . & .
\end{vmatrix}
=
\begin{vmatrix}
* & * & * & * & . & . \\
0 & * & * & * & . & . \\
0 & 0 & * & * & . & . \\
0 & 0 & 0 & * & . & . \\
. & & & & . & .
\end{vmatrix}
$$

and it is clear that the determinant is, when completely in triangular form, equal to the product of the diagonal elements, since this is the only one of its terms which does not contain at least one zero factor. The process can be continued by subtracting suitable multiples of the last row from each of the preceding rows, then suitable multiples of the last row but one from each row that precedes it, until the matrix is completely diagonal. This is unnecessary for evaluating the determinant, but provides a method for obtaining the reciprocal of a matrix.

For addition of k_1 times the first row to the second is equivalent to multiplying the matrix on the right by a matrix whose every diagonal element is unity, and all the rest zero except $a_{12} = k_1$. This matrix has determinant unity, which is one way of explaining why this operation, though changing the array as a matrix, leaves unaltered its value as a determinant (see § 7.8). The whole process described in the previous paragraph consists of a series of multiplications of the original matrix on the right by such matrices. (The resultant diagonal matrix should not be confused with the true 'diagonal form' of the original matrix!) This diagonal matrix may now be converted into I by one more multiplication on the right, this time by its own reciprocal. Now if

$$MABC... = I,$$
$$M = (ABC...)^{-1},$$
or
$$M^{-1} = ABC... = IABC....$$

Simultaneously with the above process, therefore, we carry out the same process in a parallel column on I and the final result is the reciprocal of the original matrix. The earlier and latter stages can be telescoped somewhat, and a simple layout is shown below:

original matrix
$$\begin{bmatrix} 0.889 & -0.385 & 0.250 \\ 0.254 & 0.866 & 0.433 \\ -0.383 & -0.322 & 0.866 \end{bmatrix} \quad \begin{array}{ccc} 1.000 & 0 & 0 \\ 0 & 1.000 & 0 \\ 0 & 0 & 1.000 \end{array}$$

$$\begin{array}{ccc} 0.889 & -0.385 & 0.250 \\ 0 & 0.975 & 0.361 \\ 0 & -0.488 & 0.974 \end{array} \quad \begin{array}{ccc} 1.000 & 0 & 0 \\ -0.285 & 1.000 & 0 \\ 0.430 & 0 & 1.000 \end{array}$$

$$\begin{array}{ccc} 0.889 & 0 & 0.393 \\ 0 & 0.975 & 0.361 \\ 0 & 0 & 1.154 \end{array} \quad \begin{array}{ccc} 0.887 & 0.395 & 0 \\ -0.285 & 1.000 & 0 \\ 0.288 & 0.500 & 1.000 \end{array}$$

$$\begin{array}{ccc} 0.889 & 0 & 0 \\ 0 & 0.975 & 0 \\ 0 & 0 & 1.154 \end{array} \quad \begin{array}{ccc} 0.788 & 0.224 & -0.342 \\ -0.376 & 0.843 & -0.314 \\ 0.288 & 0.500 & 1.000 \end{array}$$

$$\begin{array}{ccc} 1.000 & 0 & 0 \\ 0 & 1.000 & 0 \\ 0 & 0 & 1.000 \end{array} \quad \begin{bmatrix} 0.886 & 0.252 & -0.384 \\ -0.386 & 0.865 & -0.322 \\ 0.250 & 0.433 & 0.866 \end{bmatrix} \begin{array}{l} \text{reci-} \\ \text{procal} \\ \text{of} \\ \text{matrix} \end{array}$$

The original matrix was computed as an orthogonal one on a slide rule, and the reciprocal should, therefore, be its transpose. The numbers underlined are computed, and the rest copied; it will be seen that to obtain the reciprocal of an $n \times n$ matrix involves the computing of n^3 numbers (not counting the zeros). The determinant of the matrix

$$= 0{\cdot}889 \times 0{\cdot}975 \times 1{\cdot}154 = 1{\cdot}000.$$

By rearranging the order the process can be turned into one of repeated pivotal condensation and bordering, but the actual numerical work is if anything, increased by doing this.

7.5. Computation of eigenvalues and eigenvectors

The computation of eigenvalues and eigenvectors is most conveniently carried out, if the eigenvalues are real, by an iterative process due to Hotelling. Let the matrix be A and let X^* be an arbitrary vector whose expansion in terms of right-eigenvectors of A is

$$X^* = x_1 P_1^* + x_2 P_2^* + \ldots$$

and let the eigenvalues of A be $a_1, a_2, \ldots$. Then

$$AX^* = a_1 x_1 P_1^* + a_2 x_2 P_2^* + \ldots$$

and

$$A^r X^* = a_1^r x_1 P_1^* + a_2^r x_2 P_2^* + \ldots.$$

Then if $a_1 > a_2 > \ldots$, if r is large enough we shall have $a_1^r x_1 \gg a_2^r x_2 \gg \ldots$, provided that the x_i are not actually zero. Thus by repeatedly operating with A on an arbitrary vector the direction of the vector (that is, the ratios of its components) approaches more and more to that of the eigenvector with the eigenvalue of largest absolute value. This eigenvector is known as the 'dominant vector' of the matrix for this reason. When the dominant vector and its eigenvalue are known, the corresponding term can be removed from the proper expansion of the matrix (a separate determination of the left-eigenvector being made if the matrix is not symmetric), and the second largest eigenvalue then determined, and so on until the complete proper expansion is obtained.

Hotelling's method is therefore

1. Choose an arbitrary vector. A suitable choice is often $(1, 1, 1, \ldots)$ with signs inserted so that the row containing the largest diagonal element gives the largest total. Another is a vector made up of the square roots of the diagonal elements.

2. Operate on it repeatedly with the matrix until, to the required degree of accuracy, further operation does not change the ratios of the components but only multiplies them by the eigenvalue.
3. Normalize this vector so that its scalar square equals the eigenvalue. Form the outer product $(V**V)$ of this vector with itself. The result is the first term of the proper expansion. (This applies to symmetric matrices, to which the process is usually applied. The procedure with non-symmetric matrices is a little more complicated, as already noted.)
4. Subtract the result from the original matrix. The difference is called the first residual matrix. Repeat (1)–(3) until the analysis is complete.

In illustrating this process we shall also illustrate the whole process of factor analysis discussed in Chapter XI, applying it to a made-up example, in order that a number of points may be made clear as we go.

Consider then the matrix

$$\begin{bmatrix} 15 & 20 & 15 \\ 3 & 14 & 0 \\ 18 & 19 & 22 \\ 1 & 8 & 4 \\ 13 & 14 & 19 \end{bmatrix}$$

which may be taken to be the scores of five students in three tests. As explained in Chapter XI, the procedure is to form the correlation matrix and to evaluate its eigenvalues and eigenvectors. Our matrix is easily discovered by pivotal condensation to be of rank three but to remain so if a column of 1's is added, hence there are two significant factors only.

The calculation of the correlation matrix is set out as follows:

I	II	III	I²	II²	III²	I–II	I–III	II–III	
15	20	15	225	400	225	300	225	300	
3	14	0	9	196	0	42	0	0	
18	19	22	324	361	484	342	396	418	
1	8	4	1	64	16	8	4	32	
13	14	19	169	196	361	182	247	266	
50	75	60	728	1,217	1,086	874	872	1,016	(a)
			3,640	6,085	5,430	4,370	4,360	5,080	(b)
			2,500	5,625	3,600	3,750	3,000	4,500	(c)
			1,140	460	1,830	620	1,360	580	(d)
			228	92	366	124	272	116	(e)
			1·000	1·000	1·000	0·856	0·941	0·631	(f)

Columns 1–3 (or, in general, 1,..., t) are the original matrix. The next three (t) columns contain the squares of these numbers, and the next three ($\frac{1}{2}t(t-1)$) columns contain the products of numbers in two columns. In row (a) each column is summed, and in row (b) the total is multiplied by 5 (s). Row (c) contains in the second three columns the squares of the totals in the first three and in the last three columns the cross products of the totals. Row (d) is the difference between rows (b) and (c); the difference is positive in the square columns but may be negative in the product columns, especially if in one test good performance is registered by *low* marks. In row (e), we have divided row (d) by 5 (s); this is not necessary in calculating the correlation matrix. In row (f) the entry is 1·000 in each square column, but in the product columns the number in row (d) has been divided by the square root of the product of the numbers in row (d) in the corresponding square columns. The correlation matrix is now

$$\begin{bmatrix} 1\cdot000 & 0\cdot856 & 0\cdot941 \\ 0\cdot856 & 1\cdot000 & 0\cdot631 \\ 0\cdot941 & 0\cdot631 & 1\cdot000 \end{bmatrix}.$$

By dividing the first three sums in row (a) by 5 (s), we can obtain the mean score in each test. If this is subtracted from each score in the column it refers to, the matrix denoted in Chapter XI by μ is obtained. It, with a corresponding calculation of the correlation matrix, is given below:

I	II	III	I²	II²	III²	I–II	I–III	II–III
5	5	3	25	25	9	25	15	15
−7	−1	−12	49	1	144	7	84	12
8	4	10	64	16	100	32	80	40
−9	−7	−8	81	49	64	63	72	56
3	−1	7	9	1	49	−3	21	−7
0	0	0	228	92	366	124	272	116, etc.

It will be seen that the numbers formerly in row (e) are now obtained at row (a), and naturally the same correlation matrix is now found.

Before looking at the correlation matrix, we may apply the method of § 11.3, and apply Hotelling's method to the matrix $\tilde{\mu}\mu$. (We do not apply it to $\tilde{M}M$ as the irrelevant factor is a nuisance for the purpose of illustration.) It will be seen by an examination of their formation, that just as the correlation matrix is obtained from row (f), so $\tilde{M}M$ and $\tilde{\mu}\mu$ are obtained from rows (a) and (e) respectively.

The application of Hotelling's method to $\tilde{\mu}\mu$ is set out as follows:

$$
\begin{array}{ccccccc}
 & & & & a & b & c \\
228 & 124 & 272 & & 1 & 6 & 4 & & 16 \\
124 & 92 & 116 & & 1 & 3 & 2 & & 4 \\
272 & 116 & 366 & & 1 & 7 & 5 & & 25 \\
\hline
a' \quad 624 & 332 & 754 & & & & & & 45
\end{array}
$$

$$
\begin{array}{ccc}
1{,}368 & 744 & 1{,}632 \\
372 & 276 & 348 \\
1{,}904 & 812 & 2{,}562 \\
\hline
b' \quad 3{,}644 & 1{,}832 & 4{,}542
\end{array}
\qquad
630\begin{bmatrix} 4 \\ 2 \\ 5 \end{bmatrix}
\begin{bmatrix} 4 & 2 & 5 \end{bmatrix} =
\begin{bmatrix} 224 & 112 & 280 \\ 112 & 56 & 140 \\ 280 & 140 & 350 \end{bmatrix}.
$$

$$
\begin{array}{ccc}
912 & 496 & 1{,}088 \\
248 & 184 & 232 \\
1{,}360 & 580 & 1{,}830 \\
\hline
c' \quad 2{,}520 & 1{,}260 & 3{,}150
\end{array}
$$

The layout is simplified somewhat by the fact that it is applied to a symmetrical matrix. This operates on the vector headed by a to give the vector shown in row form as a'. Vector b has its components roughly in the same proportion as those of a', and the matrix operates on it to produce b'. Each row of the matrix is multiplied by the element of b in it, and the results are added to produce b'. The numbers in c are again a close approximation, in small integers, to those in b', and we find that, by a lucky chance owing to the artificiality of the example, this vector is the eigenvector we have been working towards, since each component of c' is exactly 630 times the corresponding one of c. The scalar square of c is evaluated as 45 and the first term of the proper expansion worked out. This is next subtracted from the original matrix, the result being

$$
\begin{bmatrix} 4 & 12 & -8 \\ 12 & 36 & -24 \\ -8 & -24 & 16 \end{bmatrix} =
\begin{bmatrix} 2 \\ 6 \\ -4 \end{bmatrix}
\begin{bmatrix} 2 & 6 & -4 \end{bmatrix}
$$

which is itself a dyad, as is to be expected since the original matrix was of order two. If we now put the two eigenvectors together we need not bother at this stage to normalize them, for we have

$$
\begin{bmatrix} 5 & 5 & 3 \\ -7 & -1 & -12 \\ 8 & 4 & 10 \\ -9 & -7 & -8 \\ 3 & -1 & 7 \end{bmatrix}
\begin{bmatrix} 4 & 1 \\ 2 & 3 \\ 5 & -2 \end{bmatrix} =
\begin{bmatrix} 45 & 14 \\ -90 & 14 \\ 90 & 0 \\ -90 & -14 \\ 45 & -14 \end{bmatrix}
$$

and we can divide the columns of this product by the scalar squares of the two vectors. Our final result by the procedure of § 11.3 is thus

$$
\begin{bmatrix}
5 & 5 & 3 \\
-7 & -1 & -12 \\
8 & 4 & 10 \\
-9 & -7 & -8 \\
3 & -1 & 7
\end{bmatrix}
=
\begin{bmatrix}
1 & 1 \\
-2 & 1 \\
2 & 0 \\
-2 & -1 \\
1 & -1
\end{bmatrix}
\begin{bmatrix}
4 & 2 & 5 \\
1 & 3 & -2
\end{bmatrix}
$$

showing the 5×3 matrix as the product of two matrices of orders 5×2 and 2×3 respectively.

The determination of the eigenvectors of the correlation matrix is more typical, because the result is not integral, and therefore not to be hit by a round figure guess. There is no need to set out the whole calculation again. The successive approximations go thus

$$R(1, 1, 1) = (2 \cdot 797, \ 2 \cdot 487, \ 2 \cdot 573)$$

$$= 2 \cdot 487(1 \cdot 12, \ 1 \cdot 00, \ 1 \cdot 07)$$

$$R(1 \cdot 12, \ 1 \cdot 00, \ 1 \cdot 07) = 2 \cdot 634(1 \cdot 14, \ 1 \cdot 00, \ 1 \cdot 05)$$

$$R(1 \cdot 14, \ 1 \cdot 00, \ 1 \cdot 05) = 2 \cdot 638(1 \cdot 131, \ 1 \cdot 000, \ 1 \cdot 044)$$

$$R(1 \cdot 131, \ 1 \cdot 000, \ 1 \cdot 044) = 2 \cdot 627(1 \cdot 130, \ 1 \cdot 000, \ 1 \cdot 0435)$$

$$R(1 \cdot 130, \ 1 \cdot 000, \ 1 \cdot 0435) = 2 \cdot 625(1 \cdot 130, \ 1 \cdot 000, \ 1 \cdot 0435)$$

It is very important not to stop one stage short of complete identity between operand and result, since the difference of two in the last place in the eigen*value* can have serious repercussions in later stages if ignored. The first dyad of the proper expansion is

$$
\begin{bmatrix}
0 \cdot 996 & 0 \cdot 001 & 0 \cdot 920 \\
0 \cdot 881 & 0 \cdot 780 & 0 \cdot 814 \\
0 \cdot 920 & 0 \cdot 814 & 0 \cdot 849
\end{bmatrix}
$$

and the first residual matrix is

$$
\begin{bmatrix}
0 \cdot 004 & -0 \cdot 025 & 0 \cdot 021 \\
-0 \cdot 025 & 0 \cdot 220 & -0 \cdot 183 \\
0 \cdot 021 & -0 \cdot 183 & 0 \cdot 151
\end{bmatrix}
$$

to which in general the same method should be applied to obtain the second eigenvector. The importance of an absolutely accurate value of the eigenvalue is that none of the first eigenvector dyad must be left in. In this case, however, the first residual matrix is in dyad form, since

$$
\begin{bmatrix} 0 \cdot 053 \\ -0 \cdot 470 \\ 0 \cdot 389 \end{bmatrix} \begin{bmatrix} 0 \cdot 053 & -0 \cdot 470 & 0 \cdot 389 \end{bmatrix} = \begin{bmatrix} 0 \cdot 003 & -0 \cdot 025 & 0 \cdot 021 \\ -0 \cdot 025 & 0 \cdot 221 & -0 \cdot 183 \\ 0 \cdot 021 & -0 \cdot 183 & 0 \cdot 151 \end{bmatrix}.
$$

The value 0·053 of the first component is in some doubt; a possible error of one in the last place of 0·004 makes its square root quite unreliable, and the value quoted is a compromise between 0·052 and 0·054 calculated from the non-diagonal terms. A value 0·056 is required to make this vector orthogonal to the first one. The conclusion is left in this form as an object lesson that it pays in the long run to keep a couple of extra figures in the calculation until the very last moment.

As explained in Chapter XI, the eigenvectors of the correlation matrix can be used to factorize the matrix of scores not only after the origin has been adjusted to a mean of zero as here, but after the scale has also been adjusted in each column to a standard deviation of unity.

The rapid success of the method depends on a wide separation of the eigenvalues—in the above examples the ratios were $630/56 = 11+$ and $2 \cdot 625/0 \cdot 375 = 7$—and if they are close it is much slower. The fact that the two ratios $11+$ and 7 are not equal suggests a method whereby in cases of difficulty equal or nearly equal eigenvalues could be separated. Complex eigenvalues present yet another problem which does not occur in factor analysis.

7.6. The orthogonality relations

The proof of the orthogonality relations given in § 5.5 is essentially that given by Littlewood (pp. 45–46) and by Bhagavantam and Venkatarayudu (p. 197), but neither proves that the regular representation contains each irreducible representation of degree m exactly m times, in a manner independent of the orthogonality relations themselves. The proof based on these relations was given, in effect, at the end of § 6.4, and an independent proof is difficult to come by. I have kept the circular proof in § 5.5 for a didactic reason—that it provides an easier understanding of the nature of these relations than does the rigorous proof which is more abstract in nature.

In the usual proof of the orthogonality relations a number of essential results are established *en route*. The first of these is that if a matrix C commutes with all matrices M_r of a representation of a group, then either C is a multiple of the identical matrix or the representation is reducible. This is Theorem 5.2.1, and applies to the simultaneous reducibility of any collection of matrices, whether a group or not.

It is necessary next to show that every representation of a finite group is equivalent to a unitary one. This we do by stating explicitly the transformation which will make it so. Let the representation consist of the matrices $M_1,..., M_n$, and let $T = \sum\limits_{1}^{n} M_r \tilde{M}_r$, where, to save over-elaboration of notation, $\tilde{M}_r$ denotes the associate, and not the transpose, of M_r. Then T is Hermitian. Let t be the transform UTU^{-1} of T to (real, since T is Hermitian) diagonal form by the unitary matrix U. (The possibility of doing this with a unitary matrix was shown in § 4.7.) Then the matrices $L_r = t^{-\frac{1}{2}}UM_rU^{-1}t^{\frac{1}{2}}$ are a unitary representation of the group. To prove this we have to show (1) that $L_r \tilde{L}_r = I$, and (2) that $L_r L_s = L_t$ if $M_r M_s = M_t$. The latter is obvious. And

$$L_r \tilde{L}_r = (t^{-\frac{1}{2}}UM_r . U^{-1}t^{\frac{1}{2}})(t^{\frac{1}{2}}\tilde{U}^{-1} . \tilde{M}_r \tilde{U}t^{-\frac{1}{2}})$$

$$= t^{-\frac{1}{2}}UM_r . T . \tilde{M}_r \tilde{U}t^{-\frac{1}{2}} \qquad \text{(since } \tilde{U}^{-1} = U\text{)}$$

$$= \sum_{s=1}^{n} t^{-\frac{1}{2}}U . M_r M_s \tilde{M}_s \tilde{M}_r . \tilde{U}t^{-\frac{1}{2}}$$

$$= t^{-\frac{1}{2}}U . T . \tilde{U}t^{-\frac{1}{2}}$$

$$= t^{-\frac{1}{2}}tt^{-\frac{1}{2}} = I.$$

Thus the representation $M_1,..., M_n$ is equivalent to the unitary one $L_1,..., L_n$.

The next stage is known as Schur's lemma, and is that if $M_1,..., M_g$ and $N_1,..., N_g$ are both irreducible representations of a group, and $XM_r = N_r X$ for all r, then either (i) $X = 0$, or (ii) X is square and non-singular, and M and N are equivalent. To prove this we make M and N unitary and then note that this implies, from all $XM_r = N_r X$ that $M_r^{-1}\tilde{X} = \tilde{X}N_r^{-1}$ (all r), i.e. $M_r \tilde{X} = \tilde{X}N_r$ (all r), whence

$$X(\tilde{X}N_r) = X(M_r \tilde{X}) = (XM_r)\tilde{X} = (N_r X)\tilde{X},$$

whence $X\tilde{X}$ is a scalar multiple of I, say kI. A similar argument applies to $\tilde{X}X$. Now $(AB)_{rs} = *A_r B_s*$, and if X is an $m \times n$ matrix, then $\tilde{X}X = I$ implies the existence of m perpendicular vectors in an n-space, while $X\tilde{X} = I$ implies n perpendicular vectors in an m-space. These can only be simultaneously possible if $m = n$, and X is square. With X square, $k = 0$ implies $X = 0$, and $k \neq 0$ implies that X^{-1}

exists, and $N_r = X M_r X^{-1}$ (every r), whence M and N are equivalent representations.

We now restate Schur's lemma in the form that if M and N are inequivalent irreducible representations, the equations $X = N_r X M_r^{-1}$ (all r) have no solution except $X = 0$. By the argument of § 5.6, these equations can be regarded as stating that there is no *vector* X which is invariant under all the n Kronecker product transformations

$$N_r \times \tilde{M}_r^{-1} = N_r \times M_r.$$

(Here again we assume that the representation M has been transformed to an equivalent unitary one.) But $\sum_{r=1}^{n} (N_r \times M_r) X$ should be invariant, whatever X, and therefore must be zero for all X, except when M and N are equivalent. But this is to say that when M and N are inequivalent $\sum_{r=1}^{n} (N_r \times M_r)$ is identically zero. Expanding this and taking the trace leads at once to the orthogonality relations for inequivalent representations. When M and N are equivalent then, again by Schur's lemma, only a scalar multiple of the unit matrix is invariant, i.e. the vector X with every $X_{kk} = 1$ and every $X_{jk} = 0$ $(j \neq k)$ is an eigenvector of $\sum_{r=1}^{n} (N_r \times M_r)$ with eigenvalue 1. Expansion of this and summation over $k = 1, ..., n$ leads to the orthogonality relation for equivalent representations. These two relations suffice to analyse the regular representation, and the other two (summation over the representations) then follow by the previous proof.

As a corollary to this work we may cite Burnside's theorem, that the N $m \times m$ matrices which form an m-dimensional irreducible representation of a group of order N span the whole algebra of $m \times m$ matrices; regarding the matrices as m^2-dimensional vectors, they span the whole m^2-space—there is no vector perpendicular to them all, no matrix L such that $\text{tr}(LU) = \sum_{k} L_{ik} U_{ki} = 0$ for all N of the matrices U.

Fundamental to any more rigorous treatment of these matters is the distinction between those sets of matrices which are simultaneously transformable to the form $\begin{bmatrix} A & 0 \\ 0 & C \end{bmatrix}$, those which cannot be transformed to this form but can be simultaneously transformed to the form $\begin{bmatrix} A & B \\ 0 & C \end{bmatrix}$, and those which cannot be simultaneously transformed to either form. The last are termed irreducible, the second type incompletely reducible or non-analysable, and the first type completely reducible or analysable. As explained in § 7.2 (though not fully), in dealing with finite groups it is unnecessary to distinguish complete and incomplete reducibility, and we shall not pursue the subject further except in so far as it is forced upon us in dealing with continuous groups, but the student will have to bear it in mind in any further reading.

7.7. Operator space

The considerations in this section are required only for Chapter XVIII, and unless the reader has made himself completely familiar with the preceding work they should probably be omitted on first reading. Throughout this section, X, Y,..., with or without stars, are vectors in an n-space; A, B,... are operators in this space when written without stars, but with stars they are the same n^2 quantities considered as vectors in an n^2-space.

If $B = X**Y$, where $X*$ is a right-eigenvector of A belonging to the eigenvalue a, then

$$AB = AX**Y = aX**Y = aB. \qquad (7.7.1)$$

If, further, $*Y$ is a left eigenvector of C belonging to the eigenvalue c, then

$$ABC = AX**YC = acB. \qquad (7.7.2)$$

The former case can be brought under the latter by putting $C = I$.

Now, by (5.6.4 a),

$$ABC = acB \sim (A \times \tilde{C})B* = acB*. \qquad (7.7.3)$$

Thus $B*$ is an eigenvector of $A \times \tilde{C}$. Further, $A \times \tilde{C}$ is an $n^2 \times n^2$ operator with n^2 eigenvalues. As there are just n^2 products ac, we have here all the eigenvalues of $A \times \tilde{C}$, and if no two a's nor any two c's are alike, then we have a unique set of orthogonal $B*$. When $C = I$, $*Y$ is arbitrary, because every vector is an eigenvector of I. In this case we must choose a set of n independent $*Y$ and we shall obtain a set of n independent $B*$ to each eigenvalue a. This procedure also holds for repeated eigenvalues (repeated less than n times) of C.

The scalar square of B^* is

$$*BB^* = \sum_{i,j} (x_i y_j)^2$$
$$= \sum_{i,j} x_i^2 y_j^2$$
$$= \sum_i (x_i^2) \sum_j (y_j^2)$$
$$= *XX^* *YY^*,$$

and the scalar product of two B's, $B_1 = X^**Y$ and $B_2 = \xi^* *\eta$, is

$$*B_1 B_2^* = \sum_{i,j} (\bar{x}_i \bar{y}_j)(\xi_i \eta_j)$$
$$= \sum_{i,j} (\bar{x}_i \xi_i)(\bar{y}_j \eta_j)$$
$$= \sum_i \bar{x}_i \xi_i . \sum_j \bar{y}_j \eta_j$$
$$= *X\xi^* *Y\eta^*, \tag{7.7.4}$$

which can be written in the clumsy but memorable form

$$*(X^**Y)(\xi^* *\eta)^* = *X\xi^* *Y\eta^*. \tag{7.7.5}$$

Thus $*B_1 B_2^*$ is zero provided *either* $*X\xi^* = 0$ or $*Y\eta^* = 0$, and *a fortiori* if both relations hold, and it is unity provided *both* $*X\xi^* = 1$ and $*Y\eta^* = 1$. We can state this as a theorem:

Theorem 7.7.6. *An orthogonal set of X^* with an orthogonal set of $*Y$ give rise to an orthogonal set of $*B$, and an orthonormal set of X^* with an orthonormal set of $*Y$ give rise to an orthonormal set of $*B$.*

The corresponding expression $(X^**Y)^**(\xi^* *\eta)$ is the same as $X^**Y \times \xi^* *\eta$ subject possibly to a reservation about the order of the components.

If
$$AB = aB$$

we shall call B an eigenoperator (on the right) of A, or sometimes an eigensymbol. The hypothesis is equivalent, as we have seen, to the statement that B^* is an eigen*vector* of $A \times I$.

If A is idempotent, then
$$AA = 1A$$

and A is its own eigensymbol with eigenvalue 1. Let A have r eigenvalues equal to 1 and $n-r$ equal to 0. Then the proper expansion of A contains r terms and the trace of A is r. We have described as 'loosely idempotent' an operator whose pth power is itself multiplied by the pth power of a scalar; such an operator is a multiple of an idempotent operator, and can be normalized to strict idempotency by dividing it by the scalar, and when this has been done its trace will be r.

If an operator B cannot be expressed in the form X^**Y with X^* an eigenvector of another operator A, this may be for one of two reasons: (1) that B cannot be expressed in this form at all, because it is not a dyad, or (2) that when B is in the form $X^*{}^*Y$, X^* is not an eigenvector of A. Let Z_1^*, Z_2^*,... be a set of normal orthogonal eigenvectors of A. (They will be unique unless A has repeated eigenvalues.) If we put

$$B = Z_1^*{}^*Y_1 + Z_2^*{}^*Y_2 + \ldots + Z_n^*{}^*Y_n,$$

then the product $\quad {}^*Z_r B = {}^*Z_r Z_r^*{}^*Y_r = {}^*Y_r$

is an explicit expression for the ${}^*Y_r$. Further, the resulting expression obviously operates on each of the n Z_r in the same way as B does, and as the n Z_r are independent, this shows that the expansion really does equal B. Thus an arbitrary operator B can be expanded in terms of n eigensymbols of a given operator A.

If B is idempotent, we can put $A = B$. Then $Y_r = 0$ for every $b_r = 0$; that is, the number of terms in the expansion is equal to the number of non-zero eigenvalues. If B is factorizable, i.e. can be expressed in the form $X^*{}^*Y$ at all, then we know that it has only one non-zero eigenvalue (§ 3.8), and we see that in this case we shall factorize it successfully by this procedure without worrying about alternative (2) of the previous paragraph.

We summarize the conclusions of § 3.8 and the present section so far:

If an operator is factorizable, it is a numerical multiple, k, of an idempotent operator, and has only one non-zero eigenvalue. On division by k, which is the non-zero eigenvalue, its trace will be unity.

The trace of an $n \times n$ idempotent operator is an integer r, $1 \leqslant r \leqslant n$, which is equal to the number of times unity appears as an eigenvalue. Unless $r = 1$ the operator is not factorizable, but it can be expressed as the sum of r factorizable operators.

A singular operator is only loosely idempotent if all its eigenvalues are equal.

An equation between operators $ABC = DEF$ may be interpreted in various ways: (1) by regarding C and F as vectors in an n^2-space, and AB and DE as the operators $AB \times I$ and $DE \times I$ in this space, (2) by regarding B and E as the vectors with $A \times \tilde{C}$ and $D \times \tilde{F}$ as the operators, or (3) by writing $ABCG = DEFG$ where G is an arbitrary vector in the n^2-space and $ABC \times I$ and $DEF \times I$ are the operators in this space, as well as (4) the usual one where $ABCG^* = DEFG^*$, and G^* is an n-vector.

Considering the equivalent relations

$$Y^* = CX^*, \qquad {}^*Y = {}^*X\tilde{C},$$

and using the relations (4.6.4), we find that

$$Y^+ = RCR^{-1}X^+, \qquad {}^+Y = {}^+X\overline{(RCR^{-1})},$$

$$Y^\circ = \tilde{R}^{-1}C\tilde{R}X^\circ, \qquad {}^\circ Y = {}^\circ X\overline{(\tilde{R}^{-1}C\tilde{R})},$$

whence it is convenient to regard

$$X^+ = RX^* \qquad \text{and} \qquad C^+ = (R \times \tilde{R}^{-1})C^*$$

as associated contravariant transformations in the n-space and in the n^2-space, and

$$X^\circ = R^{-1}X^* \qquad \text{and} \qquad C^\circ = (\tilde{R}^{-1} \times R)C^*$$

as the corresponding covariant transformations. It follows that $X^+ {}^\circ Y$ is a contravariant vector in the n^2-space and $X^\circ {}^+Y$ is a covariant vector. (This conclusion is valid in either orthogonal or unitary convention.)

7.8. Some miscellaneous proofs

We first prove the theorem that the trace of a matrix is unaltered by conjugation by a direct method. If $P = ABC$, then

$$P_{ru} = \sum_s \sum_t A_{rs} B_{st} C_{tu},$$

and hence

$$P_{rr} = \sum_s \sum_t A_{rs} B_{st} C_{tr},$$

so that the trace of P is given by

$$\sum_r P_{rr} = \sum_s \sum_t \left(\sum_r C_{tr} A_{rs} \right) B_{st},$$

and if $C = A^{-1}$, the expression in brackets is unity for $t = s$, and zero for $t \neq s$, whence the theorem is proved.

The corresponding theorem about the determinants is a special case of the theorem that the determinant of the product of two matrices is the product of their determinants. If $AB = C$, then the determinant of A may be written $\sum \pm a_{1r} a_{2s}, \ldots$ and the determinant of B similarly. If the determinants are of order $n \times n$ each contains $n!$ terms. The product of these determinants will consist of the sum of the $(n!)^2$ terms of the form $\pm a_{1r} a_{2s} \ldots b_{1p} b_{2q} \ldots$. The determinant of the product will consist of the terms

$$\pm c_{1i} c_{2j} \ldots = (a_{11} b_{1i} + a_{12} b_{2i} + \ldots)(a_{21} b_{1j} + a_{22} b_{2j} + \ldots) \ldots$$

and by counting up we find that each term in $|A||B|$ occurs once and once only in $|C|$, and with the same sign (which depends on whether the permutation $123\ldots123\ldots$ to $rst\ldots pqr\ldots$ is an even one or an odd one and vice versa). Thus the two are identical.

As particular cases of this, the determinants of A and A^{-1} are reciprocals, and the determinant of $A^{-1}BA$ is equal to that of B.

PART II

APPLICATIONS OF FINITE GROUPS

CHAPTER VIII

THE EXTERNAL FORMS OF CRYSTALS

NOTE: *For this chapter only Chapters I and II of Part I are essential to the argument; there are references to representations and to factor groups which can be passed over without disturbing the continuity.*

METAPHORICALLY, as well as literally, the study of the external forms of crystals is superficial. But to take it first is historically correct, and it enables us to isolate for preliminary study certain problems which can be solved independently of any questions of internal structure. Crystals, even those of the same substance grown under similar conditions, can show a variety of shapes (known to crystallographers as 'habits'), but characteristic of them all is the occurrence of plane faces, and a tendency for a given type of face to occur several times in symmetrically disposed positions. A crystal in which all such symmetrically disposed faces are congruent is called a perfect crystal. Imperfections in crystals, as when an expected face fails to appear, or varies in size, or varies in shape owing to variations in size of neighbouring faces, can usually be explained by factors impeding growth in certain directions—e.g. the walls of the containing vessel, or temperature or concentration gradients in the solution. It is therefore possible to classify crystals according to the types of symmetry they show when perfect, and to establish this classification on a group-theoretic basis will be our first task. Because the subject is suffering from a 'spring-clean' on the question of notation, we shall have throughout to deal with two parallel notations. This is unfortunate but necessary as long as books using the old notation remain in use. Both notations provide symbols for (a) the symmetry elements, and (b) the symmetry groups.

The symmetry elements are what we have hitherto called the proper and improper rotations of the crystal into itself. Such transformations are real and preserve lengths; they are therefore orthogonal transformations. The eigenvalues must be of modulus unity (or they would not preserve the lengths of eigenvectors) and, since the characteristic equation is a real cubic, one of the eigenvalues must be real. Since the trace is real, the other two roots, if complex, must be conjugates. These considerations restrict us to the alternatives

$$\begin{bmatrix} 1 & 0 & 0 \\ 0 & e^{i\theta} & 0 \\ 0 & 0 & e^{-i\theta} \end{bmatrix} \text{ and } \begin{bmatrix} -1 & 0 & 0 \\ 0 & e^{i\theta} & 0 \\ 0 & 0 & e^{-i\theta} \end{bmatrix}$$

for the diagonal form, since the wholly real diagonal forms can be brought under one of these with $\theta = 0$ or π, rearranging the order if necessary. The first type has a determinant equal to 1 and is a proper rotation; the second has a determinant of -1 and is an improper rotation. Except in one case of each type, the direction shown here as the X-axis has a unique character, and is known as the axis of the rotation. In real form these elements are

$$(a) \begin{bmatrix} 1 & 0 & 0 \\ 0 & \cos\theta & \sin\theta \\ 0 & -\sin\theta & \cos\theta \end{bmatrix} \text{ including } (a_1) \begin{bmatrix} 1 & 0 & 0 \\ 0 & 1 & 0 \\ 0 & 0 & 1 \end{bmatrix} \text{ and } (a_2) \begin{bmatrix} 1 & 0 & 0 \\ 0 & -1 & 0 \\ 0 & 0 & -1 \end{bmatrix}$$

and

$$(b) \begin{bmatrix} -1 & 0 & 0 \\ 0 & \cos\theta & \sin\theta \\ 0 & -\sin\theta & \cos\theta \end{bmatrix} \text{ including } (b_1) \begin{bmatrix} -1 & 0 & 0 \\ 0 & 1 & 0 \\ 0 & 0 & 1 \end{bmatrix} \text{ and } (b_2) \begin{bmatrix} -1 & 0 & 0 \\ 0 & -1 & 0 \\ 0 & 0 & -1 \end{bmatrix}$$

We are not unfamiliar with these operators, but it is worth showing without appeal to geometrical intuition that they include all the possible rotations about a given axis.

Since the improper rotations have a determinant of -1, two improper rotations performed in succession give rise to a proper rotation, and the improper rotations are therefore, in any given group, a coset of the proper rotations equal in number to them if present at all. It is thus convenient, in designing a notation, to design one first for the proper rotations, and then, selecting one arbitrary improper rotation, to show the improper rotations as products of this one with the proper rotations. Both (b_1) and (b_2) commute with all (a), and either one might be conveniently selected. (b_1) has the advantage that $(b) = (a)(b_1)$, but (b_2) has the advantage of being the one which is not associated with any particular axis. We see that $a(\theta)(b_2) = b(\theta+\pi)$, in a fairly obvious notation, so that the advantage of (b_1) in this respect is slight. (b_1) is a reflection across the plane perpendicular to the X-axis, and (b_2) is the 'inversion', by which each point becomes the one an equal distance from the centre of the crystal but in a diametrically opposite direction from it.

The order of the element (a) is $2\pi/\theta$ or the first integral multiple of it which is itself an integer, and thus if such an element is to be a member of a finite group we must have $\theta = 2k\pi/n$. If k/n is in its lowest terms, some multiple of it (mod 2π) will be equal to $2\pi/n$, and the cyclic group based on it will be the same as the cyclic group based on $2\pi/n$. Since $a(\theta)a(\phi) = a(\theta+\phi)$, if the elements $a(2\pi/p)$ and $a(2\pi/q)$ are both in a group, it will be possible (by the theorem known as Euclid's algorithm, that if p and q are prime to each other integers m and n can be found such that $mp-nq = 1$) to generate from them the element $a(2\pi/r)$, where r is the l.c.m. of p and q. This generates a cyclic group which includes all the elements generated by $a(2\pi/p)$ and $a(2\pi/q)$. Hence the only possible groups of proper rotations about a single axis are the groups $\mathfrak{c}_n$ generated by $a(2\pi/n)$.

The order of the element $b(2\pi/n)$ is n if n is even, but if n is odd, its nth power is (b_1), and its order is $2n$, its odd powers being (b) elements and its even powers (a) elements. When n is odd, therefore, the group based on $a(2\pi/n)$ is a subgroup of the group based on $b(2\pi/n)$. When n is even, the corresponding subgroup is that based on $a(4\pi/n)$; (b_1) is not a member, and by incorporating (b_1) a new group of order $2n$ is obtained.

The notations are based on these considerations, which are not difficult to reach by geometrical intuition. The old notation is due to Schönflies, and represents a proper rotation through $2\pi/n$ and the cyclic group derived from it by C_n. The new notation is due to Hermann and Mauguin, and uses for this the symbol n. The old (Schönflies) notation represents each improper rotation as the product of a proper rotation with (b_1) (reflection across the plane perpendicular to the axis) and denotes it by S_n, the new (Hermann–Mauguin) notation represents each improper rotation as the product of a proper rotation with (b_2), and denotes it by $\bar{n}$. Neither notation is completely consistent, however. The old notation denotes a reflection, which might be written S_1, by σ, and the inversion, which might be written S_2, by i. The new notation represents a reflection, which might be written $\bar{2}$, by m (from the expression 'mirror-plane'). The advantage of the latter inconsistency is that it is convenient to represent a complete rotation group about a given axis by a single typographical space, and the notation $\dfrac{n}{m}$ is convenient for the group of order $2n$ (n even) referred to in the previous paragraph. But $\dfrac{n}{m}$ is even more conveniently written n/m, which shows how the best laid schemes 'gang aft agley'. If n is odd, n/m is the same as $\bar{n}$, as shown in the previous paragraph.

Although the two symbols refer to the same *type* of element, S_n and $\bar{n}$ are, it will be seen, quite different. S_n is $b(2\pi/n)$ and $\bar{n}$ is $b\left(\dfrac{2\pi}{n}+\pi\right)$. As symmetry groups they need more careful consideration. If n is odd, then $(\bar{n})^n$ is $\bar{1}$ (i), but $(S_n)^n$ is m; both elements give rise to cyclic groups of order $2n$, but to different ones. If n is even but $\frac{1}{2}n$ is odd, then $(\bar{n})^{\frac{1}{2}n}$ is m but $(S_n)^{\frac{1}{2}n}$ is $\bar{1}$ (i). Thus, if n is odd, the groups $\bar{n}$ and S_{2n} are the same, and the groups $\overline{(2n)}$ and S_n. Only when n is divisible by 4 are $\bar{n}$ and S_n the same, and then the elements are generated in a different order. For the purpose of crystallography this means that S_3 and $\bar{6}$ are the same group, and S_6 and $\bar{3}$; both are of order 6. But S_4 and $\bar{4}$ are the same group, of order 4.

The notation for complete symmetry groups will be developed as we go. In the old notation it consists of the symbol for the proper rotation of highest order, modified as improper rotations and other axes are added. In the new notation such axes are chosen that the symmetry group may be represented as the product (not necessarily commutating) of the subgroups associated with each axis, and the symbols are written in succession. In the succeeding sections we shall use the new notation as a rule, but fall back on the old when, as sometimes happens, we wish to use numerical coefficients, and we shall add suffixes to denote the direction of the axis of a rotation more freely than is general practice.

8.2. Forms without multiple axes

We shall use the following notation whenever convenient. An element will be denoted by the coordinates of the point to which it moves the point (XYZ), minus signs being placed over the symbol. Thus rotations through $\frac{1}{2}\pi$ and π about the X-axis will be $(XZ\bar{Y})$ and $(X\bar{Y}\bar{Z})$ respectively.

Let us consider first the group which contains those rotations, proper and improper, which do not interlink X, Y, and Z, and which therefore consists simply of the eight possible combinations of sign in $(\pm X \pm Y \pm Z)$. They are:

No coordinate negative:	$(XYZ) = I$	the identity.
One coordinate negative:	$(\bar{X}YZ) = \sigma_x$ or m_x	reflections across planes
	$(X\bar{Y}Z) = \sigma_y$ or m_y	perpendicular to the axes
	$(XY\bar{Z}) = \sigma_z$ or m_z	indicated by the suffixes.
Two coordinates negative:	$(X\bar{Y}\bar{Z}) = C_x$ or 2_x	rotations through π about
	$(\bar{X}Y\bar{Z}) = C_y$ or 2_y	the axes indicated by the
	$(\bar{X}\bar{Y}Z) = C_z$ or 2_z	suffixes.
Three coordinates negative:	$(\bar{X}\bar{Y}\bar{Z}) = i$ or $\bar{1}$	inversion.

It is easily verified that every element (except I) is of order 2, and that they form a group with the structure $\mathfrak{s}_{2\times 2\times 2}$. We may write out the multiplication table. (See below.) In doing so, we combine it with a dictionary to a notation more usual among crystallographers, in which axes are distinguished by primes or by the subscripts v and h. (These stand for 'vertical' and 'horizontal', respectively, applied to mirror planes. Either the X- or the Z-axis is commonly taken to be vertical; here we take the Z-axis in anticipation of the next section, where it will conform to the usual practice, although this is the less usual convention in dealing with these simpler groups.)

$E = I$	m_z	m_x	2_y	m_y	2_x	2_z	$\bar{1}$
$\sigma_h = m_z$	I	2_y	m_x	2_x	m_y	$\bar{1}$	2_z
$\sigma_{v''} = m_x$	2_y	I	m_z	2_z	$\bar{1}$	m_y	2_x
$C_{2'} = 2_y$	m_x	m_z	I	$\bar{1}$	2_z	2_x	m_y
$\sigma_{v'} = m_y$	2_x	2_z	$\bar{1}$	I	m_z	m_x	2_y
$C_{z''} = 2_x$	m_y	$\bar{1}$	2_z	m_z	I	2_y	m_x
$C_2 = 2_z$	$\bar{1}$	m_y	2_x	m_x	2_y	I	m_z
$i = \bar{1}$	2_z	2_x	m_y	2_y	m_x	m_z	I

The arrangement of the table shows Im_z as an invariant subgroup. The associated factor group is the group of the corresponding properties of a lamina in the XY-plane, for which m_z is indistinguishable from the identity. It is easily verified that the two members of any other coset, for example m_x and 2_y, are also indistinguishable in the lamina. The matrices differ only in the last diagonal term, and become identical if this representation is omitted. This is the general principle for the interpretation of factor groups; it can only be applied if the representation is one which, on being reduced, contains among the irreducible representations one of the factor group.

If a crystal has less symmetry than this, its symmetry operations must be a subgroup of this group, and we can list the possible symmetry types by picking out the subgroups of $s_{2 \times 2 \times 2}$. In doing so, we must remember that the assignment of the coordinates X, Y, and Z is arbitrary, but the distinction between an m and a 2 is fundamental. Consequently the various subgroups are:

c_1 I only

c_2 (i) $I\bar{1}$,   (ii) Im,   (iii) IC.

$s_{2 \times 2}$ (i) $I2_p\,\bar{1}\,m_p$,   (ii) $I2_p\,m_q\,m_r$,   (iii) $I2_x\,2_y\,2_z$.

Each of these subgroups represents a possible different type of symmetry. In order to understand the symmetry properties properly, it will help to consider not only crystals but also other objects, and in the following table the possible subgroups listed above have been set out with their elements, the symbol for the symmetry group in both notations, a classification of the types which we shall want later, and various types of object showing the symmetry in question.

Elements	I	$I\bar{1}$	Im_z	$I2_z$	$I\,\bar{1}$ $m_z\,2_z$	$I\,2_x$ $m_y\,m_z$	$I\,2_x$ $2_y\,2_z$	The whole group
Old symbol	C_1	C_i S_2	C_s C_{1h}	C_2	C_{2h}	C_{2v}	D_2 V	D_{2h} V_h
New symbol	1	$\bar{1}$	m	2	$2/m$	mm $2m\,\bar{2}m$	222	mmm $2/mm$

System	Triclinic			Monoclinic			Orthorhombic	
Common objects	any irregular object	jester's bauble	chair	table laid for 2			rectangular table	brick (all sides unequal)
Brick with corners modified				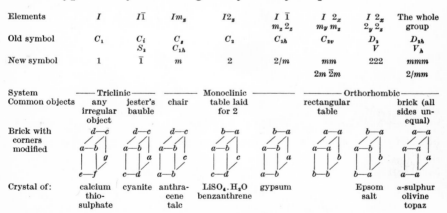				
Crystal of:	calcium thiosulphate	cyanite	anthracene talc	LiSO$_4$.H$_2$O benzanthrene	gypsum		Epsom salt	α-sulphur olivine topaz

8.3. Forms with one multiple axis

It will be shown later that the symmetry classes already considered include all those with no element of order greater than 2. A single n-fold axis is always taken as the Z-axis, and we have to consider the possible groups resulting from a combination of this with any of the elements of order 2 already considered. In doing this there are several points to take care of. First, since $2_x 2_z = 2_y$, we shall not consider 2_y as an independent element, but let it appear by combination of 2_x with 2_z. Secondly, on the other hand, we now have to discriminate between m_z ($= \sigma_h$), which is perpendicular to the n-fold axis, and m_x or m_y ($= \sigma_v$), which is parallel to it. Thirdly, 2_z, if present, will have to appear in consequence of the order of the Z-axis being even. For a reason often quoted in the form that 'triangles, squares, and hexagons can fill a plane, but not pentagons or other n-gons', but which we shall examine more closely in the next chapter, only three-, four-, and six-fold axes need be considered. The net result is that we have to consider each of the first six groups of the foregoing section (with $2/m$ in the form $I\bar{1}\, m_x\, 2_x$ and m in the two forms Im_x and Im_z) with each of $3(C_3)$, $6(C_6)$, $4(C_4)$, and $\bar{4}(S_4)$, but not all of these twenty-four combinations are independent groups, since the same elements are apt to arise by different orders of synthesis. The results are summarized in the table on the following page, in which we give, for each group, its symbol in each notation, its group-theoretic structure, and a list of the elements in it. Recalling our theory of the ƀ groups, we realize that there will be oblique twofold axes in many cases. These we denote by 2_n, where $n\pi$ is the angle the axis makes with the X-axis. In dealing with the fourfold axes the student will find the (XYZ) notation very helpful for checking the group-theoretic structures; C_4 is $(Y\bar{X}Z)$ or $(\bar{Y}XZ)$, according as it is clockwise or anticlockwise, and S_4 is $(\bar{Y}X\bar{Z})$ or $(Y\bar{X}\bar{Z})$. This notation is not so helpful with three- and six-fold axes unless the modification described in § 8.5 is used. In any case the student should again use the techniques of that section to supplement his imagination. In a few cases we have included the name of a well-known mineral crystallizing in the symmetry group; definite examples of most of the groups are known, and suspected examples of the rest.

8.4. Forms with more than one multiple axis

If we try, for example, to add a second fourfold axis at right angles to an already existing one, we are adding $(XZ\bar{Y})$ and similar elements to $(Y\bar{X}Z)$, and the result will be a group with structure $\mathfrak{s}_{2 \times 2 \times 2} \times \pi_3$ with $8 \times 6 = 48$ elements, some of which, from our knowledge of π_3, must be of order 3. This group is the group of all rotations, proper and improper, of a cube, and we can best study the remaining types of symmetry as subgroups of this. (We shall show later that 6 cannot be combined with anything inclined to it of order greater than 2.) These rotations permute the faces, edges, corners, and diagonals of the cube, but whereas there is this restriction on the three former, that adjacent

Subgroup of $S_{2\times2\times2}$		With threefold axis		With sixfold axis		With fourfold axis — C type		With fourfold axis — S type	
C_1	1 c_1	C_3	3 c_3	C_6	6 c_6	C_4	4 c_4	S_4	$\bar 4$ c_4
	E		E $2C_3$		E $2C_3$ C_z $2C_6$		E C_z $2C_4$		E C_z $2S_4$
C_i	$\bar 1$ c_2	$S_6(C_{3i})$	$\bar 3$ c_6	C_{6h}	$6/m$ $s_{6\times2}$	C_{4h}	$4/m$		$s_{4\times2}$
	E		E $2C_3$		E $2C_3$ C_z $2C_6$		E C_z $2C_4$		the same
	i		i $2S_6$		i $2S_6$ m_z $2S_3$		i m_z $2S_4$		
C_s	m c_2	$^{*}C_{3h}$	$\bar 6 = \dfrac{3}{m}$ c_6						
	E		E $2C_3$		the same		the same		the same
	m_z		m_z $2S_3$						
	ditto	C_{3v}	$3m$ d_3	C_{6v}	$6mm$ d_6	C_{4v}	$4mm$ d_4	S_{4v}	$\bar 42m$ d_4
	E		E $2C_3$		E $2C_3$ C_z $2C_6$		E C_z $2C_4$		E C_z $2S_4$
	m_x		m_x $2m_{\frac14}$		m_x $2m_{\frac14}$ m_y $2m_{\frac14}$		m_x m_y $2m_{\frac14}$		m_x m_y $2C_{\frac14}$
					(wurtzite)				
C_2	2 c_2	D_3	32 d_3	D_6	62 d_6	D_4	42 d_4		†the same viz:
	E		E $2C_3$		E $2C_3$ C_z $2C_6$		E C_z $2C_4$		E C_z $2S_4$
	C_x		C_x $2C_{\frac14}$		C_x $2C_{\frac14}$ C_y $2C_{\frac14}$		C_x C_y $2C_{\frac14}$		C_x C_y $2m_{\frac14}$
			(α-quartz)		(β-quartz)				
C_{2h}	$2/m$ $s_{2\times2}$	$D_{3d}(S_{3v})$	$\bar 3m$ d_6	D_{6h}	$6/mmm$ $d_{6\times2}$	D_{4h}	$4/mmm$		$d_{4\times2}$
	E		E $2C_3$		E $2C_3$ C_z $2C_6$		E C_z $2C_4$		the same
	C_x		C_x $2C_{\frac14}$		C_x $2C_{\frac14}$ C_y $2C_{\frac14}$		C_x C_y $2C_{\frac14}$		
	i		i $2S_6$		i $2S_6$ m_z $2S_3$		i m_z $2S_4$		
	m_x		m_x $2m_{\frac14}$		m_x $2m_{\frac14}$ m_y $2m_{\frac14}$		m_x m_y $2m_{\frac14}$		
			(calcite)						
C_{2v}	mm $s_{2\times2}$	$^{*}D_{3h}$	$\bar 6m2$ d_6						
	E		E $2C_3$						
	C_x		C_x $2C_{\frac14}$		the same		the same		the same
	m_y		m_y $2m_{\frac14}$						
	m_z		m_z $2S_3$		(beryl, ice)		(rutile, zircon)		
System:		Trigonal *except C_{3h} and D_{3h}		Hexagonal *including C_{3h} and D_{3h}		Tetragonal			

† With axes rotated through $\pi/4$.

ones must remain adjacent and opposite ones opposite, the proper rotations of the cube are just the permutation group on its diagonals. (We can, in fact, by rotating the cube, put any one diagonal where we want it, by rotation about this diagonal we can get a second where we want it, and if the other two are then wrong, a rotation through 180° about an axis perpendicular to the plane containing the correct diagonals will exchange the incorrect ones but only alter the sense of the correct ones, not their positions.) The improper rotations are obtained by multiplying each proper rotation by $\bar 1$. Thus we have the groups 43 (new notation) or O (for 'octahedral'—old notation) with structure π_4 (twenty-four elements); and $m3m$ or O_h with structure $\pi_4 \times c_2$ (forty-eight elements). Since all the elements, proper and improper, permute the faces, both of these groups are subgroups of π_6, a fact which is occasionally useful. These considerations can be summarized as follows:

Class in π_4	No. of elements	The group O			Class in π_6	Coset in O_h			Class in π_6
		Type	Description			Type	Description		
1^4	1	I	Identity		1^6	$\bar{1}$	inversion		2^3
$1^2 2$	6	2	Rotation about line parallel face diagonal		2^3	m	reflection across plane through opposite edges		$1^2 2^2$
13	8	3	Rotation about a diagonal		3^2	$\bar{3}$	inversion-axis about a diagonal		6
22	3	2	Rotation about a line perp. to a face		$1^2 2^2$	m	reflection across plane parallel to a face		$1^4 2$
4	6	4	Ditto		$1^2 4$	$\bar{4}$	inv.-axis about a line perp. to a face		24

We now need to pick out the subgroups of this which are not already dealt with in the previous section. They are, with their crystallographic symbols and elements, etc., as follows:

O_h	$m3m$	I	$6C_2$	$8C_3$	$3C_2$	$6C_4$	i	$6m$	$8S_6$	$3m$	$6S_4$	$\pi_4 \times c_2$
O	43	I	$6C_2$	$8C_3$	$3C_2$	$6C_4$						π_4
T_h	$m3$	I		$8C_3$	$3C_2$		i		$8S_6$	$3m$		$a_4 \times c_2$
T_d	$\bar{4}3m$	I		$8C_3$	$3C_2$			$6m$			$6S_4$	π_4
T	23	I		$8C_3$	$3C_2$							a_4

It will be seen in the next chapter that these groups all belong to the cubic system, the fundamental characteristic of which is the group $T = 23$ as a subgroup. This is expressed in the new notation by a 3 in the second place, but in other respects this notation is somewhat obscure here; a further comment will be found on this in § 9.7.

We have thus found thirty-two possible combinations of symmetry elements belonging to eighteen different group-theoretic types—i.e. they are thirty-two distinct three-dimensional representations of eighteen different abstract groups. The thirty-two point groups, as they are called, form the basis of the crystallographer's classification of the forms he finds. The importance of the group-theoretic types is that every property of a crystal must conform to one or another of the representations of the symmetry class to which it belongs.

8.5. Graphical representation of symmetry types

We give in concluding this chapter some graphical methods which the student may find useful in assisting his imagination when dealing with the various symmetries which an object may have.

The groups themselves are conveniently represented and pictured simultaneously by a projection of a sphere, on which one point is marked, to the front and off centre, together with all the other points into which it is converted by the elements of the group, those on the front of the sphere being given full dots, and those behind open dots. Fig. 6 should make the method clear.

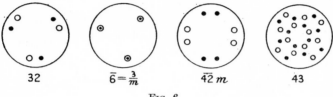

FIG. 6.

A three-dimensional solid can only be represented on paper in some sort of projection. Accuracy and convenience is usually best combined in the isometric projection

$$X' = \tfrac{1}{2}\sqrt{3}X - \tfrac{1}{2}Y,$$

$$Y' = \tfrac{1}{2}\sqrt{3}X + \tfrac{1}{2}Y + Z,$$

in which all lengths along the axes (but not oblique ones) are correct. The much cruder

$$\left. \begin{array}{l} X' = X - kZ \\ Y' = Y - kZ \end{array} \right\} \quad (\tfrac{1}{2} < k < 1)$$

will be found to suffice for many purposes, and has the advantage that it can be used on squared paper without the aid of geometrical instruments other than a ruler. The notation (XYZ) of § 8.2 is used to obtain from the coordinates of a point the coordinates of all the points into which it transforms under the group. A point, say $(3, 2, 1)$, and all its transforms, are then plotted and the points joined up to show a convex solid, full lines to the front and dotted lines for edges which are hidden. With the simpler groups a solid will probably not be obtained, but as the point $(0, 0, 0)$ always transforms into itself, this point can be included if required. By trial and error it may be found that a different

$X:Y:Z$ ratio for the initial point may give a better or an alternative interpretation, and if any of the initial coordinates are made equal a specialized form often results, since the transformed points may not all be different. In Fig. 7 we show some of the results of the use of this method. The method can be extended by considering two or three

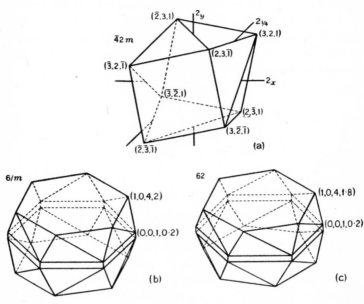

Fig. 7.

initial points; this will show how an edge or a face, respectively, transform.

With groups including a three- or six-fold axis, the (XYZ) notation does not apply, but we may use the following device. We consider three unit vectors in the XY-plane at 120° to each other, U, V, and W; then the point $uU+vV+wW$ is the same as the point

$$(u+k)U+(v+k)V+(w+k)W.$$

It will be found that the transformation $(UVW) \rightarrow (\overline{W}\overline{U}\overline{V})$ is a rotation through $\frac{1}{3}\pi$ about the Z-axis. We can now plot on the projection

$$X' = W-\tfrac{1}{2}X-\tfrac{1}{2}Y+dZ,$$

$$Y' = \tfrac{1}{2}Y-\tfrac{1}{2}X+Z.$$

Some examples of this device are included in Fig. 7. The dZ, which can be omitted if not desired, serves to separate lines which would otherwise fall on top of each other, and is a device which can be used with the (XYZ) system if required.

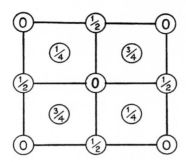

FIG. 8. Unit cell of diamond.

Less vivid, but much more serviceable when dealing with the complex internal structure of crystals and in any case more rapid, is the notation now habitually used by crystallographers. In this, two axes are drawn on the paper, oblique if necessary. Points out of this plane are projected vertically on to it and marked with a number representing the vertical coordinate. As used for internal structures this number is on such a scale that 1 represents the base of the next cell (see the next chapter if this term is not understood); for macro-structures the choice of unit is completely arbitrary. An illustrative example of this technique is given in Fig. 8.

CHAPTER IX

THE INTERNAL STRUCTURE OF CRYSTALS

THERE is one important law concerning the external forms of crystals which was not referred to in the previous chapter because its implications belong to this one; it is the Law of Rational Indices, which states:

If three independent vectors are taken parallel to three edges of a crystal from an arbitrary origin, and the intercepts made by an arbitrarily chosen face on these vectors are taken as units in each direction, then the ratio of the intercepts of any other face on these vectors may be expressed as the ratio of small integers (or infinity).

The word 'small' is to be taken relatively to the complexity of the crystal form, of course, and the inclusion of infinity as a possibility merely takes care of faces parallel to the chosen edges.

It is implied in the above statement that if the law is true for one chosen set of axes then it is true for any similarly chosen set, and we show that this is so, establishing *en route* certain relations needed later. First we assert

THEOREM 9.1.1. *The vector (through the origin) perpendicular to a plane which includes the points $f_1 P_1{}^*$, $f_2 P_2{}^*$, and $f_3 P_3{}^*$ is*

$$\frac{1}{f_1}*R_1 + \frac{1}{f_2}*R_2 + \frac{1}{f_3}*R_3,$$

where $*R_1$, $*R_2$, and $*R_3$ are the vector set reciprocal to the set P.

For such a plane consists of all the vectors $af_1 P_1{}^* + bf_2 P_2{}^* + cf_3 P_3{}^*$ for which $a+b+c = 0$, or, more precisely, is parallel to the plane consisting of all these vectors, and

$$\left(\frac{1}{f_1}*R_1 + \frac{1}{f_2}*R_2 + \frac{1}{f_3}*R_3\right)(af_1 P_1{}^* + bf_2 P_2{}^* + cf_3 P_3{}^*) = a+b+c = 0.$$

We do not, at the moment, discuss the length of the vector, though it will, for later purposes, be defined in terms of the distance of the plane from the origin, but the matter is complicated by the fact that the $*R$ are covariant vectors. (See § 9.7.)

Two such planes determine the line in which they intersect, and three such planes determine, taken two by two, three such lines. If now the original vectors $P*$ were three edges of a crystal and the three plane faces three faces of the crystal, then the law of rational indices states that all the nine quantities f_i, g_i, and h_i defining the three faces can be taken as small integers. The three lines of intersection will be three new edges which may form the basis of an alternative coordinate system, and we show that if the law is true in the old system it is true in the new one.

We can determine the direction of the line of intersection of the planes whose intercepts on the vectors P_1*, P_2*, and P_3* are f_1, f_2, f_3 and g_1, g_2, g_3 from the fact that the vector X parallel to it must be perpendicular to both of the vectors perpendicular to the planes. Expressing $X*$ as $x_1 P_1* + x_2 P_2* + x_3 P_3*$, this amounts to

$$\left(\frac{1}{f_1}*R_1 + \frac{1}{f_2}*R_2 + \frac{1}{f_3}*R_3\right)(x_1 P_1* + x_2 P_2* + x_3 P_3*) = 0$$

or

$$\frac{x_1}{f_1} + \frac{x_2}{f_2} + \frac{x_3}{f_3} = 0$$

and a similar equation in the g's. Solving these two equations,

$$x_1 : -x_2 : x_3 = \begin{vmatrix} 1/f_2 & 1/f_3 \\ 1/g_2 & 1/g_3 \end{vmatrix} : \begin{vmatrix} 1/f_1 & 1/f_3 \\ 1/g_1 & 1/g_3 \end{vmatrix} : \begin{vmatrix} 1/f_1 & 1/f_2 \\ 1/g_1 & 1/g_2 \end{vmatrix}.$$

As all the f_i and g_i are small integers, on clearing of fractions and common factors, this ratio will be one of small integers. Hence the transformation equations from the three vectors $P*$ to a set of three vectors $X*$, though formally somewhat complicated, will reduce to ones with small integers as coefficients, when fractions and common factors are removed.

If now a fourth face is described alternatively as containing the points $s_i P_i*$ or the points $t_i X_i*$, then the vector perpendicular to this plane will be described alternatively as

$$\frac{*R_1}{s_1} + \frac{*R_2}{s_2} + \frac{*R_3}{s_3} \quad \text{or as} \quad \frac{*Y_1}{t_1} + \frac{*Y_2}{t_2} + \frac{*Y_3}{t_3},$$

and these descriptions must be identical. Thus if, as the law asserts, $s_1 : s_2 : s_3$ can be expressed in terms of small integers, so also can $t_1 : t_2 : t_3$.

Of course, the law does not hold *equally* well for *any* set of axes. The combination of ratios of $4:5$ and $5:6$ may produce a ratio $4:6$, but it may produce a $24:25$. But this is simply indicative of a bad choice of basic vectors. For any given symmetry class of crystal, crystallographers have set up rules by which the axes to be used are conventionally determined. The smallest integral numbers by which the components $1/f_1$, $1/f_2$, and $1/f_3$ of the vector reciprocal to a face may be expressed, are known as the Miller indices of that face, and are conventionally enclosed in round brackets without commas as a method of naming the face.

9.2. The lattice hypothesis

The law stated in the previous section is capable of an interpretation which is far-reaching. Effectively it says that if we take three edges meeting in a corner as axes, then the coordinates of any other point which is possible as a corner are integral multiples of certain distances along these axes. To be sure, a crystal seems capable of continuous growth, and the unit must therefore be very small, and we then seem in danger of losing our 'small' integers, but this danger turns out to be more apparent than real. The only physical interpretation we can give to the point-corner of a crystal is something of the size of a single atom or molecule. There is no reason to suppose that addition of extra layers to a crystal alters the inside of it, and we therefore assume that also in the centre of a crystal the molecules only occur at points whose coordinates are integral multiples of these small units. The hypothesis is therefore that in a crystal the molecules (a word to be accepted provisionally) occur only at points on a 'lattice', which, in two dimensions, might be something like Fig. 9. In this figure the intercepts of the face BC on OA and OB are OH and OB; those of CD are OK and OI, and those of EF are OJ and ∞, etc. The validity of the law is obvious, and the validity of the qualification 'small' will appear if the student will try to construct faces whose intercepts have, for example, even the ratio $5:7$ when measured in terms of the distances between consecutive dots along OA and OB respectively.

The symmetry of the crystal we have drawn in Fig. 9 is 2 only, whereas the symmetry of the immediate surroundings of an internal point includes mirror planes (perhaps 'mirror lines' in two dimensions) as well. Such a result might have one of two causes, either unsymmetrical external conditions during growth, or a lack of full symmetry in the molecules themselves which would favour growth in certain directions at the expense of growth in others. In the latter case the internal symmetry is also only 2. In this chapter we are concerned with internal symmetry only, and we see that it depends on two factors, the symmetry of the lattice, and the symmetry of what is at the lattice points. As the pursuit of these considerations leads to 230 symmetry

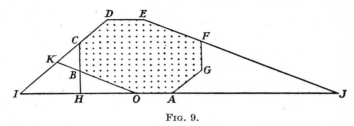

FIG. 9.

types in three dimensions but only to 17 in two dimensions, to look at the latter first will be a useful introduction to the former.

The external symmetry types possible in two dimensions are those which result from the tables in §§ 8.3 and 8.4, by taking the factor groups which result from Im_z as an invariant subgroup. They are, in effect, the groups C_n and D_n. The question is, what symmetries can a *lattice* have, and under what conditions? It always has a $2 = (\overline{XY})$, and if the axes are at right angles it has also two mirror elements, $m_y = (X\overline{Y})$ and $m_x = (\overline{X}Y)$. If the units of X and Y are equal, it again acquires two mirror elements, this time reflections across the bisectors of the angles between the axes, $m_{\nearrow} = (YX)$ and $m_{\nwarrow} = (\overline{YX})$. Combination of these conditions—the basic vectors at right angles and equal—gives a 4 and four mirror elements. An alternative possibility, easily overlooked in this trial and error method of analysis, is that if the basic vectors are equal and inclined at $2\pi/3 = 120°$, we get the hexagonal symmetry D_6. The result is that internally the lattice may have any one of *five* types of symmetry. But the symmetry may be reduced to a subgroup of the main type if the object at the lattice points has less symmetry, and this increases the number of possibilities to *thirteen*. These are all summarized in the first three columns of the table (next page); the symmetry types in the fourth and fifth columns increase the total number of types to *seventeen* and will be discussed later.

The type with the basic vectors equal but with no other symmetry-bestowing condition calls for further consideration. The lattice has the

TABLE OF PLANE SPACE GROUPS

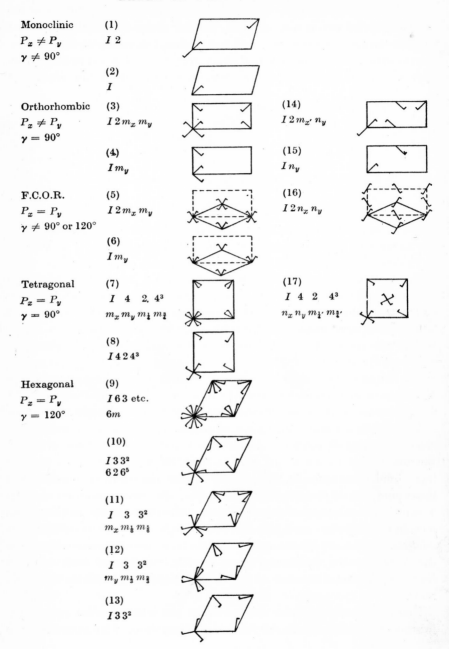

Monoclinic
$P_x \neq P_y$
$\gamma \neq 90°$

(1)
$I\,2$

(2)
I

Orthorhombic
$P_x \neq P_y$
$\gamma = 90°$

(3)
$I\,2\,m_x\,m_y$

(14)
$I\,2\,m_{x'}\,n_y$

(4)
$I\,m_y$

(15)
$I\,n_y$

F.C.O.R.
$P_x = P_y$
$\gamma \neq 90°$ or $120°$

(5)
$I\,2\,m_x\,m_y$

(16)
$I\,2\,n_x\,n_y$

(6)
$I\,m_y$

Tetragonal
$P_x = P_y$
$\gamma = 90°$

(7)
$I\quad 4\quad 2.\ 4^3$
$m_x\,m_y\,m_{\frac{1}{4}}\,m_{\frac{3}{4}}$

(17)
$I\quad 4\quad 2\quad 4^3$
$n_x\,n_y\,m_{\frac{1}{4}'}\,m_{\frac{3}{4}'}$

(8)
$I\,4\,2\,4^3$

Hexagonal
$P_x = P_y$
$\gamma = 120°$

(9)
$I\,6\,3$ etc.
$6m$

(10)
$I\,3\,3^2$
$6\,2\,6^5$

(11)
$I\quad 3\quad 3^2$
$m_x\,m_{\frac{1}{6}}\,m_{\frac{5}{6}}$

(12)
$I\quad 3\quad 3^2$
$m_y\,m_{\frac{1}{4}}\,m_{\frac{3}{4}}$

(13)
$I\,3\,3^2$

appearance of Fig. 10. It has the same symmetry properties as the one in which the basic vectors are at right angles, but it is not the same lattice. It may be referred to basic vectors at right angles but only by choosing between one of two tricks. Either (as at B below) we may use small vectors, in which case not every lattice point is occupied, or (as at C) we may use vectors twice the size, in which case we find a point at

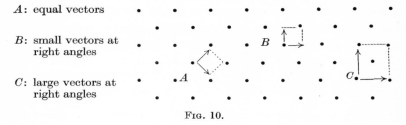

A: equal vectors

B: small vectors at
   right angles

C: large vectors at
   right angles

FIG. 10.

the centre of each lattice 'cell' as well as at its corners. Not only is aP_x+bP_y a possible point, with a and b integers, but also

$$(a+\tfrac{1}{2})P_x+(b+\tfrac{1}{2})P_y.$$

The latter convention proves more convenient, and taking over the names from the three-dimensional lattices, we can call the five lattices monoclinic, orthorhombic, centred orthorhombic, tetragonal, and hexagonal, respectively. The four types of external symmetry define four *systems*.

The four extra types in the last two columns of the table on page 106 arise only when the lattice points are occupied by objects with lower symmetry than the lattice, and they depend on the following principle:

If one of the axes is left invariant by a symmetry operation of order n, an object of lower symmetry may be repeated at intervals of $1/n$ unit along the axis, if it undergoes the symmetry operation at each repetition.

The object must be of lower symmetry, or the element transforms it into itself, and the result is simply that the basic vector is n times smaller. The principle is a logical extension of the earlier arguments, but it effects a revolutionary change in focusing attention on the contents of the 'unit cell' rather than on the lattice points; this change is an essential one for the understanding of crystal chemistry. In two dimensions the only element which can leave an axis invariant is reflection across it, and the new type of symmetry arises whenever the full symmetry of a class includes an m across an axis, and an object not possessing this symmetry can be alternated with its mirror image along the axis without breaking any other symmetry requirements. This element is denoted by C^s or n, and is known as a glide. It may be associated with a reflection across a line not through the origin, or with inversions with respect to a point not the origin; we denote this by a prime.

9.3. The three-dimensional point lattices: (i) from lattice to symmetry

The same type of reasoning can be applied in three dimensions. In certain respects the number of possibilities is greatly increased. We can contrast the situations in two and three dimensions by a table:

	Two dimensions	Three dimensions
Symmetry groups possible for a lattice . .	Plane systems 4	Space systems 6 (7)
Types of lattice, including centred ones separately	Plane lattices 5	Space lattices 14
Possible types of external symmetry . .	Plane classes 11	Space classes 32
Possible types internal symmetry with objects at lattice points only	Point plane groups 13	Point space groups 73
Possible types internal symmetry including glides, etc.	Plane groups 17	Space groups 230

In this section we discuss the systems, point lattices, and classes, postponing the point space groups and space groups until a later section.

The analysis of the possibilities in three dimensions may be set out thus:

1. A lattice inevitably has the symmetry element i. A lattice with no greater symmetry is said to be *triclinic*.
2. If the unit vectors are all different in length, one right angle between them does not help, but if two are both perpendicular to the third, the latter is a twofold rotation axis and the former define a mirror plane. Lattices with this symmetry are said to be *monoclinic*.
3. With the unit vectors still unequal but now all at right angles, we have three twofold axes and three mirror planes. This type of lattice is known as *orthorhombic*.
4. If two of the vectors are equal in length, we know that this is equivalent in their plane to a centred lattice with axes at right angles, but we have seen that this produces no new symmetry unless at least one of the two angles is a right angle. As the new or 'orthogonal' axes bisect the angles between the old, or 'primitive' axes, this means that a lattice with two vectors equal and the third equally inclined to them will give a monoclinic symmetry. Since the base, but not the other faces of the unit monoclinic cell is centred, this lattice is called a *base-centred* (or sometimes 'side-centred') *monoclinic* lattice.

5. And if two axes are equal with the third perpendicular to both, we shall have a *base-centred orthorhombic* lattice.

6. Further symmetry is attained if all three axes are at right angles and two unit vectors are equal. The symmetry is D_{4h} (4/*mmm*), and the lattice is described as *tetragonal*.

7. Retracing our steps somewhat, and still considering two equal vectors, if these two are perpendicular but the third not, no extra symmetry results unless the third vector is equally inclined to them and its length and direction so mutually adjusted that its projection on the plane of the first two is equal to half the sum of the first two, in which case a point at the end of it lies on one of the fourfold axes of the plane, and the lattice has tetragonal symmetry. The oblique vector is a diagonal of the ordinary tetragonal cell, and its end at the cell centre; hence this lattice is described as *body-centred tetragonal*.

8. Finally, so far as the case of two equal vectors is concerned, the base-centred orthorhombic lattice acquires a sixfold axis if the two equal axes are at 120°. This is the *hexagonal* lattice.

9. When the three vectors are all equal in length, the situation becomes more difficult to envisage with any certainty of not missing anything. If no other conditions (about angles) hold, it will still be true that the lattice will have the equivalent of three axes all at right angles, *each* of the perpendicular plane lattices being centred. This is the *face-centred orthorhombic* lattice.

10. If the three equal vectors are equally inclined, we introduce a threefold axis, and acquire *trigonal* or *rhombohedral* symmetry. We shall show later that this system can also be represented as a centred form of the hexagonal lattice.

11. If the three axes are also perpendicular, *cubic* symmetry results.

These are all the obvious possibilities, but a check on centred lattices not yet realized reveals three others:

12. Three equal vectors at the special angle $\cos^{-1}(-\frac{1}{3})$ produces a *face-centred cubic* lattice.

13. Three equal vectors at 60° to each other produces a *body-centred cubic* lattice, and

14. Three vectors of any length all at 60° produces a *face-centred orthorhombic* lattice.

This last result is rather a shock, and undermines our faith somewhat in this elementary scheme of search, and we shall reconsider the problem from another angle in the next section. It is, of course, possible to construct, e.g. a body-centred triclinic lattice, but there is no use in a centred lattice unless it demonstrates in the centred cell that the lattice has a higher symmetry than is obvious from the primitive cell. Centred lattices can be reduced to simple ones thus:

In a base-centred lattice, use vectors from the face centre to two adjacent cell corners and to the centre of the opposite face.

In a face-centred lattice, use vectors from any corner to the three face centres, and

In a body-centred lattice, use vectors from the cell centre to any three corners no two of which are opposite each other.

We may tabulate the above conclusions, and also pass on to the results of putting objects of lower symmetry at the lattice points in one step. The lattice symmetry is often known as the holohedral symmetry of the system, and crystals of lesser symmetry due to lack of full symmetry in the objects at the lattice points are described as hemihedral. In the following table, the types of cell are denoted by P = primitive, C = base-centred, F = face-centred, I = body-centred. The holohedral symmetry is given first in each system.

Crystal system	Types of axes	Types of cell	Possible symmetry groups (i.e. classes)
Triclinic . . .	unequal; not all at 60°	P	$\begin{cases} C_i \ C_1 \\ \bar{1} \ \ 1 \end{cases}$
Monoclinic . .	unequal; two at 90° to third	$P \ C$	$\begin{cases} C_{2h} \ \ C_2 \ C_s \\ 2/m \ 2 \ \ m \end{cases}$
Orthorhombic . .	unequal; all at 90°	$P \ C \ F \ I$	$\begin{cases} D_{2h} \ \ D_2 \ C_{2v} \\ mmm \ 222 \ mm \end{cases}$
Rhombohedral (Trigonal) . .	all equal; all angles equal	P	$\begin{cases} D_{3d} \ D_3 \ C_{3v} \ S_6 \ C_3 \\ \bar{3}m \ 32 \ 3m \ \bar{3} \ \ 3 \end{cases}$
Hexagonal . .	2 equal at 120° 3rd perp. to both	P	$\begin{cases} D_{6h} \ \ D_6 C_{6v} \ \ C_{6h} \ \ C_6 D_{3h} \ C_{3h} \\ 6/mm \ 62 \ 6mm \ 6/m \ 6 \ \bar{6}m2 \ \bar{6} \end{cases}$
Tetragonal . .	two equal; all at 90°	$P \qquad I$	$\begin{cases} D_{4h} \ \ S_{4v} \ \ D_4 \ C_{4v} \ \ C_{4h} \ \ S_4 C_4 \\ 4/mm \ \bar{4}2m \ 42 \ 4mm \ 4/m \ \bar{4} \ 4 \end{cases}$
Cubic . . .	all equal; all at 90°	$P \qquad F \ I$	$\begin{cases} O_h \quad O \ T_h \ \ T_d \ \ T \\ m3m \ 43 \ m3 \ \bar{4}3m \ 23 \end{cases}$

9.4. The complete lattice group

The considerations in the previous section were the elementary ones usually adopted in an introductory presentation. They are inadequate for introducing the space groups other than by hit-and-miss methods, and to do this a study of the symmetry properties of the lattice as such by analytical methods is necessary. Accordingly in this and the following sections we shall review the subject more thoroughly. There will be some repetition, but the previous section will serve to have introduced some idea of the aim and a great deal of the necessary nomenclature.

The essence of a crystal is its lattice; its faces are mere accidents, and in this section we ignore them and assume the lattice to extend to infinity in all directions. The operations which transform such a lattice into itself include not only the rotations, but any translation through an integral multiple of the basic lattice vectors. The translation group introduces two new features theoretically. First, it is an infinite group. This might give us trouble if we had to discuss its representations, but as we do not, this feature will not worry us unduly. Secondly, the translations do not transform the origin into itself. This precludes the use of three-dimensional matrices, but we can overcome the difficulty by the following device. We assume our space to be the hyper-plane $w = 1$ in a four-space. Then a translation of the lattice given by $x' = x+v_x$, $y' = y+v_y$, $z' = z+v_z$ is equivalent to a matrix

$$\begin{bmatrix} 1 & 0 & 0 & v_x \\ 0 & 1 & 0 & v_y \\ 0 & 0 & 1 & v_z \\ 0 & 0 & 0 & 1 \end{bmatrix}.$$

It is easily verified that

$$\begin{bmatrix} 1 & 0 & 0 & v_x \\ 0 & 1 & 0 & v_y \\ 0 & 0 & 1 & v_z \\ 0 & 0 & 0 & 1 \end{bmatrix} \begin{bmatrix} 1 & 0 & 0 & w_x \\ 0 & 1 & 0 & w_y \\ 0 & 0 & 1 & w_z \\ 0 & 0 & 0 & 1 \end{bmatrix} = \begin{bmatrix} 1 & 0 & 0 & v_x+w_x \\ 0 & 1 & 0 & v_y+w_y \\ 0 & 0 & 1 & v_z+w_z \\ 0 & 0 & 0 & 1 \end{bmatrix}$$

so that 'multiplication' in the group-theoretic or matrix sense is the same as 'addition' in the vector sense, as it must be from the nature of the translation process; the generalization to several factors and to a power of a matrix does not need explicit statement. We shall therefore take VW to be the same as $V+W$, since we have the notation $*VW*$ for the only other type of product we shall need in this connexion.

An ordinary rotation about the origin appears as its three-dimensional matrix bordered by zeros and a diagonal unity, and the most general matrix is of the form

$$\begin{bmatrix} * & * & * & * \\ * & * & * & * \\ * & * & * & * \\ 0 & 0 & 0 & 1 \end{bmatrix}.$$

It is easily verified that the reciprocal of a matrix of this type and the product of two matrices of this type are all further matrices of the same type. Furthermore, direct multiplication shows that

$$\begin{bmatrix} 1 & 0 & 0 & v_x \\ 0 & 1 & 0 & v_y \\ 0 & 0 & 1 & v_z \\ 0 & 0 & 0 & 1 \end{bmatrix} \begin{bmatrix} a & b & c & 0 \\ d & e & f & 0 \\ g & h & i & 0 \\ 0 & 0 & 0 & 1 \end{bmatrix} = \begin{bmatrix} a & b & c & v_x \\ d & e & f & v_y \\ g & h & i & v_z \\ 0 & 0 & 0 & 1 \end{bmatrix}$$

but that

$$\begin{bmatrix} a & b & c & 0 \\ d & e & f & 0 \\ g & h & i & 0 \\ 0 & 0 & 0 & 1 \end{bmatrix} \begin{bmatrix} 1 & 0 & 0 & v_x \\ 0 & 1 & 0 & v_y \\ 0 & 0 & 1 & v_z \\ 0 & 0 & 0 & 1 \end{bmatrix} = \begin{bmatrix} a & b & c & av_x+bv_y+cv_z \\ d & e & f & dv_x+ev_y+fv_z \\ g & h & i & gv_x+hv_y+iv_z \\ 0 & 0 & 0 & 1 \end{bmatrix}.$$

In view of the first of these equations we can write the general operator in the form $T(V).R$, with the commutation rule that

$$R.T(V) = T(RV).R, \tag{9.4.1}$$

then following from the second.

It follows at once that the translations are an invariant subgroup of the whole group, with a factor group which has the same structure as the rotation group. For if $T(U).Q$ is another operator, then by successive application of the rules for the reciprocal of a product, for multiplication of translations, and the commutation rule,

$$[T(U).Q]T(V)[T(U).Q]^{-1} = T(QV), \tag{9.4.2 a}$$

$$[T(U).Q][T(V).R] = T(U+QV).QR, \tag{9.4.2 b}$$

the former demonstrating the invariance of the subgroup, and the latter that its cosets multiply as do the rotations themselves. It is worth while stating explicitly as a corollary

THEOREM 9.4.3. *If R is a member of the rotation subgroup of the lattice group, and $T(V)$ a member of the translation subgroup, then all translations of the form $T(RV)$ are equivalent under the complete group.*

The rotation subgroup, on the other hand, is not invariant, since

$$[T(U).Q]R[T(U).Q]^{-1} = T(U-QRQ^{-1}U).QRQ^{-1}.$$

It is left to the student to satisfy himself that the equivalent rotation obtained in the simplest case when a rotation is conjugated by a translation $T(U)$, is simply an equal rotation about a parallel axis through the point at the end of the vector U drawn from a point on the original axis of rotation.

The mth power of the operator $T(V).R$ is, by the commutation rule, $T[(I+R+R^2+...+R^{m-1})V].R^m$. The series in the bracket demands investigation; it is

$$\begin{bmatrix} 1 & 0 & 0 \\ 0 & 1 & 0 \\ 0 & 0 & 1 \end{bmatrix} + \begin{bmatrix} \cos\theta & \sin\theta & 0 \\ -\sin\theta & \cos\theta & 0 \\ 0 & 0 & 1 \end{bmatrix} + \begin{bmatrix} \cos 2\theta & \sin 2\theta & 0 \\ -\sin 2\theta & \cos 2\theta & 0 \\ 0 & 0 & 1 \end{bmatrix} + ... = \begin{bmatrix} C & S & 0 \\ -S & C & 0 \\ 0 & 0 & m \end{bmatrix}$$

if the axes are conveniently chosen, where

$$C+iS = \sum_{1}^{m-1} e^{ri\theta} = \frac{e^{mi\theta}-1}{e^{i\theta}-1}\frac{e^{-i\theta}-1}{e^{-i\theta}-1} = \frac{-e^{mi\theta}+e^{(m-1)i\theta}-e^{-i\theta}+1}{2-2\cos\theta}$$

and the final fraction can be again separated into real and imaginary parts to obtain C and S separately. An important result is obtained when $m = n$, the order of R (so that $\theta = 2\pi/n$), for then $C = S = 0$. The student will get a better idea of the significance of this result by plotting it on the Argand diagram, or, which is the same thing, by plotting the matrix series in the XY-plane only. We have obtained the result on a special set of axes, but clearly lose no generality thereby in the special case of $m = n$, nor if we confine our attention to the trace in other cases. If the rotations are improper ones, then the $_{33}$ term of each matrix is alternately 1 and -1, and the sum is 0 for m even and -1 for m odd. In the latter case, with $\theta = 2\pi/n$, the order of the group is $2n$, of course. We can state these results in general terms thus:

THEOREM 9.4.4. *If U^* is a unit vector in the direction of the axis of a rotation R of order n (other than the identity or a simple reflection), then*

$$(I+R+R^2+...+R^{n-1})V^* = nU^* *UV^*$$

for a proper rotation and 0 for an improper one.

The exceptions are obvious when the matrices are written out in full, the l.h.s. reducing in the case of I to V^* itself, and in the case of a reflection parallel to U^* to $2(I-U^* *U)V^*$. The student should notice that Theorem 9.4.4. is essentially three-dimensional (in its reference to 'the axis' of a rotation) whereas the argument leading to it is not necessarily so; from the algebraic identity

$$(1+x+x^2+...+x^{n-1})(1-x) = 1-x^n$$

we see that if x is any nth root of unity except 1, the first of the factors on the l.h.s. is identically zero, whence the sum of the matrices of a cyclic group is zero in all representations except the identical one, and in general its trace is equal to the order of the group multiplied by the number of times the representation in question contains the identical one.

The argument has an important generalization to non-cyclic groups. Such a group may be expressed in terms of one of its cyclic subgroups and the cosets of that subgroup, and we shall have, using the group symbol to denote the sum of all the operators in it,

$$\mathfrak{G}V^* = \mathfrak{g}V^*+B\mathfrak{g}V^*+...$$

$$= 0 \text{ if } V^* \text{ is perpendicular to } U^*, \text{ the axis of } \mathfrak{g}.$$

I

But by repeating this with a second cyclic subgroup, which must have a different axis, we can show that $\mathfrak{G}X^* = 0$ if X^* is perpendicular to the axis of this second subgroup. In this way we can find three independent vectors all reduced to zero by $\mathfrak{G}$, which must therefore be identically zero.

THEOREM 9.4.5. *The sum of all the three-dimensional matrices of any non-cyclic crystallographic group is identically zero. (Reflections alone do not render a group non-cyclic for the purpose of this theorem.)*

Thus far we have been considering completely general rotations and translations. The lattice hypothesis restricts translations to the subgroup $V^* = p_1 P_1^* + p_2 P_2^* + p_3 P_3^*$, where the P_i^* are the basic lattice vectors and the p_i are integers. In the second part of this section we wish to investigate the effects of this restriction, especially its effects on permissible rotations. First of all we can prove a result hitherto based on geometrical intuition, namely,

THEOREM 9.4.6. *The only permissible rotations are those through $2k\pi/n$, where n is 2, 3, 4, or 6.*

For this purpose we remark that any transformation may be referred to cartesian coordinates or to the basic lattice vectors (which may be oblique) and that as one is a linear transformation from the other the trace of the matrix will not be changed in the process. If a general lattice vector is transformed into another lattice vector, the components of the matrix in the lattice vector system, and therefore its trace, must be integral. In cartesians, however, the trace is $\pm 1 + 2\cos\theta$, where θ is the angle of rotation, and the upper and lower signs refer to proper and improper rotations. Hence the only permissible values of θ are those for which

$$\pm 1 + 2\cos\theta = \text{an integer}$$
$$\cos\theta = 0, \pm\tfrac{1}{2} \text{ or } \pm 1,$$

which proves the theorem. It may be of interest to note that the proof, though stated in three dimensions, applies equally well in two. Its immediate application in four dimensions is vitiated by the possibility of matrices of the form

$$\begin{bmatrix} \cos\theta & \sin\theta & 0 & 0 \\ -\sin\theta & \cos\theta & 0 & 0 \\ 0 & 0 & \cos\phi & \sin\phi \\ 0 & 0 & -\sin\phi & \cos\phi \end{bmatrix}.$$

The next question is as to the possibility of more than one rotation axis—can we, for example, have a p-fold axis and a q-fold axis inclined at an angle θ? We consider the result of combining rotations of $2\pi/p$ and $2\pi/q$ inclined at this angle. It may be written as $R_p R_\theta R_q R_\theta^{-1}$, where R_p and R_q denote appropriate rotations about the *same* axis, but the latter is transferred to another axis by conjugation (or rotation of coordinates). As we may without loss of generality take the first axis to be the Z-axis and the second to be in the XZ-plane, we may write this product as follows (where $\cos 2\pi/p$ is abbreviated to c_p, etc.),

$$\begin{bmatrix} c_p & -s_p & 0 \\ s_p & c_p & 0 \\ 0 & 0 & 1 \end{bmatrix} \begin{bmatrix} c_\theta & 0 & -s_\theta \\ 0 & 1 & 0 \\ s_\theta & 0 & c_\theta \end{bmatrix} \begin{bmatrix} c_q & -s_q & 0 \\ s_q & c_q & 0 \\ 0 & 0 & 1 \end{bmatrix} \begin{bmatrix} c_\theta & 0 & s_\theta \\ 0 & 1 & 0 \\ -s_\theta & 0 & c_\theta \end{bmatrix},$$

and the result when multiplied out must be a rotation through an angle $2\pi/n$ permitted by Theorem 9.4.6. Carrying out the multiplication and equating the trace of the product to $1 + 2 \cos 2\pi/n$ we have

$$(c_p c_q - c_p - c_q + 1)c_\theta^2 - 2s_p s_q c_\theta + (c_p c_q + c_p + c_q) = -1, 0, 1, 2, \text{ or } 3.$$

There are ten pairs of values of p and q, and five integers for the r.h.s. of this equation, giving fifty quadratic equations to be solved, from which we at once reject all solutions which are complex or numerically greater than unity. In addition, certain other solutions must be ruled out— those, namely, where the results show that although $R_p R_\theta R_q R_\theta^{-1}$ is a permissible rotation, yet $R_p^m R_\theta R_q R_\theta^{-1}$ is not; in practice this means that a fourfold axis is only possible at an angle to another axis permitted for rotations of both $\frac{1}{2}\pi$ and π, and a sixfold axis at angles permitted for $\frac{1}{3}\pi$, $\frac{2}{3}\pi$, and π, while $m = -1$ implies rather indirectly what is obvious in other ways, that an angle is only permissible if its supplement is ! The results of the calculations thus set in motion may be summarized thus:

THEOREM 9.4.7. *A p-fold and a q-fold axis may only be inclined to each other at the angles given in the following table; they then imply a further n-fold axis. (Blanks denote that the solution of the equation is not a real angle; brackets that the solution is ruled out on the second count given above.)*

p	q	$n = 2$	3	4	6	0
2	2	90°	60°	45°	30°	0°
			120°	135°	150°	180°
2	3	90°	54° 44′	35° 16′	0°	
			125° 16′	144° 44′	180°	
2	4	90°	45°	0°		
			135°	180°		
2	6	90°	0°			
			180°			
3	3	70° 32′	109° 28′	(127° 33′)	(145° 14′)	180°
3	4	54° 44′	(76° 15′)	125° 16′	(33° 5′)	
3	6	0°	(79° 26′)	(144° 28′)	(145° 39′)	
		180°				
4	4	180°	(120°)	90°	(60°)	0°
4	6		(108° 33′)	(105° 33′)	(135° 48′)	
6	6	0°	(80° 7′)	(117° 39′)	180°	

Note: $\cos\theta$	$1/\sqrt{3}$	$\sqrt{2}/\sqrt{3}$	$1/3$	
θ	54° 44′	35° 16′	70° 32′	
$\pi - \theta$	125° 16′	144° 44′	109° 28′	

A further conclusion is

THEOREM 9.4.8. *The presence of two threefold axes implies the presence of four.*

(This might be regarded as a purely group-theoretic exercise. An inspection of the table at the end of Chapter VI shows that a group with more than two third-order elements always contains at least eight. Given I, A, A^2 and I, B, B^2 as distinct subgroups it is not difficult to prove, using only the methods of Chapter I, that there are at least two other subgroups c_3 if either (a) A and B commute, or (b) AB is of order 2. But it is more satisfactory in the present context to see the situation more concretely from the three-dimensional standpoint of the foregoing table.) Two oblique C_3 can only be inclined at one angle, $109° 28′ = 180° - 70° 32′$, and there must therefore be a third C_3 and a C_2. The latter, being at $125° 16′$ to both the original C_3, must be coplanar with them (since $109° 28′ + 2 . 125° 16′ = 360°$), but the former, at $109° 28′$ to both of the original C_3, lies out of this plane. Conjugation of the $3C_3$ by the C_2 performs the operation C_2 on their axes; that is, it exchanges the two original C_3 and rotates the third into a fourth on the opposite side of the plane.

Consideration of more than two oblique axes is simplified by:

THEOREM 9.4.9. *If a group contains only proper rotations, and contains s_n axes of order n, then*

(i) $$s_2 = 3 + s_4 + 3s_6,$$

(ii) *order of group* $= 1 + s_2 + 2s_3 + 3s_4 + 5s_6 = 4 + 2s_3 + 4s_4 + 8s_6.$

These are proved by considering that the rotations about the several axes contain the identity but no other element in common, whence the number of elements in the group is $1+\sum_{2}^{6}(n-1)s_n$; further, the sum of the traces of all the elements, which by Theorem 9.4.5 is zero, is, by a simple application of Theorem 9.4.4, $3+\sum_{2}^{6}(n-3)s_n$. We may recall Theorem 1.6.3 also in this connexion.

After so much preparation we come quickly to the kill so far as proper groups are concerned. A C_6 cannot exist with an oblique C_6, C_4, or C_3, and a C_4 cannot exist with a single oblique C_3 since the C_2 which it implies causes another C_3. We can have $4C_3$ which will imply at least twelve elements, and if we add a C_4 to this it must contain $3C_4$ and twenty-four elements. Thus the only possible proper rotation groups are the cyclic groups C_1, C_2, C_3, C_4, and C_6 with the following non-cyclic groups:

		s_6	s_4	s_3	s_2	Order
222	D_2	0	0	0	3	4
32	D_3	0	0	1	3	6
42	D_4	0	1	0	4	8
62	D_6	1	0	0	6	12
23	T	0	0	4	3	12
43	O	0	3	4	6	24

The programme of deducing the results of Chapter VIII analytically instead of partly intuitively is completed by adding the improper groups with the aid of the following theorem:

THEOREM 9.4.10. *All rotations groups either*

(i) *are proper groups containing no improper element; or*

(ii) *contain the inversion element, i, and are then the direct product of a proper group with the group I i; or*

(iii) *contain some improper elements but not i, in which case there is an isomorphous proper group which contains the same proper elements, these forming a subgroup of order N/2, but the coset in one group is i times the coset in the other.*

We leave the details of the proof to the student; it has practically been given in § 8.1. The complete list of possible rotation groups is now

(i) the proper rotation groups listed above;

(ii) each of these multiplied by the group I i; and

(iii) groups formed by multiplying by i the coset of any subgroup of order $N/2$ in any of the proper groups;

and the student should expand this and check it against Chapter VIII.

9.5. The three-dimensional point lattices: (ii) from symmetry to lattice

Having vindicated, by a deeper analysis, the conclusions of Chapter VIII, we now turn to a corresponding deepening of § 9.3. The lattice hypothesis limits the possible symmetries, but they are as yet only possibilities; to realize the more elaborate of them, restrictions on the translations are necessary. Our procedure is therefore the reverse of that in § 9.3; there we discovered what symmetries we could obtain by imposing conditions on the vectors, but here we know what symmetries we are entitled to expect, and by imposing them we deduce the necessary constraints on the lattice vectors.

In the first place, since the inversion element, i, in its matrix form, is simply $-I$, the condition that $R^{-1}TR$, where T is a general lattice vector, must be another lattice vector, will, if satisfied by a given T for a given R, also be satisfied by the same T for $-R$, that is, for iR. This means that none of the improper groups impose any conditions on the lattice vectors other than those imposed by the proper groups from which, by the procedure of Theorem 9.4.10, they are derived. We shall show presently that in a similar way D_n (i.e. $n2$) imposes no more restrictions than does C_n (n), if $n > 2$, and O (43) no more than T (23). In this way the only symmetries we shall need to consider will be

C_1	C_2	D_2	C_3	C_4	C_6	T
1	2	222	3	4	6	23

and we shall have shown that the only possible types of lattice symmetry divide the thirty-two classes into the seven systems. The investigation is in two stages; first we investigate possible basic vectors for each symmetry type, and then we investigate whether the vectors so discovered are necessarily primitive sets (i.e. we consider what types of centred lattice are possible).

If U^* is the axis of a proper rotation, which we had better call A to avoid confusion between R and the $^*R_i$ (the vectors reciprocal to the P_i^*), then $AU^* = U^*$, whence $(A-I)U^* = 0$, and similarly $^*U(A-I) = 0$. Expanding the first of these in terms of the lattice vectors,

$$
\begin{aligned}
0 &= (A-I)\sum_j U_j P_j^* \\
&= \sum_j U_j(A-I)P_j^* \\
&= \sum_j \sum_i U_j(A_{ij}-I_{ij})P_i^* \\
&= \sum \Big[\sum U_j(A_{ij}-I_{ij}) \Big] P_i^*,
\end{aligned}
$$

but as the $P_i{}^*$ are independent, each square bracket must separately be zero, whence, since the A_{ij} and the I_{ij} are all integers, the U_j must be in integral ratio. Hence U^* is a general lattice vector. Similarly, from $*U(A-I) = 0$, U must be a general reciprocal lattice vector. (The star can be dropped from a real vector whenever matrix multiplication is no longer in question.) Hence

THEOREM 9.5.1 a. *A rotation axis must be parallel to both a general and a reciprocal lattice vector.*

In this statement we have made a slight change of wording because the vector calculus we have been using assumes that all vectors pass through the origin, but this is merely its technique, and in the present context is irrelevant and misleading. The point becomes important only when we turn to discuss the space groups. For our present purpose we can more profitably rewrite the theorem in the alternative form:

THEOREM 9.5.1 b. *If there is a proper rotation axis, U, it is possible to choose the basic lattice vectors so that one of them, $P_u{}^*$, say, is along the axis, and the rest, $P_v{}^*,...,$ are all perpendicular to it.*

Now if R is a lattice rotation and V a lattice vector, then RV must be a lattice vector. If R is a C_2 (2), then $RP_u{}^* = P_u{}^*$ and $RP_v{}^* = -P_v{}^*$, but if the order of R is greater than two, then $RP_v{}^*$ is a new vector, equal to $P_v{}^*$ in length but not in direction. Except where there is no axis of order greater than two, therefore, it is possible to choose $P_u{}^*$, $P_v{}^*$, and $RP_v{}^*$ as basic lattice vectors. Doing so, we may summarize and proceed to the next step simultaneously:

With no rotation axis (triclinic), there are no restrictions on the basic vectors.

With one twofold axis (monoclinic), one basic vector will be along the axis (the 'b' vector), and the other two (the 'a' and 'c' vectors) at right angles to it, of any length.

With two twofold axes (orthorhombic), one basic vector must be along each axis and the third perpendicular to both; thus three axes at right angles, with still no restrictions on length.

With one fourfold axis (tetragonal), one basic vector must be along the axis, and the other two at right angles to it, equal and at $2\pi/4$, that is, at right angles, to each other.

With one threefold axis (trigonal or rhombohedral), one vector must be along the axis and the other two at right angles to it, equal, and at $2\pi/3$ to each other. But as two vectors which are at $2\pi/3$ are also at $2\pi/6$, unless we can distinguish the positive and negative directions of the vector, this lattice is also the hexagonal lattice.

Any further symmetry involves us in at least T (23), which, since it has three twofold axes, can be referred to three basic vectors at right angles. But the implications of the angles given in Theorem 9.4.7 is that rotation about the threefold axis permutes these vectors, which must therefore be equal as well as at right angles.

The statement made earlier that the conditions necessary for a lattice to have symmetry C_n (n) or T $(n > 2)$, are also sufficient for D_n $(n2)$ or O (43), can now easily be verified.

It will be realized that the reason why we have arrived at the seven (or six) systems and not at the fourteen lattices is that the vectors referred to in Theorem 9.5.1 b need not be the shortest possible ones, and, which is more to the point, need not be such as can generate all the points of the lattice. Vectors which generate the whole lattice are called 'primitive'. If there are shorter possible lattice vectors than those we have chosen, they will be of the form $aP_a^* + bP_b^* + cP_c^*$, which we may refer to more briefly as $T(a, b, c)$, and we may assume that P_a^*, P_b^*, and P_c^* are already the shortest possible which do comply with the conditions above, so that no such vectors exist for which two of the coefficients a, b, and c are zero. Further, these coefficients must be rational fractions or they could not generate the lattice, and when only two of them are not zero they must be simple reciprocals of integers and not multiples of reciprocals, since, by Euclid's algorithm, if p/q is in its lowest terms it is always possible to find integers m and n such that $m . p/q - n = 1/q$, and thus to generate the simple reciprocal. Then again, if there is a mirror plane perpendicular to one, say P_a^*, of the basic vectors, $T(a, b, 0)$ implies $T(-a, b, 0)$ and these two can generate $T(2a, 0, 0)$ and $T(0, 2b, 0)$, which we have already ruled out except if $2a$ and $2b$ equal 0 or 1; thus the only possible value for a and b with a mirror plane is $\frac{1}{2}$. This leaves us with five possibilities:

(a) The lattice is already primitive—Type P.

(b) The vector $T(\frac{1}{2}\frac{1}{2}\frac{1}{2})$ is a lattice vector. This gives us the body-centred type of lattice—Type I.

(c) One of the vectors $T(0\frac{1}{2}\frac{1}{2})$, $T(\frac{1}{2}0\frac{1}{2})$, or $T(\frac{1}{2}\frac{1}{2}0)$ is a lattice vector. This leads to the side-centred types A, B, and C. In the absence of reason for distinguishing these three, they are referred to as Type C.

(d) All three of these vectors are lattice vectors. (We cannot have two only since any two generate the third.) This gives the face-centred lattice—Type F.

(e) No mirror plane restriction and some other type of centring.

These possibilities are subject to two conditions, however. (A) The insertion of the extra points must not break the symmetry of the lattice, but (B) as already explained in § 9.3, the primitive cell must fail to show the symmetry conditions in the form in which we have laid them down, otherwise the centring merely gives us a similar lattice based on shorter vectors. Reviewing the classes in respect of these two requirements,

Triclinic lattices have no symmetry conditions imposed, and therefore by (B) the lattice must be primitive.

Monoclinic symmetry conditions are broken if P_b* is replaced by anything else on going over to a primitive lattice, but not otherwise. Detailed examination shows that only the side-centred types, A and C, cannot be reduced to an already known type based on a smaller cell. The difference between these is here merely a matter of nomenclature.

Orthorhombic conditions are broken unless all three basic vectors are at right angles, and none of the centred types preserve this when reduced to a primitive vector set; hence all are possible.

Tetragonal conditions are also broken in each type, but here condition (A) comes in, for any modification which does not treat the a and b axes alike will spoil the tetragonal symmetry. Only the primitive and body-centred types— P and I—are possible.

Cubic lattices of all types are allowed by (B), but (A) forbids the side-centred type. We may therefore have P, I, and F cubic lattices.

Rhombohedral-hexagonal lattices are the only ones where centred types are permitted by (B) but there is no mirror plane restriction, so that alternative (e) is possible. In the present approach these two systems have the same basic cell, with the formal difference that the positive octant (containing the vector $(+1, +1, +1)$) contains the long diagonal of the hexagonal cell but the short diagonal of the rhombohedral one. The geometry of this lattice is shown in Fig. 11, in the next section.

It will be found by trial and error that any attempt to centre the cell to give possibilities (b), (c), or (d) either destroys the threefold symmetry or results in a half-sized lattice, but that threefold symmetry (though not sixfold) is preserved if extra points are added one- and two-thirds of the way along one (but not both) of the long diagonals. This is centring the hexagonal lattice with $T(\frac{1}{3}, \frac{1}{3}, \frac{1}{3})$ and $T(\frac{2}{3}, \frac{2}{3}, \frac{2}{3})$, and as the lattice based on the three vectors $T(\frac{1}{3}, \frac{1}{3}, \frac{1}{3})$, $T(\frac{1}{3}-1, \frac{1}{3}, \frac{1}{3}) = T(-\frac{2}{3}, \frac{1}{3}, \frac{1}{3})$, and $T(\frac{1}{3}, \frac{1}{3}-1, \frac{1}{3}) = T(\frac{1}{3}, -\frac{2}{3}, \frac{1}{3})$ is a primitive lattice based on three equal vectors at equal angles, we see that what we formerly called the rhombohedral system appears here as a special centred form of the hexagonal system.

These extra translations form a factor group of the whole lattice group. The combination of $T(\frac{1}{2}\frac{1}{2}0)$ with $T(0\frac{1}{2}\frac{1}{2})$, for example, produces $T(\frac{1}{2}1\frac{1}{2})$, which is the point $T(\frac{1}{2}0\frac{1}{2})$ one P_b* higher, i.e. it is the point $T(\frac{1}{2}0\frac{1}{2})$ in the next cell. By regarding similar points in different cells as not different, we get $T(\frac{1}{2}\frac{1}{2}0)$ and $T(0\frac{1}{2}\frac{1}{2})$ combining to produce $T(\frac{1}{2}0\frac{1}{2})$. This is an application of the principle of addition to a modulus, discussed in § 4.3.

9.6. The conventional axes and matrices

Some of the elements of the symmetry groups have decidedly un-expected forms when referred to crystallographic axes. A review of them, while adding to the student's experience of particular matrices, will also serve for a tabulation of standard crystallographic practice in the matter of axes.

Triclinic system. The vectors from a lattice point to its three nearest non-coplanar neighbours will be the basic lattice vectors; these are a, b, and c in order of magnitude from the largest to the smallest. The only transformations are

$$E = I = \begin{bmatrix} 1 & 0 & 0 \\ 0 & 1 & 0 \\ 0 & 0 & 1 \end{bmatrix} \qquad i = \bar{1} = \begin{bmatrix} -1 & 0 & 0 \\ 0 & -1 & 0 \\ 0 & 0 & -1 \end{bmatrix}.$$

These two matrices are valid for the elements concerned throughout all the systems, since they are invariant under all transformations.

Monoclinic system. The axis perpendicular to the other two is con-ventionally taken as the b axis. The two extra elements available in this system are

$$C_2 = 2 = \begin{bmatrix} -1 & 0 & 0 \\ 0 & 1 & 0 \\ 0 & 0 & -1 \end{bmatrix} \qquad \sigma_h = m = \begin{bmatrix} 1 & 0 & 0 \\ 0 & -1 & 0 \\ 0 & 0 & 1 \end{bmatrix}.$$

Orthorhombic system. The axes a, b, and c are in order of magnitude from the longest to the shortest. As implied in the (XYZ) notation, the matrices are the eight matrices

$$\begin{bmatrix} \pm 1 & 0 & 0 \\ 0 & \pm 1 & 0 \\ 0 & 0 & \pm 1 \end{bmatrix}.$$

Tetragonal systems. The unequal axis (the fourfold one) is conven-tionally the c axis. The matrices are those of the orthorhombic system together with the following, in which upper or lower signs are to be taken together for the proper rotations C_4 and $C_{\bar{4}}$, and one upper with one lower for the improper rotations S_4 and $m_{\bar{4}}$.

$$2C_4 \text{ and } 2m_{\bar{4}} = \begin{bmatrix} 0 & \mp 1 & 0 \\ \pm 1 & 0 & 0 \\ 0 & 0 & 1 \end{bmatrix},$$

$$2C_{\bar{4}} \text{ and } 2S_4 = \begin{bmatrix} 0 & \pm 1 & 0 \\ \pm 1 & 0 & 0 \\ 0 & 0 & -1 \end{bmatrix}.$$

Cubic system. This contains all of the above elements. It also contains the matrices equivalent to those of the tetragonal system, but with the diagonal element in the first or second position, making the six of each type instead of two. The $8C_3$ and $8S_6$ are

$$
\begin{bmatrix} 0 & \pm 1 & 0 \\ 0 & 0 & \pm 1 \\ \pm 1 & 0 & 0 \end{bmatrix}
\quad \text{and} \quad
\begin{bmatrix} 0 & 0 & \pm 1 \\ \pm 1 & 0 & 0 \\ 0 & \pm 1 & 0 \end{bmatrix},
$$

those with an even number of minus signs being C_3 and those with an odd number being S_6.

Centred lattices referred to primitive axes. All the above matrices refer to the simple lattices, or to centred lattices regarded as such. If centred lattices are *referred to primitive vector sets*, the matrices are transformed. In place of those given above, we have, in the monoclinic system,

$$
C_2 = 2 = \begin{bmatrix} 0 & -1 & 0 \\ -1 & 0 & 0 \\ 0 & 0 & -1 \end{bmatrix}
\qquad
\sigma_h = m = \begin{bmatrix} 0 & 1 & 0 \\ 1 & 0 & 0 \\ 0 & 0 & 1 \end{bmatrix}
$$

and in the orthorhombic system the same distribution of unit and zero elements with all combinations of plus and minus signs. The matrices given here (M') are transformed into those given above (M) by $M \to RM'R^{-1}$, where R is the matrix giving the primitive basic vectors in terms of the conventional ones, namely,

$$
R = \begin{bmatrix} \frac{1}{2} & \frac{1}{2} & 0 \\ \frac{1}{2} & -\frac{1}{2} & 0 \\ 0 & 0 & 1 \end{bmatrix},
\qquad
R^{-1} = \begin{bmatrix} 1 & 1 & 0 \\ 1 & -1 & 0 \\ 0 & 0 & 1 \end{bmatrix}.
$$

Face-centred and body-centred lattices can be treated in a similar way; it is left as an exercise to the student to do this.

Trigonal-hexagonal system. This system needs considerably more discussion. The basic vectors in § 9.5 were one along the sixfold (or threefold) axis, and two at right angles to this. The lattice built to this prescription is shown in Fig. 11 (other layers being an arbitrary distance vertically above the one shown). The equal vectors at $2\pi/6$ are shown on the left, but the figure also shows that a base-centred orthorhombic lattice with the special ratio $a:b = 1:\sqrt{3}$ is an equivalent description. Crystallographically this description has such advantages that it is adopted in the Mauguin–Hermann notation, so that, for example, D_{3h} is written $C6m$ and not $P6m$. When the type A of base-centred lattice has to be distinguished from the type C, however, H is used and not A.

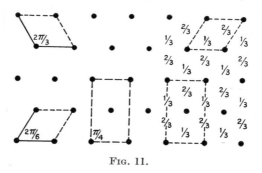

Fig. 11.

An examination of the method of expressing the results of rotating a basic vector in either system in terms of the basic vectors of that system enables the rotation matrices to be written down at once. They are

	6	**3**	**2**	**3′**	**6′**
Primary lattice	$\begin{bmatrix} 0 & -1 & 0 \\ 1 & 1 & 0 \\ 0 & 0 & 1 \end{bmatrix}$	$\begin{bmatrix} -1 & -1 & 0 \\ 1 & 0 & 0 \\ 0 & 0 & 1 \end{bmatrix}$	$\begin{bmatrix} -1 & 0 & 0 \\ 0 & -1 & 0 \\ 0 & 0 & 1 \end{bmatrix}$	$\begin{bmatrix} 0 & 1 & 0 \\ -1 & -1 & 0 \\ 0 & 0 & 1 \end{bmatrix}$	$\begin{bmatrix} 1 & 1 & 0 \\ -1 & 0 & 0 \\ 0 & 0 & 1 \end{bmatrix}$
O.R. lattice	$\begin{bmatrix} \frac{1}{2} & -\frac{3}{2} & 0 \\ \frac{1}{2} & \frac{1}{2} & 0 \\ 0 & 0 & 1 \end{bmatrix}$	$\begin{bmatrix} -\frac{1}{2} & -\frac{3}{2} & 0 \\ \frac{1}{2} & -\frac{1}{2} & 0 \\ 0 & 0 & 1 \end{bmatrix}$	$\begin{bmatrix} -1 & 0 & 0 \\ 0 & -1 & 0 \\ 0 & 0 & 1 \end{bmatrix}$	$\begin{bmatrix} -\frac{1}{2} & \frac{3}{2} & 0 \\ -\frac{1}{2} & -\frac{1}{2} & 0 \\ 0 & 0 & 1 \end{bmatrix}$	$\begin{bmatrix} \frac{1}{2} & \frac{3}{2} & 0 \\ -\frac{1}{2} & \frac{1}{2} & 0 \\ 0 & 0 & 1 \end{bmatrix}$

The inversion-rotations $\bar{6}$, etc., are obtained by reversing all signs in the above, and the various reflections and twofold rotations not included above are obtained by reversing either the sign of the bottom right-hand 1 or all the signs except this one. (Compare § 8.1, noting that the axis here is the Z-axis.) The two rows of matrices given above are, of course, equivalent representations of the group c_6, and corresponding matrices have the same trace. Yet another equivalent representation, the derivation of which we leave to the student, is obtained if the basic vectors are equal and at 120°.

The rhombohedral lattice was seen in § 9.5 to be a centred hexagonal one, with the extra points trisecting one of the longer diagonals of the cell. From Fig. 11 we see that the orthorhombic representation involves a centred cell with the extra points at $(\frac{1}{2}, \frac{1}{2}, 0)$ (as before), $(0, \frac{1}{3}, \frac{1}{3})$, $(0, \frac{2}{3}, \frac{2}{3})$, $(\frac{1}{2}, \frac{1}{6}, \frac{2}{3})$, and $(\frac{1}{2}, \frac{5}{6}, \frac{1}{3})$. This cell contains eight corner points, six points in a face, and two in the body, and thus is equivalent to $\frac{8}{8}+\frac{6}{2}+2 = 6$ primitive cells; a primitive cell is obtained by taking the vectors from $(\frac{1}{2}, \frac{1}{2}, 0)$ to $(0, \frac{1}{3}, \frac{1}{3})$, $(\frac{1}{2}, \frac{5}{6}, \frac{1}{3})$, and $(1, \frac{1}{3}, \frac{1}{3})$ as basic vectors. This ortho-rhombic representation of the trigonal symmetry is denoted by the letter R. R thus stands for a somewhat complicated factor group of the trans-lation group.

The holohedral trigonal symmetry is a subgroup of the hexagonal symmetry and no new matrices are introduced. If the lattice is referred to the primitive basis the matrices of the six elements in C_{3v} ($3m$) are those of the permutation representation of π_3, and the remaining six are these with all signs reversed.

9.7. The space groups

Molecules, in aggregating to a crystal, might be expected so to arrange themselves as to display in bulk such symmetry as they have, though guesses in this direction are more often wrong than right. Not only may unsymmetrical molecules group themselves into symmetrical arrange-ments which are the effective units for crystal building, but frequently symmetrical molecules show an unexpected refusal to take up what one would imagine to be the obvious arrangement. It can only be presumed that their finer structure is such as to bring unexpected unsymmetrical residual forces into play which control their arrangement. Nevertheless, we may say in principle that objects with any one of the thirty-two classes of symmetry, in aggregating, are likely to dispose themselves on a lattice which displays that class of symmetry, but not on a lattice which displays a higher symmetry than is necessary. (The lattice cannot help displaying the holohedral symmetry of the class to which it belongs.) The lattice may be a primitive or a centred one, and for this purpose the trigonal-hexagonal is to be considered one system. If the object has hemihedral symmetry, alternatives may arise in certain cases, for example an object lacking mirror symmetry across a plane, crystallizing in a base-centred lattice, may orient itself with this plane parallel to the centred face of the cell or perpendicular to it. And in one class of the tetragonal system, $\bar{4}2m$ (D_{2d}), the lack of full symmetry provides sufficient relief from condition (A) of § 9.5 to permit the side- and face-centred lattices normally impossible in that system. The result is that this procedure—placing objects with each of the thirty-two symmetries at the points of various appropriate lattices—leads to seventy-three distinct structures, grouped as follows:

System	Centring							Total
	P	C	A	H	R	F	I	
Triclinic . . .	2							2
Monoclinic. . .	3	3						6
Orthorhombic . .	3	3	1			3	3	13
Tetragonal. . .	7	1				1	7	16
Trigonal . . .		5		3	5			13
Hexagonal . .		7		1				8
Cubic . . .	5					5	5	15
								73

The remainder of the 230 space groups contain elements which are the three-dimensional equivalents of the two-dimensional C^s type, and these we must now consider. They are of the form $T(V).R$, and our first task is to decide which elements of this type are not equivalent to simple proper or improper rotations, about an axis not through the origin. Conjugation of this element by the translation $T(U)$ leads to

$$T(U)[T(V).R][T(U)]^{-1} = T(V+U-RU).R$$

and the element $T(V).R$ will therefore be equivalent to a simple rotation if it is possible to find U such that $(I-R)U^* = -V^*$. Now, as shown in §§ 3.6 and 8.1, the eigenvalues of a rotation are of modulus unity, and therefore if real equal to ± 1. The operator $I-R$ will have as many zero eigenvalues as R has eigenvalues $+1$. A rotation with

three such eigenvalues is simply I,

two such eigenvalues is a reflection across the plane of the two eigenvectors,

one such eigenvalue is a proper rotation about the eigenvector,

no such eigenvalue is an improper rotation not a reflection.

Now if V has components in a direction in which $I-R$ has a zero eigenvalue, it will be impossible to transform $T(V).R$ into a simple rotation, and thus $T(V).R$ is a new type of element provided either (i) R is a proper rotation and V directed along it, or (ii) R is a reflection and V in the plane. (Components of V other than those specified can still be removed if $U = (I-R)^{-1}V$, where $(I-R)^{-1}$ is the pseudo-reciprocal of § 3.8.)

By Theorem 9.4.4, if R is of order n and V is along the axis of R, $(T(V).R)^n = T(nV)$; it is therefore essential that nV shall be a lattice vector. Similarly, if R is a reflection and V in the plane perpendicular to its axis, $(T(V).R)^2 = T(2V)$, so that in this case $2V$ must be a lattice vector. It is also obvious that unless $T(V)$ and R separately are not elements of the structure, the whole discussion is trivial. We therefore define two new types of symmetry element:

A structure is said to have a *screw-axis* n_k if the lattice possesses the symmetry element n and an object of lower symmetry at a lattice point is repeated along the axis of the rotation subject to simultaneous rotations of $2\pi/n$ and displacements of k/n of the lattice vector in this direction.

A structure is said to have a *glide plane* if the lattice possesses a mirror plane and an object not possessing this symmetry element is repeated subject to simultaneous reflection in the plane and displacement by half a lattice vector in the plane.

The notation for a glide plane depends on the direction of the displacement; it is a, b, or c for displacements parallel to the corresponding axes, n for a diagonal glide, and d for a displacement which is half-way to a centring point (i.e. which is half a primitive lattice vector but needs quarters for expression in terms of the sides of the centred cell).

Assuming that we are given a structure containing such elements, (9.4.2 b) shows that the group-structure of its symmetry will be the same as though the elements R were unaccompanied by translations—the integral translation group is still an invariant subgroup, and the cosets $T(V).R$ form a factor group with the same structure as the elements R. Further, owing to the extreme smallness of the translation parts in practice in crystals, it will seem to external appearances that the crystal possesses the simple symmetry elements R. It is these two features which allow the Hermann–Mauguin notation to deal very simply with the 230 space groups.

We have used this notation freely hitherto without explaining exactly how it is meant to be applied to symmetry groups. In theory it is a complete description of the symmetry group of the structure on the following conventions as to its interpretation. (1) The integral translation group is invariably understood and not written. (2) The translation factor group in a centred lattice is symbolized by P, C, F,.... (P denotes $\mathfrak{c}_1$, of course.) (3) The elements necessary to generate the rotation group of its apparent (external) symmetry are then added in the following order: (i) the symbol n, $\bar{n}$, m, or n/m appropriate to the axis of highest n (the groups T and T_h are understandable exceptions here), (ii) similar data on the next most important axis, usually perpendicular to the first, but always, in the cubic system, one of the triad axes, (iii) similar data on any third axis which convenience may dictate—see the next paragraph. (4) But if this external symmetry is due to screw axes or glide planes in the structure, the symbols n or m are *replaced* by n_k or a, b, c, n, or d.

The student should be warned, however, that admirable as is this scheme in theory, in practice there are certain further conventions which reduce some of it to an esoteric mumbo-jumbo unless the thirty-two classes are learnt off by heart. The group structure is always expressible in terms of two axes, and in those cases where three symbols are given, either the third is unnecessary, or it is included because something else has been left out. To the first class belong 222 ($= 22$), $\overline{4}2m$ ($= \overline{4}2$ or $\overline{4}m$), $4/mmm$ ($= 4/mm$), $4mm$ ($= 4m$), and the corresponding hexagonal groups, and to the second class belong mmm $\left(= \dfrac{2}{m}m\right)$ and $m3m$ $\left(= \dfrac{4}{m}3\right)$. But the symbols in the first class pass over to the second when (as we shall see) screw axis subscripts are omitted because they can be deduced from the glide plane information in the third part of the symbol. Let us see how it all works out in practice.

A structure is said to have the symmetry Cmc. Externally this will be indistinguishable from Pmm. If the two axes are the X and the Y axes, the first m implies Im_x and the second Im_y, and the whole group will be $(Im_x)(Im_y) = Im_x m_y 2_z$. That the second m is replaced by a c means that this element is actually a glide plane, and that C replaces P means that the lattice is face-centred. That C and c are the same letter means that the glide (a vector) and the centred face (a plane) correspond, i.e. are perpendicular. The complete group so far elucidated is therefore

$$I \qquad T(000).m_x \qquad T(00\tfrac{1}{2}).m_y \qquad T(pqr).2_z$$
$$T(\tfrac{1}{2}\tfrac{1}{2}0).I \qquad T(\tfrac{1}{2}\tfrac{1}{2}0).m_x \qquad T(\tfrac{1}{2}\tfrac{1}{2}\tfrac{1}{2}).m_y \qquad T(stu).2_z$$

and by multiplying the known elements together with the aid of the commutation rule (9.4.1) and reducing (mod $T(111)$), we find that $T(pqr)$ is $T(00\tfrac{1}{2})$ and $T(stu)$ is $T(\tfrac{1}{2}\tfrac{1}{2}\tfrac{1}{2})$. The fourth element of the group is therefore a screw axis. Since the object is at $T(000)$ with both I and m_x, it possesses itself the symmetry element m_x, but not the other two (m_y and 2). A unit cell with this structure is shown in Fig. 12.

As a more elaborate study let us consider what space groups come under the class $C_{4v} = 4mm$, the rotation group of which has eight elements and is non-commutative. The eight elements of this class can be generated from a fourfold Z-axis and a reflection in the XZ-plane; the second m is superfluous as already explained. We therefore generate a complete group from $T(0,0,a).4$ and $T(b,c,d).m_y$. (We cannot put $c = 0$ at once, because we have defined the origin as lying on the fourfold axis by writing $T(0,0,a)4$, and the glide plane may be parallel to this

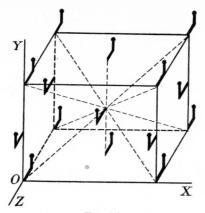

FIG. 12.

axis but not through the origin.) In writing out the cyclic subgroup
derived from $T(0, 0, a).4$ we may assume that $4a = 0$ (mod 1), and we
have, with certain simplifications of notation, the table on page 130.
The c_4 subgroup is written in first, then the second generating element,
and a 5×5 square completed; the new elements in the fifth row are
then used to complete the edges of the table, and the remainder filled
in with the aid of (9.4.1).

Now, if the lattice is primitive, I can only be associated with a lattice
translation, whence, considering this case first, the expressions

$$4a; \qquad 2b; \qquad b+c; \qquad 2c; \qquad 2d; \qquad 2a+2d; \qquad b-c$$

are all zero (mod 1). These equations lead to

$$a = 0 \text{ or } \tfrac{1}{2}; \qquad d = 0 \text{ or } \tfrac{1}{2}; \qquad b = c = 0 \text{ or } \tfrac{1}{2}.$$

Since $a = \tfrac{1}{2}$ implies a 4_2, and the m_y becomes n, c, or b if $(b, d) = (\tfrac{1}{2}, \tfrac{1}{2})$,
$(0, \tfrac{1}{2})$, or $(\tfrac{1}{2}, 0)$ respectively, this leads to eight possible primitive lattices,
namely,

	a	$b = c$	d	Symbol deduced	Normal symbol
(a)	0	0	0	$4m$	$4mm$
(b)	0	0	$\tfrac{1}{2}$	$4c$	$4cc$
(c)	0	$\tfrac{1}{2}$	0	$4b$	$4bm$
(d)	$\tfrac{1}{2}$	0	0	$4_2 m$	$4mc$
(e)	0	$\tfrac{1}{2}$	$\tfrac{1}{2}$	$4n$	$4nc$
(f)	$\tfrac{1}{2}$	0	$\tfrac{1}{2}$	$4_2 c$	$4cm$
(g)	$\tfrac{1}{2}$	$\tfrac{1}{2}$	0	$4_2 b$	$4bc$
(h)	$\tfrac{1}{2}$	$\tfrac{1}{2}$	$\tfrac{1}{2}$	$4_2 n$	$4nn$

Multiplication Table for Structures in the Class C_{4v}

	$(0, 0, 2a)2$	$(0, 0, 3a)4^3$	I	$(0, 0, a)4$	$(b, c, d)m_y$	$(b, c, a+d)m_{\frac{x}{4}}$	$(b, c, 2a+d)m_x$	$(b, c, 3a+d)m_{\frac{x}{4}}$
I	$(0, 0, 2a)2$	$(0, 0, 3a)4^3$	I	$(0, 0, a)4$	$(b, c, d)m_y$	$(b, c, a+d)m_{\frac{x}{4}}$	$(b, c, 2a+d)m_x$	$(b, c, 3a+d)m_{\frac{x}{4}}$
$(0, 0, a)4$	$(0, 0, 3a)4^3$	I	$(0, 0, a)4$	$(0, 0, 2a)2$	$(b, -c, a+d)m_{\frac{x}{4}}$	$(b, -c, 2a+d)m_y$	$(b, -c, 3a+d)m_{\frac{x}{4}}$	$(b, -c, d)m_x$
$(0, 0, 2a)2$	I	$(0, 0, a)4$	$(0, 0, 2a)2$	$(0, 0, 3a)4^3$	$(-b, -c, 2a+d)m_x$	$(-b, -c, 3a+d)m_{\frac{x}{4}}$	$(-b, -c, d)m_y$	$(-b, -c, a+d)m_{\frac{x}{4}}$
$(0, 0, 3a)4^3$	$(0, 0, a)4$	$(0, 0, 2a)2$	$(0, 0, 3a)4^3$	I	$(-b, c, 3a+d)m_{\frac{x}{4}}$	$(-b, c, d)m_x$	$(-b, c, a+d)m_{\frac{x}{4}}$	$(-b, c, 2a+d)m_y$
$(b, c, d)m_y$	$(b, c, 2a+d)m_x$	$(b, c, 3a+d)m_{\frac{x}{4}}$	$(b, c, d)m_y$	$(b, c, a+d)m_{\frac{x}{4}}$	$(2b, 0, 2d)I$	$(2b, 0, a+2d)4$	$(2b, 0, 2a+2d)2$	$(2b, 0, 3a+2d)4^3$
$(b, c, a+d)m_{\frac{x}{4}}$	$(b, c, 3a+d)m_{\frac{x}{4}}$	$(b, c, d)m_y$	$(b, c, a+d)m_{\frac{x}{4}}$	$(b, c, 2a+d)m_x$	$(b+c, b+c, a+2d)4^3$	$(b+c, b+c, 2a+2d)I$	$(b+c, b+c, 3a+2d)4$	$(b+c, b+c, 2d)2$
$(b, c, 2a+d)m_x$	$(b, c, d)m_y$	$(b, c, a+d)m_{\frac{x}{4}}$	$(b, c, 2a+d)m_x$	$(b, c, 3a+d)m_{\frac{x}{4}}$	$(0, 2c, 2a+2d)2$	$(0, 2c, 3a+2d)4^3$	$(0, 2c, 2d)I$	$(0, 2c, a+2d)4$
$(b, c, 3a+d)m_{\frac{x}{4}}$	$(b, c, a+d)m_{\frac{x}{4}}$	$(b, c, 2a+d)m_x$	$(b, c, 3a+d)m_{\frac{x}{4}}$	$(b, c, d)m_y$	$(b-c, c-b, 3a+2d)4$	$(b-c, c-b, 2d)2$	$(b-c, c-b, a+2d)4^3$	$(b-c, c-b, 2a+2d)I$

The 'normal' symbol is the one usually used by crystallographers. The second letter refers to $m_{\frac14}$, the screw axis subscript is suppressed and is understood to be present if the letters are one from each pair (m, b) and (c, n) and absent if the letters are both from one pair. How the beginner is expected to understand this is never stated!

In considering the body-centred lattice, $T(\frac12, \frac12, \frac12).I$ becomes a possibility. From the occurrence of $(2b, 0, 2d).I$ and $(0, 2c, 2d).I$ we see that $b, c,$ and d may still be 0 or $\frac12$ only, but the combination of $a = \frac14$ with b or c equal to $\frac12$ and d equal to 0 or $\frac12$ is not ruled out. These four combinations represent only two distinct structures, however, since b and c represent equivalent translations under the rotation group. (The distinction is only one of the naming of the axes, and in counting the space groups the convention that $a, b,$ and c are in descending order of magnitude is dropped.) These two combinations are $4_1 m$ and $4_1 c$, usually written $4md$ and $4cd$—the d type of glide plane can only arise when one of the quantities $a,...,d$ is $\frac14$. The eight combinations already found need re-examination to see if they are possible with a body-centred lattice. In the following table we give the translations associated with each rotation element in each of the eight combinations, adding to it, in the line below, $T(\frac12\frac12\frac12)$.

	I	4	2	4^3	m_y	$m_{\frac14}$	m_x	$m_{\frac34}$
(a)	000	000	000	000	000	000	000	000
	$\frac12\frac12\frac12$	$\frac12\frac12\frac12$	$\frac12\frac12\frac12$	$\frac12\frac12\frac12$	$\frac12\frac12\frac12$	$\frac12\frac12\frac12$	$\frac12\frac12\frac12$	$\frac12\frac12\frac12$
(b)	000	000	000	000	$00\frac12$	$00\frac12$	$00\frac12$	$00\frac12$
	$\frac12\frac12\frac12$	$\frac12\frac12\frac12$	$\frac12\frac12\frac12$	$\frac12\frac12\frac12$	$\frac12\frac12 0$	$\frac12\frac12 0$	$\frac12\frac12 0$	$\frac12\frac12 0$
(c)	000	000	000	000	$\frac12\frac12 0$	$\frac12\frac12 0$	$\frac12\frac12 0$	$\frac12\frac12 0$
	$\frac12\frac12\frac12$	$\frac12\frac12\frac12$	$\frac12\frac12\frac12$	$\frac12\frac12\frac12$	$00\frac12$	$00\frac12$	$00\frac12$	$00\frac12$
(d)	000	$00\frac12$	000	$00\frac12$	000	$00\frac12$	000	$00\frac12$
	$\frac12\frac12\frac12$	$\frac12\frac12 0$	$\frac12\frac12\frac12$	$\frac12\frac12 0$	$\frac12\frac12\frac12$	$\frac12\frac12 0$	$\frac12\frac12\frac12$	$\frac12\frac12 0$
(e)	000	000	000	000	$\frac12\frac12\frac12$	$\frac12\frac12\frac12$	$\frac12\frac12\frac12$	$\frac12\frac12\frac12$
	$\frac12\frac12\frac12$	$\frac12\frac12\frac12$	$\frac12\frac12\frac12$	$\frac12\frac12\frac12$	000	000	000	000
(f)	000	$00\frac12$	000	$00\frac12$	$00\frac12$	000	$00\frac12$	000
	$\frac12\frac12\frac12$	$\frac12\frac12 0$	$\frac12\frac12\frac12$	$\frac12\frac12 0$	$\frac12\frac12 0$	$\frac12\frac12\frac12$	$\frac12\frac12 0$	$\frac12\frac12\frac12$
(g)	000	$00\frac12$	000	$00\frac12$	$\frac12\frac12 0$	$\frac12\frac12\frac12$	$\frac12\frac12 0$	$\frac12\frac12\frac12$
	$\frac12\frac12\frac12$	$\frac12\frac12 0$	$\frac12\frac12\frac12$	$\frac12\frac12 0$	$00\frac12$	000	$00\frac12$	000
(h)	000	$00\frac12$	000	$00\frac12$	$\frac12\frac12\frac12$	$\frac12\frac12 0$	$\frac12\frac12\frac12$	$\frac12\frac12 0$
	$\frac12\frac12\frac12$	$\frac12\frac12 0$	$\frac12\frac12\frac12$	$\frac12\frac12 0$	000	$00\frac12$	000	$00\frac12$

Whether a translation is in the upper or lower line is simply the order of our discovery; hence we see at once that (a) and (e) are now identical, likewise (b) and (c), (d) and (h), and (f) and (g), which reduces our types to four. But they are still not all distinct, for the forms $(\frac12, \frac12, 0)m_{\frac34}$ and $(\frac12, \frac12, 0)m_{\frac14}$ (which $= (\frac12, -\frac12, 0)m_{\frac14}$) are not glide plane elements at all.

since the 'glide' is perpendicular to the plane, and the element is therefore equivalent to a simple reflection across a parallel plane. We are thus left with two structures, $4m = 4mm$, and $4_2 c = 4cm$.

The old notation for the space groups is uninformative, since it merely adds a serial number on to the external symmetry symbol. Complete lists of the space groups in both notations are given in works on crystallography. We conclude this section with a summary table showing the distribution of the 230 space groups among the lattices and classes, so that, if the student wishes as an exercise to repeat the above method on some other classes, he will know how many space groups he should find. In many cases the list is obvious (or nearly so) by inspection.

TABLE OF DISTRIBUTION OF SPACE GROUPS

System	Class			P or R	C, A, or H	F	I	Total	
Triclinic	C_1	1		1				1	
	C_i	$\bar{1}$	(S_2)	1				1	2
Monoclinic	C_s	m	(C_{1h})	2	2			4	
	C_2	2		2	1			3	
	C_{2h}	$2/m$		4	2			6	13
Orthorhombic	C_{2v}	mm		10	7	2	3	22	
	D_2	222	(V)	4	2	1	2	9	
	D_{2h}	mmm	(V_h)	16	6	2	4	28	59
Tetragonal	S_4	$\bar{4}$		1			1	2	
	C_4	4		4			2	6	
	C_{4h}	$4/m$		4			2	6	
	D_{2d}	$\bar{4}2m$	$(V_d; S_{4v})$	4	4	2	2	12	
	C_{4v}	$4mm$		8			4	12	
	D_4	42		8			2	10	
	D_{4h}	$4/mmm$		16			4	20	68
Trigonal	C_3	3		1	3			4	
	S_6	$\bar{3}$	(C_{3i})	1	1			2	
	C_{3v}	$3m$		2	4			6	
	D_3	32		1	6			7	
	D_{3d}	$\bar{3}m$	(S_{3v})	2	4			6	25
Hexagonal	C_{3h}	$\bar{6}$	$(3/m)$		1			1	
	C_6	6			6			6	
	C_{6h}	$6/m$			2			2	
	D_{3h}	$\bar{6}m$	$(\bar{6}m2)$		4			4	
	C_{6v}	$6mm$			4			4	
	D_6	62			6			6	
	D_{6h}	$6/mmm$			4			4	27
Cubic	T	23		2		1	2	5	
	T_h	$m3$		3		2	2	7	
	T_d	$\bar{4}3$		2		2	2	6	
	O	43		4		2	2	8	
	O_h	$m3m$		4		4	2	10	36
									230

9.8. The reciprocal lattice

We have seen that the fundamental hypothesis of crystal structure is the existence of a 'lattice' consisting of all points describable by the expression $a_1 P_1 + a_2 P_2 + a_3 P_3$, where P_1, P_2, and P_3 are three non-coplanar vectors and a_1, a_2, and a_3 are integers. (But we ought perhaps to dispel any impression that there are any unique points which are lattice points. In a given crystal, fixing an origin determines a lattice, but the origin is completely arbitrary; thus there is nothing more distinctive about 'lattice points' in a crystal than there is about the intersection of grid-lines on a map, which, on the ground, look just like any other point.) Associated with any three vectors P_1, P_2, and P_3 is the reciprocal set R_1, R_2, and R_3. If these are in their turn made the basis of a lattice, this new lattice is called the reciprocal of the old one. It is to be thought of as existing in a different space (compare § 3.2).

In Theorem 9.1.1 we showed that a plane described in terms of three vectors which terminate on it is conveniently described in terms of a vector in the reciprocal lattice, since the vector

$$p_2 p_3 R_1 + p_3 p_1 R_2 + p_1 p_3 R_3$$

is an unnormalized vector from the origin perpendicular to the plane on which the vectors $p_1 P_1$, $p_2 P_2$, and $p_3 P_3$ terminate. Conversely, any vector in the reciprocal space defines a plane in the original space—the plane made up of all vectors perpendicular to it. We may write this plane as the totality of all vectors V satisfying $*RV* = 0$ where $*R$ is the vector in the reciprocal space. The equation $*RV* = c$ defines a parallel plane not through the origin, on which all vectors V satisfying it terminate. (This is obvious from a coordinate geometry point of view, or we may say that if $U*$ is any solution of $*RV* = c$, then $U*$ added to any solution of $*RV* = 0$ gives a solution of $*RV* = c$.)

Let us now restrict the generality of the previous paragraph in two respects, first by requiring that $*R$ is a *lattice* vector in the reciprocal space, and secondly that at least one solution $V*$ of $*RV* = c$ is a lattice vector in the direct space—which means that the plane passes through at least one lattice point. Then an expansion of $*RV*$ shows that c must be an integer. Thus those planes which contain a lattice point are the planes defined by $*RV* = 0, 1, 2, \ldots$. Further, among the vectors $V*$ will be one, V_p^*, which is parallel to $*R$; the length of this vector is c divided by the length of $*R$, but it is also the perpendicular distance of the plane from the origin. Thus we see that, in general, a lattice vector $*R$ in the reciprocal space defines a series of planes through lattice points of the direct lattice spaced a distance apart equal to the reciprocal of the length of $*R$. (An exception to this would occur if the expansion of $*RV*$ showed that c must be an integral multiple not merely of unity but of some higher integer; this, however, occurs when the coefficients in $*R = r_1*R_1 + r_2*R_2 + r_3*R_3$ contain a common factor q, and this is equivalent to saying that the lattice vector $*R$ is q times a shorter lattice vector. In applying this rule we must therefore stipulate that $*R$ is the shortest reciprocal lattice vector with the given direction.)

An alternative way of putting this conclusion is to say that a lattice vector in a given direction in the reciprocal space defines a set of parallel planes in the direct space, and the length of the shortest such reciprocal lattice vector gives the number of such planes per unit length perpendicular to them. The closer such planes are—i.e. the longer the reciprocal lattice vector—the less important they are, since, as the density of the points in the direct space is given, the closer the planes are, the less dense will be the spacing of points in any one plane. This use of the reciprocal lattice finds a very important application in X-ray crystallography, because X-rays are reflected from crystal planes; indeed, in a precession camera photograph the dots obtained on the film are actually lattice points in one plane of the reciprocal space, and in some other types dots which are points in a distorted or projected form of the reciprocal lattice are obtained.

We can immediately anticipate one of the considerations of Chapter XIV, where we shall use and extend the ideas of the last paragraph but one. A contravariant vector we can understand and picture. A covariant vector may sometimes be pictured as a vector in the dual or reciprocal space; it is sometimes more usefully pictured as a lamination-quality, the vector being perpendicular to the laminations and its magnitude inversely proportional to their thickness. We shall see in Chapter XIV that in a space with a metric there are not co- and contra-variant vectors, but co- and contra-variant forms of vectors. We shall be pursuing the line of thought in this paragraph if we consider the two forms of the gradient vector on the earth's surface and the contour and hachure methods of representing it on a map. In the former, lines run perpendicular to the gradient, closer together when the gradient is stiffer; in the latter (more popular on the continent than in England) lines run with the gradient, their intensity varying with the steepness. The former is covariant thinking and the latter contravariant.

Another application of the reciprocal space is the discussion of wave propagation through crystals or other periodic structures by Brillouin. A wave of frequency ν and wavelength $\lambda = 1/a$ is described by the equation $\psi = Ae^{2\pi i(\nu t - ax)}$, where ψ is the measure of whatever disturbance is propagated and x is distance in the direction of propagation. But in a lattice structure certain types of disturbance (at least) are defined only at the lattice points $x = nd$ (n integral), where d is the lattice spacing. But with n integral, $Ae^{2\pi i(\nu t - (ad+m)n)} = Ae^{2\pi i(\nu t - adn)}$ if m is any integer. Thus a given disturbance can be described equally well as a wave disturbance with wavelength $\lambda = 1/a$ or as one with wavelength given by $1/\lambda = a \pm m/d$. The difference between these descriptions lies in the number of periods in the region between two successive lattice points where the disturbance is undefined.

In extending this to several dimensions we have to consider the wavelength as a vector in the direction of propagation of the wave. $1/\lambda$ is then a vector in the reciprocal space, parallel to λ. $1/d$ was the basic reciprocal lattice vector, and the term $\pm m/d$ generalizes to an arbitrary reciprocal lattice vector. The conclusion as to the ambiguity of the wavelength then reduces, in three dimensions, to the simple conclusion that a wave disturbance in a crystal, describable in terms of a wavelength represented by the direction and the reciprocal of the length of a vector A, may equally well be represented by any vector of the form $A + D$ (in direction and reciprocal of length) where D is any reciprocal lattice vector.

No mention has been made of the velocity of propagation in the foregoing discussion, and therefore the frequency has not been explictly used in the argument. To develop Brillouin's theories further is to do this, and to introduce dispersion, and to wander too far from our main theme. We shall return briefly to the Brillouin theory in Chapter XVII.

CHAPTER X

THE VIBRATIONS OF MOLECULES

A MOLECULE is a collection of, say, n atoms, held together by forces more or less in isolation from other material particles. In fact, as the isolation becomes more and more of an idealization, so the concept of a molecule becomes less and less useful. The intramolecular forces are, viewed from one angle, simply the whole subject of chemistry, but from another they are ordinary mechanical forces and can be discussed in mechanical terms. With even the simplest molecules, however, the problem is too complex unless the coordinates are cunningly chosen—unless, in fact, 'normal' coordinates are used. Most elementary physical and physico-chemical books explain this without making very clear what normal coordinates are or giving examples, in which they are probably justified, since the value of normal coordinates does not really show itself in the most elementary applications. There is, however, one idealized example which will serve by way of introduction.

Consider what might be an HCl or NO molecule constrained to remain in a fixed vertical line, namely two masses m_1 and m_2 constrained to move along a vertical straight line and connected by a spring of un-stretched length a and force constant k. Let the coordinates of the masses (measured along the vertical line) be x_1 and x_2. The equations of motion of m_1 and m_2 will be

$$m_1 \ddot{x}_1 = k(x_2 + a - x_1) - m_1 g,$$
$$m_2 \ddot{x}_2 = k(x_1 - x_2 - a) - m_2 g,$$

but if we change to new coordinates $X = (m_1 x_1 + m_2 x_2)/(m_1 + m_2)$ and $d = x_1 - x_2$, these equations become

$$(m_1 + m_2)\ddot{X} = (m_1 + m_2)g,$$
$$\frac{m_1 m_2}{m_1 + m_2} \ddot{d} = -k(d - a),$$

which are the elementary equations for the motion of the whole system under gravity, and for the simple harmonic motion of a mass

$$\frac{m_1 m_2}{m_1 + m_2}$$

at one end of the spring if the other end is fixed—each equation containing only one of the coordinates. The coordinates X and d are the normal coordinates for this system. It is sometimes convenient to refer to $m_1+m_2 = M$ as the external mass and to $m_1 m_2/(m_1+m_2) = \mu$ as the internal mass of the two-body system.

10.2. Procedure for transformation of coordinates

In this section we shall start with n atoms, whose coordinates are given in a cartesian system as (x_1, y_1, z_1), (x_2, y_2, z_2),..., (x_n, y_n, z_n), and we shall perform successive changes of the coordinate system until we have a set of normal coordinates.

In our first change we study the molecule in an instantaneous position. It will probably be strained, but positions can be found for each atom, close to their actual positions, in which the strain would be relieved; these positions are not unique, since the unstrained molecule can be moved as a whole, but we shall select one such position and call it the equilibrium configuration of the molecule. We now refer each atom to new axes parallel to the original ones but through the equilibrium position of that atom as origin. We could write these new coordinates (ξ_1, η_1, ζ_1), (ξ_2, η_2, ζ_2),..., and write $\xi_r = x_r - x_r^0$, etc., but we shall not need the latter relations once we have noted that although $\xi_r \neq x_r$, yet we still have $\dot{\xi}_r = \dot{x}_r$. Further, it will be convenient for summation purposes not to use different letters ξ, η, ζ but to use $\xi_1,..., \xi_{3n}$, where $\xi_{n+r} = \eta_r$ and $\xi_{2n+r} = \zeta_r$.

In these coordinates the kinetic energy takes a similar form to its form in the original cartesians, namely,

$$\text{K.E.} = \tfrac{1}{2} \sum_1^n m_r(\dot{x}_r^2 + \dot{y}_r^2 + \dot{z}_r^2)$$

$$= \tfrac{1}{2} \sum_1^{3n} m_r \dot{\xi}_r^2.$$

But we already gain in simplicity in the form for the potential energy. The potential energy is probably a very complicated function of the coordinates, but in all normal circumstances it will be possible to represent it by a Taylor series:

$$\text{P.E.} = P_0 + \sum_1^{3n} \left(\frac{\partial P}{\partial \xi_r}\right)_0 \xi_r + \frac{1}{2} \sum_1^{3n} \sum_1^{3n} \left(\frac{\partial^2 P}{\partial \xi_r \, \partial \xi_s}\right)_0 \xi_r \xi_s + \dots.$$

In this series, however, P_0 can be equal to zero because we can choose an arbitrary zero for the potential energy, and all the terms which are summed in the second term of this series will be zero because by choosing the coordinates so that they are all zero in the equilibrium position we have arranged that every $(\partial P/\partial \xi_r)_0$ is zero. So much having been arranged, we now neglect the fourth and all later terms on the ground that we shall consider only small vibrations, and we are left with

$$\text{P.E.} = \tfrac{1}{2} \sum_1^{3n} \sum_1^{3n} p_{rs} \xi_r \xi_s.$$

We now make two further changes of coordinates. The first is a simple change of scale which eliminates m_r from the expression for the kinetic energy

$$\text{K.E.} = \tfrac{1}{2} \sum_1^{3n} (m_r^{\frac{1}{2}} \dot{\xi}_r)^2 \qquad \text{P.E.} = \frac{1}{2} \sum_1^{3n} \sum_1^{3n} \frac{p_{ab}}{(m_r \, m_s)^{\frac{1}{2}}} q_r q_s$$

$$= \tfrac{1}{2} \sum_1^{3n} \dot{q}^2, \qquad\qquad = \tfrac{1}{2} \sum_1^{3n} \sum_1^{3n} \pi_{rs} q_r q_s.$$

The expressions are now in a form which makes it reasonable to use the notation of Chapter III, and, regarding the $3n$ coordinates as those of a vector in $3n$ dimensions, to write

$$\text{K.E.} = \tfrac{1}{2}{}^*\dot{q}\dot{q}{}^*, \qquad\qquad \text{P.E.} = \tfrac{1}{2}{}^*q\Pi q^*,$$

where Π is a symmetric operator. Our final coordinate change is to adopt the eigenvectors of Π as axes. This makes Π diagonal in form. Since Π is symmetric, its eigenvectors are orthogonal, and the transformation can be effected by an orthogonal matrix, thus preserving the expression for the kinetic energy (§ 4.7). We now have

$$\text{K.E.} = \tfrac{1}{2} \sum_1^{3n} \dot{Q}_r^2, \qquad\qquad \text{P.E.} = \tfrac{1}{2} \sum_1^{3n} \Pi_r Q_r^2.$$

The resulting coordinates are normal coordinates. Despite the several stages we have taken in arriving at them, they are only homogeneous linear combinations of the cartesian coordinates ξ_r, and linear but not homogeneous functions of the cartesians $x_1, ..., z_n$. Their value lies in the fact that when they are used the dynamical equations reduce to one in each coordinate, since the equation

$$\ddot{x} = -\frac{1}{2m} \frac{\partial P}{\partial x}$$

transforms to
$$\ddot{Q}_r = -\frac{\partial P}{\partial Q_r} = -\Pi_r Q_r,$$

which does not contain the other Q's. These equations now lead to a simple harmonic motion in each normal coordinate, the diagonal elements of Π being $4\pi^2$ times the squares of the frequencies.

All the theory of this section, apart from the notation and nomen-clature, is standard dynamical theory, treated in the standard textbooks of mechanics.

10.3. The normal modes of symmetrical molecules

The symmetry of a molecule is defined, as with a crystal, as the group of operations which transforms the molecule into itself. The chief difference is that there is no reason why a molecule should not have a symmetry group such as C_5 or D_5 (5 or 52) which is impossible for a crystal (consider cyclopentane, for example), whereas it is unlikely to have, say, full cubic symmetry.

In the application of the symmetry operations to a strained molecule, we consider the effect on the molecule of those operations which trans-form the *un*strained molecule into itself. The effect of such an operation on any atom can be considered as an application of the rotation in the local coordinates (ξ, η, ζ) together with a translation of the origin to a new undisplaced position. The latter part would invalidate the assump-tion that the displacements are small unless the new position is referred to the new origin. We therefore write the effect of an operation R in the form

$$R(x_r^0 + \xi_r) = x_s^0 + R\xi_r = x_s^0 + \xi_s'$$

and study the matrix relating the ξ' to the ξ. This point may be clearer after a study of Fig. 13. We shall have $r = s$ only if the rth atom in the unstrained molecule is invariant under R.

The matrices which give the conversion of the ξ_n into the ξ_n' are a $3n$-dimensional representation of the whole symmetry group. We shall refer to this as the cartesian or ξ-representation. In it, each matrix takes the form (if the ξ of each atom are taken consecutively) of $n \times n$ squares each 3×3, the only squares not filled with zeros being those corresponding to the 1's in the permutation-of-the-atoms representation, and these taking the form of the ordinary three-dimensional representa-tion of the rotation. Consequently, the trace of one of these matrices is $U_R(\pm 1 + 2\cos\phi_R)$, where U_R is the number of atoms invariant in the unstrained molecule under R, ϕ_R is the angle of rotation, and the lower sign is used for an improper rotation, computed as a rotation through ϕ with *reflection*, not inversion.

As the normal coordinates are a linear transformation of the cartesian ones, they too will give a $3n$-dimensional representation of the group, and the characters in this representation will be the same as those in the cartesian representation, viz. $U_R(\pm 1 + 2\cos\phi_R)$. But the action of a symmetry operator on a normal vibration can only reproduce that mode or produce another with the same frequency. (We are assuming, of course, that a molecule would not be described as having a given symmetry unless the potential energy relations as well as the actual atomic positions have this symmetry; the case of the second possible form of

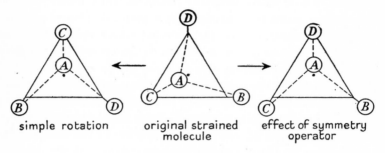

simple rotation   original strained   effect of symmetry
                              molecule   operator

Fig. 13.

ozone described below will illustrate this point.) This means that in this representation no component R_{ij} can be anything but zero if the ith and jth normal modes of vibration have different frequencies. Thus if the operator Π is of the form M of § 4.7, every symmetry operator is of the form L of the same section. But this is only another way of saying that in normal coordinates the representation of the symmetry group is already reduced into its irreducible components, except in so far as there may be p coordinates with the same frequency that are not related by an irreducible pth-degree representation, a situation described, when it occurs, as accidental degeneracy.

Consequently, we can get information about the normal coordinates not otherwise readily available by analysing the ξ-representation into its irreducible components. This procedure is much the most readily understood by an example, and for this purpose we will consider one of the classical problems of chemistry.

10.4. The structure of the ozone molecule (i)

That the ozone molecule is O_3 is demonstrated in every elementary textbook of chemistry. Classical valency theory requires that an oxygen atom is linked to other atoms by two bonds, called valency bonds, and the natural conclusion from this is that the three oxygen atoms are at the corners of an equilateral triangle with bonds along each side. But this theory has proved inadequate, and a second type of bond, the coordinate bond, has been postulated, equivalent, one might say, to two bonds at one end and none at the other, so far as counting towards the valency rule is concerned. As valency bonds at as acute an angle as 60° are unusual, and involve considerable strain in formation, an alternative structure with two atoms linked by a double bond and the third to one of these by a coordinate bond, becomes quite a possibility. Such a molecule would be bent, apart from a further development, the resonance phenomenon, which would assign to this possibility a structure in which a central atom is linked to the two others by bonds which are half double and half coordinate; in this case the molecule might well be linear. We thus have three possibilities:

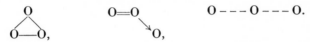

The first of these molecules would have the symmetry D_{3h} ($6m$). The second, without resonance, would have symmetry C_s (m), or with it, C_{2v} (mm), and the third would have a symmetry not met with in crystals but readily understood as $C_{\infty v}$ (∞m), since it is unchanged by any rotation whatsoever about its own axis. (We may take up a former point here, and remark that, even if the angle in the second case were 60°, the forces involved would not have the D_{3h} symmetry, so that no additional symmetry would be thus accidentally introduced.)

We now take these possibilities in turn and discover their normal coordinates, in each of which there will be one normal mode of vibration. To do this we adopt the procedure at the end of § 6.4, applying it to the characters $U_R(\pm 1 + 2\cos\phi_R)$. Before doing so, however, we must consider one further matter, namely, that among the $3n$ normal co-ordinates are the three which represent the translation of the molecule as a whole, and either two or three which represent its rotation as a whole. (Compare the first normal coordinate in the example in § 10.1.) It will be convenient if we can distinguish these from the start, and we are able to do so, because we can calculate characters for them. The translation of the molecule as a whole is a straightforward vector of the form (X, Y, Z), and its character is therefore $\pm 1 + 2\cos\phi$ (without any U_R). The rotation is not quite so simple; it is normally represented by a vector along the axis of rotation, but the direction of this vector is variously described as (*a*) making a right-handed screw with the rotation, or (*b*) looking in the direction which makes the rotation appear clockwise, and either of these descriptions requires the direction of the vector to reverse during an improper rotation as well as undergoing the usual transformation. The character of the rotation is therefore the same as that of translation for proper rotations but minus that of translation for improper ones. (A deeper analysis of this character will be found in § 13.7.)

We set out the first calculation thus:

	I	A, A^5	A^2, A^4	A^3	even B	odd B				
	I	$2S_3$	$2C_3$	m_z	$3m_v$	$3C_2$	$Tr.$	$Rot.$	All	$Rest$
Γ_1	1	1	1	1	1	1	0	0	1	1
Γ_2	1	1	1	1	-1	-1	0	1	1	0
Γ_3	1	-1	1	-1	1	-1	1	0	1	0
Γ_4	1	-1	1	-1	-1	1	0	0	0	0
Γ_5	2	1	-1	-2	0	0	0	1	1	0
Γ_6	2	-1	-1	2	0	0	1	0	2	1
U_R	3	0	0	3	1	1				
ϕ	$0°$	$120°$	$120°$	$0°$	$0°$	$180°$				
Tr. character	3	-2	0	1	1	-1				
Rot. character	3	2	0	-1	-1	-1				
Total character	9	0	0	3	1	-1				

So far as the translational coordinates are concerned, we notice that the Z coordinate is reversed by m_z, by the S_3, and by the C_2, but is unchanged by the other operations; this is therefore the coordinate which transforms by Γ_3, in which just these elements are represented by -1 and the rest by 1. Similarly, though not quite so simply, X and Y transform like the two components of the two-dimensional representation Γ_6. We can similarly identify the coordinate transforming like Γ_2 as ω_z, the z component of rotation, and those like Γ_5 as ω_x and ω_y. These identifications help us to understand the theory of the whole process, but apart from this the point is merely to remove them, as identified, from 'all' the normal coordinates, leaving just three, one transforming like Γ_1, and two transforming together like Γ_6, to be found.

All three must be of the form

$$\sum_1^9 a_r \xi_r.$$

We identify them separately by representations, and consider first the one which comes under Γ_1. We shall find it convenient to use the mixed notation

$$Q_1 = a_1 \xi_1 + a_2 \xi_2 + a_3 \xi_3 + a_4 \eta_1 + a_5 \eta_2 + \ldots + a_9 \zeta_3.$$

Now m_z changes the sign of every ζ, yet, according to the table for Γ_1, leaves Q_1 unchanged. Thus $a_7 = a_8 = a_9 = 0$. One of the C_2 similarly changes the signs of η and ζ, while simultaneously interchanging subscripts 2 and 3, yet again leaving the coordinate unchanged, whence

$a_5 = -a_6$, $a_2 = a_3$, and $a_4 = 0$. The normal coordinate we are considering now looks like this:

$$Q_1 = a_1\xi_1 + a_2(\xi_2 + \xi_3) + a_5(\eta_2 - \eta_3).$$

Some of the other operations merely yield the same equations. That they do (and not inconsistent ones) is a result of the correctness of the underlying group theory. But one C_3 transforms the cartesian coordinates thus

$$\xi_1' = \xi_2\cos 120° - \eta_2\sin 120°, \quad \text{etc.,}$$

and as this, too, must leave the normal coordinate unchanged, this coordinate is now reduced to the form

$$Q_1 = a_1\{\xi_1 - \tfrac{1}{2}(\xi_2 + \xi_3) - \tfrac{1}{2}\sqrt{3}(\eta_2 - \eta_3)\}$$

and is completely determined to within a scale factor.

The normal coordinates which transform by Γ_6 we may call

$$Q_2 = \sum_1^9 b_r\xi_r \quad \text{and} \quad Q_3 = \sum_1^9 c_r\xi_r.$$

The representation Γ_6 is a non-faithful one with matrices

$$I, A^3 = \begin{bmatrix} 1 & 0 \\ 0 & 1 \end{bmatrix}, \quad A, A^4 = \begin{bmatrix} -\tfrac{1}{2} & \tfrac{1}{2}\sqrt{3} \\ -\tfrac{1}{2}\sqrt{3} & -\tfrac{1}{2} \end{bmatrix}, \quad A^2, A^5 = \begin{bmatrix} -\tfrac{1}{2} & -\tfrac{1}{2}\sqrt{3} \\ \tfrac{1}{2}\sqrt{3} & -\tfrac{1}{2} \end{bmatrix}.$$

B matrices obtained by changing signs throughout the second column.

Since m_z still has the same matrix as the identity, the conclusion that the coefficients of ζ_1, ζ_2, and ζ_3 are zero follows as before. The C_2 which changes the sign of η and ζ while simultaneously interchanging the subscripts 2 and 3 may be taken to be the matrix

$$\begin{bmatrix} 1 & 0 \\ 0 & -1 \end{bmatrix},$$

whence, in Q_2, $b_5 = -b_6$, $b_2 = b_3$, and $b_4 = 0$ as before, but in Q_3, $c_5 = c_6$, $c_2 = -c_3$, and $c_1 = 0$, since, under this matrix, $C_2 Q_3 = -Q_3$. Q_2 and Q_3 now take the forms

$$Q_2 = b_1\xi_1 + b_2(\xi_2 + \xi_3) + b_5(\eta_2 - \eta_3),$$

$$Q_3 = c_2(\xi_2 - \xi_3) + c_4\eta_1 + c_5(\eta_2 + \eta_3).$$

We now use the A matrices, or, to be precise, one C_3, as before. The effect of this on the cartesian coordinates is to rotate them through 120°, at the same time applying the permutation (123) to their suffixes.

Assuming the C_3 is A^2 (though it could be A^4), its effect on the normal coordinates will be

$$C_3 Q_2 = -\tfrac{1}{2}Q_2 - \tfrac{1}{2}\sqrt{3}Q_3,$$

$$C_3 Q_3 = \tfrac{1}{2}\sqrt{3}Q_2 - \tfrac{1}{2}Q_3.$$

We can either substitute the transformed cartesians into Q_2 and Q_3 as given above, or we can substitute Q_2 and Q_3 as given above into these equations, to find Q_2' and Q_3'. Doing both and equating coefficients of $\xi_1, ..., \eta_3$ we get in all twelve equations from which to determine $b_1, ..., c_6$. But here we run into a difficulty. We readily find that $c_2 = b_5$, but after that we find that in all our battery of equations only three are independent, and we have five constants still distinct and independent (i.e. four ratios, for which three equations are insufficient). *This would, with more experience, be expected, owing to the fact that two normal modes come under* Γ_6. We quote as three independent equations those obtained by comparing the coefficients of ξ_1, η_1, and η_2 in the expressions for Q_2':

$$-b_1 + b_2 + \sqrt{3}b_5 = 0,$$

$$\sqrt{3}b_2 - b_5 - \sqrt{3}c_4 = 0,$$

$$\sqrt{3}b_1 - b_5 - \sqrt{3}c_5 = 0.$$

One solution of these equations is $b_5 = 0$, $b_1 = b_2 = c_4 = c_5$, but on substituting this into Q_2 and Q_3 we get $Q_2 = b_1(\xi_1 + \xi_2 + \xi_3)$ and $Q_3 = c_4(\eta_1 + \eta_2 + \eta_3)$ and since these, with b_1 and c_4 equal to $\tfrac{1}{3}$, are the coordinates of the centre of gravity of the molecule, we have little difficulty in interpreting them as the translational normal coordinates. The normal coordinate we are seeking will be orthogonal to these. We therefore put $b_2 = b_5 x$, from which we find that $b_1/b_5 = \sqrt{3}+x$, $c_4/b_5 = x - 1/\sqrt{3}$, and $c_5/b_5 = x + 2/\sqrt{3}$. We now determine x from the condition that the resulting Q shall be orthogonal to the translational ones, and find that $x = -1/\sqrt{3}$. It will be convenient to choose $b_5 = \sqrt{3}/2$, as then all the Q are normalized to the same length. We can now tabulate our results including the rotation about the Z-axis, which gives us all

Coeff. of	ξ_1	ξ_2	ξ_3	η_1	η_2	η_3
in T_x	1	1	1	0	0	0
T_y	0	0	0	1	1	1
Q_1	1	$-\tfrac{1}{2}$	$-\tfrac{1}{2}$	0	$-\tfrac{1}{2}\sqrt{3}$	$\tfrac{1}{2}\sqrt{3}$
Q_2	1	$-\tfrac{1}{2}$	$-\tfrac{1}{2}$	0	$\tfrac{1}{2}\sqrt{3}$	$-\tfrac{1}{2}\sqrt{3}$
Q_3	0	$\tfrac{1}{2}\sqrt{3}$	$-\tfrac{1}{2}\sqrt{3}$	-1	$\tfrac{1}{2}$	$\tfrac{1}{2}$
ω_z	0	$-\tfrac{1}{2}\sqrt{3}$	$\tfrac{1}{2}\sqrt{3}$	-1	$\tfrac{1}{2}$	$\tfrac{1}{2}$

the coordinates in the plane, and it will be seen that they are indeed all orthogonal.

To understand them, we should put all but one in turn equal to zero, and, by solving for the cartesian coordinates and plotting, study the distortion represented by each. But this is unnecessary, because the above table is a scalar, $\sqrt{3}$, times an orthogonal matrix. Calling this M,

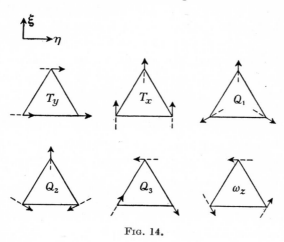

Fig. 14.

the table says that if a configuration of the molecule is given alternatively by the nine-dimensional vectors Q^* or ξ^*, then $Q^* = M\xi^*$. Hence $\xi^* = M^{-1}Q^* = \tilde{M}Q^*$, and if only one normal mode is present, $Q^* = I_r{}^*$, then $\xi^* = \tilde{M}I_r{}^*$, or $^*\xi = {}^*M_r$; thus the rows of the above table are the components, in cartesians, of the separate normal modes. These are plotted in Fig. 14.

The details of the above calculation are a diversion from the main question of the structure of ozone, but they illustrate most of the points which arise in all such calculations. The conclusion in the previous paragraph is so useful that it might have been elevated to a theorem. The difficulty associated with the two normal modes coming under the same representation is irresolvable unless we have information as to the potential energy matrix; we solved it because we knew that the translational movement had to be one normal mode; and we knew this because there is no potential energy associated with a pure translation. The immediate issue, however, is the conclusion reached early on, that in this model the nine degrees of freedom are resolved into three translational, three rotational, and three vibrational, one of the latter being unique and the other two, since they transform into one another under the symmetry operations, being degenerate, that is, having the same frequency.

We now carry through the same procedure on the other models. The student should do this as an exercise. The model lacking all symmetry yields no information at all, and in a case like this, information concerning the forces is required to solve the equations for the coefficients $a_1,...,c_9$. The isosceles triangle model follows the above very closely, except that two modes come under the identical representation as well as one of the translations. The transformation equations reduce these as far as $a_1\xi_1+a_2(\xi_2+\xi_3)+a_5(\eta_2-\eta_3)$, and by making this orthogonal to the translation $\xi_1+\xi_2+\xi_3$ we can reduce the number of coefficients by one, but this is as far as we get in the absence of information on forces.

The linear model demands for its solution a knowledge of the characters of continuous groups, discussed in a later chapter. The symmetry group is $D_{\infty h}$ with structure $\mathfrak{d}_\infty \times \mathfrak{c}_2$. The classes in this group are:

   (i) Each pair of elements C_ϕ and $C_{-\phi}$ is a class.

  (ii) I is a class of this type with $\phi = 0$.

 (iii) Each pair of elements S_ϕ and $S_{-\phi}$ is a class.

 (iv) i is a class of this type with $\phi = 0$.

  (v) All the C_2 belong to one class.

 (vi) All the m_v belong to one class.

In summing over the classes we integrate in each of these four groups from 0 to 2π, and count the result as 2π elements in each. With this hint the student should find the calculation straightforward. The only surprise is in the results, where we find that one of the representations included under the rotations does not occur among the normal modes; this result is well known, however, in elementary treatments of the specific heats of gases, the missing mode being rotation about the axis of the molecule.

When these calculations have been carried through, the results are:

Equilateral triangle: Three modes, two degenerate, therefore only two frequencies.
Bent molecule: Three distinct frequencies.
Linear molecule: Four modes, two degenerate, and therefore three frequencies.

(The number of frequencies, it might be mentioned, is the sum of the numbers in the 'rest' column of the table analysing the characters; the number of modes is the sum of the products of these numbers with the dimensionality of the representation they belong to.) As degenerate modes may split into modes with only approximately equal frequencies under the influence of small perturbations such as external fields or the effects of neighbouring molecules, we would seem already to have promise of settling the question of the structure of ozone. But the complete argument can only be given in a later chapter where we shall consider the mechanism by which spectra are produced.

10.5. Numerical determination of natural frequencies

We saw in § 10.2 that the normal coordinates of a system are those coordinates in $3n$-space in which the potential energy matrix assumes a diagonal form. The equations $\ddot{Q}_r = -\Pi_r Q_r$ show that the eigenvalues of this matrix are the squares, multiplied by $4\pi^2$, of the natural frequencies of the simple harmonic oscillations in the several normal coordinates, $t_r = 2\pi/\sqrt{\Pi_r}$ giving the periods. Consequently if the potential energy matrix is set up in *any* system of coordinates, a determination of the eigenvalues and eigenvectors is one way of determining the normal frequencies and modes. If, as is often the case, it is only the longest period that is required, this will be obtained from the smallest eigenvalue of the matrix Π, and thus from the dominant root of the reciprocal matrix Π^{-1}. The calculation is eased by the fact that it is often easier to write down Π^{-1} than Π. Writing the original equations in the form $Q_r = -\Pi_r^{-1}\ddot{Q}_r$, combined into matrix form as $Q^* = -\Pi^{-1}\ddot{Q}^*$; this, transformed to the original cartesian coordinates, becomes

$$X^* = -\Pi^{-1}\ddot{X}^* = \Pi^{-1}(F/m)^*,$$

where the F and the m in each component of the vector $(F/m)^*$ are the force necessary to produce the *static* displacement X and the mass. In many cases it is not necessary to introduce all $3n$ coordinates. An example will make this clearer, and we choose one, not from molecular structure, but which the author has occasionally set as a practical exercise in mechanics.

Consider the 'double pendulum' shown in Fig. 15, where it is shown displaced under static forces. The ordinary static equations for the two masses, after elimination of the tensions in the rods, lead to

$$\frac{m_2 g}{F_2} = \tan\phi \simeq \frac{l_2}{x_2 - x_1},$$

$$\frac{(m_1 + m_2)g}{F_1 + F_2} = \tan\theta \simeq \frac{l_1}{x_1}$$

which, after slight rearrangement, can be combined into the matrix form

$$\begin{bmatrix} x_1 \\ x_2 \end{bmatrix} = \begin{bmatrix} \dfrac{l_1}{(m_1+m_2)g} & \dfrac{l_1}{(m_1+m_2)g} \\ \dfrac{l_1}{(m_1+m_2)g} & \dfrac{l_1}{(m_1+m_2)g}+\dfrac{l_2}{m_2 g} \end{bmatrix} \begin{bmatrix} F_1 \\ F_2 \end{bmatrix}$$

which we convert to the dynamical problem by putting $F_1 = -m_1 \ddot{x}_1$ and $F_2 = -m_2 \ddot{x}_2$, and transfer the factors m_1 and m_2 into the matrix to give

$$\begin{bmatrix} x_1 \\ x_2 \end{bmatrix} = -\begin{bmatrix} \dfrac{m_1 l_1}{(m_1+m_2)g} & \dfrac{m_2 l_2}{(m_1+m_2)g} \\ \dfrac{m_1 l_1}{(m_1+m_2)g} & \dfrac{m_2 l_1}{(m_1+m_2)g}+\dfrac{m_2 l_2}{m_2 g} \end{bmatrix} \begin{bmatrix} \ddot{x}_1 \\ \ddot{x}_2 \end{bmatrix}.$$

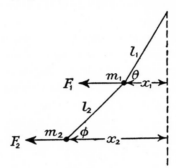

Fig. 15.

Considering now a numerical case, say $m_1 = m_2$ and $l_1 = l_2$, we have

$$\begin{bmatrix} x_1 \\ x_2 \end{bmatrix} = -\frac{l}{2g}\begin{bmatrix} 1 & 1 \\ 1 & 3 \end{bmatrix}\begin{bmatrix} \ddot{x}_1 \\ \ddot{x}_2 \end{bmatrix}.$$

The eigenproblem can now be solved either by the iteration method of § 7.6, or, as it is a 2×2 matrix, by direct solution of the characteristic equation; the latent roots are $2+\sqrt{2}$, with vector $(1, 1+\sqrt{2})$, and $2-\sqrt{2}$ with vector $(1, 1-\sqrt{2})$, and the significance of this result is that if the pendulum is initially displaced with $x_1:x_2 = 1:1+\sqrt{2}$, then x_1 and x_2 will maintain this ratio, the pendulum swinging with a period $2\pi\sqrt{\{(2+\sqrt{2})l/2g\}}$, or if the initial displacements are in the ratio $1:1-\sqrt{2}$, this ratio will also be maintained, the period being $2\pi\sqrt{\{(2-\sqrt{2})l/2g\}}$, whereas any other initial displacement will lead to a superposition of these two oscillations. A number of more complicated examples of this method of dealing with a system whose normal modes are not obvious will be found in Frazer, Duncan, and Collar, Chapter X.

CHAPTER XI

FACTOR ANALYSIS

NOTE: *For this chapter the necessary preliminary work is contained in Chapters II and III, and §§ 7.4 and 7.5 of Part I*

FACTOR analysis is a technique, hitherto associated mostly with research in psychology, which makes no use of group-theory proper, but which makes use of matrices throughout, and involves in particular the numerical determination of eigenvalues and eigenvectors. The type of problem it solves is not unknown in physical science, though usually unrecognized or put on one side, and it has direct applications where methods of teaching science are studied. Consequently, we make no apology for the inclusion of this chapter. As, moreover, the exact interpretation of some of its methods and results is still subject to controversy, it is possible that a new approach may assist in the debate.

11.2. The basic problem of factor analysis

If s students each take t tests, the marks they obtain can be arranged in the form of a matrix M of s rows and t columns, in which the element $M_{\sigma\tau}$ is the mark obtained by the σth student in the τth test. (This is the arrangement most schoolmasters would adopt; for some reason in much of the literature the transpose of this matrix is used.) At first sight these numbers are all independent, but it is common knowledge that a student good in one subject tends to be good in all, or at any rate in many of the others; such a student is described as intelligent. On the other hand, there are undoubted *biases* in which subjects group themselves together, so that a student good in one subject is more likely to be good in others of the same group than in subjects from a different group. The question arises whether a rigid analysis along these lines can be made.

Let us consider a simple case. Suppose that the t tests are not in different subjects, but are the marking of the same paper by t different examiners, and let us further suppose that the examiners have had instructions to allot a proportion of the total marks, at their discretion, to (i) spelling, (ii) writing, (iii) accuracy of facts, (iv) clarity of presentation, (v) originality of ideas, and so on, to f factors. Let us assume also that the examiners agree on the attainment by each student in each of these factors, but differ in the importance they assign to them. (In practice, this is an over-simplification, since examiners who agree on the relative attainments often disagree on absolute attainments, or on what standard deserves full marks; we shall return to this point.) Then there will be three distinct matrices: S, the students' matrix, of s rows and f columns, giving the attainment of each student in each factor; T, the tests or examiners' matrix, of f rows and t columns, giving the maximum of marks allotted by each examiner to each factor; and M, the marks matrix, already considered. Since

$$M_{\sigma\tau} = \sum_{\phi=1}^{f} S_{\sigma\phi} T_{\phi\tau}$$

we shall have $M = ST$, according to the ordinary rules of matrix multiplication.

The general case is probably not sufficiently dissimilar in principle to invalidate conclusions drawn from this example. It is considered by psychologists that there may be a quite limited number of factors— general intelligence, numerical ability, geometrical or structural sense, manual dexterity, perseverance, and so on—which contribute variously to the ability of an individual, not only in various academic subjects but also in the multifarious activities of everyday life. In physical science the method might be applied to those problems which have so far defied analysis because of the unknown factors involved, such as the analysis of meteorological observations, or the relation between chemical constitution and physiological activity. (In the former, 'days' would correspond to 'students', and the 'tests' would be the various observations such as pressure, temperature, humidity, wind, and their rates of change. In the latter, the compounds would be the 'students', and various measurable chemical and physiological properties would be the 'tests'. In this connection it is worth mentioning that artificial problems have been constructed in which the relations involved are not linear, and the method has still succeeded in disentangling which factors were involved in which tests, though sometimes a factor might be 'swamped'—see the 'box' example in Professor Thomson's book.)

The fundamental feature of the problem is easily stated. The equation $M = ST$ can be written

$$*M_{\sigma} = \sum_{\phi=1}^{f} S_{\sigma\phi} *T_{\phi},$$

thus showing that the s rows of M, considered as vectors, are linear combinations of only f basic vectors. (The same argument applies to columns as well, of course.) M is therefore of rank not greater than f.

If, conversely, M, which is the only matrix known to us initially, is of rank f less than both s and t, it is a reasonable inference that the number of factors is only f. We may then hope to factorize M into S (an $s \times f$ matrix) and T (an $f \times t$ matrix). But even at this stage it is clear that there is no unique solution, since $M = (SF)(F^{-1}T)$, where F is any non-singular $f \times f$ matrix, will be another way of factorizing M. In the sequel we shall consider whether other desiderata may not bring us nearer a unique solution.

11.3. A simple solution

It is not difficult to factorize M in the way we have indicated. Consider $\tilde{M}M = N$. We have

$$N_{\tau\tau'} = \sum_\sigma \tilde{M}_{\tau\sigma} M_{\sigma\tau'}$$

$$= \sum_\sigma M_{\sigma\tau} M_{\sigma\tau'},$$

or
$$*N_\tau = \sum_\sigma M_{\sigma\tau} *M_\sigma$$

$$= \sum_\sigma \left(\sum_\phi M_{\sigma\tau} S_{\sigma\phi} \right) *T_\phi,$$

whence (i) N is a square $(t \times t)$ symmetrical matrix, and (ii) the vectors $*N_\tau$, $*M_\sigma$, $*T_\phi$ all lie in the same f-space, which we may call the space F-1, although they are all referred to axes, t in number, which must lie partly outside this space, in a space we may call T of which F-1 is a subspace.

Because N is symmetric we can apply the theory of § 3.8 and write

$$N = \tilde{n}\nu n,$$

the $*n_\phi$ being the f normalized eigenvectors and ν the diagonal matrix of eigenvalues. These vectors are orthogonal and lie in the same space, F-1, as the vectors N_τ, and are thus a very suitable set of vectors for setting up coordinates for F-1. Now consider the expression $M\tilde{n}n$. $\tilde{n}n$ is a $t \times t$ matrix which projects on to F-1 but leaves all vectors in F-1 unaltered; hence $M\tilde{n}n = M$. But $M\tilde{n}$ is an $s \times f$ matrix, and n is an $f \times t$ matrix, so that in $M = (M\tilde{n})n$ we have solved our problem, or at any rate reduced it to the rather laborious one of finding the eigenvectors of $N = \tilde{M}M$. This was considered in § 7.5, where a worked example of the factorization of a 5×3 matrix of rank 2 was given.

It may illuminate this procedure to approach it from another direction. $M_{\sigma\tau}$ is the τth component of $*M_\sigma$ in the original t-fold coordinates, and is therefore given by $M_{\sigma\tau} = *M_\sigma U_\tau*$, where the $*U_\tau$ are the basic vectors of that system. But this relation is valid in any system of coordinates, and if we set up a coordinate system based on the vectors of the matrix n_+ (in the notation of § 3.8), since the supplementary vectors of this system are all perpendicular to all the vectors $*M_\sigma$, only the first f terms of the sum $*M_\sigma U_\tau*$ will be non-zero. Thus we solve our problem by identifying the $*S_\sigma$ with the $*M_\sigma$ in this new coordinate system, and the $T_\tau*$ with the old basic vectors in this new system, suppressing the supplementary terms as contributing nothing. The $T_\tau*$ are therefore the projections on to F-1 of the original basic vectors.

An alternative solution is, of course, available by considering

$$N' = M\tilde{M} \quad \text{(an } s \times s \text{ matrix)};$$

it will be in the form $M = n'(\tilde{n}'M)$. We are naturally curious about the relation between these two solutions. However, if $F = \tilde{n}'M\tilde{n}$, then $n'F = n'\tilde{n}'M\tilde{n} = M\tilde{n}$. We may therefore presume that $(M\tilde{n})n$ is identically the same solution as $(n'F)(F^{-1}\tilde{n}'M)$, and that the two solutions are related in the way we have already envisaged as possible. It requires only a little generalization of this argument to show that provided f has its minimum possible value, all alternative solutions are comprised within the formula $M = (SF)(F^{-1}T)$. The first solution will usually be preferred in the first instance because t will usually be smaller than s, and the numerical work involved will be less.

11.4. Correlation and rank

In the majority of cases, however, there is a more intimate relation between the $M_{\sigma\tau}$ than is betrayed by the mere rank of the matrix. First of all there is the mundane fact that small errors can completely destroy the lowness of the rank of M and we therefore need to be able to define and recognize when a matrix is 'approximately of rank f'. Secondly, there is the oversimplification referred to in § 11.2. Both of these features will be clarified by considering the process known in statistics as correlation.

Let us first, for the sake of geometrical intuition, consider the case of only two tests, in which case the vectors $*M_\sigma$ can be plotted on an ordinary two-dimensional graph. The ends of the vectors are a series of dots. If there is no correlation between the results of these two tests, then the best and the worst students in each test will probably be average in the other, and the points will fill an area which is elliptical (to a first approximation) with its axes parallel to the coordinate axes. Imperfect correlation will result in the good all-rounder being beaten in each test by students who fall short of him in the other, with a similar situation at the bottom of the scale, and the dots will lie in an inclined ellipse. Perfect correlation will give points lying on a straight line. (The case of points lying exactly on a definable curve must be regarded as beyond this stage of the discussion.)

If we have t tests, we plot in a t-dimensional space, and once again, perfect correlation between all tests produces a straight line. They may, on the other hand, lie in an f-space, in which case none of the correlations will be perfect unless this space satisfies certain conditions of parallelism with the axes.

It immediately suggests itself that the straight line is the one-dimensional subspace which exists when there is only one factor, but we must not overlook the fact that this subspace must include the origin, which the line, or the f-space, will not in general do. We can express this situation analytically, if it arises, in a number of ways, e.g. that all vectors of the form $*M_\sigma - *M_{\sigma'}$ lie in an f-space, or that, though the matrix M is not of rank f but only of rank $f+1$, the bordered matrix

$$\begin{bmatrix} M_{11} & M_{12} & \cdot & \cdot & \cdot & M_{1t} & 1 \\ M_{21} & M_{22} & \cdot & \cdot & \cdot & M_{2t} & 1 \\ \cdot & \cdot & \cdot & \cdot & \cdot & \cdot & \cdot \\ M_{s1} & M_{s2} & \cdot & \cdot & \cdot & M_{st} & 1 \end{bmatrix}$$

is still only of rank $f+1$. (We may compare this with the device we used in § 9.4, when we used an extra dimension in order to express something involving a change of origin.) But the clearest expression comes from writing

$$*M_\sigma = *M_G + *\mu_\sigma,$$

where $*M_G$ is a vector to any point in the f-space, usually the centre of gravity of the dots, and the matrix μ, still $s \times t$, is of rank f.

Let us take perfect correlation first. Then $*\mu_\sigma = r_\sigma *U$, where $*U$ is a unit vector parallel to the line, and r_σ is the distance of the σth point from the point G. The matrix M now factorizes

$$M = \begin{bmatrix} 1 & r_1 \\ 1 & r_2 \\ \cdot & \cdot \\ 1 & r_s \end{bmatrix} \begin{bmatrix} *M_G \\ *U \end{bmatrix}$$

and in this way we have reduced any number of perfectly correlated tests into *two* factors, one 'irrelevant' one which merely gives the mark assigned in each test to an *average* student, and one in which the students are 'weighted' r_1, r_2,..., r_s on a scale such that $\sum r = 0$, and which contributes to the test scores in the ratio of the direction cosines U_τ of the vector $*U$.

In the more general case of correlation to an extent that the ends of the $*M_\sigma$ lie in an f-space not including the origin, we may factorize the matrix μ as in the previous section, obtaining the alternative results

$$M = [1* (Mn_1)*...(Mn_f)*]\begin{bmatrix} *M_G \\ *n_1 \\ \cdot \\ *n_f \end{bmatrix} = [1* n_1'*...n_f'*]\begin{bmatrix} *M_G \\ *(n_1'\,M) \\ \cdot \\ *(n_f'\,M) \end{bmatrix}.$$

11.5. Correlation and error

Factor analysis is usually carried out, however, not on the original matrix of marks, but on the correlation matrix, and for this reason, and because it is essential to a discussion of errors, we must turn our attention to the quantitative side of correlation.

The calculation of a correlation coefficient between two tests is a standard statistical procedure which is carried out as follows. The units are first adjusted so that the ranges of the marks, as measured by their standard deviations, are the same in both tests; this transforms the non-inclined ellipse in the case of no correlation into a circle, and transforms inclined ellipses into ellipses whose principal axes are at 45° to the coordinate axes. Means are then taken of narrow vertical strips, and these lie, for an inclined ellipse, on a line inclined at an angle, say θ, to the horizontal. The correlation coefficient is defined as

$$r = \tan \theta,$$

so that given x, the mean (or most probable) value of y is given by $\bar{y} = rx$. The same result is obtained if the axes are interchanged; i.e. $\bar{x} = ry$ with the same r. It is shown in standard works on statistics that r can be calculated from the raw marks $M_{\sigma\tau}$ by the formula

$$r_{\tau\tau'} = \frac{s \sum_\sigma M_{\sigma\tau} M_{\sigma\tau'} - \sum_\sigma M_{\sigma\tau} \sum_\sigma M_{\sigma\tau'}}{\sqrt{\left\{s \sum_\sigma M_{\sigma\tau}^2 - \left(\sum_\sigma M_{\sigma\tau}\right)^2\right\}\left\{s \sum_\sigma M_{\sigma\tau'}^2 - \left(\sum_\sigma M_{\sigma\tau'}\right)^2\right\}}}$$

$$= \frac{\sum_\sigma \mu_{\sigma\tau} \mu_{\sigma\tau'}}{\left(\sum_\sigma \mu_{\sigma\tau}^2\right)^{\frac{1}{2}}\left(\sum_\sigma \mu_{\sigma\tau'}^2\right)^{\frac{1}{2}}},$$

where μ has the meaning already assigned. The former of these expressions is most convenient for calculation with an adding machine, and the latter for theoretical discussion (its denominator represents the change of unit already referred to). The use of the matrix μ eliminates the irrelevant factor from the discussion, and we notice

(i) that $r_{\tau\tau'}$ is the cosine of the angle between two *column* vectors $\mu_\tau{}^*$ and $\mu_{\tau'}{}^*$ of this matrix, and

(ii) that when there are t tests the various correlation coefficients form a symmetrical matrix

$$R = d^{-\frac{1}{2}}\tilde{\mu}\mu d^{-\frac{1}{2}}$$

(where d is the matrix whose only non-zero components are the diagonal elements of $\tilde{\mu}\mu$; since these are all > 0, $d^{-\frac{1}{2}}$ raises no difficulties of definition). By arguments similar to those already used on M, we see that R is of rank f, and that its eigenvectors (or latent vectors, as they are more often called in factor analysis) are a suitable basis for the factorization of the matrix $\mu d^{-\frac{1}{2}}$, which is none other than μ with changed scale, or M with changed zero and scale. (And were it not for the desirability of keeping in view the symmetry of the columns and rows, we could abandon M altogether in favour of this transform, which is what the psychologists usually do.)

Now it is highly desirable that our factors be uncorrelated, for, if our information is incomplete, it is far better that the most likely values for the data not given should be average ones than that they should have to be calculated laboriously from the given data. We have seen that the geometrical interpretation of this is that the points at the ends of the vectors $*S$ are hyperspherically distributed, or at least that the coordinate axes we have chosen should lie parallel to the principal axes of the hyper-ellipsoid of their distribution. Analytically, we have an alternative criterion—that the vectors $S_\phi{}^*$ are orthogonal, and since $S_\phi{}^* = M\tilde{n}_\phi{}^*$, this requires that $0 = *\tilde{S}_{\phi'} S_\phi{}^* = *n_{\phi'}\tilde{M}M\tilde{n}_\phi{}^*$, which we see to be identically satisfied if we substitute $\tilde{M}M = \sum_\phi \lambda_\phi \tilde{n}_\phi{}^{**}n_\phi$. Thus

the process which we used originally to obtain *any* vectors in the space F-1 has in fact given us axes along the principal axes of the hyper-ellipsoid. For some purposes, however, it is disadvantageous to be tied down to these axes, and we therefore consider transforming the ellipsoid into a sphere, since then any orthogonal axes are permissible. This point is important as it has been misrepresented in the literature; the axes which are the latent vectors of the correlation matrix are unique *until* the scales have been changed to make the distribution spherical, but *after* this has been done they cease to have any distinction over others obtained from them by rotation.

Before discussing this transformation, however, we may dispose of the question of errors. It is clear that they must reduce correlations all round, except for the diagonal elements of R which will remain at unity unless some device for establishing a self-correlation, or reliability, is adopted, such as repeating the test, or correlating two suitably chosen halves of it with each other. The wisdom of this procedure probably varies with circumstances. Some mathematical psychologists have assumed that error contributes only to the diagonal term of the correlation matrix, and, by a consideration of dimensionalities (number of equations and number of disposable unknowns), we can show that any symmetrical $n \times n$ matrix can be expressed as the sum of $n-1$ orthogonal dyads and one diagonal matrix. Hence an $n \times n$ matrix of rank f can (by transformation to an $f \times f$ matrix bordered by $n-f$ zeros using the n_+ matrix, analysis in this way, and transformation back again) be expressed as the sum of $f-1$ dyads and a diagonal matrix, whence we should be able to resolve an $s \times t$ matrix M of rank f into $f-1$ factors plus errors.

The effect of error on the vectors $*M_\sigma$, however, is to make every one of the t coordinates uncertain to a definite extent; a theoretically linear (perfectly correlated) distribution thus becoming what may be called t-dimensional cigar-shaped, and a theoretically two-dimensional distribution becoming t-dimensional currant-bun shaped. We can therefore say that the matrix M is approximately of rank f if the first f of the principal axes of the hyper-ellipsoid are significantly longer than the remainder, which we should not expect to differ significantly from each other. We shall show in the next section that this is equivalent to taking into account those terms in the proper expansion of the correlation matrix belonging to the larger eigenvalues. As the computational method which we described in § 7.5 determines the eigenvectors in order, beginning with the one with the largest eigenvalue, this is very convenient, as we stop as soon as we are satisfied that we have taken out enough factors, rejecting the rest as insignificant or error without specifying more particularly.

We are now in a position to summarize the usual procedure in factor analysis, and it may be well to do this before passing on to further theoretical matters. As matrices of various sizes and shapes are used, and the author, for one, finds this very confusing, we shall, in this paragraph, indicate the order of a matrix more explicitly by suffixes, the

$s \times t$ matrix M being written $_sM_t$. Only one subscript will come between the factors of a matrix product! The matrix $_sM_t$ is first converted into the matrix $_s\mu_t$ by subtracting from each term the mean of the column containing it, and the matrix $_s\mu_t$ is converted into $_s\mu_t d_t^{\frac{1}{2}}$ by dividing each column by the root-mean-square of the terms in it. (These two stages are in practice combined into one—compare the calculation in § 7.5.) We shall denote $_s\mu_t d_t^{\frac{1}{2}}$ by $_s\mathbf{M}_t$; we factorize this matrix first, and indeed, as the marks $\mathbf{M}_{\sigma\tau}$ are merely the $M_{\sigma\tau}$ with a new zero and scale, it is not usually considered necessary to do more. We wish to express $_s\mathbf{M}_t$ as $_s\mathbf{S}_f\mathbf{T}_t$ with the vectors $\mathbf{S}_\phi{}^*$ orthogonal and normalized. Then

$$_t R_t = {}_t\tilde{\mathbf{M}}_s\mathbf{M}_t = {}_t\tilde{\mathbf{T}}_f\tilde{\mathbf{S}}_f\mathbf{S}_f\mathbf{T}_t = {}_t\tilde{\mathbf{T}}_f\mathbf{T}_t,$$

so that if we determine the normalized latent vectors $*r_\phi$ and the latent roots ρ_ϕ of $_t\mathbf{M}_s\mathbf{M}_t$, we can put

$$_t R_t = {}_t\tilde{r}_f\rho_f r_t, \qquad _f\mathbf{T}_t = {}_f\rho^{\frac{1}{2}}{}_f r_t.$$

$_s\mathbf{S}_f$ is now determined from the fact that since $_t\tilde{r}_f r_t$ is the identical operator *so far as all vectors in* $\mathbf{M}$ *are concerned,*

$$_s\mathbf{M}_t = ({}_s\mathbf{M}_t\tilde{r}_f\rho^{-\frac{1}{2}})_f(\rho^{\frac{1}{2}}{}_f r_t) \quad \text{and thus} \quad _s\mathbf{S}_f = {}_s\mathbf{M}_t\tilde{r}_f\rho^{-\frac{1}{2}}{}_f.$$

11.6. Transformations of the f-space

Owing to the linearity of the operations involved,

$$*M_\sigma\, B = *M_G\, B + *\mu_\sigma\, B,$$

a transformation B can be thought of as applied to the $*M_\sigma$ or to the $*\mu_\sigma$, and its effect on shapes will be the same; we are concerned particularly with transformations of ellipsoids to spheres, and we need first some geometry of the ellipsoid.

The general equation

$$a_{11}\, x_1^2 + a_{22}\, x_2^2 + \ldots + a_{nn}\, x_n^2 + 2a_{12}\, x_1\, x_2 + \ldots = 1 \qquad (11.6.1)$$

may be written in the form

$$*XAX* = 1,$$

where A is symmetrical; it represents a hyper-ellipsoid centred on the origin, provided certain conditions are satisfied which exclude hyper-hyperboloids, etc. If A is diagonal, it is an equation with no cross-products, and the diagonal elements, as the coefficients of x_r^2, are the reciprocals of the squares of the semi-axes of the hyper-ellipsoid, whose equation in conventional form is

$$\frac{x^2}{a^2}+\frac{y^2}{b^2}+\ldots = 1.$$

Thus the eigenvalues of A^{-1} are the squares of the semi-axes of the hyper-ellipsoid $*XAX* = 1$, and the condition excluding hyper-hyperboloids, etc., is that all these eigenvalues shall be positive.

Writing $X* = BX'*$, then $*X'\tilde{B} = *X$ and $*X'\tilde{B}ABX'* = 1$. This transformation can be used in several ways. By obtaining the proper expansion, $\tilde{a}\alpha a$, of A and writing $B = \tilde{a}\alpha^{-\frac{1}{2}}$, we obtain at once $*X'X'* = 1$, the equation of a hypersphere. Or, if we wish to picture the transformation in more detail, we can split B up, and perform the transformation in stages. The first process in obtaining the correlation coefficients, for example, is a change of scale equivalent to the operation of a diagonal matrix D, and writing $B = CD$ separates off this stage.

The equation (11.6.1) can be rewritten in the form

$$a_{11}x_1^2+(2a_{12}x_2+2a_{13}x_3+\ldots)x_1+(a_{22}x_2^2+\ldots-1) = 0.$$

The sum of the roots of this equation is minus the first bracket divided by a_{11}, and therefore for given values of x_2, x_3,..., the mean value of x_1 is $-(a_{12}x_2+a_{13}x_3+\ldots)/a_{11}$. For a given value of x_2 and no other information, the mean (or most probable—we assume that they are the same) value of x_1 will be given by this expression with x_3, x_4,... given their most probable values. For a given x_2, therefore, we have the simultaneous equations, in which bars denote mean values, and we have taken advantage, in the notation, of the symmetry of A,

$$a_{11}\bar{x}_1+a_{12}x_2+a_{13}\bar{x}_3+a_{14}\bar{x}_4+\ldots = 0,$$

$$a_{31}\bar{x}_1+a_{32}x_2+a_{33}\bar{x}_3+a_{34}\bar{x}_4+\ldots = 0,$$

$$\cdot \quad \cdot \quad \cdot \quad \cdot \quad \cdot \quad \cdot \quad \cdot \quad \cdot$$

$$a_{n1}\bar{x}_1+a_{n2}x_2+a_{n3}\bar{x}_3+a_{n4}\bar{x}_4+\ldots = 0,$$

the solution of which, for $\bar{x}_1$, is

$$\bar{x}_1 = \frac{\begin{vmatrix} a_{12} & a_{13} & a_{14} & \cdot & \cdot \\ a_{32} & a_{33} & a_{34} & \cdot & \cdot \\ \cdot & \cdot & \cdot & \cdot & \cdot \\ a_{11} & a_{13} & a_{14} & \cdot & \cdot \\ a_{31} & a_{33} & a_{34} & \cdot & \cdot \\ \cdot & \cdot & \cdot & \cdot & \cdot \end{vmatrix}}{} x_2 = \frac{\hat{A}_{12}}{\hat{A}_{22}} x_2 = \frac{(A^{-1})_{12}}{(A^{-1})_{22}} x_2.$$

Now in the definition of a correlation coefficient we first applied a diagonal transformation which made the standard deviations in each variable the same—we called this transformation D in the previous paragraph—and this made the correlation matrix symmetric. It is clear that if this result is to be obtained in the present approach, we must have all the $(A^{-1})_{rr}$ equal; we shall assume that the transformation D produces just this result, and without any loss of generality we can make them all equal to unity. Then by the first definition of the correlation coefficient and the above result,

$$R = (D^{-1}AD)^{-1} = D^{-1}A^{-1}D.$$

Now A and A^{-1} have the same eigenvectors, and reciprocal eigenvalues; so also do $D^{-1}AD$ and $D^{-1}A^{-1}D$, though not the same ones as A and A^{-1}. The eigenvalues and eigenvectors of R are therefore the semi-axes of the distribution ellipsoid *after* transformation by D. It is perhaps open to question whether the significance of these should not be judged *before* transformation—it really turns on the nature of the errors to be expected, whether constant from test to test or proportional to the standard deviation in each test—but as stated in the previous section the usual procedure is to judge the importance of a factor from its eigenvalue in the correlation matrix.

The transformation of the ellipsoid to a sphere may be thought of as a rotation to convert A to diagonal form followed by a diagonal transformation to make its axes equal. (If A is converted into $D^{-1}AD$ before this procedure, any difference in the result can at most be a simple rotation of the axes in terms of which the spherical distribution is expressed.) But if the rank of R is actually less than t, namely f (with no errors), transformation to a t-dimensional hypersphere is impossible; all we can do, and all we want to do, is to transform to an f-dimensional hypersphere in the space F-1 of § 11.3. The transformation in directions perpendicular to this space is left indeterminate.

Ignoring this last point, for which allowance is easily made, the transformation which converts the original equation $*XAX* = 1$ into that of a hypersphere, viz. $X* = (\tilde{a}\alpha^{-\frac{1}{2}})X'*$, or $X'* = (\alpha^{\frac{1}{2}}a)X*$, converts the original basic vectors I_r* into $(\alpha^{\frac{1}{2}}a)_r*$. The vectors reciprocal to these are $*(\alpha^{\frac{1}{2}}a)_r^{-1}$ or $*(\tilde{a}\alpha^{-\frac{1}{2}})_r$. Denoting these by $*i_r$ (since R as a symbol is already in use), we have

$$*i_r \, i_s* = *(\tilde{a}\alpha^{-\frac{1}{2}})_r(\alpha^{-\frac{1}{2}}a)_s* = (A^{-1})_{rs}.$$

Thus the transformation which makes the distribution of the points hyperspherical converts the reciprocal basic vectors (usually called reference vectors in factor analysis) into vectors of length $(A^{-1})_{rr}$ inclined to each other at angles whose cosines are the corresponding correlation coefficients. It will be remembered from § 4.6 that the coordinates of a point in oblique coordinates are the scalar products of the vector to the point with the reciprocal (not the direct) basic vectors. And, of course, since from $X^* = x_1 I_1^* + \ldots$ we have $AX^* = x_1 AI_1^* + \ldots$, the transformation is equivalent to a replotting in oblique coordinates with the transformed basic vectors as new direct basic vectors.

Let us now review the whole picture, starting from the matrix M with which we started the chapter. We plot the $*M_\sigma$ in a t-space which we may call T. By a change of origin we have the vectors $*\mu_\sigma$ which we may refer to as in a new space T'. (It *is* a new 'centred space'—see § 14.7.) The coordinate system is a simple cartesian one, the basic and reciprocal vectors being identical, and those of T and T' being related by parallel displacement. By a transformation of this space which is the same whichever point we are considering as origin, we can group the points spherically. The coordinate system is now oblique, and the reciprocal basic vectors (t in number, one for each test) are inclined at angles whose cosines are the correlation coefficients and whose lengths are the standard deviations of the original marks. If we refer to t normalized orthogonal vectors in this new space, we shall have our students uncorrelated in the new coordinates. The mark obtained by any student in any test is the scalar product of his vector with the test vector.

An alternative statement, equivalent to the above, is that there are certain combinations of the original marks, 'weighted means', which are uncorrelated in the students. The number of such which are independent is t.

If the rank of M is f, less than t, or if it is approximately so, in the sense that some of the axes of the original ellipsoid are negligible within the limits of error, the original points lie within an f-subspace, F-1, and we can transform to an f-hypersphere within this space. (In the approximate case we neglect the small displacements involved in projecting on to F-1.) By reference to f normalized orthogonal vectors in this transformed space $(F'$-1), we again have our students uncorrelated in these coordinates; this time there are f independent weighted means which adequately represent a given student in all his tests. This is the valuable case in practice, of course, particularly when some new test, difficult of assessment, proves to be expressible in terms of already known factors—e.g. success in a job in terms of factors derived from laboratory tests.

We are now in a position to see the relation between the above result and that obtained by 'factorizing the other way round'. The test vectors that we have obtained will not have their end-points spherically distributed in F'-1. By another change of origin and transformation we can make these group spherically around the origin in a space which we may call F'-2. This will be the same space as we should obtain by plotting the M_τ^*, in a space S, changing the origin to obtain m_τ^* (it is confusing to use μ here) in a space S', and then transforming these by an oblique plot to an f-hypersphere. The relation is thus complicated but not unpicturable; the complications arise from (i) the 'irrelevant' factors which necessitate the changes of origin, and (ii) the fact that it is impossible in general to arrange the factors so that they are uncorrelated in both the students and the tests, and that mathematics alone cannot decide which of these alternatives is more desirable.

11.7. Rotation of axes and oblique factors

In conclusion we discuss in this and the final section two controversial questions, and in the next section we discuss a chemical application. The first question, for discussion here, is how much, by rotations or distortion, we may meddle with our axes in the space F'-1 after we have found them. A sound answer to this question depends on one point only—that we laid down the condition that the factors be uncorrelated in the 'students'. All meddling must be discussed in the light of this point.

Let us consider an example taken from the Greeks. Their four elements, earth, air, fire, and water, are often said to be combinations in pairs of the properties of hotness, coldness, wetness, and dryness. The argument may be regarded as the reduction of the properties of physical substances to two factors, and an ambiguity as to the choice of axes. If we plot hotness–coldness along one axis and wetness–dryness at right angles to it, the points for a large number of substances will lie in a circular area, with earth, air, fire, and water lying in the middle of each quadrant. If we rotate these axes through 45° they will become axes of earthiness–airiness and fieriness–wateriness, and we shall not have touched the points, which will still occupy the same circle. But suppose we replot with airiness–earthiness and hotness–coldness as perpendicular axes, at once we produce an ellipse, indicating a correlation between these properties, known to later physicists by the name of thermal change of state, coldness being on the whole associated with earthiness and hotness with a gaseous form. We may prefer to keep our circular distribution by plotting with these axes but obliquely inclined to each other, expressing our awareness of the correlation by our choice of the angle between them. The one procedure which would seem to be quite pointless would be to plot in oblique axes and not arrange for a circular distribution.

It is important to bear in mind that the correlation is in the sample we are dealing with. Obviously, more points, suitably chosen, can turn an elliptical distribution into a circular one or vice versa. In the example of the previous paragraph, the sample is so large that we feel justified in asserting a significance in the correlation, yet in an equally large sample confined, say, to organic substances, the result might turn out very different.

We are thus brought back to our starting-point. The fundamental feature, and the only fundamental feature, if even this is not obscured by errors, is the fact that the ranks of the various matrices are lower than the number of tests (which will normally be lower than the number of students). Then the expression of the results in terms of f factors only will follow. After this, transformation of this f-space is a matter of convenience. The transformation to a hyperspherical distribution has no significance beyond that of the sample, but the significance of a large or suitably chosen sample may be great enough to warrant such a transformation. In this case orthogonal axes have the advantage that lack of information really is ignorance (our best guess in the unknown factors being an average), but the precise orientation of these axes is purely a matter of convenience in interpretation—axes to which we seem able to give a definite name being preferable to ones which we find more difficult to interpret. In some cases, however, interpretation advantages may weigh in favour of correlated factors.

There is one problem which sometimes arises which it may be well to state clearly in an example, though we cannot spare much space to discuss it. Suppose s_1 men and s_2 women take t tests, and are analysed separately. The two sets of results are both plotted in the same space T, and this is our starting-point. We shall want to know (1) is $f_1 = f_2$, and (2) to what extent do the two sets of points lie in the same F-space?

If they do not, two possibilities arise: (*a*) they contain certain factors in common and certain which are different, or (*b*) the *f*-spaces separately determined are inclined at a small angle owing to sampling errors. In the latter case it is important to realize that the same errors will affect the eigenvalues as well as the eigenvectors, and that the transformation to spherical distribution will be in dispute also. These two possibilities may occur together. It would seem that the only procedure is to transform to spherical distribution on the two groups combined, and then study the groups separately.

11.8. Application to the problem of aromatic activity

As an example of the application of these methods to a chemical problem, let us consider certain data on the reactivity of aromatic compounds. Data of this sort have so far defied accurate analysis, although Hammett has shown that many of the results can be expressed in the form

$$\log k = \log k_0 + \rho\sigma,$$

where k is a rate or equilibrium constant for a reaction of a compound ϕ—X, X being the reacting group and ϕ a substituted phenyl group, k_0 refers to the reaction of the unsubstituted ϕX, σ depends only on X and the nature of the reaction, and ρ depends only on the substituent. This relation holds provided the substituent is *meta* or *para* to X but not in general when it is *ortho*, though in some cases—e.g. *para*-NO_2—ρ assumes one of two values according to the nature of X. Ignoring the latter complication, this is clearly equivalent to analysing the data into one irrelevant factor ($\log k_0$) and one relevant factor ($\rho\sigma$). This suggests the question whether the *ortho*-substituted compounds may not be included by the inclusion of further factors:

$$\log k = \log k_0 + \rho_1\sigma_1 + \rho_2\sigma_2 + \dots$$

and, if so, what interpretation is to be put upon the several factors.

Ideally, the analysis should be carried out on a matrix of data (1) obtained under comparable conditions (so far as the conditions for the different reactions can be comparable), and (2) in which there are no blanks—i.e. data on each reaction are available for every one of the series of substituted phenyl compounds. Such data are not readily available, and we shall content ourselves, for purposes of illustration, with the data which, with the sources from which they were obtained, are set out in Table 11.8.1. Gaps occur in this table due (i) to the data not having been obtained by the workers cited, and (ii) because in certain cases k

has been quoted as zero, and no data given from which even an estimate of $\log k$ could be obtained. Although it is to some extent begging the question, some of these gaps can be filled by Hammett's rule. On the other hand, although the omission of an occasional pair of values should not affect seriously the correlation coefficients, this principle can hardly be extended to cover the omission of three extreme values (the three nitro-compounds, in some columns). We have analysed the first five columns filling gaps by Hammett's rule and also the whole table on the assumption that the gaps do not affect the correlation coefficients. A check on the validity of these two procedures will appear in due course.

TABLE 11.8.1

Raw Data

	A	B	C	D	E	F	G	H	I	J
Phenyl	−3·1	0·000	0·797	0·340	0·562	2·87	4·6	2·46	0·00	−0·28
o-Cl	−4·0	0·005	2·057	0·423	0·766	−0·85	2·8	‡	−2·00	0·09
m-Cl	−3·5	0·000	1·170	0·415	0·706	1·49	3·5	1·46	−1·35	0·48
p-Cl	−3·1	0·005	1·023	0·393	0·587	0·15	4·0	1·90	−0·38	0·34
o-CH₃	−3·0	−0·052	1·092	0·336	0·500	3·57	4·4	1·48	0·46	−0·85
m-CH₃	−2·6§	−0·009	0·728	0·322	0·558	3·53	4·7	2·63	0·32	−0·41
p-CH₃	−2·7	−0·052	0·627	0·316	0·436	1·96	5·1	2·85	1·21	−0·52
o-OCH₃	−3·5	−0·235	0·906	0·196	0·538		4·5	2·22	1·97	−1·00
m-OCH₃	−3·2	−0·044	0·912	0·346	0·624	3·53	4·2	2·33‖	0·00§	−0·24
p-OCH₃	−2·0	−0·235	0·529	0·311	0·461	−0·96	5·3	2·83	3·05	−0·34
o-NO₂	−4·2	0·344	2·827	0·496	0·849	−0·44		‡		
m-NO₂	−3·4	0·063	1·506	0·480§	0·880	−0·16	2·6§	0·45		
p-NO₂	−2·3	0·344	1·575	0·526	0·954	0·49	0·9§	‡		

A. ΔF for $\phi CHO + HCN$ from Gilman, *Organic Chemistry*, p. 808, based on Lapworth and Manske, *JCS* (1928) 2533 and (1931) 1976.

B. Change in critical oxidation potential of phenol or amine, from Gilman, loc. cit., p. 816 based on Fieser *et al.*, *JACS* (see Gilman for details).

C, D, E. Strengths of $\phi COOH$, $\phi(CH_2)_2COOH$, and *trans*-$\phi(CH)_2COOH$ respectively, all from Dippy, *Chem. Rev.* **25** (1939) 206–7.

F. Decomposition ϕ—N_2—X ($\log k$), from Bunnet and Zahler, *Chem. Rev.* **49** (1951) 294, based on Crossley, Kemble, and Bembrooke, *JACS* **62** (1940) 1400.

G. pK of substituted aniline, from Bunnet and Zahler, loc. cit., p. 342, based on Hall, *JACS* **52** (1930) 5115.

H. $\log k$ for reaction between substituted aniline and 2, 4, 6, trinitrochlorobenzene, from Bunnet and Zahler, loc. cit., p. 342, based on van Opstall, *Rec. trav. chim.* **52** (1933) 901.

I. Log relative velocity constant mono-substituted diphenylchlormethane reacting with aliphatic alcohol from Gilman, loc. cit., p. 833, based on Norris, Banta, and Blake, *JACS* **50** (1928) 1804, 1809.

J. Reaction $\phi NCS + EtOH$ ($\log k$) from Gilman, loc. cit., p. 837, based on Browne and Dyson, *JCS* (1931) 3285.

‡ Quoted as $k = 0$.
§ Calculated by Hammett's rule (Hammett, *Physical Organic Chemistry*, p. 186 (McGraw-Hill)).
‖ Hammett's rule 2·30; extrapolated from lower temperature 2·36.

The analysis of the first five columns only will be more easily followed if given in more detail than is necessary for a routine calculation. The table of raw data may be expressed as follows:

	A	B	C	D	E
Mean . .	−3·1230	0·0103	1·2115	0·3769	0·6748
S.D. . .	0·6015	0·1658	0·6196	0·0871	0·1614
Phenyl .	0·0382	−0·0621	−0·6689	−0·4237	−0·5316
o-Chlor .	−1·4580	−0·0320	1·3646	0·5293	0·7323
m-Chlor .	−0·6268	−0·0621	−0·0669	0·4374	0·3606
p-Chlor .	0·0382	−0·0320	−0·3042	0·1848	−0·3767
o-Methyl .	0·2045	−0·3758	−0·1928	−0·4696	−0·9157
m-Methyl .	0·8695	−0·1164	−0·7802	−0·5303	−0·5564
p-Methyl .	0·7032	−0·3758	−0·9433	−0·6992	−1·3123
o-Methoxy .	−0·6268	−1·4795	−0·4930	−2·0769	−0·6803
m-Methoxy .	−0·1280	−0·3275	−0·4833	−0·3548	−0·1475
p-Methoxy .	1·8670	−1·4795	−1·1014	−0·7566	−1·1574
o-Nitro .	−1·7905	2·0217	2·6074	1·3674	1·2466
m-Nitro .	0·4605	0·3179	0·4753	1·1837	1·4387
p-Nitro .	1·3682	2·0127	0·5868	1·7118	1·8971

This is the matrix μ, the raw data being obtained from the above by adding to the mean at the head of the column the product of the S.D. and the entry. The correlation matrix is obtained by summing the products of corresponding entries in pairs of columns and is

	A	B	C	D	E
A	1·0000	−0·2424	−0·7028	−0·2236	−0·3796
B	−0·2424	1·0000	0·7407	0·8750	0·8033
C	−0·7028	0·7407	1·0000	0·7170	0·7708
D	−0·2236	0·8750	0·7170	1·0000	0·8761
E	−0·3796	0·8033	0·7708	0·8761	1·0000

The major part of the analysis is the expression of this as the sum of dyads. The result is

Latent root:	3·62	1·00	0·196	0·092	0·092
Vector:	a	b	c	d	e
A . .	−0·284	0·828	0·050	0·474	0·096
B . .	0·471	0·301	0·640	−0·379	0·357
C . .	0·483	−0·292	0·266	0·783	−0·019
D . .	0·476	0·340	−0·154	−0·137	−0·785
E . .	0·487	0·149	−0·702	0·015	0·497

though the last two vectors, having the same latent root, are not uniquely determined. As the latent root is a measure of the importance of the factor, clearly at most three, and probably only two factors are important. The five vectors are all of unit length, and placed side by side as here they constitute the matrix n_+, n being the first two (or three) columns. We now multiply each row of μ by each column of n_+ (i.e. multiply corresponding terms and add), and we obtain the following table, in which we have repeated the previous one for clarity.

TABLE 11.8.2

Vector (= factor)	a	b	c	d	e
Reaction: A . .	−0·284	0·828	0·050	0·474	0·096
B . .	0·471	0·301	0·640	−0·379	0·357
C . .	0·483	−0·292	0·266	0·783	−0·019
D . .	0·476	0·340	−0·154	−0·137	−0·785
E . .	0·487	0·149	−0·702	0·015	0·497
Substituent: —. .	−0·824	−0·015	0·223	−0·432	0·063
o-Cl .	1·667	−1·326	−0·326	0·328	−0·227
m-Cl .	0·501	−0·316	−0·409	−0·380	−0·245
p-Cl .	−0·268	0·118	0·136	−0·239	−0·334
o-CH$_3$.	−0·998	−0·184	0·434	0·139	−0·198
m-CH$_3$.	−1·250	0·616	0·249	−0·077	0·274
p-CH$_3$.	−1·804	0·311	0·573	−0·187	−0·153
o-OCH$_3$.	−2·077	−1·628	−0·312	0·152	0·714
m-OCH$_3$	−0·592	−0·206	−0·186	−0·269	0·085
p-OCH$_3$.	−2·683	0·992	−0·218	0·670	−0·311
o-NO$_2$.	3·974	−0·987	0·806	0·261	0·045
m-NO$_2$.	1·774	0·192	−0·885	−0·107	−0·154
p-NO$_2$.	2·582	2·432	−0·083	0·139	0·436

Any entry in μ is now reproduced by summing the five products of the entries in the two lines of the above table corresponding to the reaction and the substituent. (If it is not, this is entirely due to rounding-off errors in determining n_+.) *But it is reproduced to within a satisfactory margin by the entries in the first two columns only*, in most cases. The few exceptions, recognizable by the larger numbers in the last three columns, may be other effects, but cannot be recognized as such on the limited data provided by these five reactions.

Hammett's rule is not immediately apparent. But if we plot the first two factors, as in Fig. 16, it appears that the m- and p-substituent points all lie near to a line (not exactly through the origin) inclined at about −20° to the 'a' axis. If we plot the first three factors the tendency is less marked, though for these compounds the 'c' factor tends to be positive when 'a' is negative. (Over all thirteen substituents the factors are necessarily uncorrelated, of course.) If the axes are rotated through 20°, therefore, the new a axis resembles Hammett's factor, and the new b axis is something whose variation is small (though not zero) in *meta* and *para* substituted compounds—except, curiously, it is large in p-NO$_2$

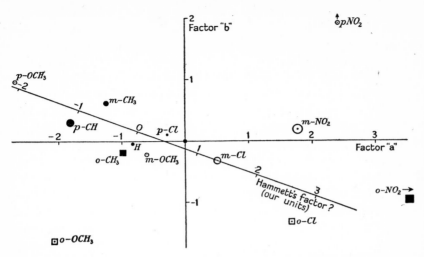

Fig. 16. Ortho points square; m- and p-points round. Size proportional to third factor: black if positive, white if negative.

compounds—but is larger in *ortho*-substituted compounds. It is the lack of variation rather than the small value which is important, since any constant value would be incorporated in the irrelevant factor (Hammett's $\log k$). The relation between Hammett's values and ours is shown in the following table:

	Hammett's value	Present value plus 0·85	Ratio
p-OCH$_3$.	−0·268	−2·00	0·134
p-CH$_3$ . .	−0·170	−1·08	0·157
m-CH$_3$.	−0·069	−0·66	0·105
m-OCH$_3$.	0·115	0·27	0·425
p-Cl . .	0·227	0·62	0·367
m-Cl . .	0·573	1·34	0·428
m-NO$_2$.	0·710	2·33	0·305
p-NO$_2$ . .	0·778 or 1·271	2·33	0·334 or 0·546

It will be seen that the order of the substituents is identical, but that the two values are not strictly proportional. The case of p-NO$_2$ in which we found a large b factor (and whose modified a factor is therefore very sensitive to the angle of rotation) is one of those to which Hammett had to give alternative values to according to whether the reaction involved substituted amines or phenols on the one hand, or carbon-based functional groups on the other. This could be very suggestive when we consider interpreting the factors. A curious point, difficult to attach any significance to, is the abrupt change of ratio values with the change in sign of the factor.

The approach to the interpretation from the chemical side strongly suggests oblique factors. The two effects most commonly considered are known as the 'inductive' and the 'tautomeric' effects; both arise from a surplus or deficient electron density, but they differ, broadly speaking, in that the former depends upon total electron density in the substituent group and is transmitted with rapidly diminishing intensity along a chain of carbon atoms whereas the latter depends only on the more mobile electrons which are not tied up in σ-bond formation (see §§ 17.2–4) and is transmitted easily to alternate members of a conjugated chain. It is obvious that in any random sample of possible substituents these two effects are likely to be correlated positively. We defer further discussion of this until we have considered the second analysis.

The ten reactions lead to a 10×10 correlation matrix whose largest latent roots and associated vectors are:

Latent root:	6·53	1·55	1·11
A	−0·21	−0·53	0·00
B	0·31	0·03	−0·54
C	0·36	0·21	0·25
D	0·35	−0·32	−0·24
E	0·38	−0·07	0·04
F	−0·18	0·51	−0·46
G	−0·35	0·07	−0·31
H	−0·32	−0·36	−0·34
I	−0·36	−0·23	0·28
J	0·28	−0·37	−0·24

As the sum of the latent roots is 10, the trace of the correlation matrix, and these three vectors account for 9·19 of this, there is only 0·81 to be shared among the other seven. The first factor is obviously the same as the first factor determined from the first five reactions, since its contributions to these reactions are in the same proportions. There is no such agreement of the second of our previous factors with either the second or the third of the above factors, nor yet with any combination of the above three. It could be that other factors have risen into prominence with the extra data—not at all unlikely since it is these data which introduce velocity constants—but this should not obscure the previous second factor so completely, and it is more likely that the deficiencies

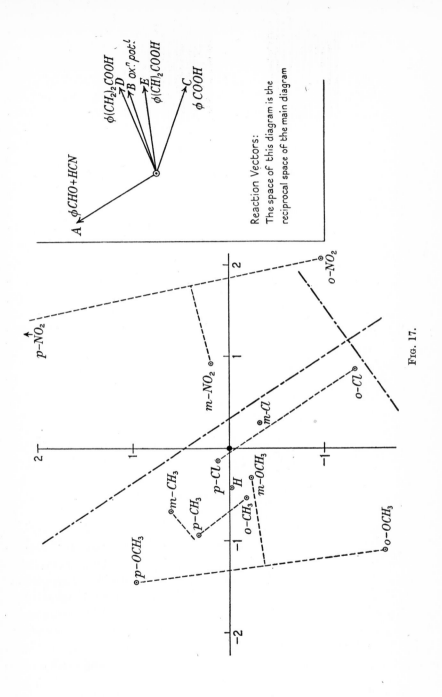

Reaction Vectors:
The space of this diagram is the
reciprocal space of the main diagram

Fig. 17.

of the new data are to blame. We shall therefore base interpretation on the first five reaction data only.

For this purpose we have re-plotted the first two factors of Table 11.8.2 in Fig. 17 after dividing the '*a*' factor numbers by 1·9 (and correspondingly *multiplying* the '*a*' factor numbers of the *reactions* by 1·9) so as to give the points a circular distribution. An interesting regularity appears which we have brought out more clearly by joining each *ortho* point to its corresponding *para* point and dropping a perpendicular from the *meta* point. Then if the chain lines are taken as axes, we see that

(1) the three points of each set are in the order *ortho*, *meta*, *para*, along the long chain line as axis (CH_3 is a possible exception), and

(2) in the perpendicular direction, if the long chain line is taken as a genuine (and not merely arbitrary) zero, the component of the *meta* point is always numerically less than those of the *ortho* and *para* points, but of the same sign.

This is the behaviour to be expected of (1) the inductive, and (2) the tautomeric effects, respectively. It is also correct that the tautomeric effect for —NO_2 should be of opposite sign to that for —OCH_3, —CH_3, and —Cl. On the other hand, our expectation that these effects should be positively correlated is not realized, nor is it possible to rotate either axis in a direction to accomplish this, without destroying one or other of the features on which our tentative interpretation is based.

An analysis of this sort should properly be done on a much larger sample of data than we have used, and also, as we have said, on data obtained for the purpose without gaps and under uniform conditions. It is therefore probable that on the data at our disposal the above conclusions go as far as is possible. The methodological significance of the analysis is that the factors are obtained directly from laboratory data— a fundamentally sound procedure—and when found, they bear an interpretation in terms of the physical treatment of mechanism.

11.9 Spearman's approach

Both the details and the overall picture in the foregoing sections have been dictated by the theoretical considerations given earlier in this book. By way of epilogue it should be said that a great deal of factor analysis, indeed all the earlier work, has taken a somewhat different form. This is due to Spearman, to whom the credit is due for attempting factor analysis at all. Spearman's argument was originally based on the fact that the correlation matrices, omitting the diagonal terms, are often approximately in dyad form, or hierarchic form, as he called it. (This name was given because if the rows of a dyad are rearranged so that the terms in one column are in numerical order, then the terms in all the columns will be in numerical order—there is a hierarchy of rows.) He then assumed that this was because the tests were each trying to measure the same thing, but each test had its own source of confusion. This is equivalent to assuming that when there are t tests there are $t+1$ factors, all uncorrelated, one of which appears in all the tests, and the others are each specific to one test. If this is the situation, then the correlation matrix should have all two-rowed minors not involving a diagonal term equal to zero, and by suitable reduction of the diagonal terms it should be possible to make the matrix of rank 1. Naturally a test has a correlation coefficient of unity with itself, but this is made up of two parts, correlation of the general factor with itself, and correlation of the specific with itself. The reduction of the diagonal terms is the removal of the latter contribution. (Compare the alternative treatment of errors in the fourth paragraph of § 11.5.)

The idea of something specific in each test is common sense, of course. In the case of the t examiners marking the essay, the analysis is as though the essay were on a subject such as 'The Atomic Bomb', and the examiners each a specialist—historian, scientist, economist, theologian, etc., and the marking scheme was (*a*) general ability and (*b*) marks for the examiner's special field. Spearman endeavoured to keep his tests as different as possible, and used the results of his analyses to eliminate tests which seemed to contain more than one common factor. But mathematically, and unless one designs the tests that way, to assume more factors than tests bedevils the whole analysis, and it would seem better to adopt the converse procedure, and try to 'break the specifics' by a deliberate attempt to make them common. (In purely academic tests, this would mean seeing that the science papers included historical questions—e.g. on the history of science—and that the history paper included questions—e.g. on the industrial revolution—designed to introduce a little of the factor most prominent in the science tests.)

Nor is the system particularly simple. In spite of the endeavour, by keeping the tests as different as possible, to ensure that the correlation matrices are hierarchic, the fact cannot be avoided that with a $t \times t$ matrix it is possible to pick out minors as large as $t/2 \times t/2$ which do not contain a diagonal element, and if these are then obstinately non-zero, more common factors must be assumed. The problem is then, in matrix form, to factorize the original matrix M (or $\mathbf{M}$) into matrices of orders $t \times (t+k)$

and $(t+k)\times s$, of the form

$$T = \begin{bmatrix} g_1 & g_2 & . & . & . & g_t \\ g_1' & g_2'' & . & . & . & g_t' \\ . & . & . & . & . & . \\ g_1^k & g_2^k & . & . & . & g_t^k \\ h_1 & 0 & . & . & . & 0 \\ 0 & h_2 & . & . & . & 0 \\ . & . & . & . & . & . \\ 0 & 0 & . & . & . & h_t \end{bmatrix} \qquad S = \begin{bmatrix} d_1 & d_1' & d_1'' & . & . & . & d_1^k & e_{11} & e_{12} & . & . & . & e_{1t} \\ d_2 & d_2' & d_2'' & . & . & . & d_2^k & e_{21} & e_{22} & . & . & . & e_{2t} \\ . & . & . & . & . & . & . & . & . & . & . & . \\ d_s & d_s' & d_s'' & . & . & . & d_s^k & e_{s1} & e_{s2} & . & . & . & e_{st} \end{bmatrix}$$

subject to the conditions that k is a minimum and the e_{pq} uncorrelated. The result is necessarily not fully determined in most cases (there being

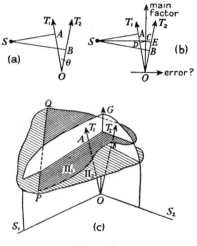

Fig. 18.

disposable constants with one value of k and no solution with k one less). The ambiguity, and the difference between the two systems of analysis, may be seen in the vector picture with two tests with correlation $r = \cos\theta$ (though, in fact, it takes three tests in Spearman's method to define a hierarchy). The picture is given in Fig. 18. The student should turn back to Fig. 4 (§ 4.6) to remind himself of the use of reciprocal vectors for coordinate determination. Fig. 18 a shows the two test vectors OT_1 and OT_2 in the plane of the paper inclined at the small angle θ (high correlation), and the point S_1 representing the attainment of student No. 1, whose scores in the tests were OA and OB. This diagram shows the facts as we are given them, the analyses add interpretative framework. Fig. 18 b shows the analysis into one factor and error; OC is the student's score in the factor, and $OD = OE$ the scores in the tests based on this factor alone. (All lines dropped from S and C are perpendiculars.) Fig. 18 c shows the Spearman analysis which requires three dimensions. OT_1 and OT_2, still at θ, are in the perpendicular planes GOS_1 and GOS_2, OG being the axis of the general factor and OS_1 and OS_2 the axes of the specifics. The planes Π_1 and Π_2 are perpendicular to OT_1 through A and to OT_2 through B, respectively. They intersect in PQ, and the student's point may be anywhere along PQ.

It might be added that there is a way of retaining the idea of general ability and specifics as required by the common-sense picture without multiplying factors, and that is by plotting the students' points in the t-space, transforming to a spherical distribution, and then stating the length of the student's vector as the general factor, and the t directional cosines on to the test vectors (of which, at most, $t-1$ are independent) as the specifics. Is there, also, an answer here to the schoolmaster's perennial poser, 'How can you really add marks in arithmetic and marks in English?'

PART III

CONTINUOUS GROUPS AND APPLICATIONS

CHAPTER XII

CONTINUOUS GROUPS: INTRODUCTION

As remarked in § 2.4, if, in the general rotation matrix in two dimensions,

$$\left[\begin{array}{cc} \cos\theta & \sin\theta \\ -\sin\theta & \cos\theta \end{array} \right],$$

the parameter θ is not limited to values which are submultiples of 2π, but may take any real value (values between 0 and 2π being sufficient to generate all possible matrices of this type), the resulting matrices form a group which differs from those considered in Part I in that (a) it has an infinite number of members, and (b) two members of the group can be found which differ infinitesimally from each other. A group of which these two statements are true is known as a continuous group. The group of all rotations in two dimensions is a natural generalization from the groups c_n derived from the rotations of an n-gon, since it is derived in the same way from the rotations of a circle into itself. It is commutative as they are, and may be called c_∞. The group of lattice translations considered in Chapter IX had the property (a) above, but not property (b); it is infinite but not continuous. On the other hand, the group of all translations in three dimensions (i.e. not restricted to lattice translations) is another example of a continuous commutative group. Other examples of continuous groups are: the generalized proper and improper rotations of a circle, $\mathfrak{d}_\infty$; the proper rotations of a sphere $\mathfrak{r}_3$; the proper and improper rotations of a sphere, $\mathfrak{r}_3 \times c_2$, and a number of matrix groups, the more important of which may be tabulated. In the table below we give two notations for several of the groups because the notation common among mathematicians does not accord well with the conventions we have developed in the earlier parts of this book.

12.2. Representations and characters in continuous groups

In the early parts of this chapter we shall sacrifice rigour in the fashion usual among those whose work is physical applications, by assuming

TABLE OF MATRIX GROUPS

No.	Name	Conventional symbol	Our symbol	Definition and properties	No. of real parameters
1	General or full linear	$GL(n, C)$	$\mathfrak{f}_n$	All non-singular $n \times n$ matrices	$2n^2$
2	Special linear	$SL(n, C)$	$\mathfrak{h}_n$	As (1), with determinant equal to 1	$2n^2 - 2$
3	General real	$GL(n, R)$		As (1), with real elements	n^2
4	Special real	$SL(n, R)$		All matrices common to (2) and (3)	$n^2 - 1$
5	Unitary	$U(n)$	$\mathfrak{U}_n$	$\tilde{M} = \bar{M}^{-1}$; preserves$*XX*$ (see § 3.5)	n^2
6	(Complex) orthogonal	$O(n, C)$		$M = \tilde{M}^{-1}$; preserves†XX† (see § 3.5)	$n(n-1)$
7	Real orthogonal	$O(n)$	$\mathfrak{o}_n$	$M = \bar{M} = \tilde{M}^{-1}$	$n(n-1)/2$
8	Special orthogonal	$SO(n)$	$\mathfrak{r}_n$	Matrices common to (2) and (7); *proper* rotations in n dimensions	$n(n-1)/2$
9	Special unitary	$SU(n)$	$\mathfrak{u}_n$	Matrices common to (2) and (5)	$n^2 - 1$
10	Symplectic	$Sp(n)$		Preserves ‡XX‡ where X‡ is a vector with quaternion components; a subgroup of $GL(2n,C)$, viz. the unitary $2n \times 2n$ matrices which preserve $$\sum_1^n (x_i\, y_{i+n} - x_{i+n}\, y_i)$$	$2n^2 + n$
11	Complex symplectic	$Sp(n, C)$		Preserves bilinear form in (10); matrices need not be unitary	$2(2n^2 + n)$
12	Spinor group	$Spin(n)$		See § 13.10	

that we can carry over the general results obtained with finite groups into continuous groups, with the proviso that whenever necessary sums will be replaced by integrals. Later in the chapter we shall inquire into some of the conditions required to justify this. We shall find some interesting results dropping out by the way.

For example, since the group $\mathfrak{c}_\infty$ is commutative, it has as many representations as it has members, that is, an infinite number. The representations, however, do not differ continuously from one another, but are discrete. We may obtain them easily by generalizing from those of $\mathfrak{c}_n$, which are $e^{i\theta}, e^{2i\theta}, ..., e^{ki\theta}, ..., e^{ni\theta}$, θ being the angle of rotation defining the element, and k defining the representation. As θ is a multiple of $2\pi/n$, $e^{ni\theta}$ is the identical representation, and is the same representation as would be obtained by setting $k = 0$. In the same way, further members of the series, forwards or backwards, merely repeat earlier ones.

But with n tending to infinity there is no repetition in either direction for the general angle θ, though of course there is for certain special angles, because c_n is an invariant subgroup of c_∞ and it is to be expected that there will be representations in which the same character belongs to several classes. As the representations are all one-dimensional, they are themselves the characters. The orthogonality relations take the forms

$$\lim \frac{1}{N} \sum e^{mi\theta} e^{-mi\theta} = 1 \quad \text{(every } \theta\text{)}, \tag{12.2.1}$$

$$\lim \frac{1}{N} \sum e^{mi\theta} e^{-mi\phi} = 0 \quad \text{(every } \theta \neq \phi\text{)}, \tag{12.2.2}$$

$$\frac{1}{2\pi} \int_0^{2\pi} e^{im\theta} e^{-im\theta} \, d\theta = 1 \quad \text{(every } m\text{)}, \tag{12.2.3}$$

$$\frac{1}{2\pi} \int_0^{2\pi} e^{im\theta} e^{-in\theta} \, d\theta = 0 \quad \text{(every } m \neq n\text{)}. \tag{12.2.4}$$

The first is trivial, since each of the N terms in the sum is identically 1. The second is equivalent to the result stated in the discussion preceding Theorem 9.4.4. The third and fourth are easily verified directly.

Now any function defined convergently for each point $\theta = 2k\pi/n$ on a circle is a possible generalized character of c_n and can be expressed using these relations as a linear combination of simple characters. Proceeding to the limit, any suitably convergent function of period 2π is a possible generalized character of c_∞ and can be similarly expressed as a linear combination of the simple ones. We have, therefore,

$$f(\theta) = a_0 + a_1 e^{i\theta} + a_2 e^{2i\theta} + \ldots + a_{-1} e^{-i\theta} + \ldots, \tag{12.2.5}$$

where the a's, which may be complex, are given by the relations

$$a_n = \frac{1}{2\pi} \int_0^{2\pi} f(\theta) e^{-in\theta} \, d\theta. \tag{12.2.6}$$

This result leads directly to the usual theory of Fourier series. The significant feature of this approach (which can, of course, be based on the limiting process leading to (12.2.3) and (12.2.4) without introducing explicitly group-theoretic considerations) is that it provides evidence that the set of terms is complete (in the sense of really reproducing the function) if n is given all positive and negative integral values.

The group $\mathfrak{d}_\infty$ can be generalized similarly from $\mathfrak{d}_n$. Its character table is

	I	Each pair of proper rotations ϕ and $-\phi$	All improper rotations	
Γ_1	1	1	1	
Γ_2	1	1	-1	(12.2.7)
Γ_{m+2}	2	$2\cos m\phi$	0	

with the two-dimensional representations taking the form

$$I = \begin{bmatrix} 1 & 0 \\ 0 & 1 \end{bmatrix} \quad C_\phi = \begin{bmatrix} \cos m\phi & \sin m\phi \\ -\sin m\phi & \cos m\phi \end{bmatrix} \quad B_\phi = \begin{bmatrix} \cos m\phi & -\sin m\phi \\ -\sin m\phi & -\cos m\phi \end{bmatrix}.$$

The symmetry group $D_{\infty h}$, which occurs frequently in molecules—we met it in one postulated form for ozone (§ 10.4)—is similarly generalized from D_{nh}. It has the structure $\mathfrak{d}_\infty \times \mathfrak{c}_2$, with classes, representations, and characters appropriate to the fact that it is a direct product group, namely,

	I	Each C_ϕ and $C_{-\phi}$	All m	i	Each S_ϕ and $S_{-\phi}$	All C_2
Γ_1	1	1	1	1	1	1
Γ_1'	1	1	1	-1	-1	-1
Γ_2	1	1	-1	1	1	-1
Γ_2'	1	1	-1	-1	-1	1
Γ_{m+2}	2	$2\cos m\phi$	0	2	$2\cos m\phi$	0
Γ_{m+2}'	2	$2\cos m\phi$	0	-2	$-2\cos m\phi$	0

12.3. The groups $\mathfrak{u}_2$ and $\mathfrak{r}_3$

We have seen that the complex numbers of modulus 1, the real rotations in a plane, and the real orthogonal matrices of order 2, if considered as generating groups, give rise to isomorphic groups, and therefore to one and the same group in abstraction. In this section we shall show that the three-dimensional rotation group and a certain two-dimensional unitary group are similarly isomorphic, and in the next section we shall discuss the representations of this group. The problem can be attacked purely algebraically, but it is easier to allow geometrical intuition to help. We therefore start by remarking that any rotation of a sphere can be accomplished by three successive rotations about two only of the coordinate axes. The point which is to be brought to the Z-axis can be got there, in fact, by first bringing it into the XZ-plane by a rotation, through an angle ϕ, about the Z-axis, and then bringing it to the Z-axis by rotating the sphere through an angle θ about the Y-axis. All the remaining points can then be brought to their appropriate places by a second rotation about the Z-axis, through an angle ψ; this rotation, since it leaves the point on the Z-axis unmoved, will not undo what we have accomplished by the first two rotations. The whole process may be described by the notation $Z(\psi)Y(\theta)Z(\phi)$, and its matrix will be

$$
\begin{bmatrix} \cos\psi & \sin\psi & 0 \\ -\sin\psi & \cos\psi & 0 \\ 0 & 0 & 1 \end{bmatrix}
\begin{bmatrix} \cos\theta & 0 & \sin\theta \\ 0 & 1 & 0 \\ -\sin\theta & 0 & \cos\theta \end{bmatrix}
\begin{bmatrix} \cos\phi & \sin\phi & 0 \\ -\sin\phi & \cos\phi & 0 \\ 0 & 0 & 1 \end{bmatrix}
$$

$$
= \begin{bmatrix} \cos\psi\cos\phi\cos\theta+\sin\psi\sin\phi & \cos\psi\sin\phi\cos\theta-\sin\psi\cos\phi & \cos\psi\sin\theta \\ \sin\psi\cos\phi\cos\theta-\cos\psi\sin\phi & \sin\psi\sin\phi\cos\theta+\cos\psi\cos\phi & \sin\psi\sin\theta \\ -\cos\phi\sin\theta & -\sin\phi\sin\theta & \cos\theta \end{bmatrix}. \quad (12.3.1)
$$

(Note: these angles are sometimes called the Eulerian angles, but this name is also sometimes applied to a different factorization in which the final rotation is about the *transformed* Z-axis.) We notice that it is not necessary that every one of these angles be allowed its full range of 0 to 2π; the full rotation group can be realized if one of the angles is restricted to any value between 0 and π.

Here we may digress for a paragraph to point out another by-product of this work, namely, the formulae of spherical trigonometry. Consider the points on the sphere which in the course of these three rotations pass through the point $(0, 1, 0)$. They form a spherical triangle with sides ψ, ϕ, and included angle θ (see Fig. 19 a). For this paragraph we shall conform to the notation of spherical trigonometry whereby sides and denoted by small letters and angles by capitals, and therefore write these as ψ, ϕ, and Θ. The side opposite to Θ is represented by the resultant movement of the point $(0, 1, 0)$; in fact,

$$\cos\theta = Y\text{-coordinate of final position of } (0, 1, 0),$$

$$\tan\Phi = \frac{Z\text{-coordinate of final position of } (0, 1, 0)}{X\text{-coordinate of final position of } (0, 1, 0)},$$

or alternatively,

$$\sin\Phi = \frac{Z\text{-coordinate of final position of } (0, 1, 0)}{\sin\theta}.$$

With the aid of the multiplied-out matrix of the previous paragraph these become (since the result of applying it to $(0, 1, 0)$ is simply the second column of the matrix)

$$\cos\theta = \cos\psi\cos\phi + \sin\psi\sin\phi\cos\Theta,$$

$$\tan\Phi = \frac{\sin\phi\sin\Theta}{\sin\psi\cos\phi - \cos\psi\sin\phi\cos\Theta},$$

$$\sin\Phi = \frac{\sin\phi\sin\Theta}{\sin\theta}.$$

The resultant movement of $(0, 1, 0)$ is, of course, a rotation through an angle ω such that $1+2\cos\omega$ is the trace of the matrix, about an axis which is the simultaneous right- and left-eigenvector of the matrix with eigenvalue unity. In this way the pole of θ can be obtained, and the calculation is considerably simplified if the matrix itself is simplified by making use of all six elements of the triangle.

We return to the rotation group. Let the radius of the sphere be unity, and the coordinates of a point P be (x, y, z), so that $x^2+y^2+z^2 = 1$. We might put

$$z = \cos\alpha, \qquad x+iy = \sin\alpha \cdot e^{i\beta}. \tag{12.3.2}$$

Then if we define W as the two-dimensional vector

$$(\cos\tfrac{1}{2}\alpha \cdot e^{\frac{1}{2}i\beta}, \quad \sin\tfrac{1}{2}\alpha \cdot e^{-\frac{1}{2}i\beta}),$$

it is easily verified that

$$\left.\begin{aligned}
W_1\overline{W}_2 + \overline{W}_1 W_2 &= x \\
\frac{1}{i}(W_1\overline{W}_2 - \overline{W}_1 W_2) &= y \\
W_1\overline{W}_1 - W_2\overline{W}_2 &= z \\
W_1\overline{W}_1 + W_2\overline{W}_2 &= {}^*WW^* = 1
\end{aligned}\right\}. \tag{12.3.3}$$

Thus any transformation in the space of W which keeps ${}^*WW^*$ constant, that is, any unitary transformation, induces in the three-dimensional space a transformation which keeps $x^2+y^2+z^2$ constant, that is, a rotation.

An alternative presentation of this argument is possible by remarking that $x^2+y^2+z^2$ is minus the determinant of the matrix

$$\begin{bmatrix} y & z+ix \\ z-ix & -y \end{bmatrix}$$

which is the general Hermitian matrix of trace zero. Transformation by a unitary matrix preserves the Hermitian character, the determinant and the trace, and thus the group of unitary transformations of this matrix is isomorphic with a group of real orthogonal transformations in the x, y, z-space. We can also supplement the geometrical intuition by reference to Fig. 19 b. Let the line ZP (where Z is the intersection of the Z-axis with the sphere) intersect the XY-plane in P'. It is easily seen that the coordinates of P' are given by $x' + iy' = \cot \frac{1}{2}\alpha \cdot e^{i\beta}$, where

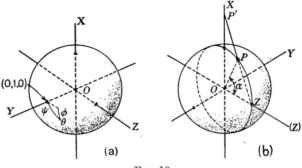

FIG. 19.

β is the angle XOP'. This shows that we can associate each point on the sphere with one in the plane, and therefore a transformation of the sphere with one of the plane. (And here, we might remark, is a possible starting-point for developing the theory of map projections.) Since $x' + iy' = W_1/W_2$, W_1 and W_2 may be regarded as the *homogeneous* co-ordinates of the point P'.

In the general unitary transformation in two dimensions as given in § 3.5, the factor $e^{i\alpha}$ is irrelevant to our present discussion (since it does not transform x, y, and z) and it may be omitted. The remainder of the expression is a *special* unitary matrix as defined in the table in § 12.1, and for our present purposes is more conveniently written

$$U = \begin{bmatrix} \cos\frac{1}{2}\theta \cdot e^{\frac{1}{2}i(\phi+\psi)} & \sin\frac{1}{2}\theta \cdot e^{\frac{1}{2}i(-\phi+\psi)} \\ -\sin\frac{1}{2}\theta \cdot e^{\frac{1}{2}i(\phi-\psi)} & \cos\frac{1}{2}\theta \cdot e^{-\frac{1}{2}i(\phi+\psi)} \end{bmatrix}$$

$$= \begin{bmatrix} e^{\frac{1}{2}i\psi} & 0 \\ 0 & e^{-\frac{1}{2}i\psi} \end{bmatrix} \begin{bmatrix} \cos\frac{1}{2}\theta & \sin\frac{1}{2}\theta \\ -\sin\frac{1}{2}\theta & \cos\frac{1}{2}\theta \end{bmatrix} \begin{bmatrix} e^{\frac{1}{2}i\phi} & 0 \\ 0 & e^{-\frac{1}{2}i\phi} \end{bmatrix} \quad (12.3.4)$$

in which all possible matrices are covered by the range of variables 0 to 2π for each of ϕ, θ, and ψ. It is merely an exercise to show (a) that the special unitary matrices form a group, and (b) that the first two factors of the above product in the unitary space induce respectively the first two factors of our original rotation matrix in the three-space. The only discrepancy is that in the latter the range of one of the angles was only 0 to π, so that two unitary matrices produce each rotation. The reason for this is that if W_1 and W_2 are both reversed in sign, x, y, z, and $*WW*$ are all unchanged, so that the unitary matrices U and $-U$ both produce the same rotation. By not distinguishing U and $-U$ we obtain a factor group of the special unitary group. Thus we have shown that

THEOREM 12.3.5. *The rotation group in three dimensions is isomorphic with a factor group of the special unitary group in two dimensions containing half the number of elements.*

The representations of the group $\mathfrak{r}_3$ *are therefore half of the representations of* $\mathfrak{u}_2$.

We shall see which half in the next section, and shall discuss this relation further in §§ 13.9 and 13.10.

It is of particular interest in connection with the theory of quaternions to notice that rotations through an angle θ about OX, OY, and OZ, respectively, correspond in the unitary group to the matrices which in § 3.9 we wrote as $\cos\theta.\eta_1+\sin\theta.\eta_4$, $\cos\theta.\eta_1+\sin\theta.\eta_3$, and $\cos\theta.\eta_1+\sin\theta.\eta_2$, respectively.

The classes of the special unitary group $\mathfrak{u}_2$ are easily stated. Let $\begin{bmatrix} x \\ y \end{bmatrix}$ be an eigenvector of $\begin{bmatrix} a & b \\ -\bar{b} & \bar{a} \end{bmatrix}$ of length unity, so that

$$\begin{bmatrix} a & b \\ -\bar{b} & \bar{a} \end{bmatrix}\begin{bmatrix} x \\ y \end{bmatrix} = \begin{bmatrix} ax+by \\ -\bar{b}x+\bar{a}y \end{bmatrix} = \lambda\begin{bmatrix} x \\ y \end{bmatrix}.$$

Then $\begin{bmatrix} x & -\bar{y} \\ y & \bar{x} \end{bmatrix}$ is unitary, and its inverse is its associate, $\begin{bmatrix} \bar{x} & \bar{y} \\ -y & x \end{bmatrix}$. We find that

$$\begin{bmatrix} \bar{x} & \bar{y} \\ -y & x \end{bmatrix}\begin{bmatrix} a & b \\ -\bar{b} & \bar{a} \end{bmatrix}\begin{bmatrix} x & -\bar{y} \\ y & \bar{x} \end{bmatrix} = \begin{bmatrix} \bar{x} & \bar{y} \\ -y & x \end{bmatrix}\begin{bmatrix} \lambda x & -\bar{\lambda}\bar{y} \\ \lambda y & \bar{\lambda}\bar{x} \end{bmatrix} = \begin{bmatrix} \lambda & 0 \\ 0 & \bar{\lambda} \end{bmatrix},$$

so that to each pair of complex conjugate numbers λ and $\bar{\lambda}$, of modulus unity, there corresponds one class of unitary matrices, the class with these numbers as eigenvalues. The character of this class is $\lambda+\bar{\lambda}$ in this representation, which may also be written $2\cos\frac{1}{2}\theta\cos\frac{1}{2}(\phi+\psi) = 2\cos\omega$, where ω is the equivalent rotation about an unspecified axis.

The properties of the full unitary group, if required, can be found from the fact that it is the direct product of the factor group of the special unitary group with the group $\mathfrak{c}_\infty$ (of which $\pm e^{i\alpha}$ are members).

12.4. Representations of $\mathfrak{u}_2$ and $\mathfrak{r}_3$

In discussing the representations of the group $\mathfrak{u}_2$, among which, by the preceding section, are the representations of $\mathfrak{r}_3$, let us first be quite clear what we are doing. The unitary matrices in two dimensions form a group from which we derive the abstract group $\mathfrak{u}_2$ which may have representations in any number of dimensions. The unitary matrices in three, four,... dimensions form other groups, but these have, for the moment, nothing to do with our problem, though we shall in fact find that for any n there is an irreducible representation of $\mathfrak{u}_2$ in n dimensions which is a subgroup of $\mathfrak{u}_n$.

We recall first two previous pieces of work. First the paragraph in § 5.2 where we showed that the vector $(1, 1, 1)$ is invariant under a group of matrices, and therefore that that representation was reducible. In this section we propose to show that nothing less than a certain complete space remains invariant under a group of matrices, and that therefore the representation is irreducible. Secondly we recall the 'induced representations' referred to in § 5.6. For in the case of the group $\mathfrak{u}_2$ the irreducible representations are simply all the induced representations of the type there discussed that can be obtained from the original unitary matrices.

It simplifies the discussion if we agree from the start that the vector $(a, b,...)$ 'is' the polynomial $ax^r + bx^{r-1}y + \ldots$. Let there be a subspace invariant under the group, and let $\sum a_p x^p y^{r-p}$ be in this subspace. We can produce a series of transformations that will generate the whole space from this vector. First, the vector is transformed by the element

$$\begin{bmatrix} e^{i\omega} & 0 \\ 0 & e^{-i\omega} \end{bmatrix} \quad \text{into} \quad a_p\, e^{(2p-r)i\omega} x^p y^{r-p},$$

and by taking sufficient different values of ω we obtain enough independent vectors to form the basis of the whole subspace spanned by those $x^p y^{r-p}$ for which a_p was not zero in the original vector. Secondly, any single $x^p y^{r-p}$ in this subspace is transformed by

$$\begin{bmatrix} \cos \pi/4 & \sin \pi/4 \\ -\sin \pi/4 & \cos \pi/4 \end{bmatrix} \quad \text{into} \quad \frac{(x+y)^p(-x+y)^{r-p}}{2^{r/2}},$$

which includes x^r, and therefore (repeating the first process) x^r is in the subspace. But now repeating the second process on x^r, we get $(x+y)^r$, in which no term can have a zero coefficient. Since it is obvious that no transformation can produce anything which is not included among the polynomials $\sum a_p x^p y^{r-p}$, and the set is therefore a complete basis, the result is proved.

THEOREM 12.4.1. *The monomials $x^p y^{r-p}$ form a basis for an irreducible representation in $r+1$ dimensions of the group $\mathfrak{u}_2$.*

Putting $r = 2l$, $p = l+m$, the monomial $x^p y^{r-p}$ becomes $x^{l+m} y^{l-m}$, and m takes all values at unit intervals from $-l$ to l inclusive. This form is more convenient for the rotation group $\mathfrak{r}_3$ since the irreducible representations of this group are those of the unitary group with integral l, that is, with even r. The student should verify that in this case, but not for odd r, the two unitary matrices corresponding to a given rotation both lead to the same matrix in the induced representation. He should also show that the induced representations are unitary, and therefore a subgroup of $\mathfrak{u}_n$.

An important result which we shall want later concerns the reduction of the Kronecker product of two representations. If $x^p y^{r-p}$ and $v^p w^{s-p}$ are the bases of two representations of degrees $r+1$ and $s+1$ respectively (the vector (v, w) undergoing the same transformations as (x, y) does), then the transformations undergone by the monomials $x^p y^{r-p} v^q w^{s-q}$ form a Kronecker product representation of the group, in $(r+1)(s+1)$ dimensions, but this representation is reducible, and the problem arises to reduce it. The answer (so far as counting representations is concerned) is that it contains each of the irreducible representations from that of degree $|r-s|$ by two's to that of degree $r+s$ exactly once. This can be shown in the usual manner from the characters. The character in the irreducible representation in $r+1$ dimensions of the class containing

$$\begin{bmatrix} e^{i\omega} & 0 \\ 0 & e^{-i\omega} \end{bmatrix} \quad \text{is} \quad \sum_{p=0}^{r} e^{(2p-r)i\omega}$$

and the problem is therefore simply one of showing that

$$\left(\sum_{p=0}^{r} e^{(2p-r)i\omega} \right) \left(\sum_{q=0}^{s} e^{(2q-s)i\omega} \right) = \sum_{\substack{n=|r-s| \\ \text{by two's}}}^{r+s} \left(\sum_{m=0}^{n} e^{(2m-n)i\omega} \right)$$

for all ω, which is solely one of algebraic manipulation. One does, however, obtain a clearer insight into the reduction by actually performing it, and this can be done.

Let $\qquad (\alpha x + \beta y)^r (\alpha v + \beta w)^s = \alpha^{r+s} \phi_0 + {}^{r+s}C_1 \alpha^{r+s-1} \beta \phi_1 + \dots,$

where $\phi_0 = x^r v^s$ and ϕ_t is a polynomial in $x^i y^j v^k w^l$ with $j+l = t$ and $i+k = r+s-t$. Then we show that the vectors $\phi_0, \dots, \phi_{r+s}$ are independent, and that the space they span is invariant under the group. They must be independent because they are independent even if we put $x = v$, $y = w$, when they become $\phi_t = x^{r+s-t}y^t$, and the basis of the $(r+s+1)$-dimensional representation. The space they span is invariant under the group since, applying the same transformation $\begin{bmatrix} a & b \\ c & d \end{bmatrix}$ to (x, y) and to (v, w),

$$(\alpha x' + \beta y')^r (\alpha v' + \beta w')^s$$
$$= \{(\alpha a + \beta c)x + (\alpha b + \beta d)y\}^r \{(\alpha a + \beta c)v + (\alpha b + \beta d)w\}^s,$$

whence

$$\sum_t {}^{r+s}C_t \alpha^{r+s-t}\beta^t \phi_t' = \sum_t {}^{r+s}C_t(\alpha a + \beta c)^{r+s-t}(\alpha b + \beta d)^t \phi_t,$$

and by equating coefficients of $\alpha^{r+s-t}\beta^t$ we can express the ϕ_t' as linear combinations of the ϕ_t.

Now $x^r v^s$ and $y^r w^s$ are already in the subspace spanned by the ϕ_t, and all other terms contain either both x and w or both y and v. Let us put the most general vector in our product representation equal to

$$\phi = (a_0 \phi_0 + a_1 \phi_1 + \ldots + a_{r+s} \phi_{r+s}) + (xw - yv) \psi.$$

We show that this is possible, that the ϕ_t and ψ are independent, and that ψ is another representation of the group. First, ϕ is identically zero only if ψ and every a are all zero. For x/y may equal v/w, in which case the second term is zero, and as we know that the ϕ_t are all independent we may conclude that every a is zero. But x/y need not equal v/w, whence in conjunction with the fact that the a's are all zero, we conclude that ψ must also be identically zero; thus the ϕ_t and ψ are all independent. It also follows that the expansion is possible if the a's are given the values they assume when $x/y = v/w$. Secondly, ψ consists of terms from the product of the representations in r and s dimensions. Since $(f+1)(g+1) = (f+g+1)+fg$, there are just enough terms in ψ to make up the required number of dimensions. Further,

$$x'w' - y'v' = xw - yv,$$

so that $(xw - yv)\psi$ transforms like ψ. Hence, in the expansion of the vector ϕ in the form at the beginning of this paragraph, we have effected a reduction

$$\Gamma_r \times \Gamma_s = \Gamma_{r+s} \dot{+} (\Gamma_{r-1} \times \Gamma_{s-1}),$$

and by repeated application of this process,

$$\Gamma_r \times \Gamma_s = \Gamma_{r+s} \dot{+} \Gamma_{r+s-2} \dot{+} \Gamma_{r+s-4} \dot{+} \ldots \dot{+} \Gamma_{|r-s|}.$$

The complete series,

$$\phi = \sum_1^{f+g+1} a_t\phi_t + (xw-yv)\sum_1^{f+g-1} b_t\psi_t + (xw-yv)^2\sum_1^{f+g-3} c_t\theta_t + ...,$$

is known as the Clebsh–Gordan series.

12.5. The numerical groups

It is easily seen that the following all fall within the definition of a group:

(a) all positive and negative integers and zero
(b) all positive and negative rational fractions and zero
(c) all real numbers including zero
(d) all complex numbers including zero
(e) all elements of a linear algebra

with addition as the law of composition,

(f) all positive rational numbers (excluding zero)
(g) all positive real numbers (excluding zero)
(h) all positive and negative rational numbers (excluding zero)
(i) all positive and negative real numbers (excluding zero)
(j) all complex numbers (except zero)

with multiplication as the law of composition,

and there are others, which the student acquainted with the theory of number fields will be able to supply for himself, but in general the elements of a linear algebra do not form a group with multiplication as the law because the product of two elements may sometimes be zero, and zero has no inverse under multiplication.

All these groups are commutative, and we may therefore expect that all their irreducible representations are one-dimensional. Since,

$$\text{if} \quad x+y = z, \quad \text{then} \quad a^x a^y = a^z$$
$$\text{or} \quad e^{kx}e^{ky} = e^{kz} \tag{12.5.1}$$

to each value (including complex ones) of a (or of k), this association of a^x (or e^{kx}) with x provides a representation of each of the addition groups (a) to (e). The identical representation is provided by the value $a = 1$ ($k = 0$).

And since, $\quad$ if $\quad xy = z, \quad$ then $\quad x^n y^n = z^n,$ $\tag{12.5.2}$

to each value (including, with certain restrictions, complex ones) of n, the association of x^n with x provides a different representation of the multiplication groups (f) to (j). The identical representation arises from the value $n = 0$.

These groups are infinite, however (though not all continuous), and they may have representations of the type referred to in § 7.6 as incompletely reducible (or reducible but non-analysable). Thus

$$\begin{bmatrix} 1 & u \\ 0 & 1 \end{bmatrix} \begin{bmatrix} 1 & v \\ 0 & 1 \end{bmatrix} = \begin{bmatrix} 1 & u+v \\ 0 & 1 \end{bmatrix} \tag{12.5.3}$$

and

$$\begin{bmatrix} 1 & \log u \\ 0 & 1 \end{bmatrix} \begin{bmatrix} 1 & \log v \\ 0 & 1 \end{bmatrix} = \begin{bmatrix} 1 & \log uv \\ 0 & 1 \end{bmatrix} \tag{12.5.4}$$

show the existence of representations of this type of the groups (a) to (e) and (f) to (g) respectively.

Since $\det A^n = (\det A)^n$ (§ 7.8), any matrix representing an element of a finite group has a determinant of modulus unity. Some of the features of the theory of finite groups are retained in continuous groups if this feature is retained, and to do this is therefore to our advantage. If an $n \times n$ matrix is multiplied by the scalar k, its determinant is multiplied by k^n, and therefore $M/|M|^{1/n}$ is a matrix with determinant unity, or $M/||M||^{1/n}$ (the double line denoting the absolute value of the determinant) a matrix with determinant of modulus unity. If

$$MN = P,$$

then

$$\frac{M}{|M|^{1/n}} \frac{N}{|N|^{1/n}} = \frac{P}{|M|^{1/n}|N|^{1/n}} = \frac{P}{|P|^{1/n}}. \tag{12.5.5}$$

Hence if every matrix in a group is divided by its determinant to the power $1/n$, the new matrices are still a representation of the group, though possibly less faithful than the original ones. There are two extremes: (1) The original group may be the direct product of a numerical group with a uni-determinantal group. The new group is then simply the latter one. Or (2) the original group may be something like, for example, the integral powers of the one-dimensional matrix ae^i (a real)—viz. $a^n e^{in}$ (n integral), and the new group, consisting of all e^{in} (n integral), is then simply isomorphic (identical in abstraction) with the original one. (The direct product of the cyclic groups on a and e^i contains all matrices $a^m e^{in}$ (both m and n integral, but not necessarily the same).)

It should be noticed that since some members of a continuous group will be of 'infinite order' (i.e. can be raised to an unlimitedly high (integral) power and never yield I thereby—compare e^i as an example), and since $\det A^n = (\det A)^n$, there is no escape from one or other of the two

conclusions (a) all the matrices of such elements have unimodular determinants, or (b) some matrices have an infinite determinant. Such groups
are distinguished as 'open' and 'closed' groups, these terms applying
naturally, in the first instance, to the group manifold discussed in the
next section.

12.6. Infinitesimal operators and the group manifold

With a continuous group there arises the possibility of infinitesimal
operators. These are operators which make an infinitesimal change in a
vector, not operators which convert a finite vector into an infinitesimal
one; $X \to X+dX$, not $X \to dX$. (More rigorously, they are operators
whose limit is I, not 0; the latter operator cannot be part of a group,
of course.) The infinitesimal rotation in two dimensions is rotation
through the angle $d\theta$, thus

$$\begin{bmatrix} \cos d\theta & \sin d\theta \\ -\sin d\theta & \cos d\theta \end{bmatrix} = \begin{bmatrix} 1 & d\theta \\ -d\theta & 1 \end{bmatrix} = \begin{bmatrix} 1 & 0 \\ 0 & 1 \end{bmatrix} + \begin{bmatrix} 0 & d\theta \\ -d\theta & 0 \end{bmatrix}.$$

$$(12.6.1)$$

In the same way, the infinitesimal special unitary operator in two
dimensions is

$$\begin{bmatrix} 1+i\,d\phi & d\theta \\ -d\theta & 1-i\,d\phi \end{bmatrix} = \begin{bmatrix} 1 & 0 \\ 0 & 1 \end{bmatrix} + i\begin{bmatrix} d\phi & -i\,d\theta \\ i\,d\theta & -d\phi \end{bmatrix} \qquad (12.6.2)$$

and is thus $I+i$(a Hermitian operator). It is usual to avoid infinitesimal
quantities inside matrices, and to write these two operators as

$$\begin{bmatrix} 1 & 0 \\ 0 & 1 \end{bmatrix} + d\theta\begin{bmatrix} 0 & 1 \\ -1 & 0 \end{bmatrix} \quad \text{and} \quad \begin{bmatrix} 1 & 0 \\ 0 & 1 \end{bmatrix} + i\,dt\begin{bmatrix} \dot\phi & -i\dot\theta \\ i\dot\theta & -\dot\phi \end{bmatrix}. \quad (12.6.3)$$

The student should show that the result that an infinitesimal unitary
operator is $I+i$(a Hermitian operator) is general, in any number of
dimensions, and should note the relation of this result to the remark
which concludes § 3.6. It will be noticed that whereas the general
special-unitary operator in two dimensions depends on three parameters,
the infinitesimal special unitary operator depends on only two. We are
here in waters deeper than our present theory will fathom, but we may
point out that infinitesimal operators always commute, since

$$(I+aA)(I+bB) = I+aA+bB+abAB, \qquad (12.6.4)$$

and if a and b are infinitesimals, the only non-commuting term is an
infinitesimal of the second order. This result is analogous to the fact
that since small areas on a sphere may be taken as plane, small rotations
must commute as do translations.

The rotation operators in two dimensions depend on a single parameter θ. They can therefore be plotted as points on a circle, one point being chosen as origin ($\theta = 0$) and labelled I, and the point an angular distance θ from this one being labelled $R(\theta)$. What is most significant about this is that the elements of the group have been plotted as points in a one-dimensional closed space. Similarly, since the members of the group $\mathfrak{u}_2$ depend on three parameters, they can be plotted in a three-space, likewise closed, as the parameters are angles. It is over these spaces that we integrate when we 'sum' over all members of the group. They are not to be confused with any of the representation spaces. In the latter, each member of the group is an operator, a matrix; in the former each member of the group is a point, a vector. For this reason we avoid calling it a space, and refer to the group manifold. In the group manifold infinitesimal operators are infinitesimally close to I. Unlike the representation spaces, the group manifold need not be euclidean, and need not be a 'single sheet'. The proper and improper rotations of a sphere, for example, are a two-sheet manifold, for no series of infinitesimal changes can convert a proper rotation, with determinant equal to $+1$, into an improper one, with determinant equal to -1.

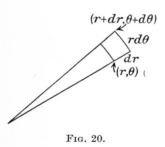

FIG. 20.

The most important property of the group manifold is its 'volume element', since only when this is known can we integrate over the whole manifold. Before discussing this we must have the theory of the metric tensor. The student who is already familiar with this could go at once to § 14.4, where the manifold of the group $\mathfrak{u}_2$ is discussed as an example. The student who is not will perhaps wish to know more clearly the nature of the problem, if not its solution, at this point. Consider therefore Fig. 20. The measure of the small increment of area, a rectangle to a first approximation, is

$$dr \times r\, d\theta = r\, dr d\theta.$$

The source of the factor r is obvious, and its presence is a warning that the $dxdydz...$ of a volume integral in cartesians becomes

$$f(r, \theta, \phi,...)\, dr d\theta d\phi...,$$

with f not necessarily equal to unity, in other systems of coordinates. The problem is to discover the form of f for the manifold of any given group.

12.7. Differential operators and Hilbert space

Suppose we are given the values $f(1)$, $f(2)$,... of a function f for all positive integral values of the argument. We can consider the numbers in this infinite sequence as the components of a vector F in a certain space with an infinite number of dimensions. In this space, any function we can construct will be represented by a vector. Only functions convergent for all positive integral values of the argument will be represented by vectors with finite coordinates, and only those for which $\sum_1^\infty \{f(n)\}^2$ converges will be represented by a vector of finite length. We shall assume this restriction in general, even if we ignore it in providing simple illustrations from time to time.

Consider now a second function, equal to $x.f(x)$. Its coordinates will be $f(1)$, $2f(2)$, $3f(3)$,...; that is, it will be the vector derived from the vector F by operating on it with the matrix

$$\xi = \begin{bmatrix} 1 & 0 & 0 & . & . & . \\ 0 & 2 & 0 & . & . & . \\ 0 & 0 & 3 & . & . & . \\ . & . & . & . & . & . \\ . & . & . & . & . & . \end{bmatrix}$$

and this matrix is therefore the operation of multiplying by x. As it is diagonal, we see that we are using the eigenvectors of this operator as axes. Interpreted as a function, the unit vector along the sth axis is the function $s(x) = \delta_x^s$ ($= 1$ or 0 as x is or is not equal to s).

Interpreting in the same way the expression $g(x)f(x)$, we need a vector F for $f(x)$ and an operator γ for $g(x)$. By this notation we are distinguishing between the functions $f(x)$ and $g(x)$ represented by vectors F and G, and the operations of multiplying by the functions represented by matrices ϕ and γ. It is clear from algebraic considerations that this distinction in notation is normally unnecessary, and we shall not consider ourselves bound to observe it; the student may find it useful to revive it from time to time to clarify the precise interpretation of an algebraic relation in matrix terms.

Let us consider next the operation

$$\begin{bmatrix} -1 & 1 & 0 & 0 & . & . \\ 0 & -1 & 1 & 0 & . & . \\ 0 & 0 & -1 & 1 & . & . \\ . & . & . & . & . & . \\ . & . & . & . & . & . \end{bmatrix} \begin{bmatrix} f(1) \\ f(2) \\ f(3) \\ . \\ . \end{bmatrix} = \begin{bmatrix} f(2)-f(1) \\ f(3)-f(2) \\ f(4)-f(3) \\ . \\ . \end{bmatrix} = \begin{bmatrix} \Delta f(1) \\ \Delta f(2) \\ \Delta f(3) \\ . \\ . \end{bmatrix} = \Delta \begin{bmatrix} f(1) \\ f(2) \\ f(3) \\ . \\ . \end{bmatrix}.$$

The effect of the matrix on the left is the same as that of the operator Δ of the calculus of finite differences—it is, in fact, the same operator in another notation. The operators ξ and Δ do not commute:

$$\begin{bmatrix} -1 & 1 & 0 & . & . \\ 0 & -1 & 1 & . & . \\ 0 & 0 & -1 & . & . \\ . & . & . & . & . \\ . & . & . & . & . \end{bmatrix} \begin{bmatrix} 1 & 0 & 0 & . & . \\ 0 & 2 & 0 & . & . \\ 0 & 0 & 3 & . & . \\ . & . & . & . & . \\ . & . & . & . & . \end{bmatrix} - \begin{bmatrix} 1 & 0 & 0 & . & . \\ 0 & 2 & 0 & . & . \\ 0 & 0 & 3 & . & . \\ . & . & . & . & . \\ . & . & . & . & . \end{bmatrix} \begin{bmatrix} -1 & 1 & 0 & . & . \\ 0 & -1 & 1 & . & . \\ 0 & 0 & -1 & . & . \\ . & . & . & . & . \\ . & . & . & . & . \end{bmatrix}$$

$$= \begin{bmatrix} 0 & 1 & 0 & 0 & . & . \\ 0 & 0 & 1 & 0 & . & . \\ 0 & 0 & 0 & 1 & . & . \\ . & . & . & . & . & . \end{bmatrix}$$

as may be verified by direct multiplication, or

$$\Delta\xi - \xi\Delta = I + \Delta,$$

which is in conformity with

$$\Delta\{xf(x)\} = (x+1)f(x+1) - xf(x)$$
$$= x\{f(x+1) - f(x)\} + f(x+1)$$
$$= x\Delta f(x) + f(x+1),$$

i.e. $$(\Delta x - x\Delta)f(x) = (1+\Delta)f(x). \tag{12.7.1}$$

Since $$\Delta a^x = a^{x+1} - a^x$$
$$= (a-1)a^x,$$

the eigenvectors of Δ are the functions a^x.

The foregoing theory has little practical importance as it stands but has been presented as an introduction to the extremely important theory obtained by passing from the calculus of finite differences to the differential calculus. To effect this passage we first increase the dimensionality of our space n-fold and specify the values of $f(x)$ at intervals $1/n$ of x. All the above theory can still be applied. But $\Delta f(x)$ is of the order of $1/n$, and it is in $\Delta f(x)/\Delta(x) = n\Delta f(x)$ that we have a quantity which remains finite as n grows larger without limit. $f(x)$ then approaches the continuous function, the operator $n\Delta$ approaches d/dx, and the space is known as Hilbert space. As we have developed it, Hilbert space contains one axis for every positive number, but in various applications other subspaces of the complete Hilbert space may be used—e.g. negative numbers may be included, or only those numbers from 0 to 1. The rigorous definition of Hilbert space also includes the proviso that all vectors are of finite length—a geometrical translation of the requirement that only convergent series or integrals are permitted.

(There is perhaps a conceptual difficulty in providing an axis for every *real* number, as this leads to a non-denumerable infinity of axes. But the conceptual difficulty of providing an axis for every rational number is no greater than that of providing one for each integer, since, as is well known, the rational numbers can all be written down in the single sequence

$$1 \quad \frac{2}{1} \quad \frac{1}{2} \quad \frac{3}{1} \quad \left(\frac{2}{2}\right) \quad \frac{1}{3} \quad \frac{4}{1} \quad \frac{3}{2} \quad \frac{2}{3} \quad \frac{1}{4} \quad \frac{5}{1} \quad \left(\frac{4}{2}\right) \quad \left(\frac{3}{3}\right) \quad \left(\frac{2}{4}\right) \quad \frac{1}{5} \quad \frac{6}{1} \quad \frac{5}{2} \quad \frac{4}{3} \quad \cdots$$

$$1 \quad 2 \quad 3 \quad 4 \qquad 5 \quad 6 \quad 7 \quad 8 \quad 9 \quad 10 \qquad\qquad 11 \quad 12 \quad 13 \quad 14 \quad \cdots$$

and thus form an infinity of the same sort as the integers. For many purposes this is all that is necessary, since the extension to irrational numbers can be made in the same way as in analysis, by using concepts similar to those of Cardan and Dedekind.)

Certain matters can be discussed without presuming any understanding of Hilbert space. For example the relations

$$\frac{d}{dx}\, a f(x) = a\frac{d}{dx}\, f(x),$$

$$\frac{d}{dx}\{f(x)+g(x)\} = \frac{d}{dx} f(x) + \frac{d}{dx} g(x)$$

parallel exactly the last two equations of § 2.2, and justify the inclusion of d/dx among linear operators. The relation

$$\frac{d}{dx}\{x\, f(x)\} = x\frac{d}{dx} f(x) + f(x),$$

or
$$\left(\frac{d}{dx} x - x\frac{d}{dx}\right) f(x) = f(x), \tag{12.7.2}$$

parallels closely equation (12.7.1) and enables us to assert that the operators x and d/dx do not commute. The eigenvectors of d/dx are therefore not the same as those of x.

But to get any farther we must at least appreciate some of the implications of the limiting process by which we passed to Hilbert space. When the function was specified at finite intervals we could write vectors and matrices in terms of their first few components and a series of dots. But now we cannot even state the second component of a vector, any more than we can identify the second point on a line. For if we measure x along a line, there is one component of our vector to each point on this line. So we simply define the vectors $F^\dagger$ and F^* as the function $f(x)$; $^\dagger F$ is also $f(x)$, but $^*F$ is, if $f(x)$ is complex, the conjugate $\bar{f}(x)$. The 'length' of the vector, which was

$$*FF^* = \sum_1^\infty \bar{f}(x)f(x),$$

now becomes

$$*FF^* = \int_{-\infty}^{+\infty} \bar{f}(x)f(x)\,dx.$$

If we are considering that part of F which lies in a subspace, the limits of integration will be different.

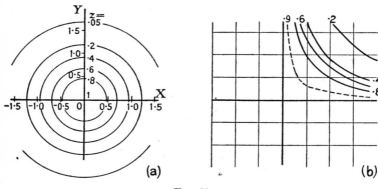

(a)   (b)

FIG. 21.

As a vector becomes a function defined along a line, so a matrix becomes a function of two variables defined on a plane, and the equation

$$Y = AX$$

takes the form

$$g(y) = \int_{-\infty}^{\infty} a(x,y)f(x)\,dx.$$

As an example, to make things more concrete, the matrix A might take either of the forms shown in Fig. 21, in which the X- and Y-axes label the 'columns' and 'rows' respectively and the Z-axis (implied by contours) gives the 'matrix elements',

$$z = a(x,y) = \begin{cases} e^{-(x^2+y^2)} & \text{(Fig. 21}\,a\text{)}, \\ e^{-xy} & \text{(Fig. 21}\,b\text{)}. \end{cases}$$

We will discuss these two cases briefly. A function derived from another in this way is known as an integral transform, and the theory of integral transforms has been developed independently of matrix concepts. By

linking the two theories we can avail ourselves of the discussions of
rigour available in integral transform theory when discussing problems
originally stated in matrix terms.

The first example is a somewhat trivial one. For $e^{-(x^2+y^2)} = e^{-x^2} \cdot e^{-y^2}$.
The consequences of this relation can be stated in two ways. From the
calculus point of view,

$$g(y) = \int_{-\infty}^{\infty} e^{-(x^2+y^2)} f(x) \, dx$$

$$= e^{-y^2} \int_{-\infty}^{\infty} e^{-x^2} f(x) \, dx$$

$$= k e^{-y^2},$$

and the function $g(y)$ is always e^{-y^2}, the influence of $f(x)$ appearing only
in the numerical factor, which, incidentally, will be zero for any odd
function. From the matrix point of view, the relation expresses the
fact that the matrix we are using is a dyad, since it is the product of the
vectors e^{-x^2} and e^{-y^2}; it therefore may be expected to do just what we
have found it to do—'project' all vectors $f(x)$ on to the vector e^{-y^2}.
The theory of integral transforms is really interested only in those
transforms for which the functional form of the 'inverse matrix' is
known, and this transformation will therefore not be found in any work
on the subject!

The second example is possibly the most important, and certainly the
best known of all integral transforms, if the range of integration is from
0 to ∞, namely, the Laplace transformation. Interest in this transformation arose (at any rate as far as physicists are concerned) because of its
use in solving the differential equations in electrical circuit theory by a
method fundamentally equivalent to that of Heaviside. Heaviside
treated d/dt as an algebraic quantity which could be the variable of a
power series expansion, or treated by the method of partial fractions,
but was subject to certain semi-empirical commutation rules. A typical
differential equation is that for a voltage $e(t)$ varying with time, which
is applied to an inductance L in series with a resistance R and a capaci-
tance C. If i is the current flowing, then

$$L\frac{di}{dt} + Ri + \frac{1}{C} \int_{-\infty}^{t} i \, dt = e(t).$$

This equation is solved by multiplying through by e^{-pt} and integrating from 0 to ∞—in other words by applying the operation of the Laplace transformation. If the transform of $i(t)$ is $I(p)$ (as yet unknown), and that of $e(t)$ is $E(p)$, then the whole equation transforms to

$$L\{pI(p) - i_{0+}\} + RI(p) + \frac{1}{pC}\{I(p) + q_0\} = E(p).$$

This is now an *algebraic* equation for $I(p)$, and its solution is

$$I(p) = \frac{E(p) + Li_{0+} - q_0/pC}{R + pL + 1/pC},$$

and by applying the inverse of the Laplace transformation to $I(p)$, the solution of the differential equation is obtained. i_{0+} and q_0 are the initial current in the inductance and the initial charge on the condenser—the $+$ in i_{0+} indicating that if there is a discontinuity at $t = 0$ due, for example, to throwing a switch, it is the limit of $i(t)$ from the positive side that is required; the incorporation of these values at the Laplace transform stage leads to the integration constants in the final results, and moreover, to the physically most convenient form.

In practice the transformations are done by means of tables, or in simple cases by rule of thumb: replace every L in a circuit by pL and every C by $1/pC$, treat these as resistances and the voltages as d.c. voltages, and solve for the current. The resulting expression for $I(p)$ is subjected to any algebraic transformation (e.g. partial fractions) which will convert it into a form to which the inverse transformation can be read directly from the tables.

We shall return to the Laplace transform to tie up some of the loose ends in the next section. Meanwhile the matrix forms of the identity and of d/dx call for investigation. Calling them $I(x, y)$ and $D(x, y)$ we require that

$$\int_{-\infty}^{+\infty} I(x, y)f(x)\, dx = f(y) \quad \text{all } f,$$

$$\int_{-\infty}^{+\infty} D(x, y)f(x)\, dx = f'(y) \quad \text{all } f.$$

Alternatively, we can try to picture them as limiting cases of the I and Δ matrices of the calculus of finite differences. As n becomes infinite, the operator $n\Delta$ is zero everywhere except at $x = y$, where 'at two successive points' it is $+\infty$ and $-\infty$, a picturable but not very rigorous conclusion concerning $D(x, y)$! In considering $I(x, y)$, the student should bear in mind that the limiting process by which a sum becomes an integral can be written

$$\sum f(x) \rightarrow \sum f(x)\,\delta x \rightarrow \int f(x)\,dx,$$

and he will find that a function such that $f(x, y)\,\delta x = \delta_y^x$ (equals 1 or 0 as x is or is not equal to y) is required at stage II, and that in proceeding to the limit $f(x, y)$ becomes infinite as $\delta x \rightarrow 0$. Dirac calls the resulting

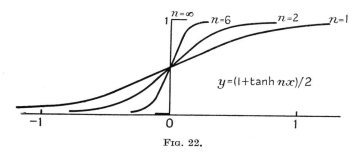

FIG. 22.

function $\delta(x-y)$, defining it as equal to zero for $x-y \neq 0$ and having at $x-y = 0$ an infinity of such a type that its integral over any range including 0 is unity, and he points out that since it differs in certain respects from the ordinary functions of analysis it is best called an 'improper function', but that its deficiencies need not worry us so long as it is only used in, and its properties deduced from, integral transform equations.

We may approach it in a slightly more rigorous way via the 'step function' (or 'Heaviside unit function'),

$$s(x) = \begin{cases} 0 & x < 0 \\ 1 & x > 0. \end{cases}$$

This function may be regarded as the limit of any function asymptotically zero at $x \rightarrow -\infty$ and unity at $x \rightarrow +\infty$, as the central portion of the scale is contracted without limit (see Fig. 22). For example,

$$\lim_{n \rightarrow \infty} \tfrac{1}{2}(1+\tanh nx) = s(x).$$

Then Dirac's δ-function as defined above is the derivative of this function.

The function $D(x, y)$ then turns out to be the derivative of the δ-function, or the second derivative of the step-function. For, if we take the risk of applying ordinary manipulative processes such as integrating by parts,

$$\int_{-\infty}^{+\infty} \delta'(x-y)f(x)\,dx = \int_{-\infty}^{+\infty} f(x)\,d\delta(x-y)$$

$$= [f(x)\,\delta(x-y)]_{-\infty}^{+\infty} + \int_{-\infty}^{+\infty} \delta(x-y)\,df(x)$$

$$= 0 + \int_{-\infty}^{+\infty} f'(x)\,\delta(x-y)\,dx$$

$$= f'(y).$$

12.8. Eigenvector theory in Hilbert space

A vector in Hilbert space being a function, eigenvectors are eigen-functions. But the fact that the space is infinity-dimensional gives rise to many difficulties, and the subject relies more and more heavily on analysis as we go deeper into it. Serious difficulties in the way of a naïve extension of n-dimensional theory (n finite) arise at the start from the familiar fact that 'a part' of an infinite number 'may be equal to the whole' as we see, for example, in the two layouts

1	2	3	4	5	6	7	8 ...		1	2	3	4	5	6	7	8 ...
	2		4		6		8 ...			2	4	6	8	10	12	14	16 ...

the first of which shows that the set of even numbers is half the set of all positive integers whereas the second shows that no matter how many positive integers we may collect, we can always find an equal number of even ones. The trouble arises in two ways. First, Theorems 2.7.3 and 5.3.1, telling us how many eigenvectors and how many representations to expect, let us down in dealing with infinite matrices and infinite groups respectively. In both cases we need some test of the *completeness* of the set we may have found. In the former case this test will probably take the form of a demonstration that an arbitrary vector can be expressed as the limit of a series whose terms are the eigenvectors we have found (with suitable numerical coefficients); in the latter some form of the orthogonality relations may meet our requirements (though (12.2.1) is disappointing as an example in this respect). Secondly, it is quite possible for what would seem to be a rectangular matrix to have an inverse. We have an example of this in the Laplace transformation.

Writing the Laplace transform in its conventional form,

$$F(p) = \int_0^\infty e^{-px} f(x)\, dx, \qquad\qquad (12.8.1)$$

the inverse is
$$f(x) = \frac{1}{2\pi i} \int_{\gamma-i\infty}^{\gamma+i\infty} e^{px} F(p)\, dp, \qquad\qquad (12.8.2)$$

where γ can often be zero, but may be any real number greater than the largest zero of $F(p)$. Thus we 'sum' from 0 to ∞ in one transformation and from $-\infty$ to $+\infty$ in the inverse. But this is obviously the wrong way to look at it. The question is not one of 'reducing the number of dimensions' but of whether functions which are linearly independent over the second range are still linearly independent over the first one. If they are, the range is to some extent at our disposal, so that other considerations can be brought in to determine our choice. In many cases a suitable choice of range enables us to gain the advantage of a property analogous to Theorem 3.6.1, which we must next discuss.

Before doing so, however, let us admit that the previous paragraph is likely to make any genuine pure mathematician extremely uncomfortable. But this book is not written for pure mathematicians, and the purpose of the previous paragraph is to convey to the reader whose outlook is primarily physical the essential unity of two lines of approach to the same problem which, without some such discussion, can appear entirely unrelated, or, if related, full of apparent inconsistencies. It *is* possible to carry the argument through completely from the vector-space point of view—the standard work for this is Stone, *Linear Transformations in Hilbert Space*—but in this treatment rigour demands the introduction of many concepts with which the reader is probably unfamiliar, and the necessary rigour can be obtained through more familiar concepts if the approach through differential equations is adopted.

We therefore discuss briefly the operator

$$L = q(x) - \frac{d^2}{dx^2}$$

which includes most of the important physical cases. If $\psi_n(x)$ is an eigenvector of this operator with eigenvalue λ_n, then

$$L\psi_n(x) = \lambda_n \psi_n(x),$$

or
$$\psi_n''(x) + \{\lambda_n - q(x)\}\psi_n(x) = 0. \qquad\qquad (12.8.3)$$

Multiplying by $\psi_m(x)$, forming the corresponding equation with m and n interchanged, and subtracting, we have

$$(\lambda_m - \lambda_n)\psi_m(x)\psi_n(x) = \psi_m(x)\psi_n''(x) - \psi_n(x)\psi_m''(x)$$

$$= \frac{d}{dx}\{\psi_m(x)\psi_n'(x) - \psi_n(x)\psi_m'(x)\}.$$

Integrating,

$$(\lambda_m - \lambda_n)\int_a^b \psi_m(x)\psi_n(x)\,dx = [\psi_m(x)\psi_n'(x) - \psi_n(x)\psi_m'(x)]_a^b. \quad (12.8.4)$$

Suppose b and a are chosen so that the right-hand side of this equation is zero—if, for example, both $\psi_m(x)$ and $\psi_n(x)$ are zero at both $x = a$ and $x = b$—then, if $\lambda_m \neq \lambda_n$, the integral on the left-hand side must be zero. As we are at the moment considering real functions, this integral is the 'scalar product', $*\psi_m\psi_n*$, of the two eigenfunctions $\psi_m(x)$ and $\psi_n(x)$ within the Hilbert space defined by the range a to b.

It can be shown that if $q(x)$ is real and continuous over the range from a to b then a solution of the equation (12.8.3) can be obtained in this range with any given values of $\psi(a)$ and $\psi'(a)$. (We may remind the student that $\psi_m(x)$ and $k\psi_m(x)$ are effectively the same solution; it is sometimes convenient to 'normalize' so that we can put $\psi(a) = \sin\alpha$, $\psi'(a) = -\cos\alpha$. The method of proof given by Titchmarsh is interesting on account of an analogy with the method of § 7.5. He puts

$$y_0(x) = \psi(a) + \psi'(a)(x - a),$$

$$y_n(x) = y_0(x) + \int_a^x \{q(t) - \lambda\}y_{n-1}(t)(x - t)\,dt,$$

and shows that, as $n \to \infty$, $y_n(x)$ approaches such a solution, since (i) it approaches

$$\phi(x) = y_0(x) + \sum_{n=1}^{\infty}\{y_n(x) - y_{n-1}(x)\},$$

and the terms in the sum on the right-hand side of this expression are each less than the corresponding term in a certain convergent power series in $x - a$ (whence the process converges), and (ii) by direct substitution $\phi(x)$ satisfies the original equation). If a second solution is similarly defined working backward from a given $\psi(b)$ and $\psi'(b)$ $(= \sin\beta$ and $-\cos\beta)$, the expression

$$\psi_1(x)\psi_2'(x) - \psi_1'(x)\psi_2(x)$$

can be shown (by differentiation and use of 12.8.3) to be independent of x, α, and β. But this expression is the Wronskian of these two functions, its vanishing being the condition that $\psi_1(x)$ is a constant multiple of $\psi_2(x)$; it is, by its method of formation, an integral function of λ, and therefore our chances of making the right-hand side of (12.8.4) zero are small except when λ takes those values which are zeros of the Wronskian. These values of λ are the eigenvalues of the operator L and the corresponding functions are the eigenfunctions (or eigenvectors).

Details of the above argument will be found in Titchmarsh, *Eigenfunction Expansions*, chap. I, together with a proof that the functions so found constitute a basis for the expansion of an arbitrary function within the interval a to b, and in later chapters of the same reference will be found discussions of the more difficult cases when a or b tend to infinity, or $q(x)$ is not as well behaved as we have assumed it to be. From this point we could also go on to equations in several variables, or to particular cases. We consider the former from another point of view in the next section. The latter are so adequately dealt with in existing works on Wave Mechanics that it is unnecessary to repeat their treatment in detail; it will suffice to enumerate the most important cases. An important feature of any particular problem is the 'nature of the spectrum', that is, whether the eigenvalues form a set of discrete points, or whether all values of λ within certain ranges may be eigenvalues.

The simplest case is $q(x) = 0$, and $(a, b) = (0, \pi)$. In this case the eigenvalues are the squares of the integers, $\lambda_n = n^2$, and the eigenfunctions are the functions $\psi_n(x) = \sin nx$. The expansion of an arbitrary function in terms of these eigenfunctions then becomes the Fourier sine series. This series has here a totally different significance, of course, from that which it had in § 12.2.

The case $q(x) = \alpha^2 x^2$ arises in the wave-mechanical treatment of the simple harmonic oscillator. The eigenvalues are given by $\lambda_n = (2n+1)\alpha$; the eigenfunctions are usually expressed in the form

$$\psi_n(x) = e^{-\alpha x^2/2} H_n(\alpha^{\frac{1}{2}} x), \qquad (12.8.5)$$

where the H_n are polynomials of degree n known as Hermite polynomials:

$$H_0(z) = 1, \qquad\qquad H_3(z) = 8z^3 - 12z,$$
$$H_1(z) = 2z, \qquad\qquad H_4(z) = 16z^4 - 48z^2 + 12,$$
$$H_2(z) = 4z^2 - 2, \qquad\qquad H_5(z) = 32z^5 - 160z^3 + 120z;$$

they are the coefficients of $s^n/n!$ in the generating function

$$S(z, s) = e^{z^2 - (s-z)^2},$$

or may be obtained from the recursion formula

$$H_{n+1}(z) = 2zH_n(z) - 2nH_{n-1}(z). \tag{12.8.6}$$

They also satisfy the differential equation

$$H_n''(z) - 2zH_n'(z) + 2nH_n(z) = 0. \tag{12.8.7}$$

This last equation suggests the study of the operator

$$L' = q(x) - p(x)\frac{d}{dx} - \frac{d^2}{dx^2}$$

which as an eigenvalue problem gives rise to the differential equation

$$\psi''(x) + p(x)\psi'(x) + \{\lambda - q(x)\}\psi(x) = 0.$$

But this equation can be reduced to the form we have been considering by the substitution $\psi(x) = e^{-\frac{1}{2}\int p(x)\,dx}\phi(x)$. It is then the functions $\phi(x)$ which have the orthogonality properties discussed earlier. There is, however, one special case which is worth extra notice. In §§ 14.2 and 14.4 we shall show that when coordinates are used which are not ortho-normal, $d^2\psi/dx^2$ becomes something which often reduces to the form

$$\frac{1}{f(x)}\frac{d}{dx}f(x)\frac{d}{dx}.$$

We thus obtain the operator

$$L'' = q(x) - \frac{1}{f(x)}\frac{d}{dx}f(x)\frac{d}{dx}$$

which on expansion proves to be of the form we are discussing, with $p(x) = f'(x)/f(x)$. The eigenfunctions of this operator being $\psi_n(x)$, the functions $\phi_n(x) = e^{\frac{1}{2}\int p(x)dx}\psi_n(x) = f(x)^{\frac{1}{2}}\psi_n(x)$ are orthogonal when integrated over x between the appropriate limits—i.e.

$$\int_a^b \psi_m(x)\psi_n(x)f(x)\,dx = 0.$$

The point to which we wish to draw attention here is that $f(x)\,dx$ is the volume element (§§ 14.2 and 14.4, or compare the last paragraph of § 12.6), and that therefore although it is the $\phi(x)$ which are orthogonal over the coordinate x, it is the $\psi(x)$ which are orthogonal over the space described by the coordinate.

Equations of this type occur in the centrally symmetric field problem of wave mechanics, which includes the hydrogen atom as a special case.

This is discussed in more detail in § 16.7, to which we refer the reader for the remaining differential operators which might have been discussed here.

We have already referred to the theorem which is the analogue of the corollary of Theorem 2.7.3 that an arbitrary vector can in general be expressed in terms of the eigenvectors of an arbitrary operator as basic vectors. This corollary follows at once from Theorem 2.7.3 if the dimensionality of the space is finite, § 4.6 providing the procedure for its practical accomplishment once the eigenvectors are known. In Hilbert space the proof is not so immediate because one cannot equate the number of dimensions and the number of eigenfunctions, but nevertheless it remains true and proven in many cases that a function which satisfies those conditions of continuity and convergency which are required to bring it within Hilbert space at all, can be expanded in terms of the eigenvectors of a given operator. Moreover, the eigenfunctions form a denumerable infinity, and thus the expansion can be expressed as a single sum or integral (or both—according as the spectrum is discrete or continuous—the point here is that the expansion will not require irreducible double infinite sums $\sum\limits_{p=1}^{\infty} \sum\limits_{q=1}^{\infty}$ or double integrals $\int\int ... \, dydx$).

We may illustrate from elementary theory by considering that a function $f(x)$ which satisfies the necessary conditions of continuity and single-valuedness may be expanded in the range $x = 0...1$ in either a power series or a Fourier series:

$$f(x) = a_0 + a_1 x + a_2 x^2 + ...$$
$$= b_0 + b_1 \cos 2\pi x + c_1 \sin 2\pi x + b_2 \cos 4\pi x + ...$$

These two expansions may be regarded as the expression of the function $f(x)$ in vector forms $(a_0, a_1, ...)$ and $(b_0, b_1, c_1, b_2, ...)$, the basic vectors in one case being the eigenvectors of the operator $x \, d/dx$ and in the other those of the operator d^2/dx^2. These two representations can be interconverted by a procedure analogous to that of (4.6.3). For

$$a_k = \left[\frac{1}{k!} \frac{d^k}{dx^k} f(x) \right]_{x=0}$$

$$= \text{real part of } \frac{1}{k!} \sum_{m} (im)^k (b_m - ic_m),$$

from which the components of the transformation matrix can be picked out. Those of the inverse matrix can similarly be picked out from

$$\left.\begin{matrix} b_k \\ c_k \end{matrix}\right\} = \int_0^1 \frac{\cos}{\sin} 2\pi kx \cdot (a_0 + a_1 x + a_2 x^2 + \dots)\, dx$$

if the integration is performed term by term.

It will be noted that the functions

$$y = x^k, \qquad y = \frac{\cos}{\sin} 2\pi kx$$

are solutions of the differential equations

$$x\frac{dy}{dx} = ky, \qquad \frac{d^2y}{dx^2} = -4\pi^2 k^2 y,$$

whether or not k is integral, yet in each case only integral values of k are required in making up the series. This illustrates the necessity of bearing in mind that when the eigenvalue problem leads to a differential equation, a formal solution of the equation is insufficient; the solutions must be discussed in relation to what in analysis is referred to as boundary conditions, or in Hilbert space theory as the domain of the transformation—that is, that subspace of a general Hilbert space in which the solutions found are actually orthogonal.

12.9. Functions of two or more variables

Any function $F(x, y)$ of two variables can be considered as a function of one of the variables by keeping the other constant. So the functions $F(x, k)$ and $F(k, y)$ can be regarded as vectors in two distinct Hilbert spaces. In these spaces the 'axes' are labelled by values of x and y respectively. To represent a function $F(x, y)$ we need a space in which each 'axis' is labelled by a pair of numbers, one the value of x and one the value of y. Such a space is the Kronecker product space of the two Hilbert spaces.

In some cases the process is fairly obvious, though it is more obvious in cases which are difficult to make rigorous, as usual! For example, if the functions x^0, x, x^2,... are chosen as axes in one space for functions of x (the coordinates of the vector being Taylor series coefficients), and the functions y^0, y, y^2,... in another for functions of y, then the Taylor series expansion of a function of both variables indicates the use of $x^0 y^0$, x, y, x^2, xy, y^2,... as basic vectors, and these are just the axes required for the Kronecker product space. More generally it would seem that if

$$f_1(x), f_2(x), \dots \quad \text{and} \quad g_1(y), g_2(y), \dots$$

are complete sets of eigenfunctions of operators F and G, then the set of functions $f_i(x)g_j(y)$ should be a complete basis for functions $\phi(x, y)$. But that this argument is not rigorous when the sets are infinite is shown by the theory of spherical harmonics, where a smaller set of functions, viz. those with $i \leqslant j$, proves to be a complete basis (cf. § 16.7). The physicist and chemist must trust to luck in such matters or else hand the problem over to the mathematician.

An important case of a different type which arises in later work is that in which x is a continuous variable but y can have only the values ± 1. Replacing y by η to mark this changed concept, we note first that $f(x, \eta)$ may be replaced, in our tool-box, by the two functions $f_+(x) = f(x, 1)$ and $f_-(x) = f(x, -1)$. It now follows that

$$f(x, \eta) = \tfrac{1}{2}\{f_+(x)+f_-(x)\}+\tfrac{1}{2}\eta\{f_+(x)-f_-(x)\}. \tag{12.9.1}$$

(It hardly needs saying that if η could have only n distinct values, a corresponding equation containing terms up to the power η^{n-1} would be obtained.) The right-hand side of (12.9.1) can be interpreted as the expression of $f(x, \eta)$ as a two-dimensional vector with components which are functions of x; in this space, η is represented by the matrix

$$Y = \begin{bmatrix} 0 & 1 \\ 1 & 0 \end{bmatrix}$$

since $\qquad Y f(x, \eta) = \begin{bmatrix} 0 & 1 \\ 1 & 0 \end{bmatrix}\begin{bmatrix} f_+(x)+f_-(x) \\ f_+(x)-f_-(x) \end{bmatrix} = \begin{bmatrix} f_+(x)-f_-(x) \\ f_+(x)+f_-(x) \end{bmatrix}$

$$= \tfrac{1}{2}\{f_+(x)-f_-(x)\}+\tfrac{1}{2}\eta\{f_+(x)+f_-(x)\} = \eta f(x, \eta)$$

since $\eta^2 = 1$.

The eigenvalues of $\begin{bmatrix} 0 & 1 \\ 1 & 0 \end{bmatrix}$ are ± 1 (the only permissible values of η) and the eigenvectors are $\begin{bmatrix} 1 \\ 1 \end{bmatrix}$ and $\begin{bmatrix} 1 \\ -1 \end{bmatrix}$, i.e. $\begin{bmatrix} g(x) \\ g(x) \end{bmatrix}$ and $\begin{bmatrix} g(x) \\ -g(x) \end{bmatrix}$. Thus any function for which $f_-(x) = f_+(x)$ is an eigenfunction of η with eigenvalue $+1$, and any function with $f_+(x) = -f_-(x)$ is an eigenfunction of η with eigenvalue -1. In the former case $\tfrac{1}{2}\{f_+(x)-f_-(x)\} = 0$ and $\tfrac{1}{2}\{f_+(x)+f_-(x)\} = f_+(x)$, whence $f(x, \eta) = f_+(x)$. In the latter case $\tfrac{1}{2}\{f_+(x)+f_-(x)\} = 0$ and $\tfrac{1}{2}\{f_+(x)-f_-(x)\} = f_+(x)$, whence

$$f(x, \eta) = \eta f_+(x).$$

Summarizing,

THEOREM 12.9.2. *Functions of the forms*

$$f(x, \eta) = g(x) \quad and \quad f(x, \eta) = \eta g(x)$$

are eigenfunctions of η belonging respectively to the eigenvalues $+1$ and -1.

The operator $\begin{bmatrix} 1 & 0 \\ 0 & -1 \end{bmatrix}$ has the interesting effect of converting $f(x, \eta)$ into $f(x, -\eta)$, that is, of interchanging $f_+(x)$ and $f_-(x)$. For

$$\begin{bmatrix} 1 & 0 \\ 0 & -1 \end{bmatrix}\begin{bmatrix} f_+(x)+f_-(x) \\ f_+(x)-f_-(x) \end{bmatrix} = \begin{bmatrix} f_+(x)+f_-(x) \\ -f_+(x)+f_-(x) \end{bmatrix}$$

$$= \tfrac{1}{2}\{f_+(x)+f_-(x)\}-\tfrac{1}{2}\eta\{f_+(x)-f_-(x)\}$$

$$= \begin{cases} f_-(x) & \text{if } \eta = +1 \\ f_+(x) & \text{if } \eta = -1. \end{cases}$$

In Chapter XVIII we shall find particles associated with such functions, and as this operator exchanges the functions in this way it may be called the interchange operator.

These results have been established with $f_+(x) \pm f_-(x)$ as basic vectors. If $f_+(x)$ and $f_-(x)$ are used as basic vectors the roles of the operators $\begin{bmatrix} 0 & 1 \\ 1 & 0 \end{bmatrix}$ and $\begin{bmatrix} 1 & 0 \\ 0 & -1 \end{bmatrix}$ are interchanged.

CHAPTER XIII

THE SYMMETRIC AND FULL LINEAR GROUPS

ANYTHING like a developed theory of the symmetric groups was omitted from Chapter VI because it is too intimately related to that of the full linear groups. It is also a much more difficult theory than that of the simpler groups. The present chapter contains a review of this theory, but for fuller details of some of the proofs, and for discussion of certain questions of rigour, the reader is referred to the standard works by Murnaghan and Littlewood.

The full linear group in n dimensions, $\mathfrak{f}_n$, is the group of all non-singular $n \times n$ matrices. Each element in such a group is defined by the n^2 components of the matrix. Since the matrix can be transformed to diagonal form by an element of the group, all matrices with the same eigenvalues are transformable into one another and belong to the same class. Any set of n complex numbers $z_1, ..., z_n$ therefore defines a class of the group $\mathfrak{f}_n$. The order of these numbers is immaterial, since they can be permuted by a matrix belonging to $\mathfrak{f}_n$. It is not surprising, therefore, that *class* functions in $\mathfrak{f}_n$, including the characters, are certain *symmetric* functions of the eigenvalues $z_1, ..., z_n$, that is, functions which are invariant if a permutation belonging to π_n is applied to the suffixes $1, ..., n$. The connexion between the two types of group is thus clear. What is not so obvious, however, is that the characters of the symmetric groups are most easily obtained as coefficients in certain expansions of symmetrical functions.

13.2. The simple symmetric functions

Three types of symmetric function of the m variables $z_1, ..., z_m$ first claim our attention. Each type can be constructed of any integral degree r in the z_i. They are (i) s_r, the sum of the rth powers of the z_i, (ii) a_r, the sum of the ^mC_r products of r of the z_i chosen without repetition from the m, and (iii) h_r the sum of the products of r of the z_i chosen without restriction on repetition, of which we shall show that there are $^{m+r-1}C_r$. Unless m is greater than r, there are no products without repetition, and a_r is then zero. We may set out the simpler results as follows:

r	m	s_r	a_r	h_r
1	2	z_1+z_2	z_1+z_2	z_1+z_2
1	3	$z_1+z_2+z_3$	$z_1+z_2+z_3$	$z_1+z_2+z_3$
2	2	$z_1^2+z_2^2$	$z_1 z_2$	$z_1^2+z_1 z_2+z_2^2$
2	3	$z_1^2+z_2^2+z_3^2$	$z_1 z_2+z_2 z_3+z_3 z_1$	$= s_2+a_2$
3	3	$z_1^3+z_2^3+z_3^3$	$z_1 z_2 z_3$	$z_1^3+z_2^3+z_3^3+z_1^2 z_2+z_2^2 z_3+$
				$+z_3^2 z_1+z_1 z_2^2+z_2 z_3^2+$
				$+z_3 z_1^2+z_1 z_2 z_3$
3	4	$z_1^3+z_2^3+z_3^3+z_4^3$	$z_1 z_2 z_3+z_1 z_2 z_4+$	$= s_3+a_3+12$ terms of the
			$+z_1 z_3 z_4+$	form $z_i^2 z_j$
			$+z_2 z_3 z_4$	

The general form of h_r is the sum of the following terms:

$$m \text{ terms } z_i^r$$

$$m(m-1) \quad \text{,,} \quad z_i^{r-1}z_j \text{ and } m(m-1) \text{ of each } z_i^{r-k}z_j^k$$
$$(r-k > k)$$

possibly $\quad \tfrac{1}{2}m(m-1) \quad \text{,,} \quad z_i^{r/2}z_j^{r/2}$

$$m(m-1)(m-2) \quad \text{,,} \quad z_i^{r-3}z_j^2 z_k \text{ and of each type } z_i^{r-a-b}z_j^a z_k^b$$
$$(\text{with } (r-a-b) > a > b)$$

$$\tfrac{1}{2}m(m-1)(m-2) \quad \text{,,} \quad z_i^{r-2a}z_j^a z_k^a \quad (\text{with } (r-2a) > a)$$

possibly $\tfrac{1}{6}m(m-1)(m-2) \quad \text{,,} \quad z_i^{r/3}z_j^{r/3}z_k^{r/3}$, etc.,

and in general,

$$Q = \frac{m!}{(m-s)!\,\rho_1!\,\rho_2!\ldots\rho_s!} \quad \text{of type} \quad z_1^{r_1}\ldots z_{\rho_1}^{r_1} z_{\rho_1+1}^{r_2}\ldots z_{\rho_1+\rho_2}^{r_2}\ldots z_r^{r_s}.$$

These terms represent the results of the operation of the $m!$ elements of π_m on the subscripts $1,\ldots,r$, each result being repeated $(m-s)!\,\rho_1!\,\rho_2!\ldots\rho_s!$ times. The total number of these terms is $\sum Q$, the sum being over all partitions $(r_1^{\rho_1} r_2^{\rho_2}\ldots r_s^{\rho_s})$ of r.

We can obtain a simpler expression for the number of terms in h_r, however, by considering the expansion of $(z_1+z_2+\ldots+z_r)^r$. Every term in it is of the rth degree, and every possible term in h_r occurs in it, often repeatedly—i.e. with a numerical coefficient. More precisely, the term $z_1^{r_1}z_2^{r_2}\ldots$ occurs $r!/r_1!\,r_2!\ldots$ times—i.e. with this coefficient. Let the number of terms in this expansion be $N(r,m)$, and denote $z_1+\ldots+z_{m-1}$ by Z. Then

$$(Z+z_m)^r = Z^r+rZ^{r-1}z_m+\ldots+z_m^r.$$

The first term of this is $(z_1+\ldots+z_{m-1})^r$, and the remaining terms are those of $(Z+z_m)^{r-1}$ multiplied by z_m and with different numerical

coefficients. Hence, counting terms,
$$N(r,m) = N(r,m-1)+N(r-1,m).$$
By breaking down the terms on the right-hand side by a repetition of this process, we obtain successively
$$N(r,m) = N(r,m-2)+2N(r-1,m-1)+N(r-2,m)$$
$$= N(r,m-3)+3N(r-1,m-2)+3N(r-2,m-1)+N(r-3,m)$$
$$\cdot \quad \cdot \quad \cdot \quad \cdot \quad \cdot \quad \cdot \quad \cdot$$
$$= N(r,m-s)+...+{}^sC_t N(r-t,m-s+t)+...+N(r-s,m).$$
But $N(p,1) = 1$ and $N(1,q) = q$, whence $N(0,q) = 1$ and
$$N(p,0) = N(p,-q) = N(-p,q) = 0,$$
so that after a certain stage terms begin to drop out of this expansion. It is easily verified that when $s = m+r-1$, and the general term is ${}^{m+r-1}C_t N(r-t,t-r+1)$, all terms have dropped out except that for which $t = r$, and we are left with
$$N(r,m) = {}^{m+r-1}C_r. \tag{13.2.1}$$

13.3. Relations between the symmetric functions

We next require certain relations between the symmetric functions which can be obtained by comparing coefficients in certain expansions. Thus, if
$$f(t) = (1-z_1 t)(1-z_2 t)...(1-z_m t)$$
$$= 1-a_1 t+a_2 t^2-a_3 t^3+..., \tag{13.3.1}$$
then
$$1/f(t) = (1+z_1 t+z_1^2 t^2+...)(1+z_2 t+z_2^2 t^2+...)...(1+z_m t+z_m^2 t^2+...)$$
$$= 1+h_1 t+h_2 t^2+.... \tag{13.3.2}$$
By multiplying the right-hand sides together, equating to 1, and therefore setting every coefficient of t^r equal to zero, we have
$$a_r-a_{r-1}h_1+a_{r-2}h_2-...+(-1)^r h_r = 0. \tag{13.3.3}$$
Further,
$$\log f(t) = \sum_p \log(1-z_p t) = -\sum_{\beta=1}^{\infty}\sum_p \frac{z_p^\beta t^\beta}{\beta} = -\sum_{\beta=1}^{\infty}\frac{s_\beta t^\beta}{\beta},$$
whence
$$1/f(t) = \prod \exp(s_\beta t^\beta/\beta) = \left(1+s_1 t+\frac{s_1^2 t^2}{2!}+...\right)\left(1+\frac{s_2 t^2}{2}+\frac{s_2^2 t^4}{2^2\, 2!}+...\right)...$$
$$= \sum_{r=0}^{\infty}\left\{\sum_{\substack{\text{all par-}\\\text{titions}\\(\rho)\text{ of } r}}\frac{1}{\rho_1!\,\rho_2!...}\left(\frac{s_1}{1}\right)^{\rho_1}\left(\frac{s_2}{2}\right)^{\rho_2}...\right\}t^r. \tag{13.3.4}$$

(Note that we have made a slight change in the notation of the partitions by putting $r_k = k$.) Comparing (13.3.2) and (13.3.4), h_r is equal to the expression in curly brackets in (13.3.4). Since each partition of r represents a class of π_r, and using the expression (6.7.1) for the number of elements in each class, we see that we can write this conclusion in the form

$$h_r = \frac{1}{r!} \sum_{\substack{\text{all elements} \\ \text{of } \pi_r}} s_1^{\rho_1} s_2^{\rho_2} \dots . \tag{13.3.5}$$

(Note that the summation is over π_r, not π_m.) By a similar expansion of $f(t)$, we obtain the relation

$$a_r = \frac{1}{r!} \sum_{\substack{\text{all elements} \\ \text{of } \pi_r}} s_1^{\rho_1} (-s_2)^{\rho_2} s_3^{\rho_3} (-s_4)^{\rho_4} \dots . \tag{13.3.6}$$

We may notice at once—it will acquire greater significance later—that the negative terms in (13.3.6) are those corresponding to odd permutations in π_r.

Other relations may be obtained by differentiating (13.3.1) and (13.3.2). In particular,

$$\frac{d}{dt} \frac{1}{f(t)} = \frac{1}{f(t)} \sum_p \frac{z_p}{1 - z_p t} = \frac{1}{f(t)} \sum_r s_r t^{r-1}$$

—the latter expression by expanding and rearranging the former. Inserting the h-series for $1/f(t)$ and comparing coefficients with those obtained by differentiating the h-series directly, gives us

$$r h_r = s_1 h_{r-1} + s_2 h_{r-2} + \dots + s_r \quad \text{(each } r\text{)}.$$

Putting $r = 1, \dots, k$ and eliminating $h_1, \dots, h_{k-1}$,

$$h_k = \frac{1}{k!} \begin{vmatrix} s_1 & -1 & 0 & 0 & . & . & . & 0 \\ s_2 & s_1 & -2 & 0 & . & . & . & 0 \\ s_3 & s_2 & s_1 & -3 & . & . & . & 0 \\ . & . & . & . & . & . & . & . \\ s_k & s_{k-1} & s_{k-2} & s_{k-3} & . & . & . & s_1 \end{vmatrix} . \tag{13.3.7}$$

A similar treatment of $f(t)$ and the associated series in the a_r leads to equations similar to the above but with alternating signs, and a determinant for a_r similar to that for h_r but with all its super-diagonal terms positive.

Perhaps the most important theorem on symmetric functions is that all symmetric functions can be expressed in terms of the a_r and thence in terms of the s_r. To prove this we first of all arrange all the partitions of r in 'dictionary order', that is, with the elements of each partition in descending order: we arrange the partitions in the order of the first part, or, if these be equal, in the order of the second part, and so on. Thus the partitions of 6 in dictionary order are (6), $(5, 1)$, $(4, 2)$, $(4, 1, 1)$, $(3, 3)$, $(3, 2, 1)$, $(3, 1^3)$, $(2, 2, 2)$, $(2, 2, 1, 1)$, $(2, 1^4)$, and (1^6). Now a symmetric function which contains $z_1^{r_1} z_2^{r_2}...$ must contain all possible terms $z_a^{r_1} z_b^{r_2}...$ with the same coefficient. Let us call the partition $(r_1, r_2, ...)$, (ρ), and denote the sum of all monomials of this type by $z^{(\rho)}$. Now

$$a_1^{r_1-r_2} a_2^{r_2-r_3}... = \left(\sum z_1 \right)^{r_1-r_2} \left(\sum z_1 z_2 \right)^{r_2-r_3}...$$
$$= \sum z_1^{r_1} z_2^{r_2}... + \sum z_1^{r_1-1}... + ...,$$

the first term on the right-hand side being $z^{(\rho)}$, and all the succeeding terms being associated with partitions later in dictionary order than (ρ). Thus we can remove the terms of a symmetric polynomial successively by subtraction of polynomials of the form $a_1^{\rho_1} a_2^{\rho_2}...$, and provided we remove them in dictionary order we shall never in removing one term replace one that we have already removed. Ultimately nothing will be left, and we can equate the original polynomial with the total function of the a_r that we have subtracted.

13.4. The Kronecker mth power

From the concept of a Kronecker product it is an obvious step to that of the Kronecker mth power of a matrix. The student should write out the Kronecker square and cube of the matrix $\begin{bmatrix} a & b \\ c & d \end{bmatrix}$ and satisfy himself that the Kronecker mth power of the $n \times n$ matrix A has terms of the type $a_{ij...,pq...} = a_{ip} a_{jq}...$, where $i, j, ..., p, q, ...$ run from 1 to n and are $2m$ in number. The Kronecker mth power of A we denote by $(A)_m$; it operates in a carrier space of n^m dimensions, and it has n^{2m} components. In this section and the next we propose to show that from the Kronecker mth powers of the matrices in $\mathfrak{f}_n$ we may obtain information concerning the group $\boldsymbol{\pi}_m$ and all the irreducible representations of $\mathfrak{f}_n$ which are (algebraically) of degree m in the a_{ij}.

We can apply the permutations P of $\boldsymbol{\pi}_m$ to the suffixes $i, j, ...$ or to the suffixes $p, q, ...$ of $(A)_m$, or to both. Application of P to both sets leaves $(A)_m$ unchanged, since it merely permutes the order of the factors $a_{ip}, a_{jq}, ...$ of $a_{ij...,pq,...}$. On the other hand, application of P to $i, j, ...$ only, results in a new matrix, which we shall call $P(A)_m$. The same matrix is produced by the application of P^{-1} to $p, q, ...$.

Let the eigenvalues of A be $z_1, z_2, \ldots$. Then the trace of A is s_1. The trace of $(A)_m$ is easily seen to be $(s_1)^m$. By slightly more elaborate manipulation we can show that the trace of $P(A)_m$ is given by

$$\operatorname{tr} P(A)_m = s_{(\mu)} = s_1^{m_1} s_2^{m_2} \ldots, \qquad (13.4.1)$$

where the partition $(\mu) = (1^{m_1} 2^{m_2} \ldots)$ defines the class to which P belongs. We now consider two important theorems. The first is that

$$(B)_m (A)_m = (BA)_m. \qquad (13.4.2)$$

This has already been proved in § 5.6 for the case $m = 2$ and the proof given there is easily extended. The second is that

$$Q(B)_m P(A)_m = QP(BA)_m. \qquad (13.4.3)$$

This is easily verified in a few simple cases, and the general proof amounts to little more than a lengthy verbal summary of the verification process. Two important corollaries follow from the second of these theorems. The first of these is that

$$Q(I)_m P(I)_m = QP(I)_m, \qquad (13.4.4)$$

which amounts, in words, to a statement that the matrices $P(I)_m$ form a representation of the group $\boldsymbol{\pi}_m$. This is important enough to illustrate in detail. With $n = 2, m = 3$, the components of a vector in the 2^3-space carry the suffixes, in dictionary order, $(abc) = (111), (112), (121), (122), (211), (212), (221), (222)$, and the operations of $\boldsymbol{\pi}_3$ convert $A_{abc,ABC}$ as follows:

$$A: A_{cab,ABC} \quad B: A_{bca,ABC} \quad C: A_{cba,ABC} \quad D: A_{acb,ABC} \quad E: A_{bac,ABC}$$

Hence we get the following representation of $\boldsymbol{\pi}_3$:

$$I = \begin{bmatrix} 1 & 0 & 0 & 0 & 0 & 0 & 0 & 0 \\ 0 & 1 & 0 & 0 & 0 & 0 & 0 & 0 \\ 0 & 0 & 1 & 0 & 0 & 0 & 0 & 0 \\ 0 & 0 & 0 & 1 & 0 & 0 & 0 & 0 \\ 0 & 0 & 0 & 0 & 1 & 0 & 0 & 0 \\ 0 & 0 & 0 & 0 & 0 & 1 & 0 & 0 \\ 0 & 0 & 0 & 0 & 0 & 0 & 1 & 0 \\ 0 & 0 & 0 & 0 & 0 & 0 & 0 & 1 \end{bmatrix} \quad A = \begin{bmatrix} 1 & 0 & 0 & 0 & 0 & 0 & 0 & 0 \\ 0 & 0 & 0 & 0 & 1 & 0 & 0 & 0 \\ 0 & 1 & 0 & 0 & 0 & 0 & 0 & 0 \\ 0 & 0 & 0 & 0 & 0 & 1 & 0 & 0 \\ 0 & 0 & 1 & 0 & 0 & 0 & 0 & 0 \\ 0 & 0 & 0 & 0 & 0 & 0 & 1 & 0 \\ 0 & 0 & 0 & 1 & 0 & 0 & 0 & 0 \\ 0 & 0 & 0 & 0 & 0 & 0 & 0 & 1 \end{bmatrix} \quad B = \begin{bmatrix} 1 & 0 & 0 & 0 & 0 & 0 & 0 & 0 \\ 0 & 0 & 1 & 0 & 0 & 0 & 0 & 0 \\ 0 & 0 & 0 & 0 & 1 & 0 & 0 & 0 \\ 0 & 0 & 0 & 0 & 0 & 0 & 1 & 0 \\ 0 & 1 & 0 & 0 & 0 & 0 & 0 & 0 \\ 0 & 0 & 0 & 1 & 0 & 0 & 0 & 0 \\ 0 & 0 & 0 & 0 & 0 & 1 & 0 & 0 \\ 0 & 0 & 0 & 0 & 0 & 0 & 0 & 1 \end{bmatrix}$$

$$C = \begin{bmatrix} 1 & 0 & 0 & 0 & 0 & 0 & 0 & 0 \\ 0 & 0 & 0 & 0 & 1 & 0 & 0 & 0 \\ 0 & 0 & 1 & 0 & 0 & 0 & 0 & 0 \\ 0 & 0 & 0 & 0 & 0 & 0 & 1 & 0 \\ 0 & 1 & 0 & 0 & 0 & 0 & 0 & 0 \\ 0 & 0 & 0 & 0 & 0 & 1 & 0 & 0 \\ 0 & 0 & 0 & 1 & 0 & 0 & 0 & 0 \\ 0 & 0 & 0 & 0 & 0 & 0 & 0 & 1 \end{bmatrix} \quad D = \begin{bmatrix} 1 & 0 & 0 & 0 & 0 & 0 & 0 & 0 \\ 0 & 0 & 1 & 0 & 0 & 0 & 0 & 0 \\ 0 & 1 & 0 & 0 & 0 & 0 & 0 & 0 \\ 0 & 0 & 0 & 1 & 0 & 0 & 0 & 0 \\ 0 & 0 & 0 & 0 & 1 & 0 & 0 & 0 \\ 0 & 0 & 0 & 0 & 0 & 0 & 1 & 0 \\ 0 & 0 & 0 & 0 & 0 & 1 & 0 & 0 \\ 0 & 0 & 0 & 0 & 0 & 0 & 0 & 1 \end{bmatrix} \quad E = \begin{bmatrix} 1 & 0 & 0 & 0 & 0 & 0 & 0 & 0 \\ 0 & 1 & 0 & 0 & 0 & 0 & 0 & 0 \\ 0 & 0 & 0 & 0 & 1 & 0 & 0 & 0 \\ 0 & 0 & 0 & 0 & 0 & 1 & 0 & 0 \\ 0 & 0 & 1 & 0 & 0 & 0 & 0 & 0 \\ 0 & 0 & 0 & 1 & 0 & 0 & 0 & 0 \\ 0 & 0 & 0 & 0 & 0 & 0 & 1 & 0 \\ 0 & 0 & 0 & 0 & 0 & 0 & 0 & 1 \end{bmatrix}$$

The usual analysis shows that this contains the identical representation four times and the two-dimensional one twice; it is already partially reduced since the identical representation appears explicitly twice, namely, in the first and eighth components.

The second corollary from (13.4.3) is deduced by substituting first $Q = I, B = C, P = R$, and $A = I$, then $Q = R, B = I, P = I, A = C$. The result is that

$$(C)_m R(I)_m = R(C)_m = R(I)_m (C)_m, \qquad (13.4.5)$$

so that $R(I)_m$ commutes with all $(C)_m$ and conversely $(C)_m$ commutes with all $R(I)_m$. Now (13.4.2) shows that the matrices $(C)_m$ form a representation of the full linear group $\mathfrak{f}_n$—to each $n \times n$ matrix corresponding the $n^m \times n^m$ matrix which is its Kronecker mth power. Let us transform to a basis in which the representation of π_m by the matrices $R(I)_m$ is fully reduced—i.e. in the case of $n = 2$, $m = 3$ which we have been considering, every matrix $R(I)_3$ is transformed to the form

$$\begin{bmatrix} 1 & 0 & 0 & 0 & 0 & 0 & 0 & 0 \\ 0 & 1 & 0 & 0 & 0 & 0 & 0 & 0 \\ 0 & 0 & 1 & 0 & 0 & 0 & 0 & 0 \\ 0 & 0 & 0 & 1 & 0 & 0 & 0 & 0 \\ 0 & 0 & 0 & 0 & * & * & 0 & 0 \\ 0 & 0 & 0 & 0 & * & * & 0 & 0 \\ 0 & 0 & 0 & 0 & 0 & 0 & * & * \\ 0 & 0 & 0 & 0 & 0 & 0 & * & * \end{bmatrix}. \qquad (13.4.6)$$

By an application of the method of § 4.7, the fact that $(C)_m$ commutes with every $R(I)_m$ implies that in this basis every $(C)_m$ is of the form

$$\begin{bmatrix} a & b & c & d & 0 & 0 & 0 & 0 \\ e & f & g & h & 0 & 0 & 0 & 0 \\ i & j & k & l & 0 & 0 & 0 & 0 \\ m & n & o & p & 0 & 0 & 0 & 0 \\ 0 & 0 & 0 & 0 & q & 0 & r & 0 \\ 0 & 0 & 0 & 0 & 0 & q & 0 & r \\ 0 & 0 & 0 & 0 & s & 0 & t & 0 \\ 0 & 0 & 0 & 0 & 0 & s & 0 & t \end{bmatrix} \qquad (13.4.7)$$

which is, of course, equivalent to

$$\begin{bmatrix} a & b & c & d & 0 & 0 & 0 & 0 \\ e & f & g & h & 0 & 0 & 0 & 0 \\ i & j & k & l & 0 & 0 & 0 & 0 \\ m & n & o & p & 0 & 0 & 0 & 0 \\ 0 & 0 & 0 & 0 & q & r & 0 & 0 \\ 0 & 0 & 0 & 0 & s & t & 0 & 0 \\ 0 & 0 & 0 & 0 & 0 & 0 & q & r \\ 0 & 0 & 0 & 0 & 0 & 0 & s & t \end{bmatrix}. \tag{13.4.8}$$

In the next section we shall show that the representations thus displayed are irreducible and that there are no others of degree m (algebraically). Expressing these conclusions generally:

THEOREM 13.4.9. *To every irreducible representation Γ_i of degree d_i of π_m which occurs f_i times in the n^m-degree representation of π_m by the $R(I)$, there corresponds a representation γ_i of $\mathfrak{f}_n$ of degree f_i which occurs d_i times in the representation of $\mathfrak{f}_m$ by the $(C)_m$.*

In this statement the word degree refers to the degree—i.e. the dimensionality—of the representation, but it is further important to notice that the matrix elements of the Kronecker mth power, and of any matrix obtained from it by a linear transformation, are homogeneous of degree m in the elements of the original matrix. Using the word degree in this sense, it is now possible to show that *all* the irreducible representations of the full linear group which are homogeneous and of degree m are obtainable in this way d_i times and d_i times only from the Kronecker mth powers of the elements of the group.

13.5. The simple characters of $\mathfrak{f}_n$

The basis of the proof is Burnside's theorem. The matrix C contains n^2 elements which we may denote by $w_1,...,w_{n^2}$. The number of terms of degree m which can be formed from these is the number of terms in the function $h_m(w_1,...,w_{n^2})$, that is $^{n^2+m-1}C_m$. Every one of these is an element of $(C)_m$, and every element of $(C)_m$ is one of these, and linearly they are all independent. If we can show that this is the number of elements in the reduced form, we shall know that all the elements in the reduced form are independent, and thence that the separate representations are neither reducible nor equivalent, and that there can be no others. But the number of elements in the reduced form (which is, for example, the number of letters $a,...,t$ which we had to use in (13.4.7) or (13.4.8)) is $\sum f_i^2$, which can be calculated as follows. The representation of π_m by the $R(I)$ is $\sum f_i \Gamma_i$, and its character is thus $\sum f_i \chi_{iR}$. If this is squared and summed over the whole group, cross products sum to zero by the orthogonality theorem, and the rest to $\sum (f_i^2 m!)$ (the $m!$ being the order of the group π_m), whence by (13.4.1) and (13.3.5) it is the value of h_m when $s_1, ..., s_m$ are all equal to n^2. This is the same as the value of $h_m(w_1, ..., w_{n^2})$ when every w_i is equal to unity, i.e. it is the number of terms in $h_m(w_1, ..., w_{n^2})$, which by (13.2.1) is $^{n^2+m-1}C_m$, the same result as before.

We can now consider the characters. Equation (13.4.4) states, in effect, that the matrices $R(C)_m$ are a representation of a group which is the direct product of π_m and $\mathfrak{f}_n$. The characters of this representation are the traces of these matrices, namely, $s_{(\mu)}$. By (5.6.8) the characters of the irreducible representations of this group are

$$\chi_{\pi_m} \chi_{\mathfrak{f}_n}. \tag{13.5.1}$$

Now the representation by the matrices $R(C)_m$ is reducible, being reduced by the process of the previous section, but this process does not reduce it as much as it does the $(C)_m$. For the sub-matrices $\begin{bmatrix} q & 0 \\ 0 & q \end{bmatrix}$, etc., of (13.4.7) become $R\begin{bmatrix} q & 0 \\ 0 & q \end{bmatrix}$ with the consequence that the matrix

$$\begin{bmatrix} q & r & 0 & 0 \\ s & t & 0 & 0 \\ 0 & 0 & q & r \\ 0 & 0 & s & t \end{bmatrix} = \begin{bmatrix} 1 & 0 \\ 0 & 1 \end{bmatrix} \times \begin{bmatrix} q & r \\ s & t \end{bmatrix} \quad \text{becomes} \quad R \times \begin{bmatrix} q & r \\ s & t \end{bmatrix}$$

and irreducible, by (6.6.2). Thus the representation of the direct product group by the $R(C)_m$ contains each irreducible representation once and once only. Hence the traces of the matrices $R(C)_m$, which by (13.4.1) are equal to $s_{(\mu)}$, are compound characters in which each of the simple characters (13.5.1) occurs with coefficient either 1 or 0. We may therefore write

$$s_{(\mu)} = \sum_{i'} \chi_{\mu i} \phi_{zi}, \tag{13.5.2}$$

where ϕ_{zi} is the character of the class defined by the values given to the z, in the representation γ_i, and the sum over i' is a sum over some, but not necessarily all, of the i (the representations of π_m). Multiplying by $h_\mu \chi_{\mu j}$ (where h_μ has the meaning from § 5.5, viz. the number of elements in the class (μ) of π_m) and summing over the classes, every sum on the right-hand side vanishes except that for which $i = j$, by the orthogonality relations, and since $N = m!$, we have

$$\phi_{zj} = \frac{1}{m!} \sum_{\mu} h_{\mu} \chi_{\mu j} s_{(\mu)} \qquad (13.5.3)$$

as an explicit expression for the ϕ_{zj}, provided the $h_{\mu} \chi_{\mu j}$ are known.

We can obtain explicit expressions for the representations of $\mathfrak{f}_n$ though the process is long except in the simplest cases. From the representation of π_m by the $R(I)_m$, we can pass to a representation of the group algebra, and thence to the moduli of the separate representations by (5.5.2). If the ith modulus is M_i, then $M_i(C)_m$ is that part of $(C)_m$ which becomes the γ_i part of $(C)_m$ when $(C)_m$ is reduced, though it is still in the original coordinate system. (Compare § 17.4 for an explicit example of this process applied to a finite group.)

Since
$$M_i(C)_m = \frac{d_i}{m!} \sum_{\text{all } R} \chi_{iR} R(C)_m, \qquad (13.5.4)$$

we can, by permuting suffixes in $(C)_m$ and taking linear combinations in this way, decompose or reduce the Kronecker mth power into parts displaying special symmetry features; these are (but in the original coordinate system) the irreducible representations of $\mathfrak{f}_n$.

Two of these representations deserve special mention—those for which the characters $\chi_{\mu j}$ are those of the identical and alternating representations of π_m. For these two, by (13.5.2) and (13.3.5) or (13.3.6) ϕ_{zj} reduces to the simple forms h_m and a_m respectively. The former representation arises naturally from the following consideration. The n^m components of a vector in the carrier space of $(C)_m$ are the n^m products of the components of m n-dimensional vectors, say X, Y,..., Z, and are thus the n^m terms (with varied coefficients) in the expansion

$$(x_1+x_2+...+x_n)(y_1+y_2+...+y_n)...(z_1+z_2+...+z_n). \qquad (13.5.5)$$

If we consider the product $(x_1+x_2+...+x_n)^m$, the terms in it are obtained by the throwing together of such terms in (13.5.5) as $x_a^r y_b^s...$, $x_b^s y_a^r...$, since $x_a^r x_b^s... = x_b^s x_a^r...$. Now if $X = Y = ... = Z$, then

$$CX = CY = ... = CZ,$$

and therefore a vector in the n^m-space derived from equal vectors X, Y,..., Z will be transformed into another vector of this type by any operator $(C)_m$—and possibly by some (though not by all) other operators in this space. This subspace of all vectors in the n^m-space which is derived from m equal vectors in the n-space is invariant under all operators $(C)_m$ and also under all permutations R, and is therefore the subspace displaying the identical representation of π_m. We call the representation of f_n which it displays, the 'symmetrized' Kronecker mth power; using a result from the previous section we see that it is in $^{n+m-1}C_m$ dimensions. We have shown that it is irreducible. For the case $n = 2$ it is not difficult to see that the symmetrized Kronecker pth power is what we have called, in § 5.6, the pth induced representation. In § 12.4 we showed independently that it is irreducible for the two-dimensional *unitary* group. This would follow from the conclusion of § 7.6 that every representation of a finite group is equivalent to a unitary one if that conclusion could be applied to continuous groups. Although this extension is not always valid, it is a general result that the symmetrized Kronecker pth powers of the matrices of the group u_n of all $n \times n$ unitary matrices form an irreducible representation of the group.

These matters deeply affect the analysis of tensors, and we shall return to them in § 14.6 and give a fuller example there.

13.6. The characters of the symmetric groups

In (13.5.3) we calculated the characters of the full linear group in terms of known functions and the characters of the symmetric groups. The latter are more difficult to obtain explicitly; known methods of calculation become increasingly involved in practice, and the values available in the literature, which go as far as the characters of π_{13}, have mostly been obtained by recurrence relations.

In this section we shall refer to two methods by which the characters of the group π_m can be calculated for a given m. In the first we demonstrate a method for the construction of the primitive idempotents of the group and class algebras independently of any knowledge of the characters; the characters are then found by inspection using (5.5.1) and (5.5.3). In the second method we go more deeply into the characters of the full linear group, and show how the characters of the symmetric group can be obtained by inspection from a simple modification of (13.5.2).

The construction in the first method is as follows. We first write out the various partitions of m in the form of rows with their first members vertically above one another; taking $m = 4$ as an example, this will be

Partition:	4	31	22	21²	1⁴
Diagram:	abcd	abc	ab	ab	a
		d	cd	c	b
				d	c
					d

Note: These diagrams are known as 'Young tableaux'.

In connection with these diagrams we may mention at once an important concept required later on and already mentioned by implication in § 6.7. Partitions which are interconverted by turning rows into columns and vice versa are described as *conjugate*; thus (4) and (1⁴) are conjugate, also (31) and (21²), while (22) is self-conjugate. We now introduce the following notation. Considering the diagram belonging to the partition (μ),

  S is any permutation of the letters a, b, c,...,
  $P^{(\mu)}$ is any permutation which does not take a letter out of its row,
  $N^{(\mu)}$ is any permutation which does not take a letter out of its column,
  $\mathfrak{p}^{(\mu)}$ and $\mathfrak{n}^{(\mu)}$ are the groups of all $P^{(\mu)}$ and all $N^{(\mu)}$, respectively,
  $p^{(\mu)}$ and $n^{(\mu)}$ are the orders of these groups, and

$$\Pi^{(\mu)} = \frac{1}{p^{(\mu)}n^{(\mu)}} \sum P^{(\mu)} \cdot \sum{}' N^{(\mu)}.$$

The symbol $\sum'$ implies that in the sum all *odd* permutations are taken *with a negative sign*. $\Pi^{(\mu)}$ is known as a 'Young symmetry operator'— it is, of course, an element of the *algebra* of π_n. The superscript (μ) can be omitted for simplicity whenever only one diagram is being considered. Finally,

$$M^{(\mu)} = \frac{1}{k} \sum_{\text{all } S} S\Pi^{(\mu)}S^{-1},$$

where k is a numerical factor to be determined. We propose to show by an example that the $M^{(\mu)}$ are the primitive idempotents of the class algebra of π_m, and that therefore, since by (5.5.1) and (5.5.3)

$$M^{(\mu)} = \frac{m_{(\mu)}}{m!} \sum_S \chi_{(\mu)s} C_s,$$

the coefficients in the $M^{(\mu)}$ thus obtained are the required characters.

If $\mathfrak{p}_r$ is the group of all permutations within the rth row only, then $\mathfrak{p}$ is the direct product $\mathfrak{p}_1 \times \mathfrak{p}_2 \times ...$; this simplifies the calculation. So, for example,

$$\Pi^4 = \frac{1}{4!} \sum \text{ all 24 elements of } \pi_4,$$

$$\Pi^{31} = \frac{1}{3!\,2!}\{I+(ab)(c)(d)+(ac)(b)(d)+(bc)(a)(d)+(abc)(d)+(acb)(d)\}\times$$
$$\times\{I-(ad)(b)(c)\}$$
$$= \frac{1}{3!\,2!}\{I+(ab)(c)(d)+(ac)(b)(d)+(bc)(a)(d)+(abc)(d)+(acb)(d)-$$
$$-(ad)(b)(c)-(adb)(c)-(adc)(b)-(ad)(bc)-(adbc)-(adcb)\},$$

$$\Pi^{22} = \frac{1}{(2!)^4}\{I+(ab)(c)(d)\}\{I+(a)(b)(cd)\}\{I-(ac)(b)(d)\}\{I-(a)(c)(bd)\}$$

$$= \frac{1}{(2!)^4}\{I+(ab)(c)(d)+(a)(b)(cd)+(ab)(cd)+(ac)(bd)+(acbd)+$$
$$+(adbc)+(ad)(bc)-(ac)(b)(d)-(a)(c)(bd)-(acb)(d)-$$
$$-(abd)(c)-(adc)(b)-(a)(bcd)-(adcb)-(abcd)\},$$

$$\Pi^{21^2} = \frac{1}{2!\,3!}\{I+(ab)(c)(d)\}\{I+(adc)(b)+(acd)(b)-(ad)(c)(b)-$$
$$-(ac)(d)(b)-(dc)(a)(b)\}$$

$$= \frac{1}{2!\,3!}\{I+(ab)(c)(d)+(adc)(b)+(adcb)+(acd)(b)+(acdb)-$$
$$-(ad)(c)(b)-(adb)(c)-(ac)(d)(b)-(acb)(d)-(dc)(a)(b)-(dc)(ab)\},$$

$$\Pi^{1^4} = \frac{1}{4!}\{\textstyle\sum \text{ all 12 even elements of } \pi_4 - \sum \text{ all 12 odd elements}\}.$$

On going over to the $M^{(\mu)}$, each permutation in the above expressions becomes $m!/h_\rho$ times the class to which it belongs; the external factor and the $m!$ can be ignored since we are interested in the ratios. Collecting the terms leading to the same class we have

from Π^4, $I+\frac{6}{6}(21^2)+\frac{3}{3}(22)+\frac{8}{8}(31)+\frac{6}{6}(4)$

,, Π^{31}, $I+\frac{2}{6}(21^2)-\frac{1}{3}(22)+\frac{0}{8}(31)-\frac{2}{6}(4)$

,, Π^{22}, $I+\frac{0}{6}(21^2)+\frac{3}{3}(22)-\frac{4}{8}(31)+\frac{0}{6}(4)$

,, Π^{21^2}, $I-\frac{2}{6}(21^2)-\frac{1}{3}(22)+\frac{0}{8}(31)+\frac{2}{6}(4)$

,, Π^{1^4}, $I-\frac{6}{6}(21^2)+\frac{3}{3}(22)+\frac{8}{8}(31)-\frac{6}{6}(4)$

and this is, to within a constant coefficient in each row, the character table. This constant can be supplied by the orthogonality requirement, and is, since the coefficient of the class I is unity, the dimensionality of the representation.

The proofs required to establish the validity of this method are lengthy and unnecessary for our purposes; they will be found in Rutherford, *Substitutional Analysis*.

In the second method we start from equation (13.5.2) with $m = n$, and multiply both sides by the determinant (2.6.4), which we may call Δ. As $s_{(\mu)}$ is a symmetric function and Δ is alternating (i.e. changing sign when any two z are interchanged), the product $s_{(\mu)}\Delta$ is alternating. It is consequently simpler than $s_{(\mu)}$ in that it can contain no terms in which two z occur with equal indices. Arranging each term with the factors in descending order of indices and then arranging the terms in dictionary order by indices, each 'dictionary entry' will include a number of terms derived from each other by permutation of suffixes. The typical term for each entry may be written

$$z_1^{\lambda_1+n-1} z_2^{\lambda_2+n-2} \ldots z_n^{\lambda_n},$$

where $\lambda_1 \geqslant \lambda_2 \geqslant \lambda_3 \geqslant \ldots \geqslant \lambda_n \geqslant 0$ and $(\lambda_1, \lambda_2, \ldots, \lambda_n)$ is a partition of m, and the other terms of the entry will carry the same coefficient but with the opposite sign if the permutation of suffixes is an odd one. Each dictionary entry is thus the determinant

$$\Delta_{(\lambda)} = \begin{vmatrix} z_1^{\lambda_1+n-1} & z_2^{\lambda_1+n-1} & . & . & . & z_n^{\lambda_1+n-1} \\ z_1^{\lambda_2+n-2} & z_2^{\lambda_2+n-2} & . & . & . & z_n^{\lambda_2+n-2} \\ . & . & . & . & . & . \\ z_1^{\lambda_n} & z_2^{\lambda_n} & . & . & . & z_n^{\lambda_n} \end{vmatrix}. \tag{13.6.0}$$

Frobenius showed, but again the proof is somewhat long and of no value to us instructionally, that when equation (13.5.2) is multiplied by Δ and written in the form

$$s_{(\mu)}\Delta = \sum_i \chi_{\mu i}(\phi_{zi}\Delta) = \sum_i \chi_{\mu i} \Phi_{zi}, \tag{13.6.1}$$

then

$$\Phi_{zi} = \Delta_{(i)}, \tag{13.6.2}$$

so that

$$\phi_{zi} = \Delta_{(i)}/\Delta. \tag{13.6.3}$$

We thus have (i) an explicit form for ϕ_{zi} not involving the characters of the symmetric groups, and (ii) in (13.6.1) an expansion from which the characters of the symmetric group may be read off as coefficients.

In illustrating this by an example we shall see that, elegant though the result may be, it involves much manipulation in practice, so that neither of the methods given here are really as workable as the recurrence formulae to be developed in § 13.8. The simplest case of any interest is π_3, and we have, in three variables,

$$s_{(3)} = x^3 + y^3 + z^3,$$

$$s_{(21)} = (x^2 + y^2 + z^2)(x + y + z),$$

$$s_{(1^3)} = (x + y + z)^3,$$

$$\Delta = \begin{vmatrix} x^2 & y^2 & z^2 \\ x & y & z \\ 1 & 1 & 1 \end{vmatrix} = x^2 y + y^2 z + z^2 x - xy^2 - yz^2 - zx^2,$$

$$\Delta_{(3)} = \begin{vmatrix} x^5 & y^5 & z^5 \\ x & y & z \\ 1 & 1 & 1 \end{vmatrix} = x^5y + y^5z + z^5x - xy^5 - yz^5 - zx^5,$$

$$\Delta_{(21)} = \begin{vmatrix} x^4 & y^4 & z^4 \\ x^2 & y^2 & z^2 \\ 1 & 1 & 1 \end{vmatrix} = x^4y^2 + y^4z^2 + z^4x^2 - x^2y^4 - y^2z^4 - z^2x^4,$$

$$\Delta_{(1^3)} = \begin{vmatrix} x^3 & y^3 & z^3 \\ x^2 & y^2 & z^2 \\ x & y & z \end{vmatrix} = x^3y^2z + y^3z^2x + z^3x^2y - x^2y^3z - y^2z^3x - x^3z^2y.$$

We now multiply out $s_{(3)}\Delta$, $s_{(21)}\Delta$, and $s_{(1^3)}\Delta$, and by collecting terms (of which there are sixty in $s_{(1^3)}$) we find that

$$s_{(3)}\Delta = \Delta_{(3)} - \Delta_{(21)} + \Delta_{(1^3)},$$

$$s_{(21)}\Delta = \Delta_{(3)} \qquad\qquad - \Delta_{(1^3)},$$

$$s_{(1^3)}\Delta = \Delta_{(3)} + 2\Delta_{(21)} + \Delta_{(1^3)},$$

and the coefficients are a character table of π_3.

The stipulation at the beginning of this proof that $m = n$ can be removed, as we shall see in the next section. Until it is removed we can only calculate the characters of the representations of algebraic degree 3 of the matrices of $\mathfrak{f}_3$ (instead of $\mathfrak{f}_n$) from the above example. There are three such representations, and the class of $\mathfrak{f}_n$ whose eigenvalues are x, y, and z has in these representations the characters:

in γ_3, $\Delta_{(3)}/\Delta = h_3(x, y, z) = x^3 + y^3 + z^3 + x^2y + xy^2 + \dots + xyz,$

in γ_{21}, $\Delta_{(21)}/\Delta = x^2y + xy^2 + y^2z + yz^2 + x^2z + xz^2 + 2xyz,$

in γ_{1^3}, $\Delta_{(1^3)}/\Delta = a_3(x, y, z) = xyz.$

13.7. Schur functions

The characters ϕ_{zj} of the irreducible representations of the group $\mathfrak{f}_n$ are, as we have seen, certain symmetric functions of the numbers $z_1, \dots, z_n$ which define the class. Considered as functions of these variables they are particular examples of what are known as bialternants or Schur functions. They are a remarkable set of functions in that their theory contains in effect only one explicit reference to the number n of the variables of which they are functions! Corresponding to any partition $(m_1, m_2, \dots, m_k) = (\mu)$, of m (with each m_j equal to or less than the previous one, for the present, and k being without upper limit by adding zeros), we define the Schur function, $\{m_1, m_2, ..., m_k\} = \{\mu\}$, by the following relations which can be shown to be equivalent:

$$\{m_1, m_2, ..., m_k\} = \frac{1}{m!} \sum_{\substack{\text{all partitions} \\ \rho \text{ of } m = \text{all} \\ \text{classes } \rho \text{ of } \pi_m}} h_\rho \, \chi_{\rho\mu} \, s_1^{\rho_2} s_2^{\rho_1} ... \tag{13.7.1}$$

$$= \begin{vmatrix} z_1^{m_1+k-1} & z_2^{m_1+k-1} & . & . & z_k^{m_1+k-1} \\ z_1^{m_2+k-2} & z_2^{m_2+k-2} & . & . & z_k^{m_2+k-2} \\ . & . & . & . & . \\ z_1^{m_k} & z_2^{m_k} & . & . & z_k^{m_k} \end{vmatrix} \Big/ \begin{vmatrix} z_1^{k-1} & z_2^{k+2} & . & . & z_k^{k-1} \\ z_1^{k-2} & z_2^{k-2} & . & . & z_k^{k-2} \\ . & . & . & . & . \\ 1 & 1 & & & 1 \end{vmatrix} \tag{13.7.2}$$

$$= \begin{vmatrix} h_{m_1} & h_{m_1+1} & . & . & h_{m_1+k-1} \\ h_{m_2-1} & h_{m_2} & . & . & h_{m_2+k-2} \\ . & . & . & . & . \\ h_{m_k-k+1} & h_{m_k-k+2} & . & . & h_{m_k} \end{vmatrix} \tag{13.7.3}$$

$$= \begin{vmatrix} a_{\bar{m}_1} & a_{\bar{m}_1+1} & . & . & a_{\bar{m}_1+\bar{k}-1} \\ a_{\bar{m}_2-1} & a_{\bar{m}_2} & . & . & a_{\bar{m}_2+\bar{k}-2} \\ . & . & . & . & . \\ a_{\bar{m}_{\bar{k}}-\bar{k}+1} & a_{\bar{m}_{\bar{k}}-\bar{k}+2} & . & . & a_{\bar{m}_{\bar{k}}} \end{vmatrix}. \tag{13.7.4}$$

In these relations, note (i) that h with a greek suffix is as defined in § 5.5, namely, the number of elements in the class of the symmetric group defined by the partition, whereas h with a roman suffix is the h-type symmetrical function of the variables $z_1, ..., z_k$, (ii) that $(\bar{m}_1, \bar{m}_2, ..., \bar{m}_{\bar{k}})$ is the partition of m conjugate to $(m_1, m_2, ..., m_k)$ as defined in § 13.6, and (iii) $\chi_{\rho\mu}$ is the character of the class ρ of π_m in the representation μ, this nomenclature by which a *representation* is associated with a *partition* being defined in effect by these relations (or by the first method of calculating the characters given in the previous section). In (13.7.1), (13.7.3), and (13.7.4) the number of variables z can have any positive integral value, but in (13.7.2) it is set a lower limit equal to the number of non-zero parts in (μ); this distinction is relatively trivial since it can be shown that the Schur function of p variables corresponding to a partition of m into more than p parts is identically zero. For example, $\bar{m}_1 = $ the number of non-zero parts in the partition, and $a_{\bar{m}_1}, a_{\bar{m}_1+1}, ...$ are all zero if $\bar{m}_1 > p$, so that the first row of (13.7.4) is a row of zeros in this case. This is the one effective reference in the theory of Schur functions to the number of variables in their argument.

(13.7.1) and (13.7.2) have been shown to be equivalent (in as much detail as we propose to go into) in the previous section. To show the equivalence of (13.7.3) we note that the remainder theorem argument which was used in § 2.6 to factorize the denominator of (13.7.2) also shows that it divides the numerator without remainder; the quotient must be a symmetric function of degree m. Now

$$z_1^r = h_r(z_1); \qquad z_1^r - z_2^r = (z_1 - z_2)h_{r-1}(z_1, z_2), \text{ etc.,} \qquad (13.7.5)$$

so that by subtracting the first column of the numerator of (13.7.2) from every succeeding one, then the second from every succeeding one, and so on, we can actually remove the factors $(z_1 - z_2)\dots$. The result is the determinant

$$\begin{vmatrix} h_{m_1+k-1}(z_1) & h_{m_1+k-2}(z_1, z_2) & h_{m_1+k-3}(z_1, z_2, z_3) & \cdot & \cdot \\ h_{m_2+k-2}(z_1) & h_{m_2+k-3}(z_1, z_2) & h_{m_2+k-4}(z_1, z_2, z_3) & \cdot & \cdot \\ \cdot & \cdot \cdot \cdot \cdot \cdot \cdot \cdot \cdot \cdot \cdot & \cdot \cdot \cdot \cdot \cdot & \cdot & \cdot \end{vmatrix}.$$

Now adding z_2 times the second column to the first, and so on, making use of the relation

$$h_r(z_1, z_2, \dots, z_{p+1}) = h_r(z_1, z_2, \dots, z_p) + z_{p+1}h_{r-1}(z_1, z_2, \dots, z_{p+1}),$$

we convert all the elements of the determinant into h-functions of all the z. The result is (13.7.3) with the order of the columns reversed. (If k is odd, the minus sign cancels with one in the denominator.)

The equivalence of (13.7.4) to (13.7.3) and thence to the other forms is demonstrated with the aid of (13.3.3), and once again it will probably be clearest if applied to an example in terms which admit of immediate generalization. We note first that $m_1 = \bar{k}$ and $\bar{m}_1 = k$, so that

$$m_1 + k - 1 = \bar{m}_1 + \bar{k} - 1.$$

The $k \times k$ determinant in (13.7.3) is now converted into an equal $(m_1 + k - 1) \times (m_1 + k - 1)$ determinant by continuing its sequences to the left (remembering that $h_0 = 1$ and $h_r = 0$ if r is negative), continuing downwards with zeros, and filling the bottom left-hand square with units on the main diagonal and zeros elsewhere. For example

$$\{3 \quad 2\} = \begin{vmatrix} h_3 & h_4 \\ h_1 & h_2 \end{vmatrix} = \begin{vmatrix} 1 & h_1 & h_2 & h_3 & h_4 \\ 0 & 0 & 1 & h_1 & h_2 \\ 1 & 0 & 0 & 0 & 0 \\ 0 & 1 & 0 & 0 & 0 \\ 0 & 0 & 1 & 0 & 0 \end{vmatrix}.$$

We now add to the last column $-a_1$ times the last but one, a_2 times the last but two, and so on. By (13.3.3) this eliminates the last column of the original determinant. Successive columns are eliminated in the same way. But when, in any row, nothing is left but a 1, the complete row and column containing it are dropped (expanding by minors of that row), a minus sign being added if necessary. Our example thus becomes

$$= \begin{vmatrix} 1 & h_1 & h_2 & h_3 & 0 \\ 0 & 0 & 1 & h_1 & 0 \\ 1 & 0 & 0 & 0 & a_4 \\ 0 & 1 & 0 & 0 & -a_3 \\ 0 & 0 & 1 & 0 & a_2 \end{vmatrix} = \begin{vmatrix} 1 & h_1 & h_2 & 0 & 0 \\ 0 & 0 & 1 & 0 & 0 \\ 1 & 0 & 0 & a_3 & a_4 \\ 0 & 1 & 0 & -a_2 & -a_3 \\ 0 & 0 & 1 & a_1 & a_2 \end{vmatrix} = - \begin{vmatrix} 1 & h_1 & 0 & 0 \\ 1 & 0 & a_3 & a_4 \\ 0 & 1 & -a_2 & -a_3 \\ 0 & 0 & a_1 & a_2 \end{vmatrix}$$

$$= - \begin{vmatrix} 1 & 0 & 0 & 0 \\ 1 & a_1 & a_3 & a_4 \\ 0 & -1 & -a_2 & -a_3 \\ 0 & 0 & a_1 & a_2 \end{vmatrix} = - \begin{vmatrix} a_1 & a_3 & a_4 \\ -1 & -a_2 & -a_3 \\ 0 & a_1 & a_2 \end{vmatrix},$$

which, on inverting about the sinister diagonal, and checking for sign, is the form required by (13.7.4), namely, since the conjugate of (3 2) is (2 2 1),

$$\begin{vmatrix} a_2 & a_3 & a_4 \\ a_1 & a_2 & a_3 \\ 0 & 1 & a_1 \end{vmatrix}.$$

13.8. Further development of Schur functions

It is convenient to remove the restriction on Schur functions that $m_1, m_2, ..., m_k$ are in descending (or stationary) order, but in doing so to adopt (13.7.2) or (13.7.3) as definition. Then, for example,

$$\{2 \ 4\} = \begin{vmatrix} h_2 & h_3 \\ h_3 & h_4 \end{vmatrix} = - \begin{vmatrix} h_3 & h_4 \\ h_2 & h_3 \end{vmatrix} = -\{3 \ 3\} \neq \{4 \ 2\}.$$

It is easily seen from (13.7.2) that any Schur function in which any m_j exceeds m_{j-k} by k is zero, two rows in the numerator being identical, and that apart from this case a general Schur function such as $\{1 \ 4 \ 1 \ 5 \ 9\}$ may be reduced to 'standard form' by adding 0, 1, 2,... from the right —giving 5 7 3 6 9—rearranging in descending order—9 7 6 5 3—again subtracting 0, 1, 2,... from the right, and prefixing a minus sign if the rearrangement—as in this example—was an odd permutation. Thus

$$\{1 \ 4 \ 1 \ 5 \ 9\} = -\{5 \ 4 \ 4 \ 4 \ 3\} = -\{5 \ 4^3 \ 3\}.$$

If (13.7.2) is multiplied by $\{1\} = \sum z$, we have the result that

$$\{m_1, m_2,..., m_k\}\{1\} = \{m_1+1, m_2,..., m_k\}+\{m_1, m_2+1,..., m_k\}+....$$

$$(13.8.1)$$

For the major diagonal term of the first factor on the left becomes the sum of the major diagonal terms of the Schur functions on the right, and similarly for all corresponding terms; it is essential that $m_k = 0$ explicitly, so that $m_k+1 = 1$, but if more zeros are added the extra functions on the right are all zero. In the same way

$$\{m_1, m_2,..., m_k\}s_p = \{m_1+p, m_2,..., m_k\}+\{m_1, m_2+p,..., m_k\}+...$$

$$(13.8.2)$$

where the last p of the m_k must be explicitly zero to realize the complete expansion; unfortunately $s_p \neq \{p\}$, $p > 1$, but

$$s_2 = 2h_2-h_1^2, \qquad s_3 = 3h_3-3h_2h_1+h_1^3, \quad \text{etc.}$$

It is possible by the use of these relations to construct the Schur functions of any order from those of lower order with a minimum of troublesome expansion of determinants, if expansion in terms of the h_r or the a_r serves the purpose in hand. For example,

$$\{5\} = h_5; \qquad \{4\ 1\} = h_4h_1-h_5; \qquad \{3\ 2\} = h_3h_2-h_4h_1,$$

and since $\qquad \{3\ 1\}\{1\} = \{4\ 1\}+\{3\ 2\}+\{3\ 1\ 1\}$

we have

$$\{3\ 1\ 1\} = \{3\ 1\}\{1\}-\{4\ 1\}-\{3\ 2\}$$
$$= (h_3h_1-h_4)h_1-(h_4h_1-h_5)-(h_3h_2-h_4h_1)$$
$$= h_5-h_4h_1-h_3h_2+h_3h_1^2,$$

and so on. With tables constructed in this way we can express the product of two Schur functions of orders p and q as the sum of Schur functions of order $p+q$. The latter should be set out in dictionary order, like terms in the same vertical column, thus:

$\{5\} =$	h_5					
$\{4\ 1\} =$	$-h_5$	$+h_4h_1$				
$\{3\ 2\} =$		$-h_4h_1$	$+h_3h_2$			
$\{3\ 1^2\} =$	h_5	$-h_4h_1$	$-h_3h_2$	$+h_3h_1^2$		
$\{2^2\ 1\} =$		h_4h_1	$-h_3h_2$	$-h_3h_1^2$	$+h_2^2h_1$	
$\{2\ 1^3\} =$	$-h_5$	$+h_4h_1$	$+2h_3h_2$	$-h_3h_1^2$	$-2h_2^2h_1$	$+h_2h_1^3$
$\{1^5\} =$	h_5	$-2h_4h_1$	$-2h_3h_2$	$+3h_3h_1^2$	$+3h_2^2h_1$	$-4h_2h_1^3+h_1^5.$

Then, for example,

$$\{2\ 1\}\{2\} = (h_2 h_1 - h_3)h_2$$
$$= 0 + 0 - h_3 h_2 + 0 + h_2^2 h_1 + 0 + 0$$
$$= \{2^2\ 1\} + \{3\ 1^2\} + \{3\ 2\} + \{4\ 1\}.$$

The terms of the second line are set out under the corresponding terms in the 'dictionary', and the terms of the third line written in so as to adjust terms in the expansion successively from the right.

There is a method of multiplying Schur functions without expanding them in any way, but it is tricky to handle. We can illustrate it on the product $\{2\ 1\}\{2\ 1\}$. The first factor is represented by the diagram of its partition (§ 13.6) using stars and not letters. The second factor is represented by the letters aab. (Similarly $\{31^2\}$ would be represented by $aaabc$.) The letters of the second factor are then added in as many different ways as possible to the diagram of the first factor subject to the following rules. (1) After the addition of each set of identical letters we must have a proper partition diagram (no row longer than any preceding row) and no two identical letters may appear in the same column. (2) At the end, summing the letters from the right, column by column, the a's keep at least level with the b's, the b's with the c's, and so on. Applied to $\{2\ 1\}\{2\ 1\}$, we have the possibilities

✱✱aa	✱✱aa	✱✱a	✱✱a	✱✱a	✱✱a	✱✱	✱✱
✱b	✱	✱ab	✱a	✱b	✱	✱a	✱a
	b		b	a	a	ab	a
					b		b

showing that

$$\{2\ 1\}\{2\ 1\} = \{4\ 2\} + \{4\ 1^2\} + \{3^2\} + 2\{3\ 2\ 1\} + \{3\ 1^3\} + \{2^3\} + \{2^2\ 1^2\}.$$

(Note: the reasons why the diagrams

(1) ✱✱ba	(2) ✱✱b	(3) ✱✱b	(4) ✱✱
✱a	✱aa	✱a	✱
		a	a
			a
			b

are excluded are (1) and (2) the diagram obtained before the addition of the b's is not a proper partition diagram, (3) when only the last column is counted there are more b's than a's, and (4) two a's in the same column.)

The importance for the theory of the full linear group of this method of expressing the product of Schur functions is that if a new representation of $\mathfrak{f}_n$ of degree $p+q$ is formed by taking the Kronecker product of two irreducible representations of degrees p and q, its characters will be the products of those of the latter representations. By expressing the product of the Schur functions in this way we are displaying the analysis of this representation into its irreducible components.

The above considerations, though helpful in analysing product representations of $\mathfrak{f}_n$, do not get us very far with π_m, because the whole discussion has been carried on in terms of the h_r. But we can substitute (13.7.1) into (13.8.1), and compare coefficients of the $s_{(\rho)}$. Comparable terms are $s_{(\sigma)}$ on the right, where (σ) is a partition of $m+1$ and $s_{(\rho)}s_1$ on the left, where (ρ) is a partition of m. (ρ) and (σ) will have $\rho_1 = \sigma_1 - 1$, $\rho_r = \rho_r$ $(r > 1)$, and to any (σ) with $\sigma_1 = 0$, there will be no corresponding terms, so that the coefficients of such terms will be put equal to zero. The result is

$$\sigma_1 \chi_{(\rho)[\mu]} = \sum_r \chi_{(\rho,1)[\mu^r]} \quad ((\sigma) = (\rho, 1)), \tag{13.8.3}$$

where the μ^r include all representations corresponding to partitions of $m+1$ derived by increasing by unity the various terms of μ and interpreting the result, if not in standard form, as explained in the first paragraph of this section.

The student should notice the notation, widely accepted, which we have introduced here for the first time, by which a partition symbol identifying a class of π_m is enclosed in round brackets, whereas one identifying a representation is enclosed in square brackets. Round brackets are also used in more general contexts, and curly brackets, of course, signify Schur functions.

A more useful result, since it takes us up the scale instead of down it, is that

$$\chi_{(\rho,p)[\mu]} = \sum_s \chi_{(\rho)[\mu^s]}, \tag{13.8.4}$$

where $\{\mu^s\}$ is any Schur function obtained by diminishing any m_k in $\{\mu\}$ by p. To prove it,

$$s_{(\rho,p)}\Delta = s_p s_{(\rho)}\Delta$$

by the definition (13.4.1), whence by (13.6.1) and (13.6.2)

$$\sum_\mu \chi_{(\rho,p)}\Delta_{(\mu)} = \sum_\lambda \chi_{\rho\lambda} s_p \Delta_{(\lambda)}$$

$$= \sum_\lambda \chi_{\rho\lambda} s_p\{\lambda\}\Delta, \qquad \text{by (13.7.2),}$$

$$= \sum_\lambda \sum_r \chi_{\rho\lambda}\{\lambda^r\}\Delta, \qquad \text{(by 13.8.1),}$$

$$= \sum_\lambda \sum_r \chi_{\rho\lambda} \Delta_{(\lambda^r)}, \qquad \text{(by 13.7.2).}$$

The $\Delta_{(\mu)}$ are linearly independent and their coefficients can be equated. On the right-hand side we shall find $\Delta_{(\mu)}$ appearing once for each (λ) which includes it in its (λ^r), and thus the theorem is proved. As an example, let us calculate the character $\chi_{(32)[31^2]}$ from the characters $\chi_{(3)(\lambda)}$. Diminishing the terms of $\{3 \ 1 \ 1\}$ in turn by two we have

$$\{1 \ 1 \ 1\} = \{1^3\} \qquad \{3 \ -1 \ 1\} = -\{3\}$$

and all the others terminate in a negative number and are therefore zero. Thus

$$\chi_{(32)[31^2]} = \chi_{(3)[1^3]} - \chi_{(3)[3]}$$
$$= 1 - 1$$
$$= 0$$

as may be verified in the table at the end of § 6.7.

In this way all the characters of π_n can be calculated from those of the symmetric groups of lower order, except those of the class (n), which must then be obtained from the orthogonality relations.

It should be noted that it is incorrect to write (13.8.4) in Schur function notation, as some authors have done, e.g.

$$\{1^3\} = \{1^2\}, \qquad \{2 \ 1\} = \{2\} + \{1^2\}.$$

Apart from anything else, the symbols on each side of such 'equations' represent expressions of different degrees in the z_i.

13.9. Subgroups of the symmetric and full linear groups

It will be remembered that any finite group of order N is a subgroup of π_N. Similarly any matrix group is a subgroup of the full linear group of the same (matrix) order. The subject of this section would therefore seem to be rather wide! Its purpose, however, is to summarize certain results which we do not intend to prove.

It is possible by inspection of the character table of a given group to deduce considerable information concerning its subgroups. This process is the main subject of study in Littlewood, *The Theory of Group Characters*, and is one of the methods of discovery of groups of high order. Otherwise the only subgroups of the symmetric groups studied as such are the alternating groups; their most important features have already been summarized in § 6.7, and need not be repeated here.

The subgroups of the full linear group are those set out in the table in § 12.1. Among them the special or unimodular linear group $\mathfrak{h}_n$, consisting of all $n \times n$ matrices with determinant equal to 1, takes a special place. It can be shown that its irreducible rational representations are the same as those of the full linear group, those which are given us by the analysis of the Kronecker mth powers. It differs from the full linear group in having a closed manifold, and it can be shown ('thence or otherwise') that, as was true of finite groups, reducibility implies complete reducibility. One may ask whether it has representations other than the rational ones. It is possible that a representation of a continuous group might be found for which infinitesimally different elements were represented by matrices whose difference was not infinitesimal; such a discontinuous representation must be 'discontinuous at every element', and we shall ignore this possibility. Denoting the original (defining) matrix by A and the matrix which represents it in the pth representation by $D_p(A)$, it can be shown that every non-analysable continuous representation of the unimodular group is irreducible and is rational integral in the real and imaginary parts of the elements of A taken separately (though not necessarily in the elements of A considered as single complex numbers), and can, in fact, be expressed in the form of a Kronecker product $D_p(A) \times D_q(\bar{A})$, where $\bar{A}$ is the conjugate of A, and D_p and D_q are two of the rational integral representations obtained by analysis of the Kronecker mth powers of A.

The extended unimodular group is that group in which the determinants are ± 1; it might well be further extended to include all $n \times n$ matrices whose determinants are $e^{i\theta}$ (θ real). In either case it has the properties we should expect of a group $\mathfrak{h}_n \times \mathfrak{c}_2$ (or $\mathfrak{h}_n \times \mathfrak{c}_\infty$), as foreshadowed in § 12.5. It has a closed manifold, though in the case of the lesser extension a two-sheet one.

When these results have been established, it can then be shown that any non-analysable continuous representation of the full linear group can be expressed as the product, scalar or Kronecker, of the following factors:

(i) a fixed power, $|\det A|^\alpha$, of the absolute value of the determinant of the defining matrix, where α may be any complex number (equations (12.5.2) and (12.5.5)),

(ii) an exponential of an imaginary integral multiple, positive or negative, of the argument of the determinant of the defining matrix, $\exp[in(\arg \det A)]$ (n positive or negative integral or zero), if $\det A$ is complex (equation 12.5.1),

(iii) an mth symmetrized Kronecker power of the matrix
$$\begin{bmatrix} 1 & \log|\det A| \\ 0 & 1 \end{bmatrix}$$
(compare equation (12.5.4)),

(iv) a representation $D_p(A) \times D_q(\bar{A})$ of the rational integral type already discussed.

If the representation is irreducible as well as non-analysable, then m (in (iii)) is zero; if it is rational integral, then α in (i) is positive integral; if rational but not integral, α is integral but negative, and so on.

The above results have been summarized from Murnaghan's book, where they are all proved in detail. Mostly they are what one might expect. In contrast, the real orthogonal and the rotation groups show features which call for discussion in a little more detail.

The real orthogonal group $\mathfrak{o}_n$ consists of all those $n \times n$ matrices whose elements are all real and whose transpose (or associate) is equal to their reciprocal; they preserve the reality and length of a real vector. It consists of all those matrices common to the complex orthogonal and the unitary groups. The determinants of its matrices are all of modulus unity and real, thus equal to ± 1. The n-dimensional rotation group $\mathfrak{r}_n$ is the subgroup of matrices with determinant $+1$. The eigenvalues of these matrices are also of modulus unity, and if they are complex they occur in conjugate pairs. It takes a complex matrix to diagonalize fully a matrix with complex eigenvalues, but any orthogonal matrix can be transformed by another orthogonal matrix to the form

$$\begin{bmatrix} R(\theta) & 0 & 0 & . & . & . & 0 \\ 0 & R(\phi) & 0 & . & . & . & 0 \\ 0 & 0 & R(\psi) & . & . & . & 0 \\ . & . & . & . & . & . & . \\ 0 & 0 & 0 & . & . & . & F \end{bmatrix}$$

where $R(\theta)$ is the two-dimensional rotation matrix with which we are now familiar (and the zeros are, where necessary, 2×2 zero matrices) and F is the matrix shown below:

	det *original matrix* $= 1$ (*proper*)	det *original matrix* $= -1$ (*improper*)
n odd	$F = 1$	$F = -1$
n even	$F = R(\omega)$	$F = \begin{bmatrix} 1 & 0 \\ 0 & -1 \end{bmatrix}.$

We note that $R(\theta)$ includes $\begin{bmatrix} 1 & 0 \\ 0 & 1 \end{bmatrix}$ and $\begin{bmatrix} -1 & 0 \\ 0 & -1 \end{bmatrix}$ as special cases ($\theta = 0$ and π respectively). We also note that a matrix which permutes the axes is orthogonal, proper for an even permutation and improper for an odd permutation. Thus the angles $\theta, \phi, \psi,...$ can be permuted by a proper rotation matrix. Since

$$\begin{bmatrix} 0 & 1 \\ 1 & 0 \end{bmatrix} R(\theta) \begin{bmatrix} 0 & 1 \\ 1 & 0 \end{bmatrix} = R(-\theta)$$

we see that the sign of any of the angles can be reversed by an improper rotation matrix, and therefore the sign of any even number of the angles by a proper rotation matrix. But $(-V)A(-V)^{-1} = VAV^{-1}$, and if n is odd (but not when it is even), if V is improper, $-V$ is proper, and thus when n is odd the sign of any of the angles θ, ϕ,... can be reversed by a proper rotation matrix.

The position is therefore that if n is even, $n = 2m$, a class of the orthogonal group is defined by (i) the absolute values of the m angles θ,..., ω, if the matrix is a proper one, or by (ii) the corresponding $m-1$ angles if the matrix is improper. In the rotation group the latter drop out, and the former are refined, each class splitting into two—one with an even number of angles negative and the other with an odd number. (We consider the range of the angles as being $-\pi$ to π.) The inverse of a matrix is obtained by reversing *all* the signs of the angles, so that a matrix and its inverse belong to the same class if m is even ($n = 4r$), but not if it is odd ($n = 4r+2$). But if n is odd, $n = 2m+1$, a class is defined by the absolute values of the m angles θ, ϕ,... and the sign of F. In the rotation group those classes with negative F drop out.

Since the orthogonal and rotation groups are subgroups of the full linear group, any representation of the latter is a representation of the former, but not necessarily irreducible. The test of irreducibility is the orthogonality relation; the character integrated over the whole group manifold must be equal to the volume of the manifold and not to some integral multiple of it. As we propose to confine our remarks on such integration to those in §§ 12.6 and 14.4, we cannot attempt even to outline this investigation. Even the results of it are somewhat complex to state. The rotation group being a subgroup of the orthogonal group of index 2 (containing 'half' of the elements), it is an invariant subgroup, and the representations of the factor group c_2 will be included in those of the orthogonal group. As with π_n and a_n, this leads to the conclusion that some of the representations can be grouped in pairs of 'associated' representations which differ only in the sign of the matrices representing elements in the coset, while others which are 'self-associated' have zero characters for all these matrices. Two associated representations of the orthogonal group lead to one representation of the rotation group, but a self-associated representation of the orthogonal group splits into two representations of the rotation group. In consequence of the class relations discussed in the previous paragraph, if n is odd there are no self-associated characters, if $n = 4r+2$ the self-associated characters split into two conjugate complex characters, but if $n = 4r$ all the characters are real. In any case all the characters of the orthogonal group are real.

They may be expressed as follows. Let $h'_r = h_r - h_{r-2}$. (This can be shown to be the character of the (reducible) representation of the orthogonal group found in the symmetrized Kronecker mth power representation after removal of an invariant part; cf. § 16.7.) Let n equal $2m$ or $2m+1$, and let (λ) be any set of m numbers, positive integers or zero, arranged in descending order. Then

$$\{\lambda\}' = \begin{vmatrix} h'_{\lambda_1} & h'_{\lambda_1+1}+h'_{\lambda_1-1} & \cdot & \cdot & \cdot \\ h'_{\lambda_2-1} & h'_{\lambda_2}+h'_{\lambda_2-2} & \cdot & \cdot & \cdot \\ \cdot & \cdot & \cdot & \cdot & \cdot \\ \cdot & \cdot & \cdot & \cdot & h'_{\lambda_m}+h'_{\lambda_m-2(m-1)} \end{vmatrix}$$

can be shown to be a simple character of the orthogonal group. Its resemblance to (13.7.3) and its greater complexity are equally obvious, It can also be written

$$\{\lambda\}' = \sum_{\substack{p \leqslant q \\ 1}}^{m} (1-\xi_p\,\xi_q)\{\lambda\},$$

where ξ_r is an operator which reduces by unity the suffix of the rth number in $\{\lambda\}$. The inverse of the above operator can be expanded as a series as though the ξ_r were algebraic quantities and in this way product representations can be analysed via the analysis of products of the $\{\lambda\}$. For example, we can prove that

$$\{\lambda_1\}'\{\lambda_2\}' = (1-\xi_1^2)(1-\xi_2^2)(1-\xi_2/\xi_1)^{-1}\{\lambda_1, \lambda_2\}$$

$$= \{\lambda_1+\lambda_2\}'+\{\lambda_1+\lambda_2-2\}'+\ldots+\{\lambda_1-\lambda_2\}'+$$

$$+\{\lambda_1+\lambda_2-1, 1\}'+\{\lambda_1+\lambda_2-3, 1\}'+\ldots+\{\lambda_1-\lambda_2+1, 1\}'+$$

$$+\{\lambda_1+\lambda_2-2, 2\}'+\ldots+\{\lambda_1, \lambda_2\}'$$

(see Murnaghan, pp. 274–7), which gives, with $\lambda_1 = 3$, $\lambda_2 = 2$, say,

$$\Gamma_3\times\Gamma_2 = (\Gamma_5+\Gamma_3+\Gamma_1)+(\Gamma_{(4,1)}+\Gamma_{(2,1)})+\Gamma_{(3,2)},$$

which is a generalized Clebsch–Gordan formula, reducing to the one in § 12.4 when $m = 1$, and all the $\{\lambda\}'$ for partitions into two or more parts are zero (two or three dimensions). It is useful for checking purposes to have the formulae for the dimensions of these representations; they are, if $l_k = \lambda_k + k - m$

$$n = 2m,\, l_m \neq 0: \quad \frac{2^m}{(2m-2)!\ldots4!\,2!} \prod_{\substack{p < q \\ 1}}^{m} (l_p^2 - l_q^2),$$

$l_m = 0$: half the above,

$$n = 2m+1: \quad \frac{2^m}{(2m-1)!\ldots3!\,1!} (l_1 + \tfrac{1}{2})\ldots(l_m + \tfrac{1}{2})\left\{ \prod_{\substack{p < q \\ 1}}^{m} (l_p - l_q)(l_p + l_q + 1)\right\},$$

but there are a number of pitfalls in interpretation (e.g. in $2\{0\}$, which may have to be put $= \Gamma_0^+ + \Gamma_0^-$, the sum of the identical and alternating representations), and the student is advised to consult more advanced works for details. The results of the analysis of a product representation are often more complex than even their appearance suggests—e.g. Murnaghan analyses the product $\{3, 2\}'\{2, 1\}'$ and shows that it contains thirty-five irreducible representations (twenty-three non-equivalent ones), but that (in the case $n = 8$) this is the analysis of a representation in 224,000 dimensions!

The rotation group has another series of representations which we deal with in the next section. As with the full linear group, all the continuous representations of the orthogonal and rotation groups are rational; in this case they are also all rational integral.

13.10. The spinor group

We saw in § 12.3 that the general rotation of a sphere can be expressed in the form $R(\psi, \theta, \phi) = Z(\psi)Y(\theta)Z(\phi)$, where two of the angles have the range $0\ldots2\pi$, and the third the range $0\ldots\pi$. We also saw that the most general member of the special unitary group can be written

$$U(\psi, \theta, \phi) = \begin{bmatrix} e^{\frac{1}{2}i\psi} & 0 \\ 0 & e^{-\frac{1}{2}i\psi} \end{bmatrix}\begin{bmatrix} \cos\frac{1}{2}\theta & \sin\frac{1}{2}\theta \\ -\sin\frac{1}{2}\theta & \cos\frac{1}{2}\theta \end{bmatrix}\begin{bmatrix} e^{\frac{1}{2}i\phi} & 0 \\ 0 & e^{-\frac{1}{2}i\phi} \end{bmatrix},$$

where each angle may vary over $0\ldots2\pi$. And we saw further that these two groups are isomorphic but not simply isomorphic, since if

$$R(\psi_1\,\theta_1\,\phi_1)R(\psi_2\,\theta_2\,\phi_2) = R(\psi_3\,\theta_3\,\phi_3),$$

then
$$U(\psi_1\,\theta_1\,\phi_1)U(\psi_2\,\theta_2\,\phi_2) = \pm U(\psi_3\,\theta_3\,\phi_3).$$

Accordingly we said that only such representations of the group u_2 as assigned the same matrix to U and $-U$ were representations of r_3. For some purposes, however, the sense of a vector is unimportant, and for these purposes all representations of u_2 are available as representations of r_3. In this case the word 'ray' is preferred to the word 'vector' in describing the operand in the real space; the associated unitary two-vector is known as a 'spinor', and the extra representations are known as 'spin representations'.

For any n, there are spin representations of the rotation group in n dimensions. We do not propose to go deeply into them, but to discuss them only in so far as may assist the student in further reading—the problem being partly that widely differing approaches are made in different books.

For example, the approach may be topological, through the geometry of the group manifold. The writer is insufficiently acquainted with topology to attempt any systematic account, however brief, of this approach, but two examples may assist the student. (1) In the Moebius strip (Fig. 23), if, starting from P, we follow the dotted line once round, we reach P but on 'the other side' of the surface—P'; we have to go round twice to reach P 'properly'. The representation $e^{in\theta}$, n half-integral, is a spin-representation of the one-dimensional rotation group. (2) The anchor ring (Fig. 24), like the sphere, is a surface on which two sets of angular coordinates define a point, but whereas on the sphere $0...\pi$ is a sufficient range for one of the angles, on the anchor ring both must range from $0...2\pi$. We may imagine the radius of the ring to be steadily diminished—first until it is less than the radius of the cross-section, and then further until it is zero; a sphere is thus obtained, but each point on the sphere being derived from two diametrically opposite points (in both coordinates) of the anchor ring is really two points. We will call this a double sphere. A feature of the anchor ring which is fundamental topologically is that if a closed curve goes round the ring a number of times, no continuous deformation of it can ever alter the odd or even character of the number, and thus there are (at least) *two* types of closed curve—the even type which can be reduced to a point by a continuous deformation and the odd type which cannot—and of which it is a further question whether all curves of this type can be deformed into each other (Fig. 25). This feature remains in the double sphere.

A space in which these complications do not occur is said to be simply connected. But the manifold of the rotation group is not simply con-

nected; it rather (in one extra dimension) resembles the double sphere
derived from the anchor ring. The proper representations of the group
associate each point of the manifold with a matrix, but the spin repre-

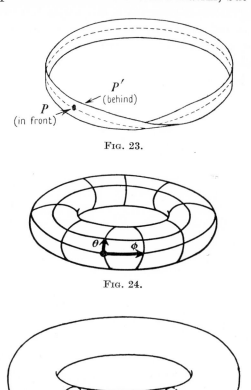

FIG. 23.

FIG. 24.

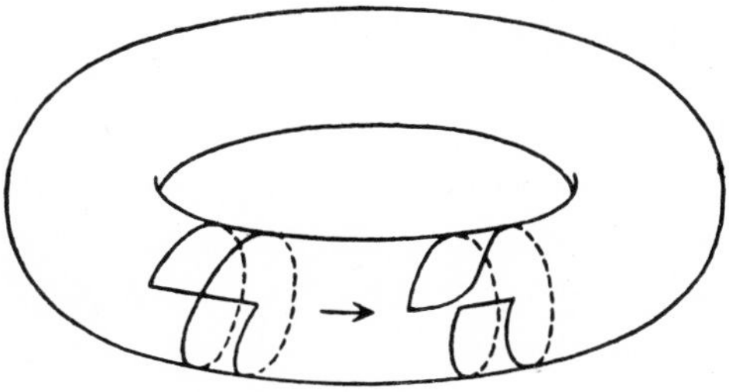

FIG. 25.

sentations associate each point with one of two matrices depending on
'how the point was reached'—starting with the identity and 'reaching'
the point by a path corresponding to a continuous variation of the
parameters. In particular, if we start from the identity ($=$ the matrix I)
and come back to it by an odd curve, its matrix will be found to be $-I$.

An alternative approach is by a generalization of quaternion theory.
The reader may have noticed that, as we have defined them, quaternion
algebra and the algebra of the quaternion group are not the same thing.

The group q_4 contains eight elements whereas quaternion algebra has only four basis elements. The basis elements of quaternion algebra constitute in fact a spin representation of the factor group $s_{2\times2}$ of the quaternion group. As they are irreducible, we see that when spin representations are allowed, it is possible to have two-dimensional irreducible representations of a commutative group.

The generalization to more dimensions is accomplished by means of the Clifford algebras. We define n basis elements $e_1,...,e_n$ satisfying the relations
$$e_i^2 = -1, \qquad e_i e_j = -e_j e_i, \qquad (13.10.1)$$
and define other basis elements $e_{pq...} = e_p e_q...$ provided $p < q < ...$ and e_0 the identity. We thus obtain in all 2^n elements, since each suffix in $e_{123...n}$ can be presumed present or absent. The relation (13.10.1) serves to interpret all products $e_p e_q...$ in which $p, q,...$ are not in ascending order. It is clear that the multiplication tables of the Clifford algebras are all similar to that of quaternion algebra in this respect, that they are, as it were, the multiplication tables of $s_{2\times2\times...}$ made non-commutative by the presence of a certain number of minus signs, and that by replacing -1 by the symbol i as in § 4.3, a true group of order 2^{n+1} is obtained, non-commutating, with I, i as an invariant subgroup and $s_{2\times2\times...}$ as factor group. The group of order 2^{n+1} is known as the covering or spinor group, and the invariant subgroup c_2 as the fundamental or Poincaré group. The covering group has structure $q_{2\times2\times...}$ if n is odd, and $q_{2\times2\times...(n\text{ factors})}\times c_2$ if n is even. In the former case only I commutes with every other element, but in the latter I and $e_{123...n}$ (all suffixes present) both do so. The student will find it a simple matter, using equation (5.6.7) (generalized to n factors) and the quaternion multiplication table in § 3.9, to check that if $n = 2k$ or $2k+1$ the following is a matrix representation of the Clifford algebra:

$$i^j e_j = \eta_4 \times \eta_4 \times ... \times \eta_4 \times \eta_3 \times \eta_1 \times ... \times \eta_1$$

(to k factors; η_3 in the jth place)

$$i^j e_{j+k} = \eta_4 \times \eta_4 \times ... \times \eta_4 \times \eta_2 \times \eta_1 \times ... \times \eta_1$$

(to k factors; η_2 in the jth place)

$$i^k e_{2k+1} = \eta_4 \times \eta_4 \times ... \text{ to } k \text{ factors (if needed—i.e. when } n \text{ is odd)}.$$

It is in 2^k dimensions, so that each matrix contains 2^{2k} elements. It would thus appear, and it can be rigidly proved, that when $n = 2k$ this representation of the Clifford algebra spans the whole matrix algebra of dimension 2^k. When $n = 2k+1$ then in this representation the element $e_{1\,2...(2k+1)} = e_1 e_2 ... \, e_{(2k+1)}$ is a scalar multiple of I, namely, $(-1)^{k^2/2}I$.

Consider now that the square of any linear combination of the *generating* elements,

$$(a_1 e_1 + a_2 e_2 + ... + a_n e_n)^2 = -(a_1^2 + a_2^2 + ... + a_n^2).$$

It follows that any transformation in the 2^k-space which preserves the relations $e_i^2 = -1$, $e_i e_j = -e_j e_i$ is a representation in that space of the $n \times n$ orthogonal group. But if B is an orthogonal matrix, the quantities $e'_j = \sum b_{ji} e_i$ satisfy these relations. Because the elements e' are elements of the e algebra which give rise to another of identical structure, the correspondence $e \to e'$ is called an 'automorphism' of the algebra. It can be shown that an automorphism $e_i \to e'_i$ of a complete matrix algebra can always be expressed as conjugation or transformation,

$$e'_i = T e_i \, T^{-1} \quad \text{(all } i).$$

Corresponding therefore to each element B of the n-dimensional orthogonal group there is a different automorphism $e_i \to \sum b_{ij} e_j$ of the 2^k-dimensional algebra, and these can be written $e_i \to T_b \, e_i \, T_b^{-1}$. Then the matrices T_b form a representation in 2^k dimensions of the n-dimensional orthogonal group, proper or spin, since

$$(-T_b) e_i (-T_b)^{-1} = T_b \, e_i \, T_b^{-1},$$

and, again, it can be shown that the representation so obtained is actually a spin representation and, over the whole orthogonal group, irreducible. It is known as the basic spin representation and its Kronecker products with the various true representations give rise to other spin representations.

The above summary is over-simplified in places but should give the student the perspective for further reading and for appreciating the following more detailed results which we give without proofs.

$n = 2$ ($k = 1$). The two-dimensional orthogonal group is $\mathfrak{d}_\infty$ and its rotation subgroup is $\mathfrak{c}_\infty$. The basic spin representation is in $2^k = 2$ dimensions, and is

$$R(\theta) = \pm \begin{bmatrix} e^{i\theta/2} & 0 \\ 0 & e^{-i\theta/2} \end{bmatrix}, \qquad F = \pm \begin{bmatrix} 0 & 1 \\ 1 & 0 \end{bmatrix}, \qquad FR(\theta) = \pm \begin{bmatrix} 0 & e^{-i\theta/2} \\ e^{i\theta/2} & 0 \end{bmatrix},$$

where F is the matrix $\begin{bmatrix} 1 & 0 \\ 0 & -1 \end{bmatrix}$ (of the original group) which we chose in the previous section to generate the improper coset from the rotation group. It will be seen at once that as far as the subgroup $\mathfrak{c}_\infty = \mathfrak{r}_2$ is concerned, the representation is reducible; there are in fact no irreducible representations of dimension greater than one, spin or otherwise, of any cyclic group. The other spin representations are the Kronecker products of this one with the true representations, and we reach the same conclusions as from the Moebius strip concerning the rotation group, together with corresponding information on the orthogonal group.

$n = 3$ $(k = 1)$. As before, $2^k = 2$; the basic spin representation is therefore in two dimensions, and is, as we saw in § 12.4, the group $\mathfrak{u}_2$. We need to relate the conclusions of § 12.4 to the present ones. Theorem 12.4.1 showed that there is a representation of $\mathfrak{r}_3$ in $s = r+1$ dimensions (every integral s, $r = 0$ giving the identical one), and the comments following it showed that the representation is true for odd s and spin for even s. Any rotation in three dimensions can be transformed into a rotation in a given plane through an angle ω; its characters in the first three representations are (1) in the identical representation, 1, (2) in the basic spin representation, $2 \cos \frac{1}{2}\omega$, and (3) in the three-dimensional (defining) representation, $1+2\cos\omega$. The formulae which relate § 12.4 to the present section and to the characters $\{\lambda\}'$ of the previous section are:

$$\{\lambda\}' = \frac{\sin(\lambda+\frac{1}{2})\omega}{\sin\frac{1}{2}\omega} \qquad \lambda = \frac{r}{2} = \frac{s-1}{2}.$$

The first of these relations follows by algebraic manipulation (summation of a geometric progression) from the form given in § 12.4 for the character. The second shows that the characters of the spin representations can be obtained formally by giving λ half-integral as well as integral values.

In general, the procedure for obtaining the basic spin representation leads to one whose character, for the proper rotation defined by the angles $\theta_1,...,\theta_k$, is

$$2^k \cos \tfrac{1}{2}\theta_1 \cos \tfrac{1}{2}\theta_2 ... \cos \tfrac{1}{2}\theta_k.$$

When n is even, the improper elements have character zero, and this representation is irreducible over the orthogonal group $\mathfrak{o}_n$ but splits into two, with characters

$$2^{k-1}(\cos \tfrac{1}{2}\theta_1 ... \cos \tfrac{1}{2}\theta_k \pm i^k \sin \tfrac{1}{2}\theta_1 ... \sin \tfrac{1}{2}\theta_k)$$

in the rotation group $\mathfrak{r}_n$. When n is odd this representation is irreducible over both groups.

CHAPTER XIV

TENSORS

In the remaining chapters of this book we shall be discussing the implications of the matter of the foregoing chapters for our understanding of physical theories. The groups may be the crystallographic ones, or the rotation group, or may be some other which the physical theory calls for. Naturally we shall deal in particular with those parts of physical theory which concern directed quantities such as vectors. As, however, vectors are not the only quantities in which direction plays an essential part, we must first enlarge the concept of vectors into that of tensors. We shall find that we have already taken the first steps towards this. For a tensor of rank r in n dimensions is defined as an ordered set of n^r numbers for which the transformation law under a change of coordinate system is the same as that of the n^r products of the components of r vectors. Thus a dyad, or a dyadic (which transforms in the same way), is a tensor of rank 2, and a tensor of rank 1 is the same thing as a vector. The transformations may be those of the products of contravariant vectors, or of covariant vectors, or both, and so we get covariant and contravariant tensors and mixed tensors. Before dealing with specific examples, however, we must look at a matter which will both develop the general ideas and considerably enlarge their usefulness.

14.2. The metric tensor

Consider the transformation, in three dimensions, from cartesians to polars. If the coordinates of a point are (x, y, z) in the former and (r, θ, ϕ) in the latter, the equations of transformation are

$$\left. \begin{aligned} r^2 &= x^2 + y^2 + z^2 & x &= r \sin\theta \cos\phi \\ \theta &= \cos^{-1} z/(x^2 + y^2 + z^2)^{\frac{1}{2}} & y &= r \sin\theta \sin\phi \\ \phi &= \tan^{-1} y/x & z &= r \cos\theta \end{aligned} \right\}. \qquad (14.2.1)$$

This is *not* a linear transformation. But consider this point as a new origin, and consider a vector V given by (dx, dy, dz) in cartesians and by $(dr, d\theta, d\phi)$ in what we may conveniently call differential polars. Then the relations

$$\begin{aligned} dx &= \sin\theta \cos\phi \, dr + r \cos\theta \cos\phi \, d\theta - r \sin\theta \sin\phi \, d\phi, \\ dy &= \sin\theta \sin\phi \, dr + r \cos\theta \sin\phi \, d\theta + r \sin\theta \cos\phi \, d\phi, \\ dz &= \cos\theta \, dr - r \sin\theta \, d\theta, \end{aligned}$$

derived in the usual way from the second set of equations constitutes a transformation which, in any region small enough to consider r, θ, and ϕ constant, *is* a linear transformation, viz. in an obvious notation

$$\begin{bmatrix} dx \\ dy \\ dz \end{bmatrix} = \begin{bmatrix} s_\theta c_\phi & r c_\theta c_\phi & -r s_\theta s_\phi \\ s_\theta s_\phi & r c_\theta s_\phi & r s_\theta c_\phi \\ c_\theta & -r s_\theta & 0 \end{bmatrix} \begin{bmatrix} dr \\ d\theta \\ d\phi \end{bmatrix}. \tag{14.2.2}$$

The components of this matrix could, with some difficulty, be expressed in terms of x, y, and z, but this is pointless; over the small region we are considering they are numerical constants, and to be thought of as such, and the whole equation is to be thought of as the equation $V* = PV^+$ of a linear transformation of local coordinates. The determinant of this transformation can be worked out; it is $r^2 \sin\theta$, and the inverse transformation is

$$\begin{bmatrix} dr \\ d\theta \\ d\phi \end{bmatrix} = \begin{bmatrix} s_\theta c_\phi & s_\theta s_\phi & c_\theta \\ c_\theta c_\phi/r & c_\theta s_\phi/r & -s_\theta/r \\ -s_\phi/r s_\theta & c_\phi/r s_\theta & 0 \end{bmatrix} \begin{bmatrix} dx \\ dy \\ dz \end{bmatrix}. \tag{14.2.3}$$

The length of this vector $V*$ is the square root of $*VV* = {}^+V\tilde{P}PV^+$. Explicitly, if we denote the length by ds, we have

$$ds^2 = dx^2 + dy^2 + dz^2 \tag{14.2.4}$$

$$= dr^2 + r^2 d\theta^2 + r^2 \sin^2\theta\, d\phi^2. \tag{14.2.5}$$

The geometrical interpretation of the latter expression is obvious; the infinitesimal displacements $(dr, 0, 0)$, $(0, d\theta, 0)$, and $(0, 0, d\phi)$ are all at right angles and represent distances dr, $r\,d\theta$, and $r\sin\theta\,d\phi$. The basic vectors of this local coordinate system are therefore at right angles but unequal in length, their lengths being 1, r, and $r\sin\theta$. Since they are at right angles, the reciprocal basic vectors are in the same directions but with lengths inversely proportional, a fact which the student may correlate with the form of the inverse matrix, P^{-1}, given above.

It is not necessary, but an accident of this example, that the basic vectors of the local system should be at right angles, and $\tilde{P}P$ therefore diagonal. In the general case the transformation is given by a series of n functions $x'_r = f_r(x_1, x_2, ..., x_r)$, and the local transformation by the expressions summarized in matrix form as

$$\begin{bmatrix} dx'_1 \\ dx'_2 \\ \cdot \\ dx'_r \end{bmatrix} = \begin{bmatrix} \dfrac{\partial x'_1}{\partial x_1} & \dfrac{\partial x'_1}{\partial x_2} & \cdot\cdot\cdot & \dfrac{\partial x'_1}{\partial x_r} \\ \dfrac{\partial x'_2}{\partial x_1} & \dfrac{\partial x'_2}{\partial x_2} & \cdot\cdot\cdot & \dfrac{\partial x'_2}{\partial x_r} \\ \cdot & \cdot & \cdot\cdot\cdot & \cdot \end{bmatrix} \begin{bmatrix} dx_1 \\ dx_2 \\ \cdot \\ dx_r \end{bmatrix} = P^{-1} \begin{bmatrix} dx_1 \\ dx_2 \\ \cdot \\ dx_r \end{bmatrix}.$$

$$\tag{14.2.6}$$

The length of a vector is, as before, $*VV* = +V\tilde{P}PV+$, and as the matrix $\tilde{P}P$, though not necessarily diagonal, is necessarily symmetrical, this results in the expression (where we write G for $\tilde{P}P$ in accordance with general usage)

$$ds^2 = g_{11}\,dx_1'^2 + g_{22}\,dx_2'^2 + \dots + 2g_{12}\,dx_1'\,dx_2' + \dots . \qquad (14.2.7)$$

In § 4.6 we called the array $G = \tilde{P}P$ the metric operator; it is more commonly known as the metric tensor.

Notice that a dyad and the metric tensor are tensors of different kinds. For the dyad $X**Y$ transforms into $P^{-1}(X**Y)P$ which is

$$(P^{-1}X)**(XP) = X+{}^{\circ}X;$$

that is to say that it transforms like the product of a covariant with a contravariant vector, and is therefore a *mixed* tensor of rank 2. But the metric tensor, which is I in cartesians, transforms to $\tilde{P}P = \tilde{P}IP$, and is thus 'covariant on both sides'.

One point which should not be passed over without mention is that we have assumed that the matrix P is non-singular. We have, in fact, evaluated its determinant in the case of the spherical polar transformation as $r^2\sin\theta$, which *is* zero for $r = 0$ or for $\theta = 0$, but not otherwise. If the student will consider lines of latitude and longitude he will see at once that at $\theta = 0$ (the poles, not the equator) there is no question of the coordinates being locally a linear transformation of cartesians, and the same is true of $r = 0$. The determinant of the matrix in the general case is the Jacobian of the transformation, and further information can be sought under this head in works on advanced calculus.

14.3. General notions

We have developed the subject of tensors hitherto in a manner designed to link it up with our former work, and also to bring out clearly the distinction between co- and contra-variance, which is often very obscure for the beginner who, reading the ordinary texts, usually fails (quite correctly) to find any difference between them in normal cartesians, and jumps straight to curvilinear coordinates, which he has every excuse for finding obscure. As we have defined these terms in § 4.6, the contra- and co-variant forms of a vector are the same vector referred to the basic and the reciprocal basic vectors respectively, and although it is often convenient for the former to be a column and the latter a row vector, there is no fixed correspondence between these concepts. In tensor analysis, the equations (4.6.4) (rewritten in algebraic form) are made the definition of a vector; this is (14.2.6) for a contravariant vector, and for a covariant vector, since P^{-1} and P are matrices of inverse transformations, the corresponding equation has $\partial x_r/\partial x'_s$ as its matrix instead of $\partial x'_r/\partial x_s$. (The student should note, as pointed out in greater detail below, that despite their appearance, $\partial x_r/\partial x'_s$ and $\partial x'_s/\partial x_r$ are not reciprocals.)

The products of the components of r vectors in n dimensions form an r-dimensional array ($n \times n \times n$... to r factors); this makes our usual notation unmanageable and forces us to abandon it temporarily in favour of the notation of tensor calculus, which we must therefore pause to describe. In n dimensions, any array of n^r quantities distinguished among themselves by r affixes which can each run through the values $1,...,n$, is called a tensor if it transforms in the same way as the product of r vectors. If it transforms as the product of p contravariant and $r-p$ covariant vectors, it is given a symbol consisting of a capital letter with p subscripts and $r-p$ superscripts. If these are numerical, the whole symbol represents a component, but if they are literal they are assumed to 'run' through the values $1,...,n$, and thus the symbol represents the complete array. The transformation law is thus

$$A'^{\;\;\;.\;cd\,..}_{\tilde{g}\tilde{h}\,:\,:\,:\,:} = \sum_p \sum_q \cdots \sum_s \sum_t \cdots \frac{\partial x'_c}{\partial x_p} \frac{\partial x'_d}{\partial x_q} \frac{\partial x_s}{\partial x'_g} \frac{\partial x_t}{\partial x'_h} A^{\;\;\;.\;pq\,.}_{st\,:\,:\,:\,:},$$

an expression implying n^r separate equations. It is usual in tensor calculus to suppress the summation signs, and to assume summation whenever the same running index occurs twice, once as a contravariant and once as a covariant index. (This occasionally gives trouble and the summation convention has to be declared suspended. Trouble is more frequent with numerical indices, but the context often disposes of it.) Thus what we have hitherto written $X^{+\circ}Y$ would in tensor notation be $X^r Y_s$ or $Y_s X^r$, with n^2 components, and what we have been writing $^\circ XY^+$ would be written $X_r Y^r$ or $Y^r X_r$, a scalar with only one component since summation over $r = 1,...,n$ is understood. Our operator A thus becomes $A^r_{.s}$, a mixed tensor of the second rank, and the products $Y^* = AX^*$ and $^*Z = ^*XA$ become

$$Y^r = A^r_{.s} X^s = X^s A^r_{.s} \quad \text{and} \quad Z_s = X_r A^r_{.s} = A^r_{.s} X_r.$$

It is easily seen that the order of the factors is immaterial in the tensor notation, the matrix order betraying itself in the arrangement of the suffixes. An important more recent development is the notation by which the rth column of the matrix A regarded as a vector, which we have denoted by $A_r{}^*$, is given the symbol $\overset{r}{A}_s$. In this notation, the s is still a subscript, showing that the components are obtained by giving s the values $1,...,n$, but the r has become part of the 'kernel', as the capital letter is called, showing that $\overset{r}{A}_s$ and $\overset{t}{A}_s$ are *two different vectors*, and not different notations for the same tensor. The quantity we have called A_{rs}, the (r, s) component of A, becomes in this notation $\overset{r}{A}$, while $*A_s$ becomes $\underset{s}{A^r}$. It is easily seen how much more powerful this notation is when tensors of high rank are under consideration.

The relation between the basic vectors and basic reciprocal vectors is a reciprocal one, and if their roles are interchanged it is easily verified that the metric tensor becomes G^{-1}, the reciprocal of the original metric tensor, G, in the matrix sense. The components of the metric tensor, which is covariant, are written g_{pq}, and those of its inverse, which from the original standpoint is contravariant, are written g^{pq}. We have already seen that a vector which takes the form V^* in normal cartesians, in which system co- and contravariant vectors have the same form, becomes $V^+ = P^{-1}V^*$ in a new system if it is contravariant, but $V^{\circ} = \tilde{P}V^*$ if it is covariant. (Each of these equations, and those which follow, may be transposed into row form if desired, but we shall take this for granted.) But $G^{-1}V^{\circ}$ may be written $(\tilde{P}P)^{-1}\tilde{P}V^* = P^{-1}V^* = V^+$. In tensor notation this result is expressed by saying that $V_r = g_{rs}V^s$ is the method of deriving the covariant form of a vector when the contravariant form is given; conversely $V^r = g^{rs}V_s$. (The student should satisfy himself that these two notations do express the same thing.)

As G is symmetrical, the quantities $g_{rt}g^{st}$ and $g_{tr}g^{ts}$ are, in matrix notation, GG^{-1} and $G^{-1}G$, and are both equal to I. In tensor notation they will be g_r^s, a mixed tensor whose components are $\begin{cases} 1 & r = s \\ 0 & r \neq s \end{cases}$ in *all* coordinate systems. It is sometimes useful to use this tensor formally for changing an index, since $g_r^s A^r = A^s$.

It is perhaps worth digressing a moment here to take up a point already mentioned which can mystify the beginner, who will be led astray if he imagines that

$$\frac{\partial x_a'}{\partial x_b} = 1 \bigg/ \frac{\partial x_b}{\partial x_a'}.$$

One would never be tempted to make this mistake if the partial differentials were written in full as $(\partial x_a'/\partial x_b)_{x_c}$ and $(\partial x_b/\partial x_a')_{x_c'}$—whence it is clear that the variables held constant are not the same in the two expressions. If, for example, we are considering the simple rotation in two dimensions,

$$y' = y\cos\theta - x\sin\theta \qquad y = y'\cos\theta + x'\sin\theta$$

$$x' = y\sin\theta + x\cos\theta \qquad x = -y'\sin\theta + x'\cos\theta,$$

then

$$\frac{\partial y'}{\partial x} = \frac{\partial x}{\partial y'} = -\sin\theta \qquad \frac{\partial y'}{\partial y} = \frac{\partial x}{\partial x'} = \cos\theta, \quad \text{etc.,}$$

so that in this case, from the first of these equations, the differentials in question are not reciprocals but are equal. The same warning against too facile reading of notation may be made in respect of the usual proof that g_s^r is invariant for all changes of coordinates, namely, that on making the coordinate change, we have, by the definition of a mixed tensor,

$$g_s'^r = \frac{\partial x_r'}{\partial x_a}\frac{\partial x_b}{\partial x_s'}g_b^a = \frac{\partial x_r'}{\partial x_a}\frac{\partial x_a}{\partial x_s'}g_a^a = \begin{cases} 1 & r = s \\ 0 & r \neq s \end{cases} = g_s^r.$$

The third expression follows because g_a^a is the only non-zero term in the sum over $1,\ldots,n$, but the fourth does not follow because of any apparent cancelling to give $\partial x_r'/\partial x_s'$ ($= 1$ or 0 as r is or is not equal to s); in fact, in the simple two-dimensional rotation example this third-stage expression is a sum $\sin^2\theta.1 + \cos^2\theta.1$. The relation underlying this step would be much clearer if it were expressed in matrix form

$$g_s'^r = \frac{\partial x_r'}{\partial x_a}\frac{\partial x_b}{\partial x_s'}g_b^a = \frac{\partial x_r'}{\partial x_a}g_b^a\frac{\partial x_b}{\partial x_s'} = P^{-1}IP = I.$$

The importance of tensors lies in two directions. First of all, just as certain physical quantities such as velocities are vectors, so certain physical quantities are tensors of higher rank. For example, when a vector reaction such as an electric moment is produced in a material medium by a vector influence such as the electric field, the 'coefficient of proportionality' is a tensor, since, in an anisotropic medium, an electric field along any given direction will, in general, induce a moment with components at right angles to itself. The relation between the field E and the moment μ has therefore to be in the form

$$\mu_x = a_{xx}E_x + a_{xy}E_y + a_{xz}E_z, \quad \text{etc.}$$

The quantity a is a tensor property of the medium. The only directions of the field which produce a moment in the *same* direction as the field itself are those parallel to the eigenvectors of the operator a.

Secondly, an equation between tensors is valid in all systems of coordinates if it is valid in one, on account of the transformation laws, a fact which is extremely useful in the theory of relativity. Tensors share this property with certain other quantities under more restricted circumstances (see § 14.7), and it is going too far to say that for this reason all equations in relativity should be tensor equations.

Since the same tensor can exist in various forms, covariant, contravariant, or mixed, it is necessary to examine the definition of any given tensor (including vectors) to find out in which form it is given. The procedure is similar to the elementary process of determining the dimensions of a quantity, but probes more finely in that each coordinate must be treated separately (a procedure recently used by Huntley for increasing the power of the method of dimensions). The cartesian coordinates and any coordinate differentials are contravariant, and in tensor notation they should be written x^1, x^2,..., dx^1, dx^2,..., though the commoner *sub*script notation is often reverted to when the summation convention is not involved, particularly if powers are to be expressed. In three dimensions, time, whether t or dt, is a scalar. Hence velocity dx^r/dt and acceleration d^2x^r/dt^2 are also contravariant vectors. Any undirected quantity independent of the coordinate system should be a scalar; besides time we have mass m as another such quantity, and we shall assume that potential energy E is a third, though full clarification of this involves §§ 14.7 and 15.8, where the relation between physical dimensions and tensor character is discussed more fully. We now come to one of the points where tensor analysis comes into its own on a really elementary application. Force may be defined as mass multiplied by acceleration, $m\ddot{X}$, and on this definition it is a contravariant vector. But it may also be defined as the gradient of the potential energy dE/dx^r, and as such, with the coordinate differential appearing in the denominator, it is of dimension -1 in the coordinate, and covariant. Before we equate these two vectors we must convert them to the same form. We therefore write Newton's second law in the form

$$m\ddot{X}^r = g^{rs}\left(\frac{dE}{dx^s}\right).$$

In normal cartesians $g^{rs} = \begin{cases} 1 & r = s \\ 0 & r \neq s \end{cases}$, and the law takes its normal form, but this tensor equation is valid in *all* systems of coordinates, and in plane polars, for example, it becomes (two equations in two dimensions) $m\ddot{r} = dE/dr$ and $mr^2\ddot{\theta} = dE/d\theta$—the latter being the familiar relation between angular acceleration, moment of inertia, and couple.

14.4. The volume element and the Laplace operator

Two problems in calculus must here claim our attention. The first is the integration of a function (such as a density) over a volume to obtain a total (e.g. from density, total mass) within the volume. This is briefly written $\int_V f(x^1,...,x^n)\,dV$, or in more detail

$$\int ... \int f(x^1,...,x^n)\,dx^1...dx^n.$$

A little thought as to the origin of this expression shows us that $dx^1...dx^n$ is the volume of the n-space contained between the hyperplanes $x^1 = x_0^1$ and $x^1 = x_0^1 + dx^1$ on one pair of opposite sides, $x^2 = x_0^2$ and $x^2 = x_0^2 + dx^2$ on another pair, and so on. But this result is valid only in normal cartesians; in oblique cartesians cosine factors will have to be introduced, and in more complicated cases the volume of this element will vary from point to point. We can obtain the general expression by the following argument. The volume $dx^1...dx^n$ can be expressed in the form of the determinant of the matrix

$$Q = \begin{bmatrix} dx^1 & 0 & . & . & . & 0 \\ 0 & dx^2 & . & . & . & 0 \\ . & . & . & . & . & . \\ 0 & 0 & . & . & . & dx^n \end{bmatrix}$$

(which has only one non-zero term). Under an arbitrary change of coordinates the columns of this matrix become the columns of the matrix $Q' = RQ$ (regarding Q not as an operator but as a set of vectors) and applying to this the theorem (proved in § 7.8) that the determinants multiply like the matrices, we see that $|Q| = |Q'|/|R| = |Q'|/(|G|)^{\frac{1}{2}}$. The matrix is not in diagonal form, however, and we still have the volume between the *original* coordinate increases. We now transform Q' to diagonal form by the process of § 7.4. Each stage of this adds to one vector a multiple of another, and thus, though changing the shape of the element of volume, changes it to another parallelepiped on the same base and between the same parallels, so that the volume is unaltered. At the end of the process it is a parallelepiped each edge of which is an infinitesimal basic vector in the new system, and the determinant, being diagonal, is the product of these vectors. We thus have

$$dV = dx^1 dx^2 ... dx^n = g^{\frac{1}{2}} dx'^1 dx'^2 ... dx'^n, \tag{14.4.1}$$

the second expression holding in all systems of coordinates.

As an example of the use of this equation let us return to the subject of the volume element in the group manifold, taking $\mathfrak{u}_2$ as an example. We begin with a process so naïve that its results will need confirming when obtained. We set, in fact, the general 'special unitary' matrix

$$U(\theta, \phi, \psi) = \begin{bmatrix} \cos\theta\, e^{i\phi} & \sin\theta\, e^{i\psi} \\ -\sin\theta\, e^{-i\psi} & \cos\theta\, e^{-i\phi} \end{bmatrix} \text{ equal to } \begin{bmatrix} w & x \\ y & z \end{bmatrix}$$

and we plot all such matrices as points in a complex four-space with w, x, y, and z as coordinates. Then

$$dw = -\sin\theta\, e^{i\phi}\, d\theta + i\cos\theta\, e^{i\phi}\, d\phi$$

$$dx = \quad \cos\theta\, e^{i\psi}\, d\theta \qquad\qquad + i\sin\theta\, e^{i\psi}\, d\psi$$

$$dy = -\cos\theta\, e^{-i\psi}\, d\theta \qquad\qquad - i\sin\theta\, e^{-i\psi}\, d\psi$$

$$dz = -\sin\theta\, e^{-i\phi}\, d\theta - i\cos\theta\, e^{-i\phi}\, d\phi.$$

As the group is a three parameter one, it forms a three-space locus in the w-x-y-z-space, and dw, dx, dy, dz are not independent if the varied matrix is still special-unitary. Assuming the four-space to be unitary-orthogonal,

$$ds^2 = dw d\bar{w} + dx d\bar{x} + dy d\bar{y} + dz d\bar{z}$$

$$= 2(d\theta^2 - \cos^2\theta\, d\phi^2 - \sin^2\theta\, d\psi^2).$$

This is therefore the metric of the three-space. Its volume element, apart from a numerical factor, is therefore

$$dV = |\cos\theta \sin\theta|\, d\theta d\phi d\psi.$$

Had we, instead of using the 'simple' representation of the 2×2 algebra, used the quaternion one, this would have amounted to a rotation of axes which leaves the essential geometry of the surface (the manifold) undisturbed. This thought removes some of the arbitrariness of our procedure.

But we do need some justification for starting with the four-space unitary-orthogonal. And, indeed, the volume element in the group manifold should be definable in terms of the abstract group, and not in terms of one of its representations (even if, as here, the representation used is the defining one). With this aim in view, we say that if the general infinitesimal operator of the group is

$$I + aA + bB + cC + \ldots$$

where a, b, c,... are infinitesimals, and the operators $I+aA$, $I+bB$, $I+cC$,... define a parallelepiped in the neighbourhood of I with volume $abc...$, then the vectors from X to $X+aXA$, $X+bXB$, $X+cXC$,... *must* define an *equal* volume in the neighbourhood of X. We may ask whether the vectors X to $X+aAX$, $X+bBX$, $X+cCX$,... will also do so consistently. The answer to this question is obtained by transferring the original volume from I to X by left multiplication and bringing it back by right multiplication—the result is the volume defined by the vectors

$$I \quad \text{to} \quad I+aXAX^{-1}, \quad I+bXBX^{-1}, \quad I+cXCX^{-1}, \quad \ldots.$$

But the transformations $A \to XAX^{-1}$, $B \to XBX^{-1}$, etc., constitute a mapping of the group manifold on itself; a transformation of the manifold. Transformations $A \to YAY^{-1}$,... associate one such mapping with each of X, Y,..., and the set of these mappings, of these transformations of the group manifold, constitute a representation of the elements X, Y,... in the group manifold as representation space, linear so long as infinitesimal elements are considered. Provided that the group is closed, the determinants of X, Y,... in this representation must be uni-modular, and therefore preserve volume in the group manifold. Subject to this proviso, therefore, that the group is a closed one, right and left translation yield the same definition of unit volume in the neighbourhood of X.

If our previous result is consistent with this theory we need not worry too much how we got it. But the immediate application of the theory to the special unitary group is complicated by the vanishing of $\sin \theta$ at I. Consider therefore the more general case of going from Y to YX instead of from I to X; consider, in fact,

$$\begin{bmatrix} w & x \\ y & z \end{bmatrix}\begin{bmatrix} f & g \\ h & k \end{bmatrix} = \begin{bmatrix} wf+xh & wg+xk \\ yf+zh & yg+zk \end{bmatrix} = \begin{bmatrix} w' & x' \\ y' & z' \end{bmatrix}.$$

Then $\qquad\qquad\qquad dw' = f\,dw + h\,dx$, etc.,

whence

$$(ds')^2 = (f\,dw + h\,dx)(\bar{f}\,d\bar{w} + \bar{h}\,d\bar{x}) + \ldots, \text{ etc.}$$

$$= (f\bar{f} + g\bar{g})\,dw\,d\bar{w} + (\bar{f}h + \bar{g}k)\,d\bar{w}\,dx + (f\bar{h} + g\bar{k})\,dw\,d\bar{x} + \ldots$$

$$= dw\,d\bar{w} + dx\,d\bar{x} + \ldots \quad \text{provided } \begin{bmatrix} f & g \\ h & k \end{bmatrix} \text{ is unitary.}$$

Since $ds' = ds$ in form, $dV' = dV$, and our method is justified in the circumstances in which we used it, though how it is to be validly applied in other cases is only suggested by this analysis—it is obvious that the unitariness of the four-space and the unitariness of the matrix $\begin{bmatrix} f & g \\ h & k \end{bmatrix}$ have together brought about the result.

As the orthogonality relations sum over classes, it is usually more convenient to express the volume element in a form adapted to this. By § 12.3 a class of the special unitary group is defined by a single parameter ω, which takes values from 0 to π, defined by

$$\cos \omega = \cos \theta \cos \phi.$$

A function, such as a character, which is the same for all elements of a class, will be of the form $f(\omega)$, and its integral over all the group will be

$$\int_0^{2\pi} \int_0^{2\pi} \int_0^{2\pi} f(\omega) \, |\cos \theta \sin \theta| \, d\theta d\phi d\psi = 2\pi \int_0^{2\pi} \int_0^{2\pi} f(\omega) \, |\cos \theta \sin \theta| \, d\theta d\phi$$

since ω does not involve ψ. We cannot so easily integrate again—θ and ϕ must both be expressed in terms of ω and another variable, and the integration performed with respect to the other. As ω and $-\omega$ define the same class, the range of ω is only half that of θ or ϕ. The resulting expression for the integral of a class function is

$$8\pi \int_0^\pi f(\omega) \sin^2\omega \, d\omega.$$

The other continuous groups can be treated similarly.

The second problem is that of the transformation of certain differential operators. The reader is probably familiar with the operator ∇ (called 'del', or sometimes 'nabla'); it is a 'vector' with components

$$(d/dx_1, d/dx_2, ..., d/dx_n),$$

and if ϕ is a scalar function of position then the product $\nabla\phi$ is a vector $(d\phi/dx_1, d\phi/dx_2, ..., d\phi/dx_n)$, the *gradient* of ϕ. The operator

$$*\nabla\nabla* = (d^2/dx_1^2 + d^2/dx_2^2 + ...)$$

is the 'Laplace operator'. In going out of cartesians a problem arises which is really one of notation in that on going over to the transpose of, say, $G\nabla\phi$, the answer is only $\phi\tilde{\nabla}\tilde{G}$ if the differentials in $\tilde{\nabla}$ are assumed to operate to the left, a highly inconvenient assumption which is sometimes made, in which case $\tilde{\nabla}$ is written $(\delta/\delta x_1, \delta/\delta x_2, ..., \delta/\delta x_n)$, but which may be evaded, so far as the Laplace operator is concerned, by the result which we now prove.

Let ϕ be any scalar function of position; then it commutes with matrices which are functions of position provided they do not contain differential operators. Thus—in matrix and expanded notations in parallel columns for clarity!—

$$(^\circ\nabla V^*)\phi = {}^\circ\nabla\phi V^* \qquad\qquad \left(\sum_s \frac{\partial}{\partial x'_s} V_s\right)\phi = \sum_s \frac{\partial}{\partial x'_s}(V_s\phi)$$

$$= \phi(^\circ\nabla V^*) + {}^\circ(\nabla\phi)V^* \qquad = \phi\sum_s \frac{\partial V_s}{\partial x'_s} + \sum_s V_s\frac{\partial\phi}{\partial x'_s}$$

$$= \phi(^\circ\nabla V^*) + {}^*V\nabla^\circ\phi \qquad = \phi\sum_s \frac{\partial V_s}{\partial x'_s} + \left(\sum_s V_s\frac{\partial}{\partial x'_s}\right)\phi.$$

Now in the special case of $V^* = \hat{P}_r{}^*$, the first sum in the last line vanishes identically, for it is the determinant

$$\begin{vmatrix} \dfrac{\partial x'_1}{\partial x_1} & \cdot\ \cdot\ \cdot & \dfrac{\partial x'_1}{\partial x_s} & \cdot\ \cdot\ \cdot & \dfrac{\partial x'_1}{\partial x_n} \\[2ex] \dfrac{\partial x'_2}{\partial x_1} & \cdot\ \cdot\ \cdot & \dfrac{\partial x'_2}{\partial x_s} & \cdot\ \cdot\ \cdot & \dfrac{\partial x'_2}{\partial x_n} \\[2ex] \cdot\ \ \cdot\ \ \cdot\ \ \cdot\ \ \cdot\ \ \cdot\ \ \cdot\ \ \cdot \end{vmatrix}$$

with the rth row replaced by the row $(\partial/\partial x_1...\partial/\partial x_s...\partial/\partial x_n)$ and on inspection this will be found to behave formally as a determinant with two rows proportional. Hence

$$(^\circ\nabla\hat{P}_r{}^*)\phi = (^*\hat{P}_r\nabla^\circ)\phi. \tag{14.4.2}$$

As ϕ is arbitrary we can drop it and use this as an operator equation; the relation is then $^\circ\nabla\hat{P}_r{}^* = {}^*\hat{P}_r\nabla^\circ = {}^*\hat{P}_r\tilde{P}\nabla^*$, the latter from the familiar equations of § 4.6. We can put these r results together in a row, suppressing the subscript r and the final stars, and if we also substitute $\hat{P} = |P|P^{-1}$, we arrive at the formula

$$^\circ\nabla|P|P^{-1} = |P|^*\nabla,$$

or $$^*\nabla = |P|^{-1}{}^\circ\nabla|P|P^{-1}. \tag{14.4.3}$$

As $\nabla^* = \tilde{P}^{-1}\nabla^\circ$ in the usual way, with no difficulties as the differentials are in the final factor, we can now write

$$^*\nabla\nabla^* = |P|^{-1}{}^\circ\nabla|P|P^{-1}\tilde{P}^{-1}\nabla^\circ$$

$$= g^{-\frac{1}{2}}{}^\circ\nabla g^{\frac{1}{2}}G^{-1}\nabla^\circ \tag{14.4.4}$$

as the form of the Laplace operator when the metric tensor is given. When G is diagonal this reduces to the form

$$\frac{1}{q_{11}\,q_{22}\cdots}\left\{\frac{d}{dx'_1}\left(\frac{q_{22}\,q_{33}\cdots}{q_{11}}\frac{d}{dx'_1}\right)+\frac{d}{dx'_2}\left(\frac{q_{11}\,q_{33}\cdots}{q_{22}}\frac{d}{dx'_2}\right)+\cdots\right\},\qquad(14.4.5)$$

where $q_{rr}=g_{rr}^{\frac{1}{2}}$. It is this result which gives rise to operators of the type of L'' of § 12.8.

14.5. Tensor properties of matter: (i) symmetrical tensors

In the tensors of elementary physics we return to a somewhat simpler situation since they need not normally be specified except in ortho-normal cartesian coordinates, and thus the distinction between covariance and contravariance can be neglected, since under these conditions $X^+ = P^{-1}X^*$ and $X^\circ = \tilde{P}X^*$ are the same transformation. The question of interest in this section and the next is the determination of the relations which must hold between the components of a tensor when more than usual symmetry conditions hold. Two questions are involved —symmetry in the nature of the tensor, and symmetry due to the crystalline nature of the medium. We discuss the former first, and the latter in the next section.

We have seen in § 13.5 that an array of n^r components specified by r indices can be broken down (decomposed, or reduced) into the sum of parts each of which displays on permutation of the indices a different irreducible representation of the group π_r.

Thus π_2 has only two irreducible representations, the identical, $[2]$, and the alternating, $[1^2]$. A tensor of rank 2 contains n^2 components, which may be represented as a matrix, say T. Consider the tensors (also in matrix form)

$$T_{[2]}=\tfrac{1}{2}(T+\tilde{T}),\qquad T_{[1^2]}=\tfrac{1}{2}(T-\tilde{T}).$$

These are unchanged and change in sign respectively if the suffixes are permuted, for

$$(T_{[2]})_{ij}=\tfrac{1}{2}(T_{ij}+T_{ji})=(T_{[2]})_{ji}$$

and

$$(T_{[1^2]})_{ij}=\tfrac{1}{2}(T_{ij}-T_{ji})=-(T_{[1^2]})_{ji}.$$

Further,

$$T=T_{[2]}+T_{[1^2]},\qquad \tilde{T}=T_{[2]}-T_{[1^2]},$$

so that T is completely determined by the two parts into which it has been split. $T_{[2]}$ has its non-diagonal terms equal in pairs; there are therefore $\tfrac{1}{2}n(n+1)$ independent terms. $T_{[1^2]}$ has diagonally opposite terms equal but opposite in sign, and the diagonal terms zero; $\frac{1}{2}n(n-1)$ independent terms in all. And

$$\tfrac{1}{2}n(n+1)+\tfrac{1}{2}n(n-1) = n^2.$$

A third rank tensor consists of terms T_{ijk} where i, j, k may be equal or unequal, and its components may be arranged in a cubic array. 'Transposing' may involve interchanging columns and rows, columns and tiers, etc., or a cyclic type of interchange—columns into rows, rows into tiers, and tiers into columns; there are five varieties of transpose (with the original tensor, 3! in all). Thus T_{ijk} may become any of the terms which head the table below. Under each we have put the characters of the class of the permutation which produced it.

	T_{ijk}	T_{jki}	T_{kij}	T_{jik}	T_{kji}	T_{ikj}
$\Gamma_{[3]}$.	1	1	1	1	1	1
$\Gamma_{[1^3]}$.	1	1	1	-1	-1	-1
$\Gamma_{[21]}$.	2	-1	-1	0	0	0

From this table we read off that T_{ijk} gives rise in the three 'symmetrical' tensors $T_{[3]}$, $T_{[1^3]}$, and $T_{[21]}$, to the following terms:

$$\text{in } T_{[3]} \qquad T_{ijk}+T_{jki}+T_{kij}+T_{jik}+T_{kji}+T_{ikj}$$

$$\text{in } T_{[1^3]} \qquad T_{ijk}+T_{jki}+T_{kij}-T_{jik}-T_{kji}-T_{ikj}$$

$$\text{in } T_{[21]} \qquad 2T_{ijk}-T_{jki}-T_{kij}.$$

We can see that each combination ijk (not each permutation) gives rise to one term in $T_{[3]}$, whether i, j, and k are the same or different, this term being repeated six times. In $T_{[1^3]}$, on the other hand, the corresponding term is zero if two of i, j, and k are the same; otherwise the term occurs three times with a positive sign and three times with a negative one. In $T_{[21]}$ each combination ijk gives rise to *six* terms provided i, j, and k are not *all* equal, viz.

$$2T_{ijk}-T_{jki}-T_{kij}, \quad 2T_{jki}-T_{kij}-T_{ijk}, \quad ...,$$

but these six terms represent only four independent terms since they are in sets of three which sum to zero.

To apply this method in more elaborate cases is illuminating, but does not lead easily to any general result for the number of independent components in a given case. The general case may be evaluated in the following manner. Imagine all the n^r terms written out in column form, and followed by successive columns in which the permutations of π_r have been applied. Each column is obtained from the first by the operation of a matrix, and these matrices constitute a representation by $n^r \times n^r$ matrices of π_r. The characters being the sum of the diagonal elements are the number of terms repeated in the same row. For instance, with $n = 2$, $r = 3$, we have

I abc	A cab	B bca	C bac	D cba	E acb
111	111	111	111	111	111
112	211	121	112	211	121
121	112	211	211	121	112
122	212	221	212	221	122
211	121	112	121	112	211
212	221	122	122	212	221
221	122	212	221	122	212
222	222	222	222	222	222

Repeated terms are underlined, and we see that the characters are: of I, 8; of A and B, 2; of C, D, and E, 4. In general it is only necessary to consider one permutation from each class, and this, for the class $(p, q, r, ...)$ may be taken as the permutation

$$(12...p)(p+1...p+q)(p+q+1...p+q+r)... .$$

Then the only terms unaltered by this permutation are those whose suffixes are p alike, followed by q alike, followed by r alike..., and there are n^k such terms, where k is the number of cycles in $(p, q, r, ...)$. This representation is now analysed in the usual manner, and the number of terms in the tensor $T_{[\rho]}$ is the number of times the representation $\Gamma_{[\rho]}$ occurs multiplied by its dimensionality. Thus for tensors of the third rank in 2, 3, 4,..., n dimensions, the number of independent terms is calculated according to the following scheme:

Class	1^3	3	21	2 dimensions	3 dimensions	4 dimensions	n dimensions
h_ρ	1	2	3				
$\Gamma_{[3]}$	1	1	1	$24/6 = 4$	$60/6 = 10$	$120/6 = 20$	$(n^3+2n+3n^2)/6$
$\Gamma_{[1^3]}$	1	1	-1	$0/6 = 0$	$6/6 = 1$	$24/6 = 4$	$(n^3+2n-3n^2)/6$
$\Gamma_{[21]}$	2	-1	0	$12/6 = 2$	$48/6 = 8$	$120/6 = 20$	$(2n^3-2n)/6$
2 dimensions	8	2	4				
3 dimensions	27	3	9				
4 dimensions	64	4	16				
n dimensions	n^3	n	n^2				

whence the number of independent components in each 'symmetrical' part of a third rank tensor is given by

$n =$	2	3	4	n
$T_{[3]}$	4	10	20	$n(n+1)(n+2)/6$
$T_{[1^3]}$	0	1	4	$n(n-1)(n-2)/6$
$T_{[21]}$	4	16	40	$2n(n^2-1)/3$
Total	8	27	64	n^3

It should be noted, however, that the decomposition in (13.5.4) does not separate repeated equivalent representations. The above analysis of the third rank tensor is therefore incomplete to that extent. We shall see that further decomposition is possible but is to such an extent arbitrary that it is best left until the particular application to be made has been defined.

The tensor under consideration is a vector in the carrier space of the 8×8 matrices of § 13.4. The effect of the moduli of the class algebra is to separate (13.4.6) into the two parts

$$\begin{bmatrix} 1 & 0 & 0 & 0 & 0 & 0 & 0 & 0 \\ 0 & 1 & 0 & 0 & 0 & 0 & 0 & 0 \\ 0 & 0 & 1 & 0 & 0 & 0 & 0 & 0 \\ 0 & 0 & 0 & 1 & 0 & 0 & 0 & 0 \\ 0 & 0 & 0 & 0 & 0 & 0 & 0 & 0 \\ 0 & 0 & 0 & 0 & 0 & 0 & 0 & 0 \\ 0 & 0 & 0 & 0 & 0 & 0 & 0 & 0 \\ 0 & 0 & 0 & 0 & 0 & 0 & 0 & 0 \end{bmatrix} \quad \text{and} \quad \begin{bmatrix} 0 & 0 & 0 & 0 & 0 & 0 & 0 & 0 \\ 0 & 0 & 0 & 0 & 0 & 0 & 0 & 0 \\ 0 & 0 & 0 & 0 & 0 & 0 & 0 & 0 \\ 0 & 0 & 0 & 0 & 0 & 0 & 0 & 0 \\ 0 & 0 & 0 & 0 & * & * & 0 & 0 \\ 0 & 0 & 0 & 0 & * & * & 0 & 0 \\ 0 & 0 & 0 & 0 & 0 & 0 & * & * \\ 0 & 0 & 0 & 0 & 0 & 0 & * & * \end{bmatrix}.$$

Now

$$\begin{bmatrix} c_\theta & 0 & s_\theta & 0 \\ 0 & c_\phi & 0 & s_\phi \\ -s_\theta & 0 & c_\theta & 0 \\ 0 & -s_\phi & 0 & c_\phi \end{bmatrix} \begin{bmatrix} p & q & 0 & 0 \\ r & s & 0 & 0 \\ 0 & 0 & q & p \\ 0 & 0 & r & s \end{bmatrix} \begin{bmatrix} c_\theta & 0 & -s_\theta & 0 \\ 0 & c_\phi & 0 & -s_\phi \\ s_\theta & 0 & c_\theta & 0 \\ 0 & s_\phi & 0 & c_\phi \end{bmatrix} = \begin{bmatrix} p & q & 0 & 0 \\ r & s & 0 & 0 \\ 0 & 0 & p & q \\ 0 & 0 & r & s \end{bmatrix}$$

$$\begin{bmatrix} c_\theta & 0 & s_\theta & 0 \\ 0 & c_\phi & 0 & s_\phi \\ -s_\theta & 0 & c_\theta & 0 \\ 0 & -s_\phi & 0 & c_\phi \end{bmatrix} \begin{bmatrix} w \\ x \\ y \\ z \end{bmatrix} \neq \begin{bmatrix} w \\ x \\ y \\ z \end{bmatrix}.$$

The student should ponder the geometrical picture of this (despite its being in four dimensions) and he will see why the complete reduction in the operators still leaves an arbitrariness in the precise mode of decomposition.

A significant choice of axes for separating the two representations is obtained by using the idempotents constructed in § 13.6. Considering the Young tableaux

$$\begin{matrix} i & j & \quad & i & k \\ k & & \quad & j & \end{matrix}$$

which are the only standard tableaux for the partition (21), and the Young symmetry elements of the form NP, we have as moduli

(i) $\frac{1}{4}\{I+(ij)(k)-(ik)(j)-(ijk)\}$,

(ii) $\frac{1}{4}\{I+(ik)(j)-(ij)(k)-(ikj)\}$,

which operate on the complete tensor T_{ijk} to give

(i) $\frac{1}{4}(T_{ijk}+T_{kji}-T_{jik}-T_{kij})$,

(ii) $\frac{1}{4}(T_{ijk}+T_{jik}-T_{kji}-T_{jki})$.

We shall refer to these as $T_{[21a]}$ and $T_{[21b]}$ respectively; their sum is $T_{[21]}$. $T_{[21a]}$ is antisymmetric in its first two indices: $(T_{[21a]})_{ijk} = -(T_{[21a]})_{jik}$ and also obeys the relation

$$(T_{[21a]})_{ijk}+(T_{[21a]})_{jki}+(T_{[21a]})_{kij} = 0. \tag{A}$$

$T_{[21b]}$ also obeys this relation, but is antisymmetric in the first and third indices:

$$(T_{[21b]})_{ijk} = -(T_{[21b]})_{kji},$$

Any tensor belonging to the representation [21] shows the symmetry (A), but there are five alternatives to the above decomposition. By using the operator PN the two parts of $T_{[21]}$ are *symmetric* in i, j and i, k respectively. By defining dictionary order as jki or kij and using PN and NP from the new tableau thus obtained, four further types of symmetry are available. $T_{[21]}$ can thus be split in six distinct ways, and either symmetry or antisymmetry in any one chosen pair of letters can be imposed simultaneously with (A). The decomposition is then complete, since any attempt to impose any new type of symmetry whatever will be found to reduce the tensor to zero.

There is a formula for the number of components in any one of these symmetrically irreducible types which is very simple, though not easily proved. To calculate, for example, the number of components in the n-dimensional tensor $T_{[431^2a]}$—a fantastic proposition, perhaps, as this is a tensor of rank nine—we set out the Young tableau thus

$$\begin{matrix} n & & n+1 & n+2 & n+3 \\ n-1 & & n & n+1 & \\ n-2 & & & & \\ n-3 & & & & \end{matrix}$$

and we take the product of all these factors with a numerical coefficient which is the dimensionality of $\Gamma_{[431^2]}$ divided by 9!. This dimensionality may be obtained from the character tables—it is 216—or in reasonably simple cases by counting the number of standard tableaux. The number of components in the partly reduced tensor $T_{[431^2]}$ is, of course, this number again multiplied by 216.

The expression of the fact that a given tensor is symmetrical is most easily achieved by an equation of the form

$$T_{[\mu]} = T,$$

or alternatively by the equations

$$T_{[\mu']} = 0 \quad (\text{all } (\mu') \text{ except } (\mu)),$$

the main advantages of the latter appear (a) with the notation for symmetrization and antisymmetrization employed by some writers in which the symbols in question are enclosed in round and square brackets respectively, e.g.

$$T_{(ijk)} = T_{[ijk]} = 0$$

implies that T has the symmetry of $T_{[21]}$, for which this notation provides no symbol, and (b) when the symmetry type is established by proving these relations directly.

Tensors of higher rank can be analysed in a similar manner. The one-dimensional representations $T_{[n]}$ and $T_{[1^n]}$ from a tensor of rank r in n dimensions contain $^{n+r-1}C_r$ and ^nC_r terms respectively.

The importance of this analysis of a tensor is that it not infrequently happens that a physical tensor shows one or other of the symmetries in question. When this is so it is of the nature of a physical law. For example, if T_{ij} is an elastic coefficient, one suffix refers to the direction of stress and one to the direction of strain. The relation between stress X and strain Y must be of the form $Y = TX$ with T a tensor, but if T is symmetrical (in the narrow sense, excluding 'antisymmetry' and other forms), this assertion is equivalent to asserting that 'the strain in the X-direction produced by a given stress in the Y-direction is equal to the strain which would be produced in the Y-direction by an equal stress in the X-direction'.

In certain cases a tensor of high rank may show symmetry in some but not all of its suffixes. This in no way invalidates the above treatment so long as the group used is the subgroup of those permutations under which the symmetry is displayed, and not the complete permutation group. For example, tensors of the fourth rank occur in the theory of elasticity which are invariant for the permutations

$$hijk \quad ihjk \quad hikj \quad ihkj \quad jkhi \quad jkih \quad kjhi \quad kjih$$

but not for others; that is, for permutations within the first and second pairs of suffixes and between the pairs as pairs, but not for permutations which break up the pairs.

The terms of a tensor of rank r can be sorted into classes corresponding to the partitions of r, and permutation of the indices does not change a term into one of another class. Thus T_{hhhh} remains T_{hhhh} under all permutations; T_{hhhi} is changed into at most three others, T_{hhih}, T_{hihh}, and T_{ihhh}. It is occasionally convenient to analyse each such class separately, which can be done by the same process with a certain amount of care. But these classes do not remain invariant under the coordinate changes on which the definition of a tensor is based, and this diminishes their usefulness. The tensors $T_{[n]}$, $T_{[1^n]}$, etc., retain their symmetry properties if transformed to a new coordinate system.

14.6. Tensor properties of matter: (ii) in crystals

The occurrence of the symmetry properties dealt with in the previous section is a physical law—if a certain tensor possesses a symmetry of the type there dealt with, it does so for all substances. In crystals, a tensor property must have the crystal symmetry as well as the general symmetry. That is, it must be invariant under those coordinate transformations which leave the crystal itself invariant. (This explicit statement is known as Neumann's principle.) Thus whereas the refractive index or compressibility of an orthorhombic crystal may be different in three directions at right angles, it must be the same in all directions in a cubic crystal. Thus the imposition of cubic symmetry reduces the number of independent components from three to one.

We are considering in general a relation of the form

$$Y = TX,$$

where X is some applied quantity, Y is the effect which it produces, and T the 'coefficient of proportionality' (in general, a tensor) which is a property only of the medium (see § 14.3). (It may be pointed out that this is a *linear* law, and its wide applicability is due to the fact that it is the first approximation in a kind of generalized Taylor series:

$$Y = TX + U(X \times X) + V(X \times X \times X) + \dots$$

in matrix notation, or

$$Y^i = T^i_j X^j + U^i_{jk} X^j X^k + V^i_{jkm} X^j X^k X^m + \ldots$$

in tensor notation.) The general problem is thus to calculate the number of independent components of a given tensor property of a given type of crystal. The method is basically that of the previous section, modified as we shall show, and leads to the formula

$$n = \frac{1}{N} \sum h_\rho \, \chi_i(R) \chi_j(R)$$

(the general formula for determining how many times the representation Γ_j is contained in the representation Γ_i) with the characters χ_j and χ_i taken from Table 14.6.1 (p. 258). The modifications compared with the previous section are as follows. (1) The group is the crystal symmetry group, not the permutation group. (2) As the property is to remain invariant, it is only necessary to determine how often the *identical* representation occurs, and were it not for one qualification to this statement we could simplify the formula by substituting $\chi_j(R) = 1$ in it. But there are certain properties—in the next section they are discussed more fully, and designated 'W-tensors' or 'pseudo-tensors'—which change in sign under improper symmetry elements. These are distinguished in Table 14.6.1 by a bar over the letter denoting the quantity, and in these cases it is the representation with characters $+1$ for proper elements and -1 for improper elements, and not the identical representation, that is required, and $\chi_j(R)$ must be modified to this form. (3) The character χ_i which is to be analysed is obtained as follows. The components of the tensor are regarded as those of a vector in 3^r dimensions, or less if the symmetry considerations of the previous section have reduced the number. The transformation law of the tensor under proper and improper rotations is written down, expressed in matrix form, and the trace of this matrix worked out for each class of the crystal symmetry elements. For a second rank tensor in three dimensions with no special symmetry, the first stages of this process are those which led to equation (5.6.3); the character can be read off from that equation as $1 + 4\cos\theta + 4\cos^2\theta$ for a proper rotation, and a similar calculation shows it to be $1 - 4\cos\theta + 4\cos^2\theta$ for an improper one. (That these are $(1 + 2\cos\theta)^2$ and $(1 - 2\cos\theta)^2$ is in accordance with (5.6.8).) The reader who is more accustomed to the other notation will not forget that in the improper rotations θ is determined by their interpretation as reflection-rotations and not inversion-rotations. If the character as we give it for proper rotations is $f(\theta)$, and ϕ is the inversion-rotation angle, then $(-1)^r f(-\phi)$ is the alternative expression for improper rotations.

The modification of (5.6.8) or of its analogue for other values of n and r, when the tensor has symmetry properties with respect to its indices, though simple, is not exactly obvious. We first rearrange the matrix, grouping together those terms of the tensor which have ceased to be independent. For $r = 2$ this gives the sequence 11, $(12, 21)$, $(13, 31)$, 22, $(23, 32)$, 33. Now consider, for example, the first bracket in this sequence.

$$a'_{12} = csa_{11} + c^2 a_{12} - s^2 a_{21} - csa_{22}.$$

In the tensors $T_{[2]}$ and $T_{[1^2]}$ the corresponding equation for a'_{21} yields no new information, and is dropped. But with $a_{12} = \pm a_{21}$, the second and third terms on the right-hand side of this equation combine to $(c^2 \mp s^2)a_{12}$. Hence the rules:

To obtain the matrix for $T_{[n]}$, in each bracketed set omit all rows but the first and add the columns.

To obtain the matrix for $T_{[1^n]}$, omit all rows in each bracketed set except the first, and add the columns after changing the sign of all columns associated by an odd permutation of the suffixes with the row that has been retained; also drop all identically zero rows and columns.

Applied to the example we have been considering (equation 5.6.3), this gives, for a proper rotation,

$$\begin{bmatrix} a'_{11} \\ a'_{12} \\ a'_{13} \\ a'_{22} \\ a'_{23} \\ a'_{33} \end{bmatrix} = \begin{bmatrix} c^2 & -2cs & 0 & s^2 & 0 & 0 \\ cs & c^2 - s^s & 0 & -cs & 0 & 0 \\ 0 & 0 & c & 0 & -s & 0 \\ s^2 & 2cs & 0 & c^2 & 0 & 0 \\ 0 & 0 & s & 0 & c & 0 \\ 0 & 0 & 0 & 0 & 0 & 1 \end{bmatrix} \begin{bmatrix} a_{11} \\ a_{12} \\ a_{13} \\ a_{22} \\ a_{23} \\ a_{33} \end{bmatrix}$$

and thence the character $3c^2 + 2c + 1 - s^2 = 4c^2 + 2c$. Starting with the matrix of an improper rotation, S_θ, the second term in this expression has a minus sign $(4c^2 - 2c)$. For the antisymmetric tensor $T_{[1^2]}$ we have

$$\begin{bmatrix} a'_{12} \\ a'_{13} \\ a'_{23} \end{bmatrix} = \begin{bmatrix} 1 & 0 & 0 \\ 0 & c & -s \\ 0 & s & c \end{bmatrix} \begin{bmatrix} a_{12} \\ a_{13} \\ a_{23} \end{bmatrix}$$

for proper rotations, a result which we record as an illustration of the more general result discussed in the next section. An alternative procedure useful in some cases is to calculate the Schur functions of the eigenvalues, 1, $e^{i\theta}$, $e^{-i\theta}$.

It remains to tabulate the more important examples of tensors of this type with their characters. In Table 14.6.1 it has been found convenient to adopt a notation which is increasingly used in the literature, that when the tensor has a symmetry or antisymmetry of the type discussed in the previous section between any of its indices, those indices are

TABLE 14.6.1: THE TENSOR EQUATION $Y = TX$

Name and type of tensor or effect	Nature and type of X	Nature and type of Y	Maximum components in T	Character of T
Dielectric permittivity $\kappa_{(ip)}$	Electric field E^i	Polarization (moment/unit vol.) P_p	6	$\pm 2c + 4c^2$
Magnetic permeability $\mu_{(ip)}$	Magnetic field $\bar{H}^i$	Induction (magnetic moment/unit vol.) $\bar{I}_p$	6	$\pm 2c + 4c^2$
Optical (refractive index)	The refractive index is the square root of the permittivity			
Optical (gyration) $\bar{G}^{(ij)}$	Direction cosines of incident light $n_i\, n_j$	Rotation of plane of polarization of incident light $\bar{g}$	6	$\pm 2c + 4c^2$
Elastic moduli $T^{((ij)(pq))}$	Stress $S_{(ij)}$	Strain $D^{(pq)}$	21	$1 - 4c^2 \pm 8c^3 + 16c^4$
Piezo-optical $T^{(ij)(pq)}$	Stress $S_{(ij)}$	Refractive index change $\Delta\nu^{(pq)}$	36	$4c^2 \pm 16c^3 + 16c^4$
P-electric (Kerr) $T^{(ij)}_p$	Stress $S_{(ij)}$	Polarization P_p	18	$2c \pm 8c^2 + 8c^3$
Piezo-magnetic $T^{(ij)}_p$	Stress $S_{(ij)}$	Induction $\bar{I}_p$	18	$2c \pm 8c^2 + 8c^3$
Magneto-optical $T^{i(pq)}$	Magnetic field $\bar{H}_i$	Refractive index change $\Delta\nu^{(pq)}$	18	$2c \pm 8c^2 + 8c^3$
Thermo-elastic $\epsilon^{(pq)}$	Temperature θ	Strain $D^{(pq)}$	6	$\pm 2c + 4c^2$
Pyro-electric T_p	Temperature θ	Polarization P_p	3	$\pm 1 + 2c$
Pyro-magnetic $\bar{T}_p$	Temperature θ	Induction $\bar{I}_p$	3	$\pm 1 + 2c$

Notes: 1. In orthonormal cartesians upper and lower indices are equivalent. But symmetry is only between indices of the same type and summation is only over indices occurring once upper and once lower.

2. A bar over a quantity denotes a W-quantity. Either two or none of Y, T, and X must be barred. If T is barred, see text, p. 256, regarding χ_j.

enclosed in round or square brackets respectively. Thus $T_{[2]}$ is written $T^{(ij)}$ and $T_{[1^3]}$ is written $T^{[ijk]}$. An extension of this notation which we do not require here is that $T^{(i|j|k)}$ denotes a third rank tensor symmetric in the indices i and k but not in all three. This table lists a number of well-known 'effects' and the type of tensor involved with the character from which the number of its components in any given case is to be calculated. In Table 14.6.2 we give the results of the calculation for each of the crystal classes, and for every type of tensor which we have discussed of rank up to three and a few of the more interesting or important of rank four. A zero indicates, of course, that the type of effect considered does not occur in crystals of the symmetry considered. The fact that some effects cannot occur in crystals possessing a centre of symmetry is very familiar.

14.7. The identification of tensor types

We are now in a position to take up the question postponed in § 3.8 concerning the description of a vector product as a vector. We shall find that this is permissible so long as we remain in certain types of coordinate system, and that it is one of a number of such identifications which are possible when appropriate restrictions hold.

If a change of coordinate system is made such that $X^* \to X^+ = RX^*$, then a pure contravariant tensor of rank p which for the purposes of this section we shall denote by A^*, undergoes the transformation

$$A^* \to A^+ = (R)_p A^*,$$

where $(R)_p$ is the Kronecker pth power of R.

Let us consider first of all the case where A^* is an antisymmetric tensor and $p = n-1$. Then A^* contains only n numerically different components, and these can be more simply labelled with the one missing index than by the $n-1$ actual contravariant ones. The expression $(R)_p A^*$ denotes n^p sums each of n^p terms. Of these sums, owing to the nature of A^*, only n are independent, and each of them can be split into n groups of terms, the terms of each group having numerically the same A-factor. The R-factor of a given group is easily seen to be a certain determinant—more precisely it is numerically that minor of R obtained by deleting the row and column whose labels are the missing indices in A^+ and A^*. Closer investigation of the signs shows that in fact

$$A^+ = \widehat{\widetilde{R}} A^* = |R| R^{-1} A^*,$$

so that provided $|R| = 1$, A^* transforms like a *covariant* vector.

Let us consider one other case in detail—p not necessarily equal to $n-1$, but R diagonal. As A^* is antisymmetric, it contains no terms with repeated index. Each term of A^* is multiplied by p of the diagonal terms of R, that is, it is multiplied by $|R|$ and by the remaining diagonal

TABLE 14.6.2—1: TENSORS OF RANKS 1-3

Tensor	Tric.		Monoc.			Orthorh.			Tetragonal							Trigonal					Hexagonal							Cubic				
	C_1	C_i	C_s	C_2	C_{2h}	C_{2v}	D_2	D_{2h}	C_4	S_4	C_{4h}	C_{4v}	S_{4v}	D_4	D_{4h}	C_3	S_6	C_{3v}	D_3	D_{3d}	C_{3h}	C_6	C_{6h}	D_{3h}	C_{6v}	D_6	D_{6h}	T	T_h	T_d	O	O_h
	1	$\bar1$	m	2	$\tfrac{2}{m}$	$2m$	222	mmm	4	$\bar4$	$\tfrac{4}{m}$	$4mm$	$\bar42m$	42	$\tfrac{4}{m}mm$	3	$\bar3$	$3m$	32	$\bar3m$	$\tfrac{3}{m}$	6	$\tfrac{6}{m}$	$\bar6m2$	$6mm$	62	$\tfrac{6}{m}mm$	23	$m3$	$\bar43m$	43	$m3m$
T^a $\pm1+2c$	3	0	2	1	0	1	0	0	1	0	0	1	0	0	0	1	0	1	0	0	0	1	0	0	1	0	0	0	0	0	0	0
T_a	3	3	1	1	1	0	0	0	1	1	1	0	0	0	0	1	1	0	0	0	1	1	1	0	0	0	0	0	0	0	0	0
T^{ab} $1\pm4c+4c^2$	9	9	5	5	5	3	3	3	3	3	3	2	2	2	2	3	3	2	2	2	3	3	3	2	2	2	2	1	1	1	1	1
T_{ab}	9	0	4	5	0	2	3	0	3	2	0	1	1	2	0	3	0	1	2	0	0	3	0	0	1	2	0	1	0	0	1	0
$T^{(ab)}$ $\pm2c+4c^2$	6	6	4	4	4	3	3	3	2	2	2	2	2	2	2	2	2	2	2	2	2	2	2	2	2	2	2	1	1	1	1	1
$T_{(ab)}$	6	0	2	4	0	1	3	0	2	2	0	0	1	2	0	2	0	0	2	0	0	2	0	0	0	2	0	1	0	0	1	0
$T^{[ab]}$ $1\pm2c$	3	3	1	1	1	0	0	0	1	1	1	0	0	0	0	1	1	0	0	0	1	1	1	0	0	0	0	0	0	0	0	0
$T_{[ab]}$	3	0	2	1	0	1	0	0	1	0	0	1	0	0	0	1	0	1	0	0	0	1	0	0	1	0	0	0	0	0	0	0
T^{abc}	27	0	14	13	0	7	6	0	7	6	0	4	3	3	0	9	0	5	4	0	2	7	0	1	4	3	0	2	0	1	1	0
T_{abc} $\pm1+6c\pm12c^2+8c^3$	27	27	13	13	13	6	6	6	7	7	7	3	3	3	3	9	9	4	4	4	7	7	7	3	3	3	3	2	2	1	1	1
$T^{(abc)}$ $-2c+4c^2+8c^3$	10	0	6	4	0	3	1	0	2	2	0	2	1	0	0	4	0	3	1	0	2	2	0	1	2	0	0	1	0	1	0	0
$T_{(abc)}$	10	10	4	4	4	1	1	1	2	2	2	0	0	0	0	4	4	1	1	1	2	2	2	0	0	0	0	1	1	0	0	0
$T^{[abc]}$ ±1	1	0	0	1	0	0	1	0	1	0	0	0	0	1	0	1	0	0	1	0	0	1	0	0	0	1	0	1	0	0	1	0
$T_{[abc]}$	1	1	1	1	1	1	1	1	1	1	1	1	1	1	1	1	1	1	1	1	1	1	1	1	1	1	1	1	1	1	1	1
$T_{[21]}$ $\pm8c^2+8c$; halve these figures for $T_{[21\,a]}$ etc.	16	0	8	8	0	4	4	0	4	4	0	2	2	2	0	4	0	2	2	0	0	4	0	0	2	2	0	0	0	0	0	0
$T_{[21]}$	16	16	8	8	8	4	4	4	4	4	4	2	2	2	2	4	4	2	2	2	4	4	4	2	2	2	2	0	0	0	0	0
$T^{(abc)}$ $2c\pm8c^2+8c^3$	18	0	10	8	0	5	3	0	4	4	0	3	2	1	0	6	0	4	2	0	2	4	0	1	3	1	0	1	0	1	0	0
$T_{(abc)}$	18	18	8	8	8	3	3	3	4	4	4	1	1	1	1	6	6	2	2	2	4	4	4	1	1	1	1	1	1	0	0	0
$T^{[abc]}$ $\pm1+4c+4c^2$	9	0	4	5	0	2	3	0	3	2	0	1	1	2	0	3	0	1	2	0	0	3	0	0	1	2	0	1	0	0	1	0
$T_{[abc]}$	9	9	5	5	5	3	3	3	3	3	3	2	2	2	2	3	3	2	2	2	3	3	3	2	2	2	2	1	1	1	1	1

TABLE 14.6.2—2: FOURTH RANK TENSORS

	Tric.		Monoc.			Orthorh.			Tetragonal							Trigonal					Hexagonal						Cubic				
	C_1	C_i	C_s	C_2	C_{2h}	C_{2v}	D_2	D_{2h}	C_4	S_4	C_{4h}	C_{4v}	S_{4v}	D_4	D_{4h}	C_3	S_6	C_{3v}	D_3	D_{3d}	C_{3h}	C_6	C_{6h}	D_{3h}	C_{6v}	D_6	T	T_h	T_d	O	O_h
	1	$\bar1$	m	2	2/m	2m	222	mmm	4	$\bar4$	4/m	4mm	$\bar42m$	42	4/mmm	3	$\bar3$	3m	32	$\bar3m$	3/m	6	6/m	$\bar6m2$	6mm	6/mmm	23	m3	$\bar43m$	43	m3m
T_{abcd} $1\pm8c+24c^2\pm32c^3+16c^4$	81	81	41	41	41	21	21	21	21	21	21	11	11	11	11	27	27	14	14	14	19	19	19	10	10	10	7	7	4	4	4
$\bar{T}_{abcd}$	81	0	40	41	0	20	21	0	21	20	0	10	10	11	0	27	0	13	14	0	8	19	0	4	9	0	7	0	3	4	0
$T'_{(abcd)}$ $1\mp2c-8c^2\pm8c^3+16c^4$	15	15	9	9	9	6	6	6	5	5	5	4	4	4	4	5	5	4	4	4	3	3	3	3	3	3	2	2	2	2	2
$\bar{T}'_{(abcd)}$	15	0	6	9	0	3	6	0	5	4	0	1	2	4	0	5	0	1	4	0	3	3	0	1	3	0	2	0	0	2	0
$T_{[31]}\,3(-1+8c^2\pm8c^3)$ Divide by 3 for $T_{[31a]}$ etc.	45	45	21	21	21	9	9	9	9	9	9	6	6	6	6	15	15	6	6	6	15	15	15	9	9	9	3	3	3	0	0
$T_{[31]}$	45	0	24	21	0	12	9	0	12	12	0	4	4	4	0	15	0	9	6	0	0	15	0	0	6	0	3	0	2	0	0
$T_{[2^21]}\,2(\pm2c+4c^2)$ Divide by 2 for $T_{[1^2a]}$ etc.	12	12	8	8	8	6	6	6	4	4	4	4	2	4	4	4	4	4	4	4	4	4	4	4	4	4	2	2	2	2	2
$T_{[2^2]}$	12	0	8	8	0	2	6	0	4	4	0	0	0	0	0	4	0	0	0	0	0	4	0	0	0	0	2	0	0	2	0
$T_{[21^2]}\,3(1\mp2c)$ Divide by 3 for $T_{[21^2a]}$ etc.	9	9	4	8	8	3	6	6	3	3	3	3	0	0	0	3	3	3	0	0	3	3	3	0	3	0	0	0	0	0	0
$T_{[21^2]}$	9	0	3	3	0	3	0	0	3	3	0	0	0	0	0	3	0	0	0	0	3	3	0	3	0	0	0	0	0	0	0
$T_{[1^4]} \equiv 0$																															
$T'_{(ab)(cd)}$ $4c^2\pm16c^3+16c^4$	36	36	20	20	20	12	12	12	10	10	10	7	7	7	7	12	12	8	8	8	8	8	8	6	6	6	4	4	3	3	3
$\bar{T}'_{(ab)(cd)}$	36	0	16	20	0	8	12	0	10	10	0	3	5	7	0	12	0	4	8	0	4	8	0	2	2	0	4	0	1	3	0
$T_{(ab)(cd)}$ $1-4c^2\pm8c^3+16c^4$	21	21	13	13	13	9	9	9	7	7	7	6	6	6	6	7	7	6	6	6	5	5	5	5	5	5	3	3	3	3	3
$\bar{T}_{(ab)(cd)}$	21	0	8	13	0	4	9	0	7	6	0	1	3	6	0	7	0	1	6	0	5	5	0	1	0	0	3	0	0	3	0

terms of R^{-1}. Again, if $|R| = 1$, A^* behaves like a *covariant* tensor of rank $n-p$.

The general result of which these two are special cases is most easily expressed with the aid of a definition. We saw in § 14.4 that the volume defined by the basis vectors in an oblique system is, in the notations of 14.2, 14.4, and the present section,

$$g^{\frac{1}{2}} = (\,|G|\,)^{\frac{1}{2}} = |P| = 1/\,|R|.$$

Consider, for definiteness, a uniform distribution of like atoms, ν per unit volume. We refer to this number as the density. The number of atoms ν' in a unit coordinate volume (i.e. a parallelepiped of unit basis vectors) in an oblique system will then be $\nu' = \nu/\,|R|$. If each of these carries a contravariant vector V^* (e.g. a momentum) then the total of the vector in unit volume will be νV^* in the orthonormal, and $\nu' V^+$ in the oblique system. Calling this the density of V and denoting it by $\mathfrak{V}$, the transformation law is

$$\mathfrak{V}^* \to \mathfrak{V}^+ = R\mathfrak{V}^*/\,|R|.$$

Thus $\mathfrak{V}$ is not a vector. We call it a vector-Δ-density of weight 1, and, in general, define a tensor-Δ-density of weight k as a quantity whose transformation law resembles that of a tensor of similar rank and variance but includes the factor $(\,|R|\,)^{-k}$.

Our two results then become special cases of the first part of the following theorem (which we shall not prove in any more detail).

THEOREM 14.7.1. *An antisymmetric contravariant tensor of rank p in an n-space is also a covariant tensor-Δ-density of rank $n-p$ and weight -1. An antisymmetric covariant tensor of rank p is also a contravariant tensor-Δ-density of rank $n-p$ and weight $+1$.*

Thus a vector product in three dimensions may be regarded as a vector provided we remain in coordinate systems for which $|R| = 1$, i.e. provided we restrict our coordinate transformations to proper rotations. For improper rotations, $|R| = -1$; we have already had occasion to note the change of sign consequent upon this in § 10.4.

If we regard volumes as essentially positive, as is usual in forming densities, we introduce new types of quantity equal to the old ones when $|R|$ is positive but of opposite sign when it is negative. Quantities obeying these transformation laws are known as tensor-densities (instead of tensor-Δ-densities) and W-tensors (instead of tensors). A negative $|R|$ is associated with a transformation from right-handed to left-handed axes, and the necessity for distinguishing these types is associated with the ideas of 'handedness' (also known as 'chirality'), and screw sense.

The plethora of types introduced above can be codified by restricting ourselves to certain groups of coordinate transformations. The method is that of Klein's 'Erlanger Programm' for the systematization of geometry. We start with a space in which the most general transformations are possible. The geometry of this space is defined as those theorems which remain true when the figure to which the theorem applies is subjected to all of the allowed transformations. When we restrict ourselves to a subgroup of the allowed transformations, two points of interest arise. First, certain figures remain invariant, and secondly, more theorems remain true. We regard the space in which the subgroup of transformations only is allowed as a new space. Klein's principle is that the geometry of any figure in the second space is its geometry in the first together with that of the invariant figures of the second space in the first space.

The most general real linear group in n dimensions is the 'affine' group, which consists of all coordinate transformations of the type

$$x^{k'} = \sum_{1}^{n} R_{k}^{k'} x^{k} + a^{k'}, \quad |R| \neq 0$$

with real constant coefficients—i.e. movements of the origin are included. A space in which all these transformations are allowed is called an E_n. Little is lost or gained if we restrict ourselves to the group $\mathfrak{h}_n$ of homogeneous transformations in which every $a^{k'} = 0$ and the origin is invariant; a space in which these transformations only are allowed is called a centred E_n. Under the affine group straight lines remain straight, concurrent lines concurrent, and parallel lines parallel; ratios of segments of parallel lines are preserved, but not ratios of non-parallel segments, nor lengths nor angles. Hence a theorem such that the medians of a triangle are concurrent belongs to this geometry, but very few other elementary theorems.

In this space it is necessary to preserve distinct all the types of quantity we have been discussing. The distinctive feature of a 'geometric object' is that it has an intrinsic nature and identity of its own, with a unique expression in terms of any given coordinate system, and a definite rule by which its expression in a second coordinate system can be deduced from its expression in the first if the coordinate transformation is known. A geometric object is called a geometric quantity if, in addition to the above requirements, its transformation is linear in its own parts, homogeneous in the $R_k^{k'}$, and does not involve the $a^{k'}$. Thus scalars, co- and contravariant vectors and tensors, mixed tensors, W-tensors, tensor-Δ-densities, and tensor densities are all distinct types of geometric quantity. Points, planes, and lines are geometric objects, on the other hand.

The two most straightforward subgroups of the affine and homogeneous groups are those (1) for which $|R|$ is positive, (2) for which $|R| = \pm 1$, and (3) combining the restrictions, for which $|R|$ is $+1$. Subgroups (1) and (3) preserve chirality and screw-sense, while subgroups (2) and (3) preserve volumes. (This is for $n = 3$; they preserve areas if $n = 2$ or hyper-volumes if $n > 3$.) Accordingly, the distinction between quantities and W-quantities is abolished in (1) and (3), and the distinction between tensors and their Δ-densities in (2) and (3).

The next step is the introduction of the metric—we restrict ourselves to those transformations which leave the metric tensor invariant. As this implies $(|R|)^2 = 1$, we must have $|R| = \pm 1$, so that we are committed to preservation of volume, but not, unless we wish it, to preservation of screw-sense. The form of the metric is important. By introducing relations of the type $A^r = g^{rs}A_s$, it abolishes the distinction between co- and contravariant quantities, but leaves a distinction between the co- and contravariant expression of a quantity. In euclidean space (and we postpone discussion of curved spaces to the next chapter), it is possible to choose a coordinate system in which the metric has the form of the identity. Under these conditions the co- and contravariant expressions of a quantity are identical, as we have already seen in § 14.5, and have assumed throughout the early parts of this book in using the single notation V^* for ortho-normal coordinate systems in place of the double notation V^+ and V° necessary in more general coordinate systems.

The above summary needs further consideration if complex numbers are included in the scheme. The number of types of quantity is again doubled.

Suppose we are given an ordinary contravariant vector V^s in one system of coordinates which in a second becomes

$$V^\sigma = R_s^\sigma V^s, \qquad\qquad (a)$$

where the σ and the s both run from $1 \ldots n$, and the R_s^σ may be complex. Then an ordinary covariant vector V_s becomes

$$V_\sigma = (R^{-1})_\sigma^s V_s. \qquad\qquad (b)$$

(The $\sim$ of (4.6.4) is allowed for here by exchanging the positions of s and σ between (a) and (b).) But two further types of transformation are possible. A quantity $V^{\bar{s}}$ which transforms by

$$V^{\bar{\sigma}} = \bar{R}^{\sigma}_s V^{\bar{s}} \qquad\qquad\text{(c)}$$

may be called an extraordinary contravariant vector, and a quantity $V_{\bar{s}}$ transforming by

$$V_{\bar{\sigma}} = (\bar{R}^{-1})^s_{\sigma} V_{\bar{s}}, \qquad\qquad\text{(d)}$$

an extraordinary covariant vector. Note that the $^-$ in $V^{\bar{s}}$ and $V_{\bar{s}}$ is not to be thought of as modifying the s but rather as being *in lieu* of finding two more positions for the index with which to represent the two new kinds of vector. It is clear that if V^s and $V^{\bar{s}}$ are real and equal, then $V^{\bar{\sigma}} = \bar{V}^{\sigma}$. But one can no more add $V^{\bar{\sigma}}$ and V^{σ} than one can V^{σ} and V_{σ}, so that one does not consider separation into real and imaginary parts.

The result of restricting ourselves to the unitary group is somewhat surprising. For if $\bar{\bar{R}} = R^{-1}$ (and $\bar{\bar{R}}^{-1} = R$), transformations (b) and (c) are the same, and also transformations (a) and (d); that is, under this group an ordinary covariant vector and an extraordinary contravariant vector are the same thing; also an ordinary contravariant and an extraordinary covariant vector. This situation demands the dropping of the terms co- and contravariant in favour of something new, and we therefore introduce Dirac's nomenclature and define

  a 'ket' as an ordinary contravariant (or extraordinary covariant) vector,

  a 'bra' as an ordinary covariant (or extraordinary contravariant) vector.

Thus, as hinted in § 3.2, the names 'bra' and 'ket' should be used only when we are restricting ourselves to unitary transformations of the coordinate system, but in work involving unitary geometry they are really the only names which are free from confusion. As we have defined them in § 3.2, X^* is a ket and $^*X$ is a bra.

Although the above includes all the systematic identifications, there are others. For example, Whittaker shows that if

$$R_{01} = iR_{23}, \qquad R_{02} = iR_{31}, \qquad R_{03} = iR_{12},$$
$$R_{01}{}^2 + R_{02}{}^2 + R_{03}{}^2 = 0,$$

then this second rank tensor is equivalent by the relations

$$(R_{01} + iR_{02})^{\frac{1}{2}} = \phi_1,$$
$$(-R_{01} + iR_{02})^{\frac{1}{2}} = \phi_2,$$

to a spinor $(\phi_1 \phi_2)$.

CHAPTER XV

RELATIVITY THEORY

THE special theory of relativity arose from the observation that the velocity of light as determined by observers in relative motion did not seem to be affected by that motion. If light is a corpuscle phenomenon it should have a constant velocity relative to its source, or if it is a wave phenomenon, a constant velocity relative to the medium (the ether) in which it is propagated, and neither of these is consistent with a velocity which is constant relative to an arbitrary receiver of the light. Indeed, the experimental results seem fantastic at first glance, for at their most paradoxical they amount to this, that if observer A is moving from west to east, and at the moment of passing a stationary observer B, light pulses are sent out both eastwards and westwards, then at some later time, when A and B are not at the same point, they both consider themselves to be equidistant from the two light pulses.

Now if two observers describe the same phenomenon differently, that is, in the same general terms but with different numerical values, the relation between their descriptions can be regarded as a change of the basic frame of reference. In observing the velocity of light the observers are recording the moments at which light reaches certain positions—or possibly recording more complex phenomena such as interference bands which can, however, be reduced to this form—and therefore the variables involved are time and three-dimensional space, an event being pin-pointed by the four numbers (x_1, x_2, x_3, t). Such a constellation of numbers is what we have, throughout this book, been calling a vector. And lest any reader should be tempted to jump too quickly to metaphysical conclusions, we would point out that we can string any series of observations together in this way—in § 10.5, for example, we grouped together the horizontal accelerations of several weights on a string under the title of vector, because it suited our needs. If there is any underlying significance in grouping these four numbers together, it will only appear when we discuss the transformation equations of the carrier space of the vector. The same event will be described by another observer as (x_1', x_2', x_3', t'), and the transformations which relate (x_1, x_2, x_3, t) to this will be formally descriptive of the physical relation between the two observers. Our immediate problem is the nature of the transformation equations when the observers are described as being in uniform relative motion.

15.2. The Galilean transformation

Until the discovery of the constancy of the velocity of light, it had been assumed, following Newton, that time was something unique, the same for everybody. One could put the origin at any moment one pleased, of course, and change one's units, but apart from these elementary considerations all observers would agree as to the times of events. In particular they would agree when two events were simultaneous. The space coordinates were more subject to individual arrangements, for a rotation of the axes would give rise to new space coordinates related to the old ones by the relatively complicated transformations of the rotation group. Further, if one observer was moving with velocity V relative to another, the space coordinates assigned would be relative to the position of the observer's origin at the time of the event, and in particular, if the two sets of axes were originally parallel and remained so (excluding the transformations of the rotation group), then the transformation equations

$$x_1' = x_1 - v_1 t,$$
$$x_2' = x_2 - v_2 t,$$
$$x_3' = x_3 - v_3 t,$$
$$t' = t$$

or, in vector notation,

$$X' = X - Vt,$$
$$t' = t,$$

would hold. Such transformations, with V independent of t, are called Galilean transformations. The most general transformation of coordinates from one observer to another moving with uniform relative velocity was therefore the totality of all transformations in which these (with all values of V) are combined with any transformation of the rotation group.

If two transformations of the above type are performed successively, we have

$$X'' = X' - Ut = X - (U+V)t$$
$$t'' = t' = t$$

showing that the result is a third transformation of the same type, the composition law being vector addition of the velocities. Since further $X' = X + Vt$ is the inverse of the former transformation, the Galilean transformations form a group which is known as the Galilean group.

A double differentiation of the transformation equations with respect to time shows that acceleration has the same value for all observers in uniform relative motion. It is also clear that coordinate *differences* have the same values for all such observers, so that the configurations from which the stresses and strains in a system are calculated are also unchanged. Hence the basic equation Force = mass × acceleration of Newton's second law is carried over without change of numerical values from one observer to another. With equations involving velocities the situation is not quite so simple, as the numerical values ascribed to velocities will be different in the two systems. But, for example, from

$$v^2 = u^2 + 2fs$$

—the familiar equation of school mechanics—we have

$$(v'+V)^2 = (u'+V)^2 + 2f(s'+Vt)$$

which, since $t = (v'-u')/f$, reduces to

$$v'^2 = u'^2 + 2fs'$$

and both observers agree on the *form* of the equation. We therefore say that Newtonian mechanics is invariant under the Galilean group. Notice that we are treating mass as an absolute constant.

15.3. The Lorentz group

The equations of optics, on the other hand, are not invariant under the Galilean group. A light wave, for example, starting at time $t = 0$, becomes a sphere of radius ct after a time t, where c is the velocity of light. The equation of this sphere is

$$x_1^2 + x_2^2 + x_3^2 - c^2t^2 = 0 \qquad (15.3.1)$$

and if the substitutions of the Galilean transformation are made in this equation, no amount of rearrangement will restore its original form. But the experimental result, we have seen, is that this form is obtained by all observers in uniform relative motion. We therefore conclude that, simple and obvious though the Galilean transformation may seem, it is not the correct transformation for relating the results of observers in uniform relative motion.

Instead of the Galilean group, therefore, we seek another group of transformations which will leave this fundamental equation of optics unchanged. Writing $ict = x_4$, the equation becomes

$$x_1^2 + x_2^2 + x_3^2 + x_4^2 = 0, \qquad (15.3.2)$$

and we see at once that the group we require is the real orthogonal group in this four-space. It simplifies things, with no real loss of generality, if we confine our investigations in the first instance to those transformations which leave x_2 and x_3 unchanged. Returning to the time as a variable, this amounts to replacing our original Galilean transformation by

$$x_1' = x_1 \cos\theta - ict \sin\theta \left.\vphantom{\begin{matrix}a\\b\end{matrix}}\right\} . \qquad (15.3.3)$$
$$ict' = x_1 \sin\theta + ict \cos\theta$$

The infinitesimal transformation of this type is

$$x_1' = x_1 - ict\theta \left.\vphantom{\begin{matrix}a\\b\end{matrix}}\right\} , \qquad (15.3.4\,\text{a})$$
$$ict' = x_1\theta + ict$$

which may also be written

$$x_1' = x_1 - ic\theta t \left.\vphantom{\begin{matrix}a\\b\end{matrix}}\right\} , \qquad (15.3.4\,\text{b})$$
$$t' = t - \frac{ic\theta}{c^2} x_1$$

and this is identical with a Galilean transformation if we set $ic\theta = V$, and neglect the small term of order V/c^2 in the second equation. As the Galilean group with V small compared with c was extremely successful in mechanics, we must preserve this result by setting θ equal to something which tends to V/ic when V is small, but also keeps $\cos\theta$ real. This can be done by putting

$$V/ic = \tan\theta, \qquad (15.3.5\,\text{a})$$

which leads to

$$\cos\theta = (1 - V^2/c^2)^{-\frac{1}{2}} = \beta, \qquad (15.3.5\,\text{b})$$

$$\sin\theta = \tan\theta \cos\theta = \beta V/ic, \qquad (15.3.5\,\text{c})$$

and thus to the transformation equations

$$x_1' = \beta(x_1 - Vt) \left.\vphantom{\begin{matrix}a\\b\end{matrix}}\right\} . \qquad (15.3.6)$$
$$t' = \beta(t - Vx_1/c^2)$$

Note that although $\beta = \cos\theta$, it is greater than unity, because θ is imaginary.

The identification of V/ic with $\tan\theta$ will perhaps be more clearly justified if we remark that V is the constant value of x_1/t for the various positions of the 'moving' origin, that is, the constant value of icx_1/x_4—and of course x_1/x_4 is very naturally interpreted as the tangent of an angle. The composition law of the rotation group in two dimensions, that $AB = C$ if $\theta_C = \theta_A + \theta_B$, together with the relation $\tan ix = i\tanh x$, leads to the composition law

$$\tanh^{-1}\frac{v_C}{c} = \tanh^{-1}\frac{v_A}{c} + \tanh^{-1}\frac{v_B}{c}, \qquad (15.3.7)$$

when v_A and v_B are parallel (instead of the $v_C = v_A + v_B$ of the Galilean group). The space of the vectors (x_1, x_2, x_3, x_4) which has a euclidean geometry, is known as the Minkowski world; it was very fashionable at one time for discussions of special relativity, but the mathematical simplicity of the treatment is obtained at such cost in terms of difficulty of physical intuition that its utility is distinctly doubtful. From this point onwards, therefore, we shall abandon it, modify our notation, and use x_4 to denote the real quantity, ct.

It is obvious from the method of derivation that the transformations we have been discussing, with all possible values of V less than c (i.e. all real values of θ), form a group, since they have a one-to-one correspondence with the rotation group in the Minkowski world. This group of transformations is known as the Lorentz group.

It might be objected by the reader at this point that we may have acquired invariance of the optical laws at the expense of the invariance of the mechanical laws, and there would be some reason in the objection. But all our mechanical laws have been discovered experimentally with objects moving at velocities small compared with that of light, and we know that under such conditions the Lorentz transformations approximate to the Galilean ones. The question is not therefore whether the mechanical laws as we know them are invariant, but what are the (invariant) laws to which the Newtonian ones are a good approximation at small velocities. We postpone this question until the next section but one.

The 'spatial dimensions' of an object, such as a parallelepiped, are, of course, the differences between the space coordinates of its ends for *equal* values of the time coordinates. If they should be l_x, l_y, l_z, for the system in which the object or the points are at rest, the equations show that they are

$$l'_x = l_x/\beta, \qquad l'_y = l_y, \qquad l'_z = l_z, \qquad (15.3.8)$$

for the moving system of coordinates, if V is directed along the X-axis. This apparent contraction in the ratio $\beta : 1$, which has been aptly likened to the 'contraction' of a circle when looked at obliquely, is known as the Fitzgerald–Lorentz contraction.

15.4. The representations of the Lorentz group

The Galilean group, apart from the part of it which is the three-dimensional rotation group, is commutative. It is, in fact, structurally the same as the three-dimensional translation group (continuous), since to each velocity there corresponds a unit-time translation. There is therefore no need to discuss its representations here.

As with the rotations, there are proper and improper Lorentz transformations; the latter have a determinant of -1, and the former make up an invariant subgroup of the complete Lorentz group known as the restricted Lorentz group. In the Lorentz group there is also another invariant subgroup (factor group c_2); this consists of all those transformations which do not change the sign of a time-like interval. These two twofold divisions cut the group manifold into four disconnected sheets.

The equations (15.3.6) can be put into the following form, in which we write z for x for future convenience

$$\left.\begin{array}{l} z'-ct' = \beta\left(1+\dfrac{V}{c}\right)(z-ct) = \gamma(z-ct) \\[2mm] z'+ct' = \beta\left(1-\dfrac{V}{c}\right)(z+ct) = \gamma^{-1}(z+ct) \end{array}\right\}, \qquad (15.4.1)$$

where γ is defined by these expressions, and may easily be shown to be $\exp\tanh^{-1}V/c$. The eigenvalues of the Lorentz transformations are thus γ and γ^{-1}, all real values $0 < \gamma \leqslant 1$ being permissible. (This conclusion also follows directly from the relation between circular rotations and Lorentz ones.) This transformation, i.e. (15.4.1), is sufficient, when joined to the rotation group, to generate the Lorentz group, for a general Lorentz change of axes can be effected by rotating the first system until the velocity of the origin of the second is along the Z-axis, then applying (15.4.1), and then readjusting the orientation of the space axes again. But the Lorentz group is a six-parameter group, three parameters being required to define the spatial relation between the two frames, and three to specify the relative velocity of the origins. Denoting a transformation of type (15.4.1) by $L(V)$, and using the notation of § 12.3 for rotations, $L(V)$ commutes with $Z(\theta)$, but not with $Y(\theta)$. The general Lorentz transformation is therefore $Z(\theta)Y(\phi)L(V)Z(\psi)Y(\chi)Z(\omega)$.

If, analogously (to 12.3.3), we write

$$W_1\overline{W}_2+\overline{W}_1W_2 = x, \qquad W_1\overline{W}_1-W_2\overline{W}_2 = z,$$
$$W_1\overline{W}_2-\overline{W}_1W_2 = iy, \qquad W_1\overline{W}_1+W_2\overline{W}_2 = ct, \qquad (15.4.2)$$

then
$$c^2t^2-x^2-y^2-z^2 = 0, \qquad (15.4.3)$$

and we have extended the unit sphere which was to be invariant under the rotation group into the null cone, the experimentally invariant expanding sphere of the light wave. Noting that $z+ct = 2W_1\overline{W}_1$ and $z-ct = -2W_2\overline{W}_2$, we see that the unitary matrices operating on W which correspond to the rotation group are to be supplemented, to generate the Lorentz group, by the matrix $L(V) = \begin{bmatrix} \gamma^{\frac{1}{2}} & 0 \\ 0 & \gamma^{-\frac{1}{2}} \end{bmatrix}$. Inspection of (15.4.2) shows that any element of $\mathfrak{f}_2$ will preserve (15.4.3), but this is actually too much. All our generating elements have a determinant of unity, thus only those elements of $\mathfrak{f}_2$ with determinant unity can be generated; these are the group $\mathfrak{h}_2$. (The expression in (15.4.3) being zero, it is a special case, for unlike non-zero expressions, it is unchanged by a mere change of scale.) As mentioned in § 13.9, the irreducible representations of $\mathfrak{f}_n$ are also irreducible in its subgroup $\mathfrak{h}_n$; the theory of the irreducible representations of the Lorentz group is thus reduced to that of $\mathfrak{f}_2$. It should be noted that unlike the rotation group, the Lorentz group is an open group.

It is not difficult to verify from (15.4.2) that the transformations we have been discussing cannot change the sign of t, nor yet produce an improper rotation (e.g. the inversion). The former are not of immediate physical application, but the latter are, and must be incorporated into the scheme. We can reverse the signs of x, y, and z by replacing (W_1, W_2) by $(\overline{W}_2, -\overline{W}_1)$. But because a number and its complex conjugate are linearly independent, there is no way of showing this as a matrix operation on W. It is necessary to resort to some device such as

$$\begin{bmatrix} \overline{W}_2 \\ -\overline{W}_1 \\ W_2 \\ -W_1 \end{bmatrix} = \begin{bmatrix} 0 & 0 & 0 & +1 \\ 0 & 0 & -1 & 0 \\ 0 & +1 & 0 & 0 \\ -1 & 0 & 0 & 0 \end{bmatrix} \begin{bmatrix} W_1 \\ W_2 \\ \overline{W}_1 \\ \overline{W}_2 \end{bmatrix}. \qquad (15.4.4)$$

The square of this matrix, incidentally, is $-I$; the representation is a spin representation still. The extension from 2×2 to 4×4 matrices raises some very interesting questions which we shall discuss later (§§ 16.5 and 16.9). It should be noticed that it is required equally whether or not the Lorentz transformations are added to the rotation group. But whereas it appears unnecessarily complicated to discuss the proper and improper rotations, which can be represented in 3×3 matrices, in terms of 4×4 matrices, the situation is not so absurd after the addition of the Lorentz matrices; nevertheless, we shall see that the implications of the discussion are profound, even if only the rotation group is in question.

15.5. The four-dimensional principle

So long as time was unique, three-dimensional vectors existed in their own right, but as the group of transformations which is available to us with a physical meaning now includes ones which interconnect space and time, this is no longer so; all physical quantities must now be represented as scalars or as vectors or tensors in a four-space. This involves identifying a fourth component of every three-dimensional vector.

The most fundamental vector to be treated in this way is, of course, the vector $(\Delta x, \Delta y, \Delta z)$ which is the difference in position between two points. It generalizes obviously into $(\Delta x, \Delta y, \Delta z, \Delta t)$. The quantity

$$\Delta s = (c^2\Delta t^2 - \Delta x^2 - \Delta y^2 - \Delta z^2)^{\frac{1}{2}}$$

with, if real, the same sign as Δt, is invariant under Lorentz transformations, and is the four-dimensional analogue of the length of a three-dimensional vector; it is known as the 'interval' between the ends of the vector. Unlike length, it can be zero, in which case the vector is known as a null-vector.

Next in importance is velocity, which, however, is exceptional, because the usual components of velocity, dx/dt, dy/dt, and dz/dt are three of the direction cosines of the interval vector, disguised by a proportionality factor. The direction cosines of the interval vector are, in fact,

$$\frac{d(ct)}{ds} = \beta,$$

$$\frac{dx}{ds} = \frac{dt}{ds}\frac{dx}{dt} = \frac{\beta}{c}V_x,$$

with corresponding expressions in y and z. This situation can be clarified by noting that if a particle is at rest in a coordinate system, then for that particle in that system $ds = c\,dt = dx_4$. Such coordinates are known as proper coordinates for the particle. Moreover, $ds = dx_4$ is still accurate to terms of the first order in v/c if v is small compared with c, since the first-order term in the expansion of β is zero. It is therefore convenient to define the four-dimensional velocity vector as a unit vector in the direction of the tangent to the 'world-line' of the particle—the world-line being the locus of the various points in the four-space which are taken up by the particle.

It is then natural to define momentum as a similar vector whose length is equal to the mass of the particle, since, apart from a factor c arising from our choice of units, this agrees with the usual definition of momentum as the product of mass and velocity, and for velocities small compared with that of light no Newtonian concepts will be upset. In particular, Newton's third law, in the form of the conservation of momentum, will hold in such systems.

Adherence to this principle when velocities are large leads to an important new conclusion which has been abundantly verified in experimental work with fast moving particles—e.g. radioactive disintegration particles. For two particles moving in the X direction (for simplicity) and interacting with conservation of momentum, we have conservation of the quantity (in which subscripts denote the two particles)

$$m_1\frac{dx_1}{ds} + m_2\frac{dx_2}{ds} = \{(m_1\beta_1)V_1 + (m_2\beta_2)V_2\}/c,$$

and thus of the quantity in curly brackets. If therefore three-dimensional velocity is still defined as differentiation of the space coordinates with respect to the time, as it will be in experimental work, it is necessary to assume that at high speeds the inertial mass of a particle is $m_0\beta$, where m_0 is the 'rest-mass', the value of the mass at low speeds. This apparent increase of mass in a moving particle, which is negligible up to, say, 1 per cent. of the velocity of light, but which becomes infinite as the velocity of light is approached, is one of the most characteristic differences between Newtonian and special-relativity physics.

Concealed in the foregoing paragraphs is an important general conclusion, namely, that 'rate of change' in mechanical laws is to be interpreted as $c\,d/ds$ rather than as d/dt. Tensorially this is essential. For dt is now one component of a vector—contrast the three-dimensional conclusion in § 14.3—but ds is a scalar. Thus if T is any tensor, dT/ds is a tensor of the same rank and variance, while dT/dt is unmanageable, except as part of the larger group of quantities which includes dT/dx, etc. (We discuss quantities of the latter type in the next section. It is necessary in defining dT/ds to specify the path along which ds is measured, of course.)

We have thus dealt with the requirement that Newton's third law be put into a form invariant under a Lorentz transformation before considering the second law, by using that form of the third law which does not involve force explicitly—namely, the conservation of momentum, To consider the second law we have to consider the definition of force, particularly in view of the fact that now that mass depends on velocity, the definitions 'rate of change of momentum' and 'mass multiplied by acceleration' will not be equivalent. The former has the advantages. First, equality of action and reaction, measured as forces, will be preserved. Secondly, it is logically more satisfactory in that it continues the line of our argument rather than demanding an examination of acceleration similar to that which we conducted for velocity. And thirdly, though we shall not go into details, it proves most satisfactory when electromagnetic phenomena are to be included. In accordance with the preceding paragraph, however, 'rate of change' is to be interpreted as $c\,d/ds$, rather than as d/dt. The resultant four-vector is called the Minkowski force, and, as before, it has to be related to the ordinary force calculated from experimental observations made in terms of the observer's time by the introduction of β-factors. From its method of derivation, the Minkowski force is a contravariant vector. Denoting its components by (F^1, F^2, F^3, F^4) and those of the ordinary force by (F_x, F_y, F_z), we have

$$F^1 = c^2 \frac{d}{ds}\left(m_0 \frac{dx}{ds}\right) = \beta \frac{d}{dt}(\beta m_0 V_x) = \beta F_x, \quad \text{etc.,}$$

and
$$F^4 = c^2 \frac{d}{ds}\left(m_0 \frac{d(ct)}{ds}\right) = \beta \frac{d(\beta m_0 c^2)}{c\,dt} = \beta \frac{d(mc^2)}{c\,dt}.$$

It will be convenient to define F_t by $F^4 = \beta F_t$, by analogy with the expressions we have obtained for F_x, F_y, and F_z.

A very important tensor quantity is the mixed tensor formed from the force and the interval vectors. Since $g_{11} = g_{22} = g_{33} = -1, g_{44} = 1$, and all other g's are zero, the covariant form of the Minkowski force will differ from the contravariant form only in a change of sign for all its spatial components. The tensor in question may therefore be written

$$\begin{bmatrix} F_1 \Delta x_1 & F_2 \Delta x_1 & F_3 \Delta x_1 & F_4 \Delta x_1 \\ F_1 \Delta x_2 & F_2 \Delta x_2 & F_3 \Delta x_2 & F_4 \Delta x_2 \\ F_1 \Delta x_3 & F_2 \Delta x_3 & F_3 \Delta x_3 & F_4 \Delta x_3 \\ F_1 \Delta x_4 & F_2 \Delta x_4 & F_3 \Delta x_4 & F_4 \Delta x_4 \end{bmatrix} = \beta \begin{bmatrix} -F_x \Delta x & -F_y \Delta x & -F_z \Delta x & F_t \Delta x \\ -F_x \Delta y & -F_y \Delta y & -F_z \Delta y & F_t \Delta y \\ -F_x \Delta z & -F_y \Delta z & -F_z \Delta z & F_t \Delta z \\ -cF_x \Delta t & -cF_y \Delta t & -cF_z \Delta t & cF_t \Delta t \end{bmatrix}.$$

In tensor notation this is $F_r \Delta x^s$; the sum of the diagonal terms is the 'contracted' tensor $F_r \Delta x^r$, which is a tensor of zero rank, that is, a scalar, unchanged by transformation of coordinates. This sum (which is in vector notation the scalar product $*F\Delta s*$) is

$$\beta\{-(F_x \Delta x + F_y \Delta y + F_z \Delta z) + \Delta(mc^2)\}.$$

The three terms in the first bracket of this equation represent the work done on the particle over the change Δ, and the last term the change in the mass $m = m_0\beta$, in units c^2 times smaller than usual. Let us choose a coordinate system in which $(\Delta x, \Delta y, \Delta z)$ is zero—i.e. in which during the time Δt the particle returns to the point it started from. Then if the system is conservative, at the end of the time increment the particle will have the same kinetic energy, hence the same velocity (in magnitude, though not necessarily in direction), and therefore the same values of β and m. For a conservative system, therefore, this scalar product is zero in these coordinates, and therefore in all systems of coordinates. Thus the increase in the kinetic energy of the particle, which by definition is equal to the work done on it, is given by

$$\Delta E = \Delta(mc^2) = \Delta(m_0\beta c^2) = \Delta\{\tfrac{1}{2}m_0 V^2 + \tfrac{3}{8}m_0 V^4/c^2 + ...\}$$

which, for values of V small compared with c, is equal to the Newtonian expression $\Delta \tfrac{1}{2}m_0 V^2$. If the system is not conservative owing to frictional dissipation of energy, it is still conservative on the atomic scale, since the heat produced is the random motion of the molecules. Thus the mass of a hot body will be greater than that of a cold one by the energy equivalent of the heat divided by c^2. Similar arguments apply to other forms of energy, though we shall not go into detail.

This conclusion, that increase in energy is always accompanied by an increase in mass, and vice versa, the increments being proportional with the conversion factor c^2, is the second distinctive feature of special relativity. It has received considerable practical application in nuclear physics, where the mass 'defect' of a nucleus from the sum of the masses of the more elementary particles of which it is assumed to consist, is regularly used as an estimate of the binding energy in the nuclear structure, and of the energy relations to be expected if nuclear transformations take place. The conclusion may be summed up in the statement that in relativity theory the conservation of mass and the conservation of energy are one and the same principle.

An even more important tensor is that formed from the momentum and velocity vectors. This is usually considered in its purely contravariant form and written T^{rs}. Thus

$$T^{rs} = m_0 \frac{dx^r}{ds}\frac{dx^s}{ds} = m\beta\frac{dx^r}{dt}\frac{dx^s}{dt}.$$

It is clear that T^{rs} is symmetrical. Now owing to the apparent contraction (15.3.8), in the ratio $1:\beta^{-1}$, of lengths measured along the direction of motion of an object, lengths perpendicular to this direction being unaffected, if we take m not as the mass of a particle but as the mass of a quantity of extended matter, $m\beta$ will be proportional to the apparent density of the matter, and equal to it if m_0 is replaced by ρ_0, the density as observed by an observer moving with the matter. Doing this throughout, which, since it involves a scalar factor only, will not alter the tensor character, T^{44} will be c^2 times the observed density, $T^{r4} = T^{4r}$ will be momentum density in the direction of the r-axis, the diagonal non-temporal terms will be of the form of density of kinetic energy, and the remaining terms something rather more difficult to give an interpretation to; *in toto*, however, remembering the identity of mass and energy, this symmetrical tensor gathers up into one quantity of sixteen components (ten of them independent) all the significant terms which represent the occurrence of matter. It is variously known as the 'matter' or as the 'energy-momentum' tensor.

15.6. Curvature of space

We have seen in § 14.2 that by adopting non-cartesian coordinate systems, certain forms of the metric tensor are obtained in which this tensor is a function of position. If we consider the distance along a great circle of a sphere, small enough to be regarded as a straight line, we obtain for its length in terms of the two angular coordinates the expression

$$ds^2 = d\theta^2 + \sin^2\theta \, d\phi^2. \qquad (15.6.1)$$

This form of the metric tensor must contain within itself some indication that the geometry of the surface of the sphere is that of a curved and not a flat surface—in other words that it is non-euclidean.

We have also seen that the translation group on the surface of a sphere —that is, the rotation group—is non-commutative. It is therefore more interesting than surprising to find that the test for the euclidean character of a space with a given metric is one that is related to the commutability of displacements along the axes. In order to justify this statement it will be necessary to summarize certain well-known results which are dealt with in more detail in most works on relativity.

The nearest equivalent to a straight line in a curved space is a curve defined by the condition that subject to its remaining wholly within the space and joining the same terminal points, any slight change in its shape increases its length. (In certain metrics a maximum length must be admitted as an alternative to a minimum.) Such a curve is known as a geodesic. The definition of a geodesic can be translated into symbolic form as

$$\delta \int ds = 0, \tag{15.6.2}$$

where ds is an increment of its length, δ refers to any change in its path, and the integration is taken between the prescribed terminal points A and B of the curve. If every increment ds is zero, the curve is a 'null-geodesic'. An equation in the form of an integral is inconvenient, however, and this equation is transformed into differential form by making use of the relation $ds^2 = g_{rs}\,dx^r dx^s$. Our first problem is to define what we mean by the 'same' point on the geodesic and on the nearly identical curve represented by the variation δ. This we do by introducing an arbitrary (but continuous) function of position λ and defining δ as a variation from a point on the geodesic to that point on the varied curve which has the same value of λ. λ will vary along the geodesic, and it will be convenient to denote $d\lambda/ds$ by $1/w$, so that

$$w^2 = g_{rs}\frac{dx_r}{d\lambda}\frac{dx_s}{d\lambda}.$$

With the aid of w and λ we can now write

$$0 = \delta \int_A^B ds = \int_A^B \delta w\, d\lambda$$

$$= \int_A^B \left\{ \frac{1}{2w}\frac{dx_r}{d\lambda}\frac{dx_s}{d\lambda}\,\delta g_{rs} + \frac{g_{rp}}{w}\frac{dx_r}{d\lambda}\,\delta\!\left(\frac{dx_p}{d\lambda}\right)\right\}\, d\lambda$$

$$= \int_A^B \left\{ \frac{1}{2w}\frac{dx_r}{d\lambda}\frac{dx_s}{d\lambda}\frac{\delta g_{rs}}{\delta x_p}\,\delta x_p + \frac{g_{rp}}{w}\frac{dx_r}{d\lambda}\frac{d\,\delta x_p}{d\lambda}\right\}\, d\lambda$$

$$= \left[\frac{g_{rp}}{w}\frac{dx_r}{d\lambda}\delta x_p\right]_A^B + \int_A^B \left\{ \frac{1}{2w}\frac{dx_r}{d\lambda}\frac{dx_s}{d\lambda}\frac{\delta g_{rs}}{\delta x_p} - \frac{d}{d\lambda}\!\left(\frac{g_{rp}}{w}\frac{dx_r}{d\lambda}\right)\right\}\, d\lambda\, \delta x_p.$$

(The second line here is obtained by differentiating the expression for w^2, dividing by $2w$ and substituting. Both the second and the third lines will probably be clear to the student if, but only if, he is prepared to write out the implications of the summation convention, at least in respect of the suffix p. In the fourth line integration by parts has been used.) Now at the limits of integration the quantities δx_p are all zero, and thus the first term in the last line vanishes. In the integral that remains the δx_p are arbitrary and therefore the integrand must be identically zero. (Otherwise we could, for example, vary the curve in such a way that the δx_p were everywhere of the same sign as their coefficients, so that the integrand was everywhere positive.) Now as λ is arbitrary, there is no reason (except in a null-geodesic) why it should not be equal to s, the distance along the geodesic from the point A, in which case $w = 1$. Making this substitution the vanishing of the integrand becomes

$$\frac{1}{2}\frac{dx_r}{ds}\frac{dx_s}{ds}\frac{\partial g_{rp}}{\partial x_p} - \frac{d}{ds}\left(g_{rp}\frac{dx_r}{ds}\right) = 0,$$

which can be transformed into

$$g_{rp}\frac{d^2x_r}{ds^2} + \frac{1}{2}\left(\frac{\partial g_{rp}}{\partial x_s} + \frac{\partial g_{sp}}{\partial x_r} - \frac{\partial g_{rs}}{\partial x_p}\right)\frac{dx_r}{ds}\frac{dx_s}{ds} = 0 \qquad (15.6.3)$$

by expanding the second term and making use of the 'dummy' nature of repeated suffixes. (Once again the student is advised to write out the sums in full.) The three-term expression in the bracket is called a Christoffel three-index symbol of the first kind, and is written $\begin{bmatrix} r & s \\ p \end{bmatrix}$.

If we define $g^{qp}\begin{bmatrix} r & s \\ p \end{bmatrix} = \begin{Bmatrix} q \\ r & s \end{Bmatrix}$ as a three-index symbol of the second kind, we can multiply (15.6.3) by g^{qp} and write the differential equation of the geodesic in the form

$$\frac{d^2x_q}{ds^2} = -\begin{Bmatrix} q \\ r & s \end{Bmatrix}\frac{dx_r}{ds}\frac{dx_s}{ds}. \qquad (15.6.4)$$

(The scientist will probably feel that this result is rather in the air and may ask for something more down to earth. As an example, therefore, consider plane polar coordinates, where $ds^2 = dr^2 + r^2\,d\theta^2$, so that

$$g_{11} = 1, \qquad g_{12} = 0, \qquad g_{22} = r^2,$$

whence, by direct calculation,

$$g^{11} = 1, \qquad g^{12} = 0, \qquad g^{22} = r^{-2}.$$

We could use either equations (15.6.3) or equations (15.6.4). In the general case (15.6.3) involves several of the d^2x_r/ds^2 owing to the summation of the first term over r, and we should have simultaneous equations to solve; by the use of (15.6.4) the labour of this is eliminated, being replaced by the extra work involved in calculating curly bracket symbols over that involved in the square bracket ones. Using (15.6.4), we have, remembering that $x_1 = r$ and $x_2 = \theta$,

q	r	s	$\begin{Bmatrix} q \\ r\ \ s \end{Bmatrix}$	The equations (15.6.4)
1	1	1	0	
1	1	2	0	$\dfrac{d^2r}{ds^2} = r\left(\dfrac{d\theta}{ds}\right)^2,$ (15.6.5)
1	2	1	0	
1	2	2	$-r$	
2	1	1	0	
2	1	2	r^{-1}	$\dfrac{d^2\theta}{ds^2} = -\dfrac{2}{r}\dfrac{dr}{ds}\dfrac{d\theta}{ds}.$ (15.6.6)
2	2	1	r^{-1}	
2	2	2	0	

The second of these equations on division by $d\theta/ds$ and integration gives

$$\log \frac{d\theta}{ds} = -2\log r + \log A$$

or

$$\frac{d\theta}{ds} = \frac{A}{r^2},$$

whence, from the formula for the metric (which is simpler than using (15.6.5)),

$$\left(\frac{dr}{ds}\right)^2 = 1 - r^2\left(\frac{d\theta}{ds}\right)^2 = 1 - \frac{A^2}{r^2},$$

so that

$$\frac{dr}{d\theta} = \frac{dr}{ds}\frac{ds}{d\theta} = \frac{r}{A}(r^2 - A^2)^{\frac{1}{2}},$$

which integrates to

$$\cos^{-1}\frac{A}{r} = \theta + C,$$

$$r\cos(\theta + C) = A,$$

the equation of a straight line in polar coordinates.

While we are digressing we may also note that the equations for the geodesic are often more conveniently obtained from the equation

$$\frac{\partial}{\partial s}\frac{\partial L}{\partial \dot{q}_r} - \frac{\partial L}{\partial q_r} = 0,$$

which is the equation known in dynamics as Lagrange's equation with t replaced by s. In Lagrange's equation the q_r are the coordinates and L is the kinetic energy minus the potential energy. Setting the latter equal to zero and putting an obvious interpretation on the former gives

$$2L = g_{pq}\left(\frac{dx_p}{ds}\right)\left(\frac{dx_q}{ds}\right)$$

in which the g_{pq} are functions of the q_r and the dx_p/ds are the $\dot{q}_p$. For example, with $ds^2 = dr^2 + r^2 d\theta^2$, we have

$$2L = \dot{r}^2 + r^2\dot{\theta}^2$$

and

$$0 = \frac{d}{ds}\frac{\partial L}{\partial \dot{r}} - \frac{\partial L}{\partial r} = \frac{d\dot{r}}{ds} - r\dot{\theta}^2 = \ddot{r} - r\dot{\theta}^2,$$

$$0 = \frac{d}{ds}\frac{\partial L}{\partial \dot{\theta}} - \frac{\partial L}{\partial \theta} = \frac{d}{ds}(r^2\dot{\theta}),$$

the same equations as before.)

To return to the main argument, we already know that given a scalar function of position ϕ, its derivatives $\partial\phi/\partial x_r$ at any given point are the components of a covariant vector at that point. (The strict proof of this is actually in the following argument.) The second derivatives $\partial^2\phi/\partial x_r\,\partial x_s$ are not, however, the components of a tensor unless certain conditions are satisfied. (We shall see that they are satisfied in flat space.) To investigate this, let us introduce an arbitrary point in the neighbourhood of the first, and consider the geodesic joining these two points. We have

$$\frac{d\phi}{ds} = \frac{\partial\phi}{\partial x_r}\frac{dx_r}{ds} \qquad = A_r\frac{dx_r}{ds}$$

$$\frac{d^2\phi}{ds^2} = \frac{\partial^2\phi}{\partial x_r\partial x_s}\frac{dx_r}{ds}\frac{dx_s}{ds} + \frac{\partial\phi}{\partial x_r}\frac{d^2x_r}{ds^2}$$

$$= \left(\frac{\partial^2\phi}{\partial x_r\,\partial x_s} - \begin{Bmatrix} q \\ r\ s \end{Bmatrix}\frac{\partial\phi}{\partial x_q}\right)\frac{dx_r}{ds}\frac{dx_s}{ds} = \left(\frac{dA_r}{dx_s} - \begin{Bmatrix} q \\ r\ s \end{Bmatrix}A_q\right)\frac{dx_r}{ds}\frac{dx_s}{ds}.$$

In each of these two expressions, the fact that the left-hand side is independent of the coordinate system shows that the right-hand side must be. Since it is a theorem (proved in the standard treatments) that a quantity which, multiplied into a tensor, produces a tensor, must itself be a tensor, the first of these equations shows that A_r is a covariant vector (as we knew, though this is the formal proof), and the second shows that

$$\frac{\partial A_r}{\partial x_s} - \begin{Bmatrix} q \\ r\ s \end{Bmatrix}A_q = A_{rs}$$

is a covariant tensor of rank two. Thus the condition that the second derivatives themselves constitute a tensor is that the three-index symbol is either zero or, possibly, another tensor, which is not usually the case.

It follows that the nine (or sixteen) differential coefficients of the components of a vector do not in general transform like a tensor, but that the quantities A_{rs} defined above (*a*) transform as a tensor, and (*b*) *are* simply the differential coefficients in question *if* the space is flat, and the g_{rs} therefore all constant. Hence when, in Newtonian or special relativity mechanics, we consider these nine or sixteen differential coefficients, it will be a reasonable generalization in a non-euclidean space to consider the tensor A_{rs} as the correct generalization. The tensor A_{rs} is known as the covariant derivative of A_r.

A covariant tensor of higher order is either the product of several covariant vectors, or is the sum of such products, and can be covariantly differentiated in this form. The result can be expressed thus:

$$(F_{hjk\ldots})_p = \frac{dF_{hjk\ldots}}{dx_p} - \begin{Bmatrix} r \\ h\ p \end{Bmatrix} F_{rjk\ldots} - \begin{Bmatrix} r \\ j\ p \end{Bmatrix} F_{hrk\ldots} - \cdots .$$

If there are contravariant indices, it can be shown that the corresponding terms are added, and that the three-index symbol has the form $\begin{Bmatrix} h \\ r\ p \end{Bmatrix}$, etc.

We are now in a position to return to the statement with which we opened this section, and see that differentiations (and therefore infinitesimal displacements) with respect to the coordinates are not necessarily commutative, a fact we associated with their analogy with rotations. Expanding the second covariant derivatives $(A_h)_{kp}$ and $(A_h)_{pk}$ in full and subtracting, we find that

$$A_{hkp} - A_{hpk} = R^s_{hkp} A_s,$$

where

$$R^s_{hkp} = \frac{\partial}{\partial x_k}\begin{Bmatrix} s \\ h\ p \end{Bmatrix} - \frac{\partial}{\partial x_p}\begin{Bmatrix} s \\ h\ k \end{Bmatrix} + \begin{Bmatrix} r \\ h\ p \end{Bmatrix}\begin{Bmatrix} s \\ r\ k \end{Bmatrix} - \begin{Bmatrix} r \\ h\ k \end{Bmatrix}\begin{Bmatrix} s \\ r\ p \end{Bmatrix} .$$

From the first of these equations R^s_{hkp} is a tensor; from the second it is zero in flat space, since it is zero when the g_{rs} are constants. It is called the Riemann–Christoffel tensor, and its vanishing can also be shown to be the condition that the space is flat.

From its expansion we see that R^s_{hkp} is antisymmetrical in k and p. Expanding it further, other symmetry properties can be verified. In the form R_{shkp} it is

    (i) antisymmetrical in k and p,
    (ii) antisymmetrical in s and h,
    (iii) symmetrical in the pairs $k\ p$, and $s\ h$,
    (iv) has $R^s_{hkp} + R^s_{kph} + R^s_{phk} = 0$.

What these amount to is that it has the symmetry properties of one of the two tensors $T_{[22a]}$ or $T_{[22b]}$, and therefore $\frac{1}{12}n^2(n^2-1)$ independent components. For $n = 2, 3, 4,...$ this equals 1, 6, 20,... .

There is another definition of this tensor based on the notion of parallel displacement. From Fig. 26 we see that a set of coordinate axes taken always parallel to itself (as this is naturally defined on a curved surface) around a finite closed circuit, finishes the circuit *not* parallel to its original orientation. If the vector V^h at $(x_1, x_2,...)$ becomes V'^h when taken first to $(x_1+d_1x_1, x_2+d_1x_2,...)$ and then to

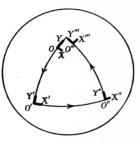

FIG. 26.

$$(x_1+d_1x_1+d_2x_1, x_2+d_1x_2+d_2x_2,...),$$

but becomes V''^h if taken via $(x_1+d_2x_1, x_2+d_2x_2,...)$, then

$$(V'-V'')^s = R^s_{hkp} V^h d_1x^k d_2x^p.$$

To go into this approach is beyond the scope of this book, but we mention it in connexion with § 14.7 because as so defined it is not antisymmetrical in s and h; this property only appears after the introduction of the metric. It should be noted that the quantity $V'-V''$ is an infinitesimal of the second order, and the above statement in no way clashes with our former statement that infinitesimal displacements commute to the first order.

15.7. The basic principles of general relativity

It was natural that the problem should be attacked of generalizing the ideas of special relativity to all relative motion. This is not the place to recapitulate the arguments from the standard works on the subject that

(1) the effects of an accelerated frame of reference are mechanically indistinguishable from those of a gravitational field, and

(2) conversely (so far as a region small enough to consider the field as uniform is concerned), together with

(3) that gravitation may be interpreted on the hypothesis that *all* bodies move along geodesics in space-time, if gravitational fields are also interpreted as deviations of the geometry of space-time from the flat,

but we shall need to record the mathematical expression of these conclusions for use in Chapter XVIII.

The first question that arises is that asking after the possible geometries of empty space, and any answer we may give is a physical hypothesis, to be tested by experiment. The equation $R^s_{hkp} = 0$ is the expression of $4^4 = 256$ conditions (only twenty of them independent) which the metric tensor must satisfy if space-time is to be flat; that is, it is too stringent for the purpose. Einstein suggested that the $4^2 = 16$ conditions (ten of them independent), obtained by equating to zero the contracted Riemann–Christoffel tensor, $R^s_{hks} = R_{hk}$, might be a suitable description of space which, though empty, might contain an irreducible gravitational field (i.e. one which cannot be made to vanish identically by change of coordinate system) and therefore not be flat.

Next comes the nature of space when matter is present. The absence of matter or energy in any form is given by the vanishing of the energy-momentum tensor. It immediately suggests itself that the vanishing of the energy-momentum tensor and the vanishing of the contracted Riemann–Christoffel tensor may be expressions of the same fact. Although this would seem to be true, the picture is somewhat oversimplified in this form. Einstein set the energy-momentum tensor equal to the following function of the metric

$$T_{rs} = -\frac{c^4}{8\pi\kappa}(R_{rs} - \tfrac{1}{2}Rg_{rs} + \Lambda g_{rs}),$$

where R is the scalar obtained by contracting R_{rs} still further, Λ is a universal constant, small and possibly zero, κ the ordinary constant of gravitation $6\cdot7 \times 10^{-8}$ cm.^{3}/gm.-sec.^{2}, and c is as usual the velocity of light. The advantage of this form is that the right-hand side of this equation is the most general function of the metric tensor which satisfies the requirement of agreeing with Newtonian mechanics to a first approximation, and also does not involve needlessly high derivatives of the metric tensor.

15.8. Relativistic and quantum-relativistic units

The student will be acquainted with the elementary theory of units and dimensions, according to which arbitrary units are set up of length, time, and mass, and possibly of something electrical, and all other units are related to these. Thus velocity being the quotient of a length by a time, is expressed in units of feet per second or metres per second. It is also said to have the dimensions L/T or LT^{-1}.

The relation $x_4 = ct$ of § 15.3 suggests that this scheme is ripe for further simplification. Once there was a separate unit of heat, the calorie, and the discoveries of Joule showed that a calorie was $4 \cdot 2 \times 10^7$ ergs. Do not the formulae of special relativity show that there is a similar equivalence between one second and 3×10^{10} cm.? If we take as our units the second and the light-second, or the metre and $3 \cdot 3 \times 10^{-9}$ seconds, then $c = 1$ and our formulae are essentially simplified. $V/ic = \tan \theta$ becomes $V = i \tan \theta$, $E = mc^2$ becomes $E = m$, and the factors c and c^2 disappear from the energy-momentum tensor. The convenience of this arrangement is so obvious that units such that $c = 1$ are almost invariably used in theoretical work involving relativity.

The result is to reduce all kinematics to geometry. To reduce dynamics also to geometry, as general relativity requires, means that only one unit can be permitted. But there is no such obviously satisfactory way of relating the unit of mass to the other two. The course which most readily suggests itself is that the constant of gravitation be put equal to unity. In classical theory $\kappa(m_1 m_2/r^2)$ gives the force between two gravitating masses, whence the dimensions of κ are $M^{-1}L^3T^{-2}$, or LM^{-1} if L and T are already assumed to have the same dimensions. Thus M and L must be the same if the constant of gravitation is to be a pure number. This gives us the centimetre or the metre as the unit of length, mass, and time, according to the following scheme

$$1 \text{ centimetre} = 1 \text{ centimetre}$$
$$= 3 \cdot 335 \times 10^{-11} \text{ seconds}$$
$$= 1 \cdot 349 \times 10^{28} \text{ grammes,}$$
$$1 \text{ metre} = 1 \text{ metre}$$
$$= 3 \cdot 335 \times 10^{-9} \text{ seconds}$$
$$= 1 \cdot 349 \times 10^{27} \text{ kilogrammes.}$$

This reduces the Einstein law of gravitation to the simpler form

$$-8\pi T_{rs} = R_{rs} - \tfrac{1}{2} R g_{rs} + \Lambda g_{rs}.$$

In the work which we shall be discussing in our final chapter, however, Eddington uses a different scheme, relating the constant of gravitation to Planck's constant from quantum theory by the formula

$$\frac{1}{8\pi\kappa} = \left(\frac{h}{2\pi}\right)^2,$$

whence
$$T_{rs} = -\left(\frac{h}{2\pi}\right)^2 (R_{rs} - \tfrac{1}{2} R g_{rs} + \Lambda g_{rs}).$$

Dimensionally this is putting $M^{-1}L^3T^{-2} = M^{-2}L^{-4}T^2$, or $M = L^{-3}$ if L is already equal to T. The advantage of this is that the energy-momentum tensor, $M^{**}V$ (M = density of momentum; V = velocity) can then be equated to the $\psi^{**}\psi$ of quantum theory, where ψ is a momentum vector, both expressions representing the occurrence of matter. It will be seen from the table below that this is possible on Eddington's scheme but not on the one discussed in the previous paragraph. The transformation equations are rather fantastic:

$$1 \text{ centimetre} = 1 \text{ centimetre}$$
$$= 3\cdot335 \times 10^{-11} \text{ seconds}$$
$$= (2\cdot84 \times 10^{-102} \text{ grammes})^{-\frac{1}{3}},$$
$$1 \text{ metre} = 1 \text{ metre}$$
$$= 3\cdot335 \times 10^{-9} \text{ seconds}$$
$$= (2\cdot84 \times 10^{-99} \text{ kilogrammes})^{-\frac{1}{3}}.$$

We give a table of dimensions in the various systems:

Quantity	Classical	Special relativity	General relativity	Quantum relativity
Length	L	L	L	$L = M^{-\frac{1}{3}}$
Area	L^2	L^2	L^2	$L^2 = M^{-\frac{2}{3}}$
Volume	L^3	L^3	L^3	$L^3 = M^{-1}$
Particle density . .	L^{-3}	L^{-3}	L^{-3}	$L^{-3} = M$
Velocity . . .	LT^{-1}	..	..	..
Acceleration . .	LT^{-2}	L^{-1}	L^{-1}	$L^{-1} = M^{\frac{1}{3}}$
Mass	M	M	L	$L^{-3} = M$
Density	ML^{-3}	ML^{-3}	L^{-2}	$L^{-6} = M^2$
Force	MLT^{-2}	ML^{-1}	..	$L^{-4} = M^{\frac{4}{3}}$
Momentum . . .	MLT^{-1}	M	L	$L^{-3} = M$
Energy	ML^2T^{-2}	M	L	$L^{-3} = M$
Pressure . . .	$ML^{-1}T^{-2}$	ML^{-3}	L^{-2}	$L^{-6} = M^2$
Angular momentum; action .	ML^2T^{-1}	ML	L^2	$L^{-2} = M^{\frac{2}{3}}$
Constant of gravitation .	$ML^{-3}T^2$	$M^{-1}L$	..	$L^4 = M^{-\frac{4}{3}}$

One further point remains to be discussed here. The most natural representation of a velocity is by a line equal in length to the distance gone in unit time. A change in the unit of time will change this, but a change in the unit of length will only alter its description, not its length. (For example, a velocity of 4 metres/sec. will be represented by a line 4 metres long, and one of 400 cm./sec. by a line 400 cm. long!) We might reasonably regard the dimensions of a velocity as T^{-1}, therefore, if we are thinking more of geometrical than of arithmetical representation.

But this is true only while we are thinking of contravariant components. If we introduce covariant components, the considerations discussed at the end of § 4.6 come in. As stated there, without a unit of length the reciprocal basic vectors cannot be defined; this is approaching from the opposite direction the statement in § 14.7 that co- and contravariant *quantities* become co- and contravariant *forms of a quantity* when the metric tensor is introduced.

In order to avoid this possible source of confusion it is necessary to divorce the basic vectors from the unit of length, as was done in § 4.6, and discuss changes of basic vector and of unit independently. If we start with a vector V^* in an orthonormal system and (*a*) change to basic vectors k times as large, and then (*b*) change to a new unit of length n times as large, then the components of V^+ will be those of V^* multiplied by $1/k$, but the components of V° will be those of V^* multiplied by k/n^2. The ordinary physical dimensions are based on the assumption that $k = n$; tensor character depends on the index of k; the dimensions suggested in the previous paragraph depend on the index of n only. Generalizing this argument we see that it is possible to distinguish physical or relative dimensions from geometrical or absolute dimensions, and that if the physical dimensions of a quantity of contravariance p and covariance q are D, then its geometrical dimensions are DL^{q-p}. These dimensions give the change in size of the geometrical object (line segment, area, etc.) which naturally represents the physical quantity in question, when the units of length, mass, etc., are changed, in contrast to the physical dimensions which give the change in magnitude of the number(s) representing it.

CHAPTER XVI

QUANTUM THEORY

THERE is a longer history of misunderstanding (or of 'partial under-standing') in the quantum theory than there is in relativity theory. It is true that for a time the apparent contraction in the ratio $\beta:1$ of the longitudinal dimension of a body in motion was regarded as a real contraction, due to an in principle determinable velocity through the aether. But the main lines of special relativity were correctly laid down from the start, and general relativity is an extension, not a correction, of special relativity. In contrast, the quantum theory has suffered from a remarkably successful initial mis-statement of its underlying nature, which still survives in the word 'quantum', and is still too useful to be abandoned entirely. Just as the first stage in relativity was to keep Newtonian mechanics and add the Lorentz contraction, and this was followed by the more satisfactory abandonment of Newtonian mechanics for Lorentz-invariant mechanics, so the first stage of quantum mechanics was to keep Newtonian mechanics and to graft on to it the 'quantum restrictions', only later abandoning the Newtonian mechanics in favour of something differing radically from the start. (We use the phrase 'Newtonian mechanics' to include the whole of nineteenth-century mechanical and electromagnetic theory.) The differences are that in relativity the first stage lasted some ten years and in quantum theory nearer thirty years, and that the second stage of quantum mechanics was a radical correction, not extension, of the first.

In consequence, the considerations which led historically to the quantum revision of Newtonian mechanics cannot be developed from one simple experimental result, as were those outlined in the previous chapter. Rather there was an increasing mass of work, the theoretical interpretation of which was sufficiently unsatisfactory to cause an inquiry studying more deeply the fundamental processes of physical observation and interpretation. We shall not review the course of that inquiry but shall presume on its conclusions by attempting to develop quantum theory, as we did relativity theory, from one basic considera-tion, but in this case it will be an epistemological one—that *the process of observing a system inevitably produces an effect upon the system*. In con-sequence of this it may not be the same system after the observation as it was before. This leads to great difficulties if our theoretical treatment is, in principle, to be firmly rooted in experiment. In order to base discussion of a system on experiment we must assume that we can start by observing enough about the system to define it, and yet, granting this principle, we cannot guarantee that the first of these defining observations will not turn it into a different system even before we start the second of them. We can only define a system with $p = p_0$ and $q = q_0$ as one in which we have measured p and found it to be p_0 and have measured q and found it to be q_0, and there is apparently no guarantee whatever that if we perform our verifications in the reverse order we shall get the same final system. In brief, *observations* are *operations which are not necessarily commutative.*

There are two approaches to the problem of dealing with this situation which converge mathematically on to the same ultimate results. The first is to accept the fact that since a second measurement may upset the first we can never have precise knowledge of all the variables of a system, and therefore to set up a calculus in which the basic quantities are probability distributions rather than exact values. The other is to seize on the word 'non-commutative' and to try to apply non-commutative, operator, algebra, rather than ordinary elementary algebra, in developing a mathematical theory. We might denote the whole system by S, and measurements of p and q by the operators P and Q, and suppose that after measuring p on the system S, the system will have changed into PS. If we now measure q it will become QPS, but had we measured these quantities in the reverse order it would have become PQS. The condition that these final states are the same is that P and Q commute. It must be remembered, of course, that the theory is to be judged on its results. At a more elementary level, we can develop *theories* of inverse square attraction, of inverse cube attraction, or of first power attraction, all of which are mathematically satisfactory, but only one of which will yield conclusions in accordance with experiment in dealing with any particular phenomenon. There is really nothing more abstruse in developing a theory involving non-commutating quantities, except the relative unfamiliarity of the mathematical technique.

16.2. The basic postulates

As an operand is a vector (leaving aside § 7.7 for the present), we assume that any precise state of the system can be represented by a vector. It is unnecessary, and indeed possibly inadvisable, to say more at this stage, except perhaps to repeat the warning in § 15.1 concerning the metaphysical implications of forming *ad hoc* vectors. But 'off the record' it may be said that the type of vector we shall ultimately need will turn out to be something very different from any of the classical vectors—vectors in phase space not excluded—since they will have to be vectors in a Hilbert space. For the moment these operand vectors are purely conceptual and will be called wave vectors when it is necessary to distinguish them from physical vectors such as velocity, momentum, or electric field. Their carrier space will similarly be referred to as wave space.

Any quantity which can be measured (observed) will now be represented by an operator in wave space. It is necessary to find room in the theory for the results of the measurement, and for the fact that information obtained by measurement does not necessarily remain trustworthy. This has been done by the assumptions (1) that the result of the measurement is the expectation $*\psi A\psi*/*\psi\psi*$, where ψ is the vector and A the observable, (2) that this is only statistically true—the result of making the measurement A on a single system will be one of the eigenvalues of A, and (3) that the single system will be modified by the process of observation so that after the observation it is represented by the eigenvector belonging to the eigenvalue which was observed. The whole theory contains no reference at all to whatever it may be that decides into which eigenstate a particular single system jumps when it is observed.

The third of these assumptions may be contrasted with two other alternatives, (4) that the system remains unaltered as ψ, and (5) as suggested in the previous section, that it changes to $A\psi$. We shall see that (4) remains tenable with (3) to a certain extent.

In the foregoing paragraphs we have tried to show first why it might be advantageous to attempt to apply non-commutative algebra to physical systems, and secondly, how it might be done. The 'how', the scheme of association of the mathematical symbols with the physical realities, is admittedly bizarre to anyone accustomed to associating each property of a system with one of the natural numbers, without the process of association reacting in any way on the system. But before being unduly concerned about this, the student should pause to consider what other method of association he can devise. In any case, there is no harm in speculating; the ultimate test is agreement with experiment, and quantum mechanics has stood this test very well.

There are one or two immediate conclusions. In the first place, one does not observe imaginary quantities in the laboratory, and hence the operators which represent observable quantities must be Hermitian and the geometry of wave space a unitary one. Thus $\psi*$ and $*\psi$ will be ket and bra vectors (§ 14.7). In consequence of this the eigenvectors of an observable will be orthogonal to one another. Let these eigenvectors (normalized) be $\psi_1, \psi_2,..., \psi_r$, with eigenvalues $a_1, a_2,..., a_r$, and let the vector ψ be expanded in the form

$$\psi = c_1\psi_1+c_2\psi_2+...+c_r\psi_r.$$

Then since the eigenvectors are orthogonal we shall have

$$*\psi\psi* = c_1^2 *\psi_1\psi_1*+c_2^2 *\psi_2\psi_2*+...+c_r^2 *\psi_r\psi_r*+$$
$$+c_1 c_2 *\psi_1\psi_2*+...$$
$$= c_1^2+c_2^2+...+c_r^2 \quad \text{(square terms only)}$$

and

$$*\psi A\psi* = c_1^2 a_1+c_2^2 a_2+...+c_r^2 a_r,$$

so that by assumption (1) above, the result of making the measurement A on the system ψ will be

$$\frac{*\psi A\psi*}{*\psi\psi*} = \frac{c_1^2 a_1+c_2^2 a_2+...+c_r^2 a_r}{c_1^2+c_2^2+...+c_r^2}.$$

But the meaning of this result is essentially statistical, namely, that if the observation is made on an assembly of identical systems, they will give the results $a_1, a_2,..., a_r$ in the proportions $c_1^2, c_2^2,..., c_r^2$, a system giving the result a_i being transformed in the process into the state ψ_i. Thus $c_i^2/\sum c_i^2$ is the fraction of the assembly which goes to ψ_i and yields the observational result a_i; it is the *probability* that any given single system will do so. A repetition of the measurement on the assembly will lead to the same result as before, but for a different reason—that the assembly is now a mixture of the different types of system $\psi_1, \psi_2,..., \psi_r$ in the proportions $c_1^2, c_2^2,..., c_r^2$. Thus *the assembly*, if it is still in existence, might well continue to be described by the original vector ψ, which is assumption (4) above. (We make the proviso 'if it is still in existence' because certain methods of measurement—the mass spectrograph, for example —actually analyse the assembly into physically separate parts. In the case of the mass spectrograph it is arguable that the assembly always was heterogeneous, but in the Stern–Gerlach experiment where spin, not mass, is the measurable, this argument is not valid: see below.)

Measurements made on assemblies of many systems therefore remain trustworthy in a statistical sense—which explains how classical mechanics did so well—and a single system which has once given the measurement a_r will continue to do so if the measurement is repeated. But if we measure a second property B, of this single system, then unless A and B commute, and thus have common eigenvectors, ψ_r will not be an eigenvector (or, in physical language, eigenstate) of B. In this case a consequence of the measurement of B will be the changing of the state of the system to an eigenstate of B—say ψ. As this in its turn is not an eigenstate of A, on remeasurement of A after measuring B the system may give any one of the eigenvalues of A (the probability of any one being worked out as before, by expanding ψ in terms of the ψ_r), and not merely that one, a_r, which it gave with certainty before we measured B. An example of such non-commutating measurements is that of the components of the spin of an elementary particle along two of the coordinate axes. A beam of such particles may be split into two parts with spins in the positive and negative directions of, say, the X-axis. One part may then be split according to the Y-axis component of the spin. One of these quarter parts of the original beam may then be re-examined for its X-axis component and will be found *not* homogeneous.

16.3. Vector observables

The concept of a physical vector arises from a type of observation the result of which is not unique unless a direction is specified, but in which, given the direction, the result is predictable according to a familiar rule when the results to be obtained in three mutually perpendicular (or otherwise independent) directions are known. As both eigenvalues and expectation values are single numbers, we see that complete determination of a physical vector really involves three separate measurements. Each of these will have its operator form, so that to determine a quantity like momentum, $(p_1 p_2 p_3) = \mathbf{p}$, we need a triad of operators, or operator-vector, $\mathbf{P} = (P_1 P_2 P_3)$. It is not necessary that these three components should be the components of the momentum parallel to any axes already set up for any purpose; it is sufficient that they should be independent and defined in direction relative to any such pre-existent set of axes. In tensor notation we can write this triad P^r. Then if the system is specified by a normalized wave vector ψ, we have the three equations

$$*\psi P^r \psi^* = p^r, \tag{16.3.1}$$

where p^r is the (average) observed value for an assembly of like systems.

We have to work on such an assembly and not on a simple system for two reasons—first because the classical concepts are based on such systems, and, secondly, because of the great difficulty we should find in applying the vector transformation laws both reasonably and rigorously to a single system. The example of the spin of an elementary particle quoted above warns us that the three members of the triad may not commute with each other. In such a case we would do well to get as far as we can on expectation values. Position, on the other hand, occupies such a fundamental place in our scheme of analysis in mathematical physics that it will be very hard if it is not possible to assign the three components of a position vector simultaneously and accurately— but let us postpone pleading hardship.

It will be seen that there are three different coordinate systems to be distinguished—we shall refer to them as bases to avoid confusion with the 'system' being studied. The first is the basis of as yet unknown dimensionality in the wave space: we shall call this basis A. The second is the three-dimensional basis in terms of which all our ordinary physical discussion is carried on: this we shall call basis B. And, thirdly, there is the basis used to express the vector P, which we have explicitly stated need not be the same as B: this we shall call C. There is obviously some connexion between A and B, since if the system denoted by ψ is rotated in space but otherwise unchanged, it becomes a new system ϕ, with new wave coordinates. For several reasons the notation of Chapter IV is inconvenient here, and we shall therefore denote the rotation of the system in space coordinates by O, and the rotation in wave coordinates by Ω. If the vector P^r of the rotated system ϕ is numerically π^r, then

$$\pi^r = O^r{}_s p^s, \qquad \phi^* = \Omega \psi^*. \tag{16.3.2}$$

It is clear that the operators Ω must be a faithful representation of the group r_3 to which O belongs. Since physically significant results appear only in the form $*\psi P \psi^*$, however, and are thus independent of the sign of ψ^*, spin representations are allowable, and ψ^* should properly be referred to as a spinor. Substituting (16.3.2) into (16.3.1), and remembering that Ω is unitary,

$$*\psi \Omega^{-1} P^r \Omega \psi^* = *\psi \overline{\overline{\Omega}} P^r \Omega \psi^* = \pi^r = O^r{}_s p^s. \tag{16.3.3}$$

The results π^r obtained by this process will be exactly the same as those obtained by leaving the system alone but rotating the measuring apparatus in the reverse direction. This will be equivalent to expressing the vector p in new coordinates, replacing p^r by p'^r, and therefore replacing P^r by P'^r. (Bases A and B remain but C becomes a new one, C'.) Thus

$$*\psi P'^r\psi* = O^r_s p^s. \tag{16.3.4}$$

Equations (16.3.3) and (16.3.4) being valid for any ψ, imply the equality of the operators concerned. (To prove this, consider the results in the last paragraph of § 4.6.) Hence

$$\Omega^{-1}P^r\Omega = P'^r. \tag{16.3.5}$$

And since from (16.3.4)

$$*\psi P'^r\psi* = O^r_s *\psi P^s\psi*,$$

for all ψ, we have $P'^r = O^r_s P^s = \Omega^{-1}P^r\Omega. \tag{16.3.6}$

(The results $\pi^r = p'^r$ will also be obtained if we rotate the measuring apparatus and physical basis (bases B and C) but not the system. In this case the operators remain as P^r, because they describe the measuring apparatus in terms of the physical basis, and the relation of these is not changed. Equations (16.3.3) are now to be interpreted, not that the P^r have become $P'^r = \Omega^{-1}P^r\Omega$, but that the $\psi*$ has become $\Omega\psi*$, showing, as we should expect, that this is the transformation of ψ if basis B is changed.)

If p^r is replaced by some other type of tensor there will be a number of obvious modifications throughout the above argument, but it will hold its validity in essence.

Equation (16.3.6) has a number of important consequences. Its most interesting features are (1) that it shows that the result of any one of a certain group of *conjugating* operators on *one* of the P^r is always equal to a *linear combination* of *all* the P^r, (2) that the eigenvalues of P'^r are the same as those of P^r, and therefore that all the P^r have the same eigenvalues, but (3) that the eigenvectors of P'^r and P^r corresponding to the same eigenvalue, are different. It does not show that an eigenvector of P^r is necessarily an eigenvector of P'^r. In fact we can find examples either of the validity or of the non-validity of this latter conclusion.

An operator with only two eigenvalues may without loss of generality be supposed to have eigenvalues $+1$ and -1. In one coordinate system it will be $\begin{bmatrix} 1 & 0 \\ 0 & -1 \end{bmatrix}$. Since the operators Ω are a representation of the rotation group, in this application they can only be the identical representation occurring twice or the two-dimensional irreducible representation. If U is the operator defined by (12.3.4), it is easily verified that

$$U^{-1}\begin{bmatrix} 1 & 0 \\ 0 & -1 \end{bmatrix} U = \cos\theta\begin{bmatrix} 1 & 0 \\ 0 & -1 \end{bmatrix} + \sin\theta\sin\psi\begin{bmatrix} 0 & i \\ -i & 0 \end{bmatrix} + \sin\theta\cos\psi\begin{bmatrix} 0 & 1 \\ 1 & 0 \end{bmatrix},$$

which should be compared with the transformation of the vector $(0, 0, 1)$ by (12.3.1). If the three matrices here are denoted by S_z, S_y, and S_x respectively, it will be found that they exemplify completely the relations (16.3.6). Further, their eigenvalues, and those of any S', are only ± 1, but if S' is obtained from S_z by rotation through an angle ω, and $\psi_z{}^*$ is an eigenvector of S_z, then $^*\psi_z S' \psi_z{}^*$, the *expectation value*, will be found to be $\pm\cos\omega$, which is the 'resolved part' of ± 1 in the direction of S'.

At the other extreme, let P^1, P^2, and P^3 have as eigenvalues all the real numbers, so that their carrier space is an infinity-dimensional space, and let them be completely independent, so that the carrier space is actually the Kronecker product space of three such spaces. Let $\psi(\xi, \eta, \zeta)$ be their simultaneous eigenvector with eigenvalues ξ, η, ζ; then $\psi(\xi, \eta, \zeta)$ is the Kronecker product of the three factor eigenvectors $\psi_1(\xi)$, $\psi_2(\eta)$, and $\psi_3(\zeta)$, and P^r commutes with ψ_s. Then, if I^r denotes the identical operator in the r factor-space, we have

$$Or_s P^s \psi(\xi, \eta, \zeta) = (Or_1 P^1 I^2 I^3 + Or_2 I^1 P^2 I^3 + Or_3 I^1 I^2 P^3)\psi(\xi, \eta, \zeta)$$

$$= Or_s p^s \psi(\xi, \eta, \zeta)$$

(the student should fill in the formal intermediate steps), which shows that $\psi(\xi, \eta, \zeta)$ is an eigenfunction of every P'.

Both of these extremes occur in quantum mechanics. The second is the classical picture, in which a state in which the coordinates (x, y, z) are known precisely in one coordinate system is one in which they are known precisely in any other obtained by rotation. The first occurs in connexion with electron spin, the eigenvalues of which are (conventionally) $\pm\frac{1}{2}$, but the expectation value of which, in a direction inclined to one in which a previous measurement has given one of these values precisely, is the resolved part of that value. In particular, if one measurement sorts electrons out into those with spin $+\frac{1}{2}$ along the Z-axis and those with spin $-\frac{1}{2}$ in this direction, then a second measurement applied to the first set along, say, the X-axis, will show the values $+\frac{1}{2}$ and $-\frac{1}{2}$ in equal proportions (average 0).

16.4. The commutation rules and wave functions

The foregoing considerations are enlightening as to possibilities but get us nowhere on probabilities. To guide us as to the most likely laws in quantum physics we must look elsewhere. The most significant fact in this direction is the success of classical physics. It has been remarked by several writers that the epistemological principle of quantum theory establishes an absolute meaning to the word 'small', which, in this context, means 'not large enough for the reactions consequent on observations to be negligible'. It is when these reactions *are* negligible that classical physics applies. This implies that somewhere in the quantum laws there must be incorporated a unit of size. It also implies that if this unit is treated as a variable and made to tend to zero, the laws must go over into those of classical physics. The scheme we have developed so far is not incompatible with classical physics if all our operators commute, though it is absurdly clumsy, when we can perfectly well work with natural numbers, to replace them all by operators in an infinity-dimensional space. Our earliest qualitative considerations also suggested that the essential features of atomic physics will only appear when non-commuting variables are introduced into our mechanics.

We therefore expect the essential nature of quantum mechanics to appear in the existence of certain variables, typically A and B, for which $AB-BA$ is not zero, but tends to zero if the natural unit of size does so. The simplest assumption would be that this expression, the 'commutator' of A and B, is equal to this unit—or rather (since if A and B are Hermitian, $AB-BA$ must be i times a Hermitian operator) equal to i times this unit. Actually this is not as simple an assumption as it appears to be. The variables S^r of the previous section, which are as simple as anything non-commutating could be, have

$$S_z S_y - S_y S_z = 2iS_x; \qquad S_y S_x - S_x S_y = 2iS_z; \qquad S_x S_z - S_z S_x = 2iS_y,$$

which is altogether different.

The difficulty appears acutely when we study the matrix form of A and B. Let A be diagonal; then

$$(AB-BA)_{ik} = \sum_j (A_{ij} B_{jk} - B_{ij} A_{jk})$$

$$= A_{ii} B_{ik} - B_{ik} A_{kk}$$

$$= B_{ik}(A_{ii} - A_{kk}),$$

and if, in suitable units, we are to have $AB - BA = iI$, then

$$B_{ik}(A_{ii} - A_{kk}) = 0 \quad i \neq k$$
$$B_{ii}(A_{ii} - A_{ii}) = i.$$

The difficulties are obvious! But they disappear if the carrier space is of a Hilbert or more general type, for in equation (12.7.2), omitting the operand, we have

$$\frac{d}{dx} x - x \frac{d}{dx} = 1,$$

which is exactly, apart from the factor i, of the type we are proposing. The discussion in § 12.7 of the matrix form of d/dx adequately exposes the origin of the difficulties in spaces of finite or denumerable dimensionality. It is thus possible to write $B = i \, d/dA$. More precisely, the vector is a function $\psi(\alpha)$; the observable A has as its operator form multiplication by α, and B has as its operator form i times differentiation with respect to α. More than this, Dirac has shown, and we need not repeat the proof here, that if B is not $i \, d/dA$, then since $B - i \, d/dA$ commutes with A, it differs from it at most by a function of A (and any other variables that commute with A) which can be eliminated by replacing $\psi(\alpha)$ by $e^{i\phi(\alpha)}\psi(\alpha)$—that is, by changing the basic vectors in such a way as to coordinate the phases of the components in a certain way, leaving only one overall phase indeterminate. This phase adjustment alters $*\psi(\alpha)G\psi(\alpha)*$ to $*\psi(\alpha)e^{-i\phi(\alpha)}Ge^{i\phi(\alpha)}\psi(\alpha)*$ which produces no change in its numerical value provided G commutes with α and therefore with $e^{i\phi(\alpha)}$. It does produce changes, however, if G includes B.

It is instructive to note that, by the end of § 3.6, if A is Hermitian and k is real, then $\exp ikA$ is unitary, and multiplication of $\psi(\alpha)$ by $\exp ikA$ is a permissible coordinate change in wave space. So is multiplication by $\exp ikB$. What is its interpretation? We have

$$\exp ikB \, \psi(\alpha) = \exp\left\{-k\frac{d}{d\alpha}\right\} \psi(\alpha)$$
$$= \psi(\alpha - k)$$

by Taylor's theorem. Now α has the definite value a_1 if $\psi(\alpha)$ is the eigenfunction $\psi_1(\alpha) = \delta(\alpha - a_1)$; for this vector

$$\alpha \, \delta(\alpha - a_1) = a_1 \, \delta(\alpha - a_1).$$

But

$$\psi_1(\alpha - k) = \delta(\alpha - k - a_1),$$

and thus

$$\alpha \, \psi_1(\alpha - k) = \alpha \, \delta(\alpha - k - a_1)$$
$$= (a_1 + k) \, \psi_1(\alpha - k).$$

From this we see (1) that if A has the eigenvalue a_1 it also has the eigenvalue a_1+k, where k is any real number, and (2) that the eigenfunction belonging to the latter is $\exp ikB$ times the eigenfunction belonging to the former. Both of these are significant results. The former implies that a variable which enjoys the commutation rule $AB-BA = i$ with another must have as eigenvalues all the real numbers from $-\infty$ to $+\infty$ if it has any real eigenvalues at all. The latter associates the operator $\exp ikB$ with a change in zero of A, or, in more realistic terms, a displacement k of the apparatus used to measure A.

It is possible that in the limiting process in which the unit of size tended to zero such difficult limits would be encountered as would render necessary the definition of new variables. But this seems unlikely, and if it is not so then the same variables must occur in quantum mechanics as occur in classical mechanics—possibly with others which are essentially of the magnitude of the unit itself. In the dynamics of particles these are six per particle, the three components of the position vector, and the three components of the momentum vector. To these must be added the time and the function of these $6n+1$ variables which is the energy; this is the type of analysis we used in Chapter X. We are therefore on stronger ground than some writers would give one to think in assuming that we shall need just these variables in quantum theory, for though there are some macro-variables—e.g. temperature—which have no micro-counterpart, others of them are almost bound to be micro-variables which survive when the unit tends to zero. (We might even suppose that all the spurious ones, like temperature, would have given some cause for suspicion in kinetic theory analyses.)

It is also possible, of course, that space is atomic, and the eigenvalues of position are discrete. In that case we are committed to something worse than $AB-BA = i$ for our commutation laws. We shall ignore this possibility!

We are committed, then, to discovering which are the non-zero commutators among the $6n+1$ variables of a classical system. It will be remembered from § 4.8, that a coordinate system in wave space is conveniently set up using the simultaneous eigenvectors of a 'complete set of commuting operators'. Thus every non-zero commutator means that not both of the operators in it take part in the construction of the coordinate system in wave space—or in other words that the wave vector function ψ is a function of one or other but not of both of such a pair. It follows that if two parts of a system can be conceived of as distinct, the variables used to describe them must commute. This leaves only the variables of a single particle to consider. In the previous section we suggested that although it is not necessary that a quantity which behaves as a vector should in fact consist of three independent components, yet it would 'be very hard if' we could not 'assign the three components of a position vector simultaneously and accurately'—that is to say, if the position vector cannot be treated as a whole in this respect. The practice of taking linear combinations of positional coordinates of several particles also suggests that the independence which we have assumed between the coordinates of different particles should also hold between the three coordinates of one particle. Such an argument applying to $x_1,...,z_n$ will also apply to $m_1 \dot{x}_1,..., m_n \dot{z}_n$—i.e. to the momenta—at any rate in non-relativistic work. We thus reach the conclusion that $AB-BA = 0$ if A and B belong to what are classically different degrees of freedom. This leaves only $pq-qp = i\hbar$, where $\hbar$ is the natural unit, if p and q are position and momentum coordinates belonging to the same degree of freedom. These we must retain if quantum mechanics is not to degenerate into classical mechanics.

These relations are usually derived by a consideration of the Poisson bracket relations of contact transformation theory. This treatment shows quantum mechanics as a natural generalization of classical mechanics and ensures the passage to classical mechanics as $\hbar \to 0$. It is probably possible to find other generalizations, and thus it is perhaps impossible to *prove* the quantum conditions. We have attempted an alternative justification for them with two objects in mind—first to make the justification slightly less dependent on classical concepts and, secondly, because many readers will be unfamiliar with contact transformations.

A treatment which seems to demand a brief comment is the one which is based on invariance under rotations (compare Temple, *Quantum Theory*). The argument seems suspiciously likely to apply equally to spin measurements where, if applicable, it leads to a definitely wrong result. To sort this out an extension of the previous section to a detailed consideration of second rank tensors $P^r Q^s$, dealing with both expectations and eigenvalues, and with P and Q commuting or not, is necessary. We would also remark in connexion with earlier treatments in general that quantum results tend to the classical in two distinct ways (1) as $\hbar$ tends to zero, and (2) as quantum numbers (which we have not yet introduced) tend to infinity. These ways are often but not always equivalent. The former is necessary; the latter is a hypothesis (Bohr's correspondence principle) which was extremely useful in the early days of quantum theory.

Although we have halved the number of classical independent variables we have actually extended enormously the range of variation of a system. Whereas formerly we could have $p = p_0$, $q = q_0$, now we must drop one of these, but we can have a system in which the other has a range of values with varying probability. It can be shown (e.g. Corson, p. 38) that the product of the standard deviations (see § 11.5) of p and q is not less than $\hbar/2$ (Heisenberg's uncertainty principle) and that thus, unless an uncertainty in p amounting to an infinite energy is to be permitted, q can never be known exactly. Nor can p be known exactly unless we have an infinite space to play with.

These remarks complete the picture of wave space. A wave vector is most conveniently expressed as a function $\psi(x_1,...)$; we lose no generality in our summary if we describe $\psi(x)$, a function of one variable only. The number $\psi(x_0)$ is its x_0 component in terms of basic vectors which are eigenfunctions of the coordinate x, every real value of x being permitted. But physically these eigenfunctions are themselves impossible, or possible only as limiting cases. The eigenfunctions themselves are $\delta(x-x_0)$, and are infinite in length, but physically possible vectors are finite in length. Thus the physically possible vectors are taken from a Hilbert space but are conveniently referred to in terms of a more general space which includes the Hilbert space. According to the discussion in § 16.2, the value $\psi(x_0)$ gives the probability of the value x_0 being obtained if the coordinate x is measured on the system; this is to be interpreted in the usual way that $|\psi(x_0)|^2 \, dx$ is the probability of a value between x_0 and x_0+dx being found.

It remains to introduce the energy and the time. As scalars these are of less interest here, though in other contexts they are as interesting as the position and momentum variates. We assume that the wave vectors are functions of time. We assume that the relation between the energy and the other coordinates is the same as in classical theory, problems such as the order of the factors in a product and the existence of variates which have no classical analogue (see the next section) being discussed as they arise. But—and this is the step which is significant—the formal relations between energy and time in classical theory parallel those between positions and momenta to some extent, and we assume this parallelism to the extent that we consider $-i\hbar \, d/dt$ to be an alternative operator form for the energy. (This is the form usually adopted, but the sign of an imaginary term introduced *ad hoc* is always a matter of convention. This sign is independent of others we have introduced, though it should be noted that if $q_r = i\hbar\, d/dp_r$, then $p_r = -i\hbar\, d/dq_r$, and vice versa, but the form here is again the conventional one.)

Equating these two forms of the energy operator, and applying them to an arbitrary operand, gives Schrödinger's equation, which is the basic equation of Wave Mechanics, the form of quantum mechanics in which (as explained in § 12.8) the problems associated with infinite matrices are resolved by translating the situation into the language of analysis. The derivation of this equation may be summarized thus:

$$\text{kinetic energy} + \text{potential energy} = \text{total energy},$$

$$\sum_{r=1}^{3n} \frac{p_r^2}{2m_r} + V(q_1, ..., q_{3n}) = E.$$

Substitute into this $p_r = -i\hbar\, d/dq_r$; $E = -i\hbar\, d/dt$. Replace $\hbar$ by $h/2\pi$, a procedure justified by later comparison of results with experiment, h being Planck's constant, and supply $\psi(q_1, ..., q_{3n})$ as operand, and we have

$$-\frac{h^2}{8\pi^2}\left[\sum_{r=1}^{3n} \frac{1}{m_r} \frac{\partial^2}{\partial q_r^2}\right]\psi(q_1, ..., q_{3n}) + V(q_1, ..., q_{3n})\psi(q_1, ..., q_{3n})$$

$$= -\frac{h}{2\pi i} \frac{d}{dt}\psi(q_1, ..., q_{3n}),$$

which is Schrödinger's equation.

16.5. The Schrödinger equations

Whatever the merits and demerits of the foregoing analysis, from this point on we accept the fact that wave mechanics has proved itself a satisfactory medium for the description of phenomena. A system in a given state, that is to say, is representable as a vector in a system or wave space which is a Hilbert space; a potential observation of any property of that system is representable as an operator whose eigenvalues are its potential results, the probabilities of the various alternatives being proportional to the squared moduli of the components of the vector when expressed in terms of the eigenvectors of the operator as a coordinate basis; and if the observation is actually made the system is altered unpredictably by the observation in such a way that after the observation it is to be represented by the eigenvector appropriate to the eigenvalue actually observed. (So far this is a summary of quantum mechanics in general.) A coordinate system can be set up in this Hilbert space such that

(i) the coordinates and the time are the argument of the wave function which is the vector in the Hilbert space,

(ii) coordinate measurements are represented by the operation of multiplication by the coordinate,

(iii) momentum measurements are represented by $-h/2\pi i$ times the operation of differentiation with respect to the corresponding coordinate,

(iv) energy is represented by $-h/2\pi i$ times the operation of differentiation with respect to the time, and

(v) the classical relation between energy, momenta, and position holds when applicable,

and thus in this sytem, if $\psi(x, y, z, t)$ is the wave vector of a single particle of mass m in a field V, and x, y, and z are the space coordinates, the equation

$$\left\{\sum_{x,y,z} \frac{1}{2m}\left(\frac{h}{2\pi i}\frac{\partial}{\partial x}\right)^2 + V(x,y,z)\right\}\psi^* = -\frac{h}{2\pi i}\frac{\partial}{\partial t}\psi^*, \quad (16.5.1\,a)$$

or, more briefly,

$$-\frac{h^2}{8\pi^2 m}\nabla^2\psi^* + V(x,y,z)\psi^* = -\frac{h}{2\pi i}\frac{\partial\psi^*}{\partial t} \quad (16.5.1\,b)$$

holds. Wave mechanics is the study of quantum mechanics through this equation, the Schrödinger equation. We first consider the form of the general solution of this equation.

Drop stars for the time, substitute

$$\psi(x, y, z, t) = \phi(x, y, z)\chi(t)$$

into (16.5.1) and divide through by $\phi(x, y, z)\chi(t)$; the right-hand side is independent of x, y, and z, and the left-hand side of t, whence each is a constant, say W. This gives

$$-\frac{h^2}{8\pi^2 m}\nabla^2\phi(x,y,z) + \{V(x,y,z) - W\}\phi(x,y,z) = 0, \quad (16.5.2)$$

$$-\frac{h}{2\pi i}\frac{\partial\chi(t)}{dt} = W\chi(t). \quad (16.5.3)$$

The first of these equations gives rise to a series of orthogonal functions $\phi_n(x, y, z)$ with eigenvalues W_n. The second then gives rise to

$$\chi_n(t) = c_n e^{-(2\pi i/h)W_n}, \quad (16.5.4)$$

where c_n is a constant of integration. Consider now an arbitrary $\psi(x, y, z, t)$. Its form at any given value of t may be expanded in terms of the solutions of (16.5.2) and as it varies from moment to moment the coefficients in this expansion will change. Owing to the expansion theorem, therefore, we may write

$$\psi(x, y, z, t) = \sum_n a_n(t)\phi_n(x, y, z) \tag{16.5.5}$$

without restricting in any way the form of ψ. The substitution of this into (16.5.1) gives

$$-\frac{h^2}{8\pi^2 m}\sum_n a_n(t)\nabla^2\phi_n(x, y, z) + V(x, y, z)\sum_n a_n(t)\phi(x, y, z)$$

$$= -\frac{h}{2\pi i}\dot{a}_n(t)\phi_n(x, y, z)$$

which reduces to

$$\sum_n W_n\, a_n(t)\phi_n(x, y, z) = -\frac{h}{2\pi i}\sum_n \dot{a}_n(t)\phi_n(x, y, z)$$

since $a_n(t)$ commutes with the space-differential operators. Multiplying by $\phi_m(x, y, z)$ and integrating, i.e. right-starring the above equation and multiplying on the left by $*\phi_m$, we obtain

$$W_m\, a_m(t) = -\frac{h}{2\pi i}\dot{a}_m(t),$$

or
$$a_m(t) = c_m\, \chi_m(t)$$

as the condition that (16.5.5) satisfies (16.5.1). The general solution of (16.5.1) is thus

$$\psi(x, y, z, t) = \sum_n a_n\, \phi_n(x, y, z)\chi_n(t). \tag{16.5.6}$$

As this proof recurs at intervals in the sequel and will not be repeated in detail, we take note of the conditions requisite for its applicability. First, V is independent of t—though it is sufficient that it be the sum of terms in x, y, z only and terms in t only. Secondly the differential operators separate in the same way. Thirdly, owing to the expansion theorem, there is no restriction on the form of ψ at a given moment, say $t = 0$; it is this which enables us to assert the complete generality of the solution we have obtained. The applicability of a proof of this nature to any given equation is summed up by saying that *the variables x, y, z and t separate*. The equations (16.5.1) and (16.5.2) are known as the Schrödinger equations with and without the time, or as the full and amplitude equations. The reason for the latter names is very important. The energy being an observable must have real eigenvalues. Further, as i does not appear explicitly in (16.5.2), if any ϕ satisfying (16.5.2) should be complex, then by substituting it in (16.5.2) and equating real and imaginary parts separately to zero we see that the real and imaginary parts of ϕ separately satisfy (16.5.2), and unless ϕ is complex merely by reason of a complex numerical coefficient, it consists of a linear combination of two real solutions. In either case we reach the conclusion that

THEOREM 16.5.7. *The solutions of the Schrödinger equation without the time can all be expressed as linear combinations of real functions of the coordinates.*

When magnetic fields are introduced, however, it is sometimes convenient to let V contain i explicitly, in which case this theorem need not apply. Ignoring this case, since ϕ is real and χ the exponential of a pure imaginary, the use of the word amplitude for ϕ is obvious.

There are very few forms of the potential field for which the amplitude equation can be solved in exact terms. Three are discussed in all the standard texts, the free particle, the harmonic oscillator, and the central force field. We shall discuss the former two briefly for the sake of results we shall need, and the latter more thoroughly owing to the insight it gives into later problems if approached in a manner different from the orthodox one. We shall also, before discussing more specific problems, discuss how the Schrödinger equation stands in the light of relativity theory.

Let us consider the last point first. In Chapter XVIII we shall give reasons for supposing that the Schrödinger equation is specially adapted to one system of coordinates—namely, it describes the internal features of a system in coordinates which are proper coordinates for the system as a whole. (This internal character appears, for example, in the fact that in the equation for the electron in a hydrogen atom a reduced mass is used.) It is thus not necessarily to be expected that the equation is invariant under Lorentz transformations. But there is the variation of mass with velocity to consider, as also that the four-vector principle requires a parallel treatment for momentum and energy—and the Schrödinger equation is quadratic in the one and linear in the other. Dirac has dealt with this with startling results. He first replaced the classical arbitrary-zero form of the energy by the relativistic one which includes the mass, viz.

$$\frac{1}{2m}(p_x^2+p_y^2+p_z^2) \quad \text{by} \quad c(m_0^2 c^2+p_x^2+p_y^2+p_z^2),$$

where the p are momenta to be used in the wave equation in their operator form, and then, writing the full Schrödinger equation for the free particle in the form

$$(p_t-(m_0^2 c^2+p_x^2+p_y^2+p_z^2)^{\frac{1}{2}})\psi^* = 0 \qquad (16.5.8)$$

he compares it with the equation

$$(p_t+\alpha_x p_x+\alpha_y p_y+\alpha_z p_z+\beta)\psi^* = 0 \qquad (16.5.9)$$

which shows much more respect for the four-vector principle. The comparison is effected by multiplying each equation by its 'conjugate' (in which p_t is replaced by $-p_t$), all variables commuting except the α and β among themselves, and then comparing coefficients of the p in the two forms. The resulting equations

$$(p_t^2-m_0^2 c^2-p_x^2-p_y^2-p_z^2)\psi^* = 0 \qquad (16.5.10)$$

and

$$\left(p_t^2-\sum_{x,y,z}[\alpha_x^2 p_x^2+(\alpha_x \alpha_y+\alpha_y \alpha_x)p_x p_y+(\alpha_x \beta+\beta\alpha_x)p_x]-\beta^2\right)\psi^* = 0$$

are the same provided that α_x, α_y, α_z, and β/mc (which may conveniently be called α_m) are quantities whose squares are unity and which anticommute.

Now since the α commute with all the other variables, they must represent some new property of the particle which is separately observable; since they anticommute among themselves, only one can be made diagonal at once; since their squares are unity their only eigenvalues are ± 1. There being four of them they are, in fact, i times the basis elements of a Clifford algebra of order 2^4 ($k = 2$) which involves us in 4×4 matrices (§ 13.10). In view of the considerations of § 12.9, this seems to imply that the new variable involved has an argument restricted to four values, but as the eigenvalues of α are equal in pairs this needs closer scrutiny. As α does not appear in (16.5.8), nor in the non-relativistic (16.5.1), it 'separates', and the full solution of the equation, now of the form $\psi(x,y,z,\alpha,t)$, can be expressed as

$$\psi_k(x,y,z)\sigma(\alpha)e^{-(2\pi i/h)W_k t}$$

or as a linear combination of such terms. We now see that one given $\psi_k(x,y,z)$ occurs in four distinct solutions of Dirac's final equation, namely, in

$$\psi_k\, \sigma(1)e^{-(2\pi i/h)W_k t} \qquad \psi_k\, \sigma(-1)e^{-(2\pi i/h)W_k t},$$

and in two others in which the sign of W_k is reversed—these latter arising from the fact that the solutions of his final equation are those of the original one *and its conjugate*. In his 'hole' theory of the positron Dirac attempted to interpret physically the latter, but for our purposes they may be ignored.

The coordinate α remains separable in all purely mechanical or electrostatic problems but a further discussion, the details of which have no bearing on the further matter of this book, shows that it affects the behaviour of the system in magnetic (and electromagnetic) fields in a way which is naturally interpreted as the possession by the particle of a magnetic moment, or more picturesquely, as it already carries a charge, of a spin. If we accept this conclusion we can further say that (*a*) it can be ignored for single particles in the absence of magnetic fields, but (*b*) it will cause interaction between particles extra to the obvious ones due to electrostatic interaction.

The function $\psi(x, y, z, \alpha, t)$ in which α can take only the two values ± 1 is often more conveniently described as the two functions $\psi_+(x, y, z, t)$ at $\alpha = 1$ and $\psi_-(x, y, z, t)$ at $\alpha = -1$. But ψ_+ and ψ_- are identical as algebraic functions, and the situation is often reduced to the simple statement that each independent solution of the non-relativistic equation actually represents two solutions. (Compare § 12.9.)

(*Note*: The student who wishes to compare Dirac's matrices for the α as given in his *Quantum Mechanics* with our discussion of the Clifford algebras should note that *any* selection of four basis elements from the five defined for the algebra of order 2^5 will meet the purpose in hand.)

16.6. The free particle and the simple harmonic oscillator

For a free particle V is a constant; writing E for the total energy, the Schrödinger equation in one dimension reduces to

$$-\frac{h^2}{8\pi^2 m} \frac{d^2\psi}{dx^2} + V\psi = E\psi,$$

or

$$\frac{d^2\psi}{dx^2} = -\frac{8\pi^2 m}{h^2}(E-V)\psi,$$

the immediate solution of which is the complex one

$$\psi = A \exp\left\{\pm i\left(\frac{8\pi^2 m}{h^2}(E-V)\right)^{\frac{1}{2}} x\right\}$$

$$= A e^{\pm i\alpha x} \tag{16.6.1}$$

(the latter form for short). As shown in the previous section, the real and imaginary parts of this solution, $A \cos \alpha x$ and $A \sin \alpha x$ must also be solutions; they are easily verified to be orthogonal over a range of x which includes an integral number of wavelengths. The general solution for a given W is a linear combination of these, viz.

$$\psi = B_1 \cos \alpha x + B_2 \sin \alpha x \qquad (16.6.2)$$

$$= C \sin(\alpha x + \lambda), \qquad (16.6.3)$$

where B_1, B_2, C, and λ may be complex; the most general solution in real terms is the same with B_1, B_2, C, and λ real. Any two such functions with λ's differing by $\frac{1}{2}\pi$ will be orthogonal over an integral number of wavelengths.

By suitable choice of zero we could make $V = 0$; E is then the kinetic energy of the particle—as, of course, $E - V$ is in any case. But we avoid this simplification for the sake of a future application.

If the particle is confined to a length L but otherwise free, a situation arises in which all the peculiar features of quantum physics are displayed. The constraint means that V rises to an infinite value at the extremities of this length, and qualitative examination of the wave equation shows that if ψ is not to become infinite also, it must be zero at these points. If x is measured from one extremity, the condition that $\psi = 0$ at $x = 0$ forces $\lambda = 0$, and the condition that $\psi = 0$ at $x = L$ forces the conclusion that L is an integral number of half wavelengths, or

$$\left(\frac{8\pi^2 m}{h^2}(E - V)\right)^{\frac{1}{2}} L = n, \quad n \text{ an integer}, \qquad (16.6.4)$$

whence
$$E - V = \frac{n^2 h^2}{8\pi^2 m L^2}, \qquad (16.6.5)$$

so that the only permitted values of $E - V$ are given by the above expression with n integral. The corresponding momentum is

$$[2m(E - V)]^{\frac{1}{2}} = \pm n h / 2\pi L \qquad (16.6.6)$$

and the minimum values of these expressions are their values when $n = 1$. In these results we see (1) the appearance of quantum numbers, (2) the appearance of a non-zero minimum of kinetic energy (zero-point energy), and (3) that if the position of the particle is known to within $\frac{1}{2}L$, it has a minimum uncertainty of momentum (uncertainty because of the double sign) of the order of $h/\frac{1}{2}L$ (Heisenberg's uncertainty principle).

It should also be noted that if we know the form of ψ at $t = 0$ and it does not conform to the requirements of the previous paragraph—suppose, for example, that the particle is definitely in one half of the box— then expansion of ψ as a Fourier sine-series over the length L is an expansion in eigenfunctions of the problem. By inserting in each term of the series the time factor $e^{-\{2\pi i(E-V)/h\}t}$ we have a solution of the full Schrödinger equation, and thus know how the instantaneous form of ψ will change with time. The conclusion is a general one—it depends merely on the fact that the amplitude equation is an eigenvalue equation in Hilbert space and therefore, whatever the form of the potential field, its solutions, the eigenfunctions, form a basis for the expansion of any 'well-behaved' function.

The free particle in three dimensions does not differ significantly from that in one; the variables separate and three identical equations are obtained, the total kinetic energy being the sum of its three resolved parts. In a three-dimensional box we meet with degeneracy—eigen-subspaces—but not in a form which will interest us in the sequel.

The harmonic oscillator in one dimension has $V = V_0 + kx^2$ and leads to the equation which has already been discussed in as much detail as we shall require in § 12.8. Consequently we proceed at once to a discussion of the central-force-field problem. The importance of this problem to us is that the operator is invariant for all rotations about the origin.

16.7. Central force fields and spherical harmonics

We consider first the effects of the rotation group on an arbitrary ψ— or rather on one which is subject to the condition that it can be expanded in a Taylor series about the origin

$$\psi = a + b_1 x + b_2 y + b_3 z +$$
$$+ c_1 x^2 + c_2 y^2 + c_3 z^2 + c_4 xy + c_5 yz + c_6 xz +$$
$$+ \sum_1^{10} d_n x^p y^q z^{3-p-q} + \dots. \tag{16.7.1}$$

The terms of degree k are, by (13.2.1), $^{3+k-1}C_2 = {}^{k+2}C_2$ in number. Let x, y, z, x', y', z' be a rotation about the origin and let the distribution function in the new coordinates be ψ'; i.e.

$$(x, y, z) = R(x', y', z'), \tag{16.7.2}$$

$$\psi(x, y, z) = \psi'(x', y', z'). \tag{16.7.3}$$

Substituting the first of these equations into (16.7.1), it is clear that R induces a linear transformation in the coefficients a, $b_1, \dots$. We may regard this as a transformation in Hilbert space which is a representation in that space of r_3. Since the substitution of (16.7.2) into any one term of (16.7.1) can only give terms of the same degree, it is clear that the subspaces spanned by the $^{r+2}C_2$ monomials of degree r (each r) are invariant subspaces under $\mathbf{r}_3$.

Since, however, $x^2+y^2+z^2$ is invariant under the rotation group, any set of terms of the form $(x^2+y^2+z^2)\xi_{k-2}$, where ξ_i is a homogeneous polynomial of degree i, will transform into another polynomial of this form, and thus the $^{k+2}C_2$-dimensional space spanning ξ_k is itself reducible if $k \geqslant 2$, since it contains an invariant subspace of dimensions $^kC_2$. The difference, $^{k+2}C_2 - {}^kC_2 = 2k+1$, has the dimensions of an irreducible representation of $\mathbf{r}_3$ (see the comment following Theorem 12.4.1) and we propose to show that it is irreducible. Deferring the proof so as not to interrupt the present argument, we can apply the same reasoning to ξ_{k-2} and thus reach the following conclusion:

THEOREM 16.7.4. *A homogeneous polynomial of degree k in x, y, z represents a vector in a subspace of Hilbert space of dimensions*

$$^{k+2}C_2 = \tfrac{1}{2}(k+1)(k+2). \tag{16.7.4}$$

This subspace is invariant under the rotation group and breaks down into irreducible representations of dimensions

$$2k+1, 2k-3, 2k-7,\ldots \begin{cases} 3 \text{ if } k \text{ is odd} \\ 1 \text{ if } k \text{ is even.} \end{cases} \tag{16.7.5}$$

Applying this to the general function, the whole Hilbert space breaks down as follows

	Representation of dimensions				
Terms of degree	1	3	5	7	9
0 . . .	*				
1 . . .		*			
2 . . .	*		*		
3 . . .		*		*	
4 . . .	*		*		*
: . . .	:	:	:	:	:

each representation occurring an infinite number of times.

If we now go over to polar coordinates by the substitution

$$z = r\cos\theta, \qquad x = r\sin\theta\cos\phi, \qquad y = r\sin\theta\sin\phi, \tag{16.7.6}$$

the terms of degree k take the form $r^k f_k(\theta, \phi)$. A set of functions $f_{ki}(\theta, \phi)$ $(i = 1,\ldots, 2k+1)$ such that the functions $r^k f_{ki}(\theta, \phi)$ span the irreducible space of dimensions $2k+1$ is known as a set of spherical harmonics of degree k. Any homogeneous polynomial of degree k can thus be expressed as r^k multiplied into a linear combination of spherical harmonics of degrees $k, k-2,\dots$. We can denote any single vector in the $(2k+1)$-space by f_k, suppressing the i since such a vector could be one of the basis vectors for this subspace, and write

$$\xi_k = r^k(f_k + f_{k-2} + \cdots + f_{1 \text{ or } 0}).$$ (16.7.7)

The spherical harmonic of degree 0 is 1; those of degree 1 are x/r, y/r, z/r, viz. $\cos\theta$, $\sin\theta\cos\phi$, $\sin\theta\sin\phi$. The spherical harmonics of higher order are more arbitrary in their definition by this approach; their most convenient form will be discussed later.

The Laplace operator ∇^2 is invariant under the rotation group. For under a change of coordinates its new form as given by (14.4.4) is determined by the new metric, and the metric is invariant under $\mathbf{r}_3$. Consequently, since

$$R\nabla^2 R^{-1} = \nabla^2 \quad \text{implies} \quad R\nabla^2 = \nabla^2 R,$$ (16.7.7 a)

it commutes with every R, and can be made diagonal in any representation of R which is in reduced form. To investigate this, we write the general homogeneous polynomial of degree k as $\xi_k = r^k\zeta_k$, where ζ_k is a function of θ and ϕ, independent of r, and containing contributions from the spherical harmonics of degrees $k, k-2,\dots$. In polars, by (14.4.5), the Laplace operator takes the form

$$\nabla^2 = \frac{1}{r^2}\frac{\partial}{\partial r}r^2\frac{\partial}{\partial r} + \frac{1}{r^2\sin\theta}\frac{\partial}{\partial\theta}\sin\theta\frac{\partial}{\partial\theta} + \frac{1}{r^2\sin^2\theta}\frac{\partial^2}{\partial\phi^2}$$

$$= \frac{1}{r^2}\frac{\partial}{\partial r}r^2\frac{\partial}{\partial r} + \frac{1}{r^2}[\ ],$$

the second line defining $[\ ]$. Using this form, we see that

$$\nabla^2\xi_k = \nabla^2 r^k\zeta_k$$
$$= \{k(k+1)\zeta_k + [\ ]\zeta_k\}r^{k-2}.$$

Now $\nabla^2\xi_k$ is, by the cartesian form of ∇^2, of the form of ξ_{k-2} since every term in ξ_k gives rise to three terms in $\nabla^2\xi_k$ in which the exponents of x, y, and z are respectively reduced by two. (In case any exponent is less than two, the corresponding term is zero.) But ξ_{k-2} has only ${}^kC_2$ independent terms as against ${}^{k+2}C_2$ in ξ_k, whence it is obvious that different ξ_k may yield the same ξ_{k-2}. Let ξ'_k and ξ''_k be two such, and let

$$\xi'_k - \xi''_k = \xi^0_k = r^k\zeta^0_k.$$

Then
$$\nabla^2\xi^0_k = \nabla^2\xi'_k - \nabla^2\xi''_k = 0$$

and
$$[\ ]\zeta^0_k = -k(k+1)\zeta^0_k.$$ (16.7.8)

The number of independent terms in ξ_k^0 (or ζ_k^0) is $^{k+2}C_2 - {}^kC_2 = 2k+1$, and it suggests itself that ξ_k^0 may be a spherical harmonic of degree k (or a linear combination of the $2k+1$ spherical harmonics in case the basic ones have already been decided on). That this is so may be proved by induction. For equation (16.7.8) shows that ζ_k^0 is an eigenfunction of [ ] with eigenvalue $-k(k+1)$, and as such it must be independent of eigenfunctions with different eigenvalues. Then expressing ξ_k as in equation (16.7.7), if $f_0, f_1, ..., f_{k-2}$ are already known to be eigenfunctions of [ ] with eigenvalues $0, -2, ..., -(k-1)(k-2)$, and if, as we have seen, there is a portion of ξ_k/r^k which is an eigenfunction with eigenvalue $-k(k+1)$, this can only be f_k. The relations

$$\nabla^2(\text{constant}) = 0,$$

$$\nabla^2(ax+by+cz) = 0$$

prove the theorem for ζ_0, ζ_1, whence it is true for all f_k.

THEOREM 16.7.9. *The spherical harmonics of degree k are eigenfunctions of the angular part of the Laplace operator in polars, with eigenvalue $-k(k+1)$.*

The equation (16.7.8) provides the most convenient method of determining explicit functions for the spherical harmonics of degrees two and above. For if in

$$\left\{ \frac{1}{\sin\theta}\frac{\partial}{\partial\theta}\sin\theta\frac{\partial}{\partial\theta} + \frac{1}{\sin^2\theta}\frac{\partial^2}{\partial\phi^2} \right\}\psi(\theta,\phi) = -k(k+1)\psi(\theta,\phi)$$

we write $\Theta(\theta)\Phi(\phi)$ for $\psi(\theta,\phi)$, it takes the form

$$\Phi(\phi)\frac{1}{\sin\theta}\frac{\partial}{\partial\theta}\sin\theta\frac{\partial}{\partial\theta}\Theta(\theta) + \Theta(\theta)\frac{1}{\sin^2\theta}\frac{\partial^2}{\partial\phi^2}\Phi(\phi) = -k(k+1)\Theta(\theta)\Phi(\phi)$$

or $$-\frac{1}{\Phi(\phi)}\frac{\partial^2}{\partial\phi^2}\Phi(\phi) = \frac{1}{\Theta(\theta)}\sin\theta\frac{\partial}{\partial\theta}\sin\theta\frac{\partial}{\partial\theta}\Theta(\theta) + k(k+1)\sin^2\theta,$$

in which left-hand side and right-hand side are functions of ϕ only and of θ only, respectively, and must therefore be independent of either, i.e. a constant, conveniently m^2, so that

$$\frac{\partial^2}{\partial\phi^2}\Phi(\phi) = -m^2\Phi(\phi)$$

and $$\left\{ \sin\theta\frac{\partial}{\partial\theta}\sin\theta\frac{\partial}{\partial\theta} + k(k+1)\sin^2\theta - m^2 \right\}\Phi(\theta) = 0.$$

There are many expositions of the latter equation to which the student will have access, and we content ourselves with giving its simpler solutions in both polar and cartesian form in Table 16.7.1. It is important to realize, however, that the $2k+1$ functions thus determined are merely *one possible* set of orthogonal basic functions in the Hilbert subspace. Others are obviously obtained by orienting the axes differently.

TABLE 16.7.1: SPHERICAL HARMONICS

Quantum label	k	m	ζ_{km}	ξ_{km}	Reference label
s	0	0	1	1	$s\sigma A$
	1	0	$\cos\theta$	z	$p\sigma B$
$p\left\{\vphantom{\begin{matrix}1\\1\\1\end{matrix}}\right.$	1	$\left.1\right\}$	$\left(\sin\theta\cos\phi\right.$	x	$p\pi D_1$
	1	$\left.-1\right\}$	$\left.\sin\theta\sin\phi\right.$	y	$p\pi D_2$
	2	0	$3\cos^2\theta-1$	$x^2+y^2-2z^2$	$d\sigma A$
	2	$\left.1\right\}$	$\left(\sin\theta\cos\theta\cos\phi\right.$	xz	$d\pi D_1$
$d\left\{\vphantom{\begin{matrix}2\\2\\2\\2\\2\end{matrix}}\right.$	2	$\left.-1\right\}$	$\left.\sin\theta\cos\theta\sin\phi\right.$	yz	$d\pi D_2$
	2	$\left.2\right\}$	$\left(\sin^2\theta\cos 2\phi\right.$	x^2-y^2	$d\delta A$
	2	$\left.-2\right\}$	$\left.\sin^2\theta\sin 2\phi\right.$	xy	$d\delta B$
	3	0	$5\cos^3\theta-3\cos\theta$	$z(3x^2+3y^2-2z^2)$	$f\sigma B$
	3	$\left.1\right\}$	$\left(\sin\theta(5\cos^2\theta-1)\cos\phi\right.$	$x(x^2+y^2-4z^2)$	$f\pi D_1$
	3	$\left.-1\right\}$	$\left.\sin\theta(5\cos^2\theta-1)\sin\phi\right.$	$y(x^2+y^2-4z^2)$	$f\pi D_2$
$f\left\{\vphantom{\begin{matrix}3\\3\\3\\3\\3\\3\end{matrix}}\right.$	3	$\left.2\right\}$	$\left(\sin^2\theta\cos\theta\cos 2\phi\right.$	$z(x^2-y^2)$	$f\delta B$
	3	$\left.-2\right\}$	$\left.\sin^2\theta\cos\theta\sin 2\phi\right.$	xyz	$f\delta A$
	3	$\left.3\right\}$	$\left(\sin^3\theta\cos 3\phi\right.$	x^3-3xy^2	$f\phi D_1$
	3	$\left.-3\right\}$	$\left.\sin^3\theta\sin 3\phi\right.$	$3x^2y-y^3$	$f\phi D_2$

Notes:

1. The expressions given are not normalized.

2. For the meaning of the reference label and quantum label see § 16.9.

3. The bracketed expressions with values of m equal but opposite in sign have been bracketed because these values of m usually refer to the complex forms $e^{\pm im\phi}$.

4. The choice of expressions within each set, s, p,..., is determined by ease of subsequent decomposition into representations of the subgroup C_∞. A more symmetrical looking set of d functions is the set of six:

$$xy \qquad yz \qquad xz \qquad x^2-y^2 \qquad y^2-z^2 \qquad z^2-x^2$$

of which the last three sum to zero and are not independent. The equivalence of the two types here is seen on applying the rotation $x'=x+y$, $y'=x-y$, when $x'y'=x^2-y^2$, etc. The types in the table above are not equivalent in this simple way.

5. Spherical harmonics of higher degree are given in several of the references in the bibliography.

To prove the irreducibility of the space of $2k+1$ dimensions derived above, we consider the characters of the irreducible representation of r_3. These were shown at the end of Chapter XIII to have the value

$$\frac{\sin(k+\tfrac{1}{2})\theta}{\sin\tfrac{1}{2}\theta}$$

for the representation of dimension $2k+1$. The sum of the series

$$\frac{\sin(k+\frac{1}{2})\theta}{\sin\frac{1}{2}\theta} + \frac{\sin(k-2+\frac{1}{2})\theta}{\sin\frac{1}{2}\theta} + \cdots$$

to $\frac{1}{2}k+1$ or $\frac{1}{2}(k+1)$ terms is easily evaluated as the imaginary part of the geometrical progression

$$(e^{(k+\frac{1}{2})i\theta} + e^{(k-2+\frac{1}{2})i\theta} + \cdots)/\sin\tfrac{1}{2}\theta$$

and is

$$\frac{\sin\frac{1}{2}\theta + \sin\frac{3}{2}\theta + \sin(k+\frac{1}{2})\theta - \sin(k+2+\frac{1}{2})\theta}{(2-2\cos 2\theta)\sin\frac{1}{2}\theta}.$$

(The denominator, $1-e^{2i\theta}$ by the usual formula, is 'realized' by multiplying both numerator and denominator by $1-e^{-2i\theta}$.) This can be transformed further by the 'sum and difference rules' to

$$\frac{4\sin\theta\sin\frac{1}{2}(k+1)\theta\sin(k+\frac{1}{2})\theta}{4\sin^2\theta\sin\frac{1}{2}\theta} = \frac{\sin\frac{1}{2}(k+1)\theta\sin(\frac{1}{2}k+1)\theta}{\sin\theta\sin\frac{1}{2}\theta}.$$

$$(16.7.9\,a)$$

The representation in ξ_k is, by the arguments following equation (13.5.5), the irreducible representation of the full linear group with character h_k—reducible here because we are considering only the subgroup $\mathfrak{d}_3$. The eigenvalues, z_1, z_2, z_3 of a rotation operator are $e^{i\theta}$, $e^{-i\theta}$, and 1, whence by (13.7.2),

$$h_k = \begin{vmatrix} e^{(k+2)i\theta} & e^{-(k+2)i\theta} & 1 \\ e^{i\theta} & e^{-i\theta} & 1 \\ 1 & 1 & 1 \end{vmatrix} \Bigg/ \begin{vmatrix} e^{2i\theta} & e^{-2i\theta} & 1 \\ e^{i\theta} & e^{-i\theta} & 1 \\ 1 & 1 & 1 \end{vmatrix}$$

$$= \frac{\sin(k+1)\theta + \sin\theta - \sin(k+2)\theta}{2\sin\theta - \sin 2\theta}$$

$$= \frac{\sin\frac{1}{2}(k+1)\theta\sin(\frac{1}{2}k+1)\theta}{\sin\theta\sin\frac{1}{2}\theta}, \qquad (16.7.9\,b)$$

the first step by direct evaluation of the determinants, and the second in the usual way by applying the 'sum and difference rules'. As this final expression is identical with (16.7.9 a), we see that

$$h_k(e^{i\theta}, e^{-i\theta}, 1) = \frac{\sin(k+\frac{1}{2})\theta}{\sin\frac{1}{2}\theta} + \frac{\sin(k-2+\frac{1}{2})\theta}{\sin\frac{1}{2}\theta} + \cdots, \quad (16.7.10)$$

and since it is a part of the general theory based on the orthogonality theorem that a compound character can be expressed as the sum of simple characters in only one way, this equation proves our assertion.

We may take advantage of this digression to add some other purely mathematical results. First, equation (13.3.5) yields alternative forms of this compound character, viz. since

$$s_1 = e^{i\theta} + e^{-i\theta} + 1 = 1 + 2\cos\theta$$

$$\cdot \quad \cdot \quad \cdot \quad \cdot \quad \cdot \quad \cdot \quad \cdot \quad \cdot$$

$$s_n = e^{ni\theta} + e^{-ni\theta} + 1 = 1 + 2\cos n\theta$$

$$\cdot \quad \cdot \quad \cdot \quad \cdot \quad \cdot \quad \cdot \quad \cdot \quad \cdot$$

we have

$$h_1 = s_1 \qquad\qquad = 1 + 2\cos\theta$$

$$h_2 = \tfrac{1}{2}(s_1^2 + s_2) \qquad = \tfrac{1}{2}\{(1 + 2\cos\theta)^2 + (1 + 2\cos 2\theta)\}$$

$$\qquad\qquad\qquad = 4\cos^2\theta + 2\cos\theta$$

$$h_3 = \tfrac{1}{6}(s_1^3 + 2s_3 + 3s_1^2 s_2) = \tfrac{1}{6}\{(1 + 2\cos\theta)^3 + 2(1 + 2\cos 3\theta) +$$

$$+ 3(1 + 2\cos\theta)^2(1 + 2\cos 2\theta)\}, \text{ etc.} \quad (16.7.11)$$

Secondly, the expression (16.7.9 a) yields the correct dimensionality, $\tfrac{1}{2}(k+1)(k+2)$, if θ is put equal to zero (character of identical element equals dimensionality of representation). It is necessary to expand the sine functions as far as the cube of θ to avoid indeterminate expressions. Thirdly, from the equation

$$\frac{\sin(k+\tfrac{1}{2})\theta}{\sin\tfrac{1}{2}\theta} - \frac{\sin(k-1+\tfrac{1}{2})\theta}{\sin\tfrac{1}{2}\theta} = 2\cos k\theta$$

(proved as usual by sum and difference rules), we see that

$$\frac{\sin(k+\tfrac{1}{2})\theta}{\sin\tfrac{1}{2}\theta} = 2\cos k\theta + 2\cos(k-1)\theta + \ldots + 2\cos\theta + 1. \quad (16.7.12)$$

The expressions on the right are the characters of the classes of c_∞ in $\mathfrak{d}_\infty$ (Table 12.2.7) and this equation provides the answer to a problem which will arise later—that of reducing into its irreducible components the representation of D_∞ obtained from an irreducible representation of $\mathfrak{r}_3$ by restricting consideration to a subgroup. The answer—that the $(2k+1)$-dimensional representation of $\mathfrak{r}_3$ contains each representation of $\mathfrak{d}_\infty$ up to the $(k+2)$th, with the exception of one of the one-dimensional representations, exactly once—could have been obtained in the direct manner from the orthogonality relations by integrating over the group manifold, but this relation saves us some of the difficulties inherent in that procedure. The one-dimensional representation present is determined by the character of the coset of c_∞ (which is zero in the two-dimensional representations) and is Γ_1 or Γ_2 according as k is even or odd.

The solution of the Schrödinger equation for a central force field now takes a fairly definite form. The equation is

$$-\frac{h^2}{8\pi^2 m}\nabla^2\psi + V(r)\psi = W\psi$$

and it separates, if ∇^2 is expressed in polars, and ψ expressed as

$$R(r)\Theta(\theta)\Phi(\phi),$$

into (1) $\qquad\qquad [\ ]\Theta(\theta)\Phi(\phi) = \beta\,\Theta(\theta)\Phi(\phi)$

in which we know that the only permissible values of β are $-k(k+1)$, and (2)

$$\frac{1}{r^2}\frac{d}{dr}r^2\frac{d}{dr}R(r) + \left[-\frac{k(k+1)}{r^2} + \frac{8\pi^2 m}{h^2}(W - V(r))\right]R(r) = 0$$

in which we have already substituted $\beta = -k(k+1)$. Calling the solutions of this equation $\psi_{k1}(r)$, $\psi_{k2}(r)$,... with eigenvalues $W_{k1} < W_{k2} < ...$, we see that the original equation has solutions $\psi_{kj}(r)\zeta_k^0$ with energy W_{kj}, this level being $2k+1$ degenerate, owing to the $2k+1$ independent ζ_k^0. In the hydrogen atom, $V(r) = e^2/r$, and in this case the degeneracy is even greater, because $W_{kj} = W_{k'j'}$ if $k+j = k'+j' = n$. We shall not go into details because they are well known and easily accessible. The extra degeneracy disappears if, for example, a second electron is present, although the symmetry remains central.

16.8. Perturbation theory

Problems in wave mechanics which do not admit of an exact solution are dealt with by perturbation theory. This has two forms which we shall refer to as static and dynamic perturbation theory. Both are applied to a system whose Hamiltonian (the energy operator in the amplitude equation) can be expressed in the form $\mathcal{H} + \mathcal{G}$, where $\mathcal{H}$ is of such a form that if $\mathcal{G} = 0$ the problem is one whose solutions $\psi_1,...,\psi_k,...$ are known, or can be assumed known.

The static form of the theory assumes that each ψ_k is an approximation to a solution ψ_k' of the system under discussion, and that, by the general expansion theorem, ψ_k' can be expressed in the form $\sum \alpha_j \psi_j$, where, if $\mathcal{G}$ is small, $\alpha_k \simeq 1$ and the other α_j are small. It calculates the α_j and the corrections to the W_k. It is particularly suited to systems which, though intrinsically simple, contain intractable mathematical features.

The dynamic form is based on the fact that while ψ_k is not an eigenfunction of the system, yet it must be a possible *unstable* state, and this form of the theory calculates the way in which ψ_k changes with time, expressing the result as an expansion in terms of $\psi_1, \ldots, \psi_k \ldots$, in which the coefficients are functions of time. It is particularly suited to systems subject to outside interference which may vary with time—including both reaction with radiation and systems in which $\mathscr{G}$ is constant but is 'switched on' at $t = 0$.

Both forms of the theory can be simplified in specific cases by an application of group theory, and though there are a number of expositions of both forms of the theory available, it will be convenient to summarize them here both in order to have the principal results available for reference, and so that they may be stated in terms of the notation which we have used throughout the other parts of this book.

The static form is relatively simple as applied to non-degenerate systems. Let

$$\mathscr{H}\psi_k^* = W_k \psi_k^*, \tag{16.8.1}$$

$$(\mathscr{H} + \lambda \mathscr{G})(\psi_k^* + \lambda \phi_k^* + \ldots) = (W_k + \lambda V_k + \ldots)(\psi_k^* + \lambda \phi_k^* + \ldots) \tag{16.8.2}$$

where the omitted terms are of higher order in λ. Multiplying out and equating coefficients of λ^0 and λ^1, the first gives equation (16.8.1) back again, and the second gives

$$\mathscr{G}\psi_k^* + \mathscr{H}\phi_k^* = W_k \phi_k^* + V_k \psi_k^*$$

or

$$(\mathscr{G} - V_k)\psi_k^* = (W_k - \mathscr{H})\phi_k^*. \tag{16.8.3}$$

Higher degrees of approximation can be obtained by equating coefficients of λ^2, $\lambda^3, \ldots$, but we shall not need them. Expanding ϕ_k^* as $\sum_j a_{kj} \psi_j^*$, equation (16.8.3) becomes

$$(\mathscr{G} - V_k)\psi_k^* = \sum_j (W_k - \mathscr{H}) a_{kj} \psi_j^*$$

$$= \sum_j (W_k - W_j) a_{kj} \psi_j^*,$$

whence

$$*\psi_k(\mathscr{G} - V_k)\psi_k^* = 0, \tag{16.8.4}$$

since for $j = k$ we have $W_j = W_k$ and for $j \neq k$ we have $*\psi_k \psi_j^* = 0$. Thus

$$V_k = \frac{*\psi_k \mathscr{G}\psi_k^*}{*\psi_k \psi_k^*}. \tag{16.8.5}$$

Similarly,

$$*\psi_i(\mathscr{G} - V_k)\psi_k^* = (W_k - W_i) a_{ki} *\psi_i \psi_i^*,$$

$$a_{ki} = \frac{*\psi_i \mathscr{G}\psi_k^*}{(W_k - W_i) *\psi_i \psi_i^*}, \tag{16.8.6}$$

since $*\psi_i V_k \psi_k^* = V_k *\psi_i \psi_k^* = 0$. The $\psi_1, \ldots, \psi_k, \ldots$ are necessarily orthogonal since they belong to different eigenvalues of $\mathscr{H}$; if they are also normalized, the divisors $*\psi_k\psi_k^*$ and $*\psi_i\psi_i^*$ are unity and can, of course, be omitted from these results.

When the unperturbed system is degenerate there is a complication, since there are eigen-subspaces of $\mathscr{H}$ in wave space. It then becomes important to choose as axes within these spaces those vectors which are the limits of the eigenvectors of the perturbed system as $\mathscr{G}$ tends to zero. The problem closely resembles that of finding the eigenvectors of a certain operator within the subspace (§ 2.7). We write, instead of (16.8.1),

$$\mathscr{H}\,\psi_{k\alpha}^* = W_k\,\psi_{k\alpha}^*, \tag{16.8.7}$$

where α distinguishes the different members of a degenerate level. Let the correct zeroth approximations (as they are called) be $\chi_{k\alpha}$, where

$$\chi_{kp}^* = \sum_q c_{pq}\psi_{kq}^*. \tag{16.8.8}$$

Let

$$(\mathscr{H}+\lambda\mathscr{G})(\chi_{kp}^*+\lambda\phi_{kp}^*+\ldots) = (W_k+\lambda V_{kp}+\ldots)(\chi_{kp}^*+\lambda\phi_{kp}^*+\ldots)$$

as before (equation 16.8.2), whence

$$(\mathscr{G}-V_{kp})\chi_{kp}^* = (W_k-\mathscr{H})\phi_{kp}^*,$$

so that

$$*\psi_{kr}(\mathscr{G}-V_{kp})\chi_{kp}^* = 0 \tag{16.8.9}$$

as before (equation 16.8.4), but now there is one such equation for each r. Writing these equations as

$$\sum_q c_{pq}*\psi_{kr}(\mathscr{G}-V_{kp})\psi_{kq}^* = 0 \quad \text{each } r \tag{16.8.10}$$

they form a consistent set of equations for the c_{pq} provided that

$$\begin{vmatrix} *\psi_{k1}(\mathscr{G}-V_{kp})\psi_{k1}^* & *\psi_{k1}(\mathscr{G}-V_{kp})\psi_{k2}^* & . & . & . \\ *\psi_{k2}(\mathscr{G}-V_{kp})\psi_{k1}^* & *\psi_{k2}(\mathscr{G}-V_{kp})\psi_{k2}^* & . & . & \\ . & . & . & . & . & . \end{vmatrix} = 0 \tag{16.8.11}$$

or, if the ψ_{kp}^* are orthogonal (which is not necessary in a degenerate level) and normalized,

$$\begin{vmatrix} *\psi_{k1}\,\mathscr{G}\psi_{k1}^*-V_{kp} & *\psi_{k1}\,\mathscr{G}\psi_{k2}^* & . & . & . \\ *\psi_{k2}\,\mathscr{G}\psi_{k1}^* & *\psi_{k2}\,\mathscr{G}\psi_{k2}^*-V_{kp} & . & . & \\ . & . & . & . & . & . \end{vmatrix} = 0. \tag{16.8.12}$$

This is an equation for V_{kp}; we can substitute each root in turn back in (16.8.10) and evaluate a set of c_{pq}, thus obtaining a χ_{kp} to correspond with each possible V_{kp} ($p = 1, 2,\ldots$).

Equation (16.8.11) or (16.8.12), known as the *secular equation*, takes on the form most currently in use if we introduce the notations $\mathscr{G} = \mathscr{H}'$ and

$$*\psi_{k\rho}\psi_{k\sigma}^* = \int \bar{\psi}_{k\rho}\psi_{k\sigma}\,d\tau = \Delta_{\rho\sigma}, \qquad (16.8.13)$$

$$*\psi_{k\rho}\,\mathscr{G}\psi_{k\sigma}^* = \int \bar{\psi}_{k\rho}\,\mathscr{G}\psi_{k\sigma}\,d\tau = H'_{\rho\sigma},$$

namely,

$$\begin{vmatrix} H'_{11}-\Delta_{11}V & H'_{12}-\Delta_{12}V & \cdot & \cdot & \cdot \\ H'_{21}-\Delta_{21}V & H'_{22}-\Delta_{22}V & \cdot & \cdot & \cdot \\ \cdot & \cdot & \cdot & \cdot & \cdot & \cdot & \cdot \end{vmatrix} = 0.$$

In Dirac's notation $\Delta_{\rho\sigma}$ is $\langle k\rho|k\sigma\rangle$ and $H'_{\rho\sigma}$ is $\langle k\rho|\mathscr{G}|k\sigma\rangle$. An alternative form for (16.8.12) is

$$\begin{vmatrix} *\psi_{k1}(\mathscr{H}+\lambda\mathscr{G})\psi_{k1}^*-(W_k+\lambda V) & *\psi_{k1}(\mathscr{H}+\lambda\mathscr{G})\psi_{k2}^* & \cdot \\ *\psi_{k2}(\mathscr{H}+\lambda\mathscr{G})\psi_{k1}^* & *\psi_{k2}(\mathscr{H}+\lambda\mathscr{G})\psi_{k2}^*-(W_k+\lambda V) & \cdot \\ \cdot & \cdot & \cdot & \cdot & \cdot & \cdot & \cdot & \cdot & \cdot \end{vmatrix} = 0.$$

$$(16.8.14)$$

The solution of the secular equation is one of the bugbears of perturbation theory, and one of the main contributions of group theory to quantum theory is in the simplification of this problem. If the $\chi_{k\rho}$ have, by accident or design, been chosen so that they are already the correct zeroth approximations, then all non-diagonal terms in the above determinants will be zero, and the equation becomes

$$(*\psi_{k1}\,\mathscr{G}\psi_{k1}^*-V_{kp})(*\psi_{k2}\,\mathscr{G}\psi_{k2}^*-V_{kp})\ldots = 0$$

with roots $*\psi_{kr}\,\mathscr{G}\psi_{kr}^*$. Group theory rarely achieves this, but if it reduces any of the above determinants to a series of diagonal blocks, $p\times p, q\times q,\ldots$, then the equation factorizes into separate equations of degrees $p, q,\ldots$, instead of being one equation of degree $p+q+\ldots$. If $p, q,\ldots$ can be kept below five, the advantages are considerable. Before examining how this is done, however, we ought to complete the review of perturbation theory by considering the dynamic form.

For this purpose we consider the general solution

$$\Psi^* = \sum a_k e^{-2\pi i(W_k/h)t}\psi_k^*$$

(i.e. 16.5.5) of the full Schrödinger equation for the unperturbed system

$$\mathscr{H}\Psi^* = -\frac{h}{2\pi i}\frac{d}{dt}\Psi^*,$$

$\mathscr{H}$ not containing the time explicitly, and in modifying the left-hand side by adding $\mathscr{G}$ to $\mathscr{H}$, we simultaneously modify the right-hand side by making the a_k functions of t. We obtain

$$(\mathscr{H}+\mathscr{G})\Big[\sum_k a_k(t)e^{-2\pi i(W_k/h)t}\psi_k^*\Big] = -\frac{h}{2\pi i}\frac{d}{dt}\Big[\sum_k a_k(t)e^{-2\pi i(W_k/h)t}\psi_k^*\Big]$$

whence, eliminating the terms which remain when $\mathscr{G}$ and the $\dot{a}_k(t)$ are zero (since these merely assert the correctness of the original solution for the unperturbed system), we have

$$\mathscr{G}\Big[\sum_k a_k(t)e^{-2\pi i(W_k/h)t}\psi_k^*\Big] = -\frac{h}{2\pi i}\sum_k \dot{a}_k(t)e^{-2\pi i(W_k/h)t}\psi_k^*.$$

The dual of $e^{-2\pi i(W_k/h)t}\psi_k^*$ is $*\psi_k e^{2\pi i(W_k/h)t}$ (nothing changing but the sign in the exponential and the formal consideration of the function ψ as a row instead of as a column), and if $\mathscr{G}$, though it may contain t, does not contain d/dt, then these exponential factors commute with $\mathscr{G}$, as also do the $a_k(t)$. Analogously to (16.8.4) and (16.8.9) we now have

$$\sum_k a_k(t)e^{2\pi i\{(W_j-W_k)/h\}t}*\psi_j\,\mathscr{G}\psi_k^*$$

$$= -\frac{h}{2\pi i}\sum_k \dot{a}_k(t)e^{2\pi i\{(W_j-W_k)/h\}t}*\psi_j\,\psi_k^* = -\frac{h}{2\pi i}\dot{a}_j(t)*\psi_j\,\psi_j^*$$

since every product on the right-hand side is zero for $j \neq k$ and the exponential is unity for $j = k$. Rearranging

$$\dot{a}_j(t) = -\frac{2\pi i}{h}\sum_k a_k(t)e^{2\pi i\{(W_j-W_k)/h\}t}*\psi_j\,\mathscr{G}\psi_k^*/*\psi_j\,\psi_k^*.$$

This, a series of simultaneous differential equations with $j = 1, 2,...,$ is the general result.

An important class of special cases consists of those in which we start with a pure state—$a_k(0) = 1$, $a_j(0) = 0$ $(j \neq k)$—and $\mathscr{G}$ is either altogether independent of time, or has a constant value for positive values of t. Then (assuming the ψ's normalized)

$$\dot{a}_k(t) = -\frac{2\pi i}{h}*\psi_k\,\mathscr{G}\psi_k^*\,a_k(t)$$

and

$$a_k(t) = a_k(0)\,e^{-(2\pi i/h)*\psi_k\,\mathscr{G}\psi_k^*t}$$

provided that t is small enough that the a_j are still approximately zero.

Also
$$a_j(t) \simeq \dot{a}_j(0)\, t$$
$$= -\frac{2\pi i}{h} {}^*\psi_j \, \mathcal{G} \psi_k^* \, t.$$

Thus the ${}^*\psi_j \, \mathcal{G} \psi_k^*$ measure probabilities of transition from the initial state ψ_k^* into the state ψ_j^*.

We can sum up the results of perturbation theory quite simply as follows:

In the presence of a perturbation, a stable state ψ_k^* of the unperturbed system is an approximation to a stable state
$$\psi_k'^* = \psi_k^* + \sum a_{kj} \psi_j^*$$
of the perturbed system. A term does not appear in this sum (i.e. the a_{kj} is zero) if ${}^*\psi_j \, \mathcal{G} \psi_k^* = 0$, and the important terms (i.e. the a_{kj} are large) are those for which $W_j \simeq W_k$.

Alternatively, the effect of the perturbation is to give the system a probability of jumping from ψ_k^* to any other state ψ_j^* for which ${}^*\psi_j \, \mathcal{G} \psi_k^* \neq 0$.

The usual contribution of group theory will be in proving that ${}^*\psi_j \, \mathcal{G} \psi_k^* = 0$ under certain circumstances, and in some cases in arranging this favourable feature.

16.9. Symmetry considerations

To be more precise, group theory has a bearing on the results of the preceding section whenever $\mathcal{H}$ and $\mathcal{G}$ are invariant under a certain group $\mathfrak{g}$. In the central field problem this is the whole rotation group $\mathfrak{r}_3$; in other cases it will be a subgroup of this. As (compare 16.7.7 a) invariance under the group implies that $\mathcal{H}$ commutes with all the operators of the group, and as both $\mathcal{H}$ and the operators of the group are operators in wave space, this implies that axes can be chosen in wave space such that $\mathfrak{g}$ is completely reduced and $\mathcal{H}$ is a multiple of the unit matrix in each subspace displaying a representation of $\mathfrak{g}$. Although this follows from the results established in Chapter XIV, it is so important that a more elementary discussion would not seem out of place.

By the invariance of $\mathcal{H}$ under $\mathfrak{g}$, if R belongs to $\mathfrak{g}$ then
$$\mathcal{H} R \psi_1^* = R \mathcal{H} R^{-1} R \psi_1^* = R \mathcal{H} \psi_1^* = R W_1 \psi_1^* = W_1 R \psi_1^*$$
and thus if ψ_1^* is an eigenvector of $\mathcal{H}$ belonging to the eigenvalue W_1, every $R\psi_1^*$ is also an eigenvector of $\mathcal{H}$ belonging to the same eigenvalue. If $\mathfrak{g}$ is of order N, this eigen-subspace will be of not more than N dimensions, and the representation of $\mathfrak{g}$ in it may be reducible; if it is, axes can be chosen so that it is reduced. We can then choose another eigenvector of $\mathcal{H}$, ψ_2^*, orthogonal to the space already defined (this will be automatic

if $W_1 \neq W_2$, since $\mathcal{H}$ is Hermitian), carry out the same procedure, and continue thus until the whole space is reduced under the group and $\mathcal{H}$ is a multiple of the unit matrix in each subspace. (Compare Theorem 5.2.1, and § 14.5—the latter more in connexion with the following paragraph.)

Consider now the reverse approach. We can separate the inequivalent representations of $\mathfrak{g}$. If any one of them occurs only once, $\mathcal{H}$ will necessarily be a scalar multiple of the unit matrix in that subspace. Repeated representations are not quite so straightforward. But every eigenvector of $\mathcal{H}$ (except when $\mathcal{H}$ has accidentally equal eigenvalues—which does not matter) is contained entirely within one of the spaces sorted out. The theory of the hydrogen atom illustrates this. Here $\mathcal{H} = \nabla^2 + e^2/r$, and is invariant under r_3. In the complete reduction of Hilbert space following Theorem 16.7.4, it is certain that the components of an eigenfunction of $\mathcal{H}$ will be found entirely in one column, but since the different subspaces represented by items in the same column display equivalent representations of r_3 they do not necessarily represent—and do not in fact represent—invariant subspaces under $\mathcal{H}$. The complete orthogonal functions which are the eigenfunctions of $\mathcal{H}$ in the hydrogen atom problem are in fact linear combinations of terms taken from one column only, and if the substitution transforming to polars is made, the spherical harmonic is a common factor. When this is taken out the series in r which are left are the Laguerre orthogonal functions—each from one column.

We may summarize this as follows. When $\mathcal{H}$ is invariant under every R of $\mathfrak{g}$, it is possible to choose axes in wave space such that the representation of $\mathfrak{g}$ is completely reduced and $\mathcal{H}$ is completely diagonal—a scalar multiple of the unit matrix in each subspace which displays an irreducible representation of $\mathfrak{g}$. The reduction of wave space into the *inequivalent* representations of $\mathfrak{g}$ is a first step towards putting $\mathcal{H}$ in diagonal form and determining its eigenvectors and eigenvalues.

But an extra comment is required here on the meaning of irreducible in this context. If there is an n-fold axis, the subgroup of proper rotations about this axis has representations similar to those discussed in § 5.2 for $\mathfrak{c}_6$. The complex ones may be grouped in conjugate pairs, in which rotation through $2\pi/n$ is represented by $e^{i2k\pi/n}$ and $e^{i2(n-k)\pi/n}$ respectively. Putting these together, as we know, the forms

$$\begin{bmatrix} e^{i2k\pi/n} & 0 \\ 0 & e^{-i2k\pi/n} \end{bmatrix} \quad \text{and} \quad \begin{bmatrix} \cos 2k\pi/n & \sin 2k\pi/n \\ -\sin 2k\pi/n & \cos 2k\pi/n \end{bmatrix}$$

are equivalent, the latter being *irreducible in real terms*. (If the group is extended to $\mathfrak{d}_n$, the additional matrices required are

$$\begin{bmatrix} 0 & e^{-i2k\pi/n} \\ e^{i2k\pi/n} & 0 \end{bmatrix} \quad \text{and} \quad \begin{bmatrix} \cos 2k\pi/n & -\sin 2k\pi/n \\ -\sin 2k\pi/n & -\cos 2k\pi/n \end{bmatrix}$$

and the complex form is no more reduced than the real one, though for some purposes it is still the simpler form.) Now if ψ conforms to the $e^{i2k\pi/n}$ representation of $\mathfrak{g}$ it cannot be real, and its real and imaginary parts must both be eigenfunctions belonging to the same W. The upshot of this is that for the purpose at present under consideration we may interpret 'irreducible' as 'irreducible in real terms'. This conclusion will be incorporated in the notation we shall be adopting for representations. It does not apply, of course, to any calculations made using the orthogonality relations of the characters. It is to some extent unexpected. It means, for example, that if an electron is in a ring (closed one-dimensional space) in which there is a saw-tooth potential field, then for each permitted value of the energy there are two distinct wave functions —one, in complex form, running, as it were, with the teeth, and one against them. It is not immediately obvious on physical grounds why these should have the same energy, unless the fact that they have the same charge distribution is sufficient.

Similar considerations apply to $\mathscr{G}$, and it is here that the usefulness of the process appears even more clearly. For in numerical applications of perturbation theory, if $\mathscr{G}$ is invariant under $\mathfrak{g}$ and ψ_j and ψ_k belong to different inequivalent representations of $\mathfrak{g}$, then $\mathscr{G}\psi_k$ belongs to the same representation as ψ_k and $*\psi_j \mathscr{G}\psi_k^* = 0$. This means that if, in the static perturbation theory with degeneracy, the ψ_{kp} are chosen so that $\psi_{k1},...,\psi_{ka}$ belong to one representation of $\mathfrak{g}$, $\psi_{k(a+1)},...,\psi_{k(a+b)}$ to another, and so on, the secular determinant consists of zeros except in squares $a \times a$, $b \times b$,... on the main diagonal, and the secular equation of degree $a+b+...$ factorizes into equations of degree $a, b,...$. In the dynamic form of the theory it means that if ψ_k belongs to (i.e. has components in) one only of the irreducible representations of $\mathfrak{g}$, then $\mathscr{G}$ will never induce a transition to any ψ associated with an inequivalent representation of $\mathfrak{g}$.

It may be that $\mathscr{G}$ does not conform to the identical representation of $\mathfrak{g}$ but to some other representation; it will then usually conform to the identical representation of some subgroup, and, with $\mathfrak{g}$ replaced by its subgroup, the above conclusions will hold. But in certain circumstances we can go further. If $\mathscr{G}$ conforms to a one-dimensional representation of g, then analogously to the above, if ψ_k^* is a correct zeroth approximation, and $*\psi_k \mathcal{G} \psi_k^* = V_k$, then

$$*\psi_k R^{-1} \mathcal{G} R \psi_k^* = \chi_R^{-1} *\psi_k \mathcal{G} \psi_k^* = \chi_R^{-1} V_k.$$

Now $*\psi_k R^{-1}$ is the dual of $R\psi_k^*$ provided $R^{-1} = \tilde{R}$, which is so for real unitary operators such as we have in the representations we are dealing with, so that we can write the above relation

$$*(R\psi_k) \mathcal{G} (R\psi_k)^* = \chi_R^{-1} *\psi_k \mathcal{G} \psi_k^* = \chi_R^{-1} V_k$$

and express the result thus:

THEOREM 16.9.1. *If $\mathcal{H}$ is invariant under g and $\mathcal{G}$ conforms to a one-dimensional representation of g, then if ψ_k is a wave function which is an eigenfunction of $\mathcal{H}$ with the eigenvalue W_k and the correct zeroth approximation to an eigenfunction of $\mathcal{H} + \mathcal{G}$ with eigenvalue $W_k + V_k$, then $R\psi_k$ is a correct zeroth approximation to an eigenfunction of $\mathcal{H} + \mathcal{G}$ with eigenvalue $W_k + \chi_R^{-1} V_k$ where χ_R^{-1} is the reciprocal of the character of R in the representation of g to which $\mathcal{G}$ conforms.*

An example of this theorem would be the Stark effect, where the unperturbed atom has cylindrical symmetry about the direction of the field—it has more, of course—and the perturbing field is reversed by certain rotations. It follows that the level W_k splits in the form $W_{ka} \pm V_{ka}$, where the a serves to distinguish the levels into which W_k would be already split by a completely cylindrically symmetrical perturbation.

We can sum up our conclusions so far in the statement that if the Hamiltonian operator in the Schrödinger equation is invariant under a group g, then the acceptable wave functions either (1) separately conform to a one-dimensional representation of the group, or (2) fall into degenerate sets which conform to a multi-dimensional representation of the group. If the perturbation reduces the symmetry, a multi-dimensional representation may well become reducible, and some at least of the degeneracy be resolved. Following up the implications of this process will be a considerable part of the remainder of this chapter and of the next.

The question of a suitable nomenclature for the various representations of the symmetry groups now becomes an urgent one, for it is clear that this nomenclature will also be a nomenclature for the wave functions themselves. The Γ_1, Γ_2,... notation tells us nothing. Somewhat more informative is the notation devised by Placzec in which the totally symmetric representation is labelled A, the other one-dimensional ones B_1, B_2,..., two-dimensional ones E_1, E_2,..., and three-dimensional ones

T_1, T_2,.... The subscripts are replaced by primes and stars for various purposes. The most valuable feature such a notation can have is that it carries over from one realization of a group to another with the minimum of difficulty and from a group to its subgroups by definite rules with a physical significance. With this end in view we shall use a modified form of Placzec's nomenclature.

As in § 9.4, we deal first with the proper groups, and if there is a multiple axis we call it the Z- or main axis. (In the cubic system the three axes are equivalent and it does not matter which we select. In the class mm the axis of the real rotation is chosen, and in 222 and mmm the choice is arbitrary.) Our nomenclature is as follows:

One-dimensional real representations	A, B, C, D
Totally symmetric	A
Symmetric all main axis rotations	B
Symmetric 180° main axis rotations; antisymmetric smaller main axis rotations	C
Antisymmetric 180° main axis rotations	D

One-dimensional complex representations. These always occur in conjugate pairs. Each conjugate pair is equivalent to a two-dimensional representation which is irreducible in real form; the latter is usually all that is of physical interest, and is denoted by a cursive form of the letters for two-dimensional representations. Its character is the sum of those for the two one-dimensional complex representations.

Two-dimensional representations	E, F
Positive character for 180° main axis rotation	E
Negative character for 180° main axis rotation	F
Three-dimensional representations	T, U
Positive character for 90° main axis rotations	T
Negative character for 90° main axis rotations	U

(Positive and negative characters correspond roughly to symmetry and antisymmetry, but the latter words are not strictly appropriate in multi-dimensional representations.) In $\mathfrak{d}_3$ the only two-dimensional representation will normally be called E and the only three-dimensional representation of $\mathfrak{a}_4$ will normally be called T; in each case the criterion fails and F or U would be equally appropriate. Some further distinctions are required in certain cases, but in all of these suffixes are resorted to for a reason which an example will make clear. In D_4 there are two distinct type C representations, one is symmetrical for rotations about the X- and Y-axes and antisymmetrical for rotations about the diagonals, the other conversely. But which are the axes and which are the diagonals is a matter of convention or arbitrary choice. We shall take the subscript

1 to indicate symmetry about the X-axis and axes equivalent to it under the group.

In those symmetry groups which contain i ($\bar{1}$), the number of representations is doubled, and we denote by A_g, B_g,..., U_g those representations in which R and iR have the same character as that which R has in A, B,..., U, and by A_u, B_u,..., U_u those in which iR has minus the character of R. These subscripts, which derive from the German *gerade* and *ungerade* ('even' and 'odd') will already be familiar to students acquainted with spectroscopy.

Those symmetry groups which contain improper elements but not i must be considered as subgroups of the group obtained by adding i. The group $C_s(m)$ will serve as an example. On adding i we obtain $C_{2h}(2/m)$, with characters as in the first five columns of the following table:

	I	2_z	i	m_z	I	2_z		I	m_z		
A_g .	1	1	1	1	1	1	A	1	1	A	$\bar{D}$
A_u .	1	1	-1	-1	1	1	A	1	-1	D	$\bar{A}$
D_g .	1	-1	1	-1	1	-1	D	1	-1	D	$\bar{A}$
D_u .	1	-1	-1	1	1	-1	D	1	1	A	$\bar{D}$

On the right of this we have picked out the columns which remain when the symmetry drops to (a) C_2, (b) C_s. The representations become the same in pairs, but not the same pairs in the two cases. We have labelled the representations of C_s in two ways, (i) based on its abstract structure alone, ignoring the difference between m_z and 2_z, and (ii) first reversing the sign of the character of the improper element m_z, labelling it as before, but putting a bar over the symbol. The result is two alternative systems of labelling the representations of the improper group:

First system: Those implications of the character table which defined the nomenclature for the isomorphic real group remain and the same nomenclature is used as for the corresponding proper group.

Second system: If the character denoted P in the first system becomes Q when the signs of the characters of all improper elements are reversed, then P is denoted by $\bar{Q}$.

And we notice that

The representations P_g and P_u of the group with i degenerate into the representations P and $\bar{P}$ of the improper subgroup.†

We shall find it convenient later to distinguish different wave functions of the same symmetry type in terms of their origin as the symmetry is

† 'Improper subgroup' here means any subgroup containing improper rotations, of course, and has no reference to the term defined in § 1.6.

reduced from $\mathfrak{d}_3$ to whatever it may actually be. Then P and $\bar{Q}$, which except in this context are equivalent designations of a certain symmetry type, become labels for distinct functions of the same symmetry type. For this purpose we can even write P and $\bar{P}$ when referring to entirely proper groups.

In atomic and molecular theory symmetries impossible to a crystal can occur. The simpler ones—$\mathfrak{c}_5$, for example—need no discussion. For $\mathfrak{r}_3$ we use the spectroscopic notation and denote the 1, 3, 5,... dimensional representations by $s, p, d, f, g,...$; spectroscopy also provides the notation $\sigma_+, \sigma_-, \pi, \delta, \phi,...$ for the representations (two one-dimensional and the rest two-dimensional) of $\mathfrak{d}_\infty$.

Table 16.9.1 gives character tables for all the crystal symmetry groups other than those containing i. The nomenclature according to the above rules is given—in the first system for all groups in the column headed with the symbol of the proper group, and in the second system in the column headed with the symbol of the improper group in question. The table also gives the representation according to which the coordinates transform in the proper groups. In groups containing i they transform by the corresponding u representation, and in the improper groups by the representation denoted by the same letter barred. Rotations transform by the same representation in the proper groups, by the corresponding g representation in the group containing i, and by the same representation in the improper groups. (The student should prove these assertions as an exercise.)

TABLE 16.9.1

The following tables are substantially as given by Mulliken with certain changes of notation. According to the rules for translational and rotational degrees of freedom given in the text, if x, y, z transform by the representation P in the proper group, then

1. $\omega_x, \omega_y, \omega_z$ transform by P in all isomorphic groups, and by P_g in the group with i added, and

2. x, y, z transform by $\bar{P}$ (that is, the representation whose characters are those of P with the sign changed for all improper elements) in all isomorphic groups, and by P_u in the group with i added.

1. $\mathfrak{c}_1$

C_1	I	(C_i)
$A : x,\ y,\ z$	1	

2. $\mathfrak{c}_2$

C_2		$\}\ I\ \{$	2_z	(C_{2h})
	C_s		m_z	
$A : z$	$\bar{D}$	1	1	
$D : x, y$	$\bar{A}$	1	-1	

3. $\mathfrak{c}_3$ (C_{3i})

C_3	I	3_z	3_z^{-1}
$A:z$	1	1	1
$\mathscr{E}:x\pm iy$	1	ω	ω^2
	1	ω^2	ω

$$\omega = \cos\tfrac{2}{3}\pi + i\sin\tfrac{2}{3}\pi$$
$$\omega + \omega^2 = -1$$

4. $\mathfrak{c}_4$ (C_{4h})

C_4	S_4	$\}\,I$	2_z	$\{\,\dfrac{4_z}{\overline{4}_z}$	$\dfrac{4_z^{-1}}{\overline{4}_z^{-1}}$
$A:z$	$\bar{C}$	1	1	1	1
$C:$	$\bar{A}$	1	1	-1	-1
$\mathscr{E}:x\pm iy$	$\bar{\mathscr{E}}$	1	-1	i	$-i$
		1	-1	$-i$	i

5. $\mathfrak{c}_6$ (C_{6h})

C_6	C_{3h}	$\}\,I$	3_z	3_z^{-1}	$\{\,\dfrac{2_z}{m_z}$	$\dfrac{6_z}{\overline{6}_z}$	$\dfrac{6_z^{-1}}{\overline{6}_z^{-1}}$
$A:z$	$\bar{D}$	1	1	1	1	1	1
$D:$	$\bar{A}$	1	1	1	-1	-1	-1
$\mathscr{E}:$	$\overline{\mathscr{F}}$	1	ω	ω^2	1	ω^2	ω
		1	ω^2	ω	1	ω	ω^2
$\mathscr{F}:x+iy$	$\bar{\mathscr{E}}$	1	ω	ω^2	-1	$-\omega^2$	$-\omega$
		1	ω^2	ω	-1	$-\omega$	$-\omega^2$

6. $\mathfrak{S}_{2\times2}$ (D_{2h})

D_2	C_{2v}	$\}\,I$	2_z	$\{\,\dfrac{2_y}{m_y}$	$\dfrac{2_x}{m_x}$
$A:$	$\bar{B}$	1	1	1	1
$B:z$	$\bar{A}$	1	1	-1	-1
$D_1:y$	$\bar{D}_2$	1	-1	1	-1
$D_2:x$	$\bar{D}_1$	1	-1	-1	1

7. $\mathfrak{d}_3$ (D_{3d})

D_3	C_{3v}	$\}\,I$	$2C_3$	$\{\,\dfrac{3C_2}{3m}$
$A:$	$\bar{B}$	1	1	1
$B:z$	$\bar{A}$	1	1	-1
$E:x\pm iy$	$\bar{E}$	2	-1	0

8. $\mathfrak{d}_4$

(D_{4h})

D_4	C_{4v}	S_{4v}	I	2_z	$2C_4$ / $2C_4$ / $2S_4$	$C_{x,y}$ / $m_{x,y}$ / $m_{x,y}$	$2C'_4$ / $2m'_4$ / $2C'_4$
A:	$\bar{B}$	$\bar{C}_2$	1	1	1	1	1
B:z	$\bar{A}$	$\bar{C}_1$	1	1	1	-1	-1
C_1:	$\bar{C}_2$	$\bar{B}$	1	1	-1	1	-1
C_2:	$\bar{C}_1$	$\bar{A}$	1	1	-1	-1	1
E:$x \pm iy$	$\bar{E}$	$\bar{E}$	2	-2	0	0	0

9. $\mathfrak{d}_6$

(D_{6h})

D_6	C_{6v}	D_{3h}	I	$2C_3$	2_z / 2_z / m_z	$2C_6$ / $2C_6$ / $2S_6$	$3C_2$ / $3m$ / $3C_2$	$3C_2$ / $3m$ / $3m$
A:	$\bar{B}$	$\bar{D}_1$	1	1	1	1	1	1
B:z	$\bar{A}$	$\bar{D}_2$	1	1	1	1	-1	-1
D_1:	$\bar{D}_2$	$\bar{A}$	1	1	-1	-1	1	-1
D_2:	$\bar{D}_1$	$\bar{B}$	1	1	-1	-1	-1	1
E:	$\bar{E}$	$\bar{F}$	2	-1	2	-1	0	0
F:$x \pm iy$	$\bar{F}$	$\bar{E}$	2	-1	-2	1	0	0

10. $\mathfrak{a}_4$

(T_h)

T	I	$3C_2$	$4C_3$	$4C_3^{-1}$
A:	1	1	1	1
$\mathscr{E}$:	1	1	ω	ω^2
	1	1	ω^2	ω
T:x, y, z	3	-1	0	0

11. π_4

(O_h)

O	T_d	I	$3C_2$	$8C_3$	$6C_2$ / $6m$	$6C_4$ / $6S_4$	
A:	$\bar{C}$	1	1	1	1	1	$[4]$
C:	$\bar{A}$	1	1	1	-1	-1	$[1^4]$
E:	$\bar{E}$	2	2	-1	0	0	$[2^2]$
T:	$\bar{U}$	3	-1	0	-1	1	$[21^2]$
U:x, y, z	$\bar{T}$	3	-1	0	1	-1	$[31]$

Notes:

1. See text for C_∞, D_∞, $\mathfrak{r}_3$, etc.
2. The improper group 'with i' is added in brackets at the side of the table.
3. Placzec's notation has not the advantages of ours when dealing with electron spin, but is widely used and we therefore give the following 'dictionary'.

Crystal class	\multicolumn{10}{c}{Our notation}									
	A	B	C_1	C_2	D_1	D_2	E	F	T	U
C_1	A									
C_2	A				B					
C_s	A				A''					
C_3	A						E			
$C_4\ S_4$	A		B				E			
C_6	A				B		E*	E*		
C_{3h}	A'				A''		E'	E''		
D_2	A	B_1			B_2	B_3				
C_{2v}	A_1	A_2			B_1	B_2				
$D_3\ C_{3v}$	A_1	A_2					E			
$D_4\ C_{4v}\ S_{4v}$	A_1	A_2	B_1	B_2			E			
D_6	A_1	A_2			B_1	B_2	E*	E*		
C_{6v}	A_1	A_2	B_2	B_1			E*	E*		
D_{3h}	A_1'	A_2'			A_1''	A_2''	E'	E''		
T	A						E		T	
$O\ T_d$	A_1		\multicolumn{4}{c}{A_2}				E		T_1	T_2

Returning once more to the proper groups, we can arrange the more significant of them as follows (the remainder are only omitted for clarity):

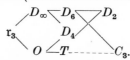

Here each group is a subgroup of any group to which it is connected on the left; T and C_3 are connected by a dotted line because in making the passage the direction of the Z-axis has to be altered. It is now possible to examine how the multi-dimensional representations of the more complex groups split up in passing to simpler subgroups. For this purpose the orthogonality relations are used for the finite groups and the trigonometric relations between the characters obtained in § 16.7 for the continuous groups. The results are contained in Table 16.9.2, and the student should verify a portion of them.

The meaning of the table will be clearer to the student if he will copy out just those columns which form one of the continuous chains in the above diagram. He will find that on passing from a group to a subgroup two things happen. First, with the dropping of certain symmetry elements certain representations become indistinguishable. Thus, for

TABLE 16.9.2

DECOMPOSITION OF REPRESENTATIONS

Proper group:	$\mathfrak{r}_3$	D_∞	O	T	D_6	D_3	C_6	C_3	D_4	C_4	D_2	C_2	C_1
Group structure:	$\mathfrak{r}_3$		π_4	$\mathfrak{a}_4$	$\mathfrak{d}_6$	$\mathfrak{d}_3$	$\mathfrak{c}_6$	$\mathfrak{c}_3$	$\mathfrak{d}_4$	$\mathfrak{c}_4$	$\mathfrak{s}_{2\times2}$	$\mathfrak{c}_2$	$\mathfrak{c}_1$
Isomorphic groups without i (see note)			T_d		C_{6v} D_{3h}	C_{3v}	C_{3h}		C_{4v} S_{4v}	S_4	C_{2v}	C_s	
Group with i:	$\mathfrak{o}_3$	$D_{\infty h}$	O_h	T_h	D_{6h}	D_{3d}	C_{6h}	C_{3i}	D_{4h}	C_{4h}	D_{2h}	C_{2h}	O_i
	s	σ_+	A	A	A	A	A	A	A	A	A	A	A
	p	σ_-	T	T	B	B	A	A	B	A	B	A	A
		π			F	E	$\mathscr{F}$	$\mathscr{E}$	E	$\mathscr{E}$	D_1	D	A
											D_2	D	A
	d	σ_+	E	E	A	A	A	A	A	A	A	A	A
		δ			E	E	$\mathscr{E}$	$\mathscr{E}$	C_1	C	A	A	A
									C_2	C	B	A	A
		π	U	T	F	E	$\mathscr{F}$	$\mathscr{E}$	E	$\mathscr{E}$	D_1	D	A
											D_2	D	A
	f	σ_-	T	T	B	B	A	A	B	A	B	A	A
		π			F	E	$\mathscr{F}$	$\mathscr{E}$	E	$\mathscr{E}$	D_1	D	A
											D_2	D	A
		δ	C	A	E	E	$\mathscr{F}$	$\mathscr{E}$	C_1	C	A	A	A
									C_2	C	B	A	A
		ϕ	U	T	D_1	A	D	A	E	$\mathscr{E}$	D_1	D	A
					D_2	B	D	A			D_2	D	A
	g	σ_+	A	A	A	A	A	A	A	A	A	A	A
		π	U	T	F	E	$\mathscr{F}$	$\mathscr{E}$	E	$\mathscr{E}$	D_1	D	A
											D_2	D	A
		δ	E	E	E	E	$\mathscr{E}$	$\mathscr{E}$	C_2	C	B	A	A
									C_1	C	A	A	A
		γ			E	E	$\mathscr{E}$	$\mathscr{E}$	A	A	A	A	A
									B	A	B	A	A
		ϕ	T	T	D_1	A	D	A	E	$\mathscr{E}$	D_1	D	A
					D_2	B	D	A			D_2	D	A

Note: The improper groups are not subgroups of $\mathfrak{r}_3$; in decomposing $\mathfrak{o}_3$, s_g, p_g,..., etc. decompose as in the table and s_u, p_u,... to the representations obtained by barring the symbol in the table. See text for details.

obvious reasons, on passing from D_n to C_n, the representations A and B become indistinguishable, and are called A; we also find representations distinguished only by a suffix losing the suffix, and E and F becoming $\mathscr{E}$ and $\mathscr{F}$. Secondly, a representation, say U of the group O, however often it occurs, always behaves in the same way on passing to a subgroup. (The reorientation needed in passing from T to C_3 betrays itself in the fact that the $\mathscr{E}$ of C_3 corresponds to the E of T, only after a rearrangement of order. This is an unimportant fact in itself, it may be said, but the student who has fully satisfied himself how and why it happens may be sure that he understands fully the implications of the whole table.)

These results are an expansion of those first derived by Bethe (by the method used here) for the purpose of determining the effects of a crystalline environment on the spectrum of an atom. We remember that a wave function belonging to an n-dimensional representation is one of an n-fold degenerate set. The table shows, for example, that a d level, which in a free atom is fivefold degenerate, splits under the perturbing action of neighbouring atoms in a cubic crystal into two levels, one three- and one twofold degenerate; in a hexagonal crystal it splits into three levels (two of them twofold); in a tetragonal crystal into four levels (one twofold) and in crystals of lower symmetry is completely split up. This argument applies indiscriminately to all d levels, whether $3d$, $4d$, $5d$,..., etc.

Bethe was concerned only with atoms—i.e. with $\mathfrak{r}_3$ direct to any one crystal symmetry. Later Mulliken realized that the same method will apply to certain molecular problems.

The table is easily extended, using the foregoing rules, to include improper groups. Every line is duplicated, carrying g and u subscripts if the group contains i, or with and without bars if it does not. But this formal extension of the table needs closer examination.

A wave function has been regarded hitherto as a function of the three coordinates x, y, z, viz. $\psi(x, y, z)$. If the symmetry is $\mathfrak{r}_3$ then there is some rotation which carries (ξ, η, ζ) into $(-\xi, -\eta, -\zeta)$, though the carriage of every x, y, z into $-x, -y, -z$ simultaneously is an improper rotation which is not a member of $\mathfrak{r}_3$. We considered the representations of $\mathfrak{r}_3$ in § 16.7, and found them to be certain homogeneous functions of the coordinates. On replacement of ξ, η, ζ by $-\xi$, $-\eta$, $-\zeta$ these will change their sign if of odd degree or keep it if of even degree; s, d, g,... levels are apparently essentially s_g, d_g, g_g,..., while p, f,... are p_u, f_u,.... . How can we discover the missing representations? There are two ways of doing it. One is to regard the symmetry elements not as physical movements but as coordinate changes. We can then invoke § 14.7, and supply them by means of W-functions, viz. $\psi(x, y, z) \Delta/|\Delta|$. ($|\Delta|$ is identically unity for all transformations of $\mathfrak{o}_3$, of course, and can be omitted from this expression.) The second is to include an extra variable, and we must examine the relation between these two methods of approach.

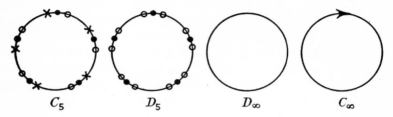

$$C_5 \qquad\qquad D_5 \qquad\qquad D_\infty \qquad\qquad C_\infty$$

Fig. 27.

The problem in geometrical form is illustrated in two dimensions in Fig. 27, where we see that there is no difficulty in drawing a figure having C_n but not D_n as long as n is finite, because a point infinitesimally clockwise or anticlockwise from a given point is not equivalent to it. To obtain a figure invariant under C_∞ but not under D_∞, we must have a circle, but it must be a circle with a sense; the distinction between clockwise and anticlockwise must be maintained, not by a difference between neighbouring points in opposite directions, but by something at the point itself. The simplest physical situation represented by such a diagram is the magnetic field around a current-bearing wire—an observation of considerable portent.

Thus a scalar function is inadequate to display the full implications of representation theory. It need only be supplemented by a 'sense', i.e. a variable consisting only of a sign, though we shall probably be happier if we allow it to be ± 1. The full implications of representation theory are thus displayed by a function $\psi(x, y, z, \eta)$, similar to the function $f(x, \eta)$ discussed in § 12.9, in which η takes only the values ± 1. A point now has four coordinates; we shall say that $(x, y, z, +1)$ is the point (x, y, z) in the 'real' world, whereas $(x, y, z, -1)$ is the point (x, y, z) in the 'inverted' or 'mirror' world; the same axes being used, and the two worlds superposed and coexisting—the natural reaction which puts a virtual image in a plane mirror *behind* the mirror. The transformations of $\mathfrak{o}_3$ now all have a determinant equal to $+1$; every x, y, z can be carried into $-x$, $-y$, $-z$ provided η is simultaneously carried into $-\eta$. Then writing $F(r)\xi_k^0$ for s_g, p_u,..., where r is essentially positive and ξ_k^0 is as defined in § 16.7, s_u, p_g,... are $\eta\,F(r)\xi_k^0$. (Different wave functions of the same symmetry will differ in the form of F.) We saw in § 12.9 that these states are eigenstates of η.

This introduction of a 'dichotomous variable'—one taking only two values—has occurred twice before. We were on the point of introducing it in § 15.4 for the same reason as here, for the extension of the vector W to double the number of components to provide for improper rotations was in effect Kronecker multiplication of wave space by a two-space, and we could write $(W_1, W_2, \overline{W}_1, \overline{W}_2)$ in the form $W + \eta\overline{W}$. Then it appeared in § 16.5 when we were discussing Dirac's relativistic modification of the Schrödinger equation, and as, here as well as there, its chief manifestation seems to be magnetic (since only magnetic effects obey inverted laws in the inverted world) we shall assume that the two wave functions $\psi(x, y, z)$ and $\eta\,\psi(x, y, z)$ which behave identically in the ordinary Schrödinger equation do in fact represent the two wave functions which are identical except in respect of spin. The interesting thing is that in this section we have been led to this conclusion by an entirely non-relativistic argument.

In discussing spin we meet with degeneracy in a peculiarly acute form. For spin does not enter into the simple Schrödinger equation, and $\psi(x, y, z)$ and $\eta\,\psi(x, y, z)$ give rise to equal energy levels, although they belong to different representations. This problem also occurs elsewhere. For $3s$, $3p$, and $3d$ levels are also degenerate in this sense. Were they not, the π levels from the $3p$ and the π levels from $3d$ would, under an infinitesimal perturbation, contribute infinitesimal correction terms to each other, but as they are, these two levels present us with a correct zeroth approximation problem to solve. The same thing happens with $\psi(x, y, z)$ and $\eta\,\psi(x, y, z)$. Although they belong to different representations of $\mathfrak{o}_3$, there is a complete degeneracy arising from a cause which has nothing to do with symmetry. All the necessary data for analysing this situation are contained in the table on the following page, which supplements Table 16.9.2, and the new problem is to decide which physical situations give rise to the various mathematical situations it reveals.

Observation of the spin of a particle yields the result $+$ or $-$, irrespective of the direction of observation. We remind the reader of this before remarking that if the nucleus has a spin, this will reduce the symmetry from $\mathfrak{o}_3$ to $\mathfrak{r}_3$, and not to anything cylindrical. It will also, by acting

TABLE 16.93

Stars denote classes surviving						$\mathfrak{o}_3$	$\mathfrak{r}_3$	$D_{\infty h}$	D_∞	$C_{\infty v}$	$C_{\infty h}$
*	*	*	*	*	*			$D_{\infty h}$			
*	*	*							D_∞		
*	*			*						$C_{\infty v}$	
*	*		*	*							$C_{\infty h}$
I	C_ϕ	2_ϕ	i	S_ϕ	m_ϕ						
1	1	1	1	1	1	s_g	s	σ_{+g}	σ_+	σ_+	σ_g
1	1	1	-1	-1	-1	s_u	s	σ_{+u}	$\bar\sigma_+ = \sigma_+$	$\bar\sigma_+ = \sigma_-$	σ_u
1	1	-1	1	1	-1	p_g	p	σ_{-g}	σ_-	σ_-	σ_g
2	$2\cos\phi$	0	2	$2\cos\phi$	0			π_g	π	π	π_g
$z{:}1$	1	-1	-1	-1	1	p_u	p	σ_{-u}	$\bar\sigma_- = \sigma_-$	$\bar\sigma_- = \sigma_+$	σ_u
$x,\,y{:}2$	$2\cos\phi$	0	-2	$-2\cos\phi$	0			π_u	$\bar\pi = \pi$	$\bar\pi = \pi$	π_u

with the spin of the electron, cause the latter to affect the energy. The correct zeroth approximations will be combinations of the original functions described as s in the column headed $\mathfrak{r}_3$. With an externally applied field, the position is different. The field defines an axis and a sense along this axis. If the field is electric, the symmetry becomes $C_{\infty v}$, but as a magnetic field is reversed by an improper rotation, a magnetic field produces the symmetry $C_{\infty h}$. In these cases the correct zeroth approximations are combinations of those wave functions which have the same symbol in the columns headed $C_{\infty v}$ and $C_{\infty h}$ respectively. It might be thought that with nuclear spin and an external field, only the real symmetry groups are possible, but before asserting this too confidently some more detailed examination of the effect of the external field on the nucleus should be undertaken.

We do not propose to develop this subject further at this stage. The possible states of n-electron systems derived from an analysis of the Kronecker product of the representations of separate wave functions will be discussed in the next section; the introduction of spin complicates the results but does not affect the basic principles. It is exceedingly important in spectroscopy, being the basis of 'multiplet' theory. Elsewhere, except in nuclear studies, the effect of spin is usually considered qualitatively, as already mentioned, in the form that *two* electrons can occupy any wave function.

We conclude with two matters. The first is the relatively simple one that in performing a product $*\psi_i\,\psi_j*$ it is now necessary to integrate over x, y, and z, and sum over η. (The current tendency to refer to 'integration' over spin coordinates is not a happy one.) If $\psi_i = \psi_j$ over the whole of real space, but $\psi_i = -\psi_j$ over the whole of mirror space, then the two functions are orthogonal, since the product is zero when summed over both spaces.

The second is that we are now in a position, if we wish to do so, to label uniquely all the possible independent wave functions in a system that can be obtained by imposing a continually increasing perturbation on an atom. Inspection of Table 16.9.2 will show that one of its rows can be uniquely specified by quoting the letters in the columns headed r_3, D_∞, and D_2—sometimes by less but there is an advantage in uniformity here. The complete specification of a wave function can therefore be made in an expression of the form $3d\pi D_{1u}$—adding the principal quantum number and the behaviour under improper rotations which are ignored in Table 16.9.2. In a free atom a wave function so specified would be just one of the possible $3p$ wave functions, the correct zeroth approximations to a certain problem being our method of making the arbitrary choice of basic independent wave functions. In an atom in an orthorhombic crystal, on the other hand, it is a certain D_1 wave function, viz. that one which changes adiabatically into a $3d\pi_u$ level if the orthorhombic perturbation is gradually reduced to zero.

16.10. n-Electron systems

Molecules, with which we shall be largely concerned in the sequel, are collections of heavy positively charged nuclei, and light negatively charged electrons, in equilibrium under their mutual interactions. A preliminary investigation of such systems leads to the Franck–Condon principle, that owing to the high inertia of the nuclei these may be regarded as fixed in discussing the wave functions in so far as concerns the electrons. We therefore consider a molecule here as an n-electron system with a force field defined by our choice of nuclear configuration. Later we shall reconcile this picture with that of a vibrating system of nuclei such as we considered in Chapter X.

Ignoring spin, the Schrödinger equation for n particles is obtained in the same way as that for one, and may be written

$$\left(-\sum_{p=1}^{n}\frac{h^2}{8\pi^2 m_p}\nabla_p^2 + \sum_{p=1}^{n}V_p + \sum_{p,q=1}^{n(n-1)}U_{pq}\right)\psi = W\psi. \qquad (16.10.1)$$

This is the amplitude form; ψ is a function of the $4n$ coordinates $x_1, y_1, z_1, \eta_1, x_2,..., \eta_n$ of the n electrons, and expresses the chance of the n electrons being simultaneously observed to have the assigned values of their coordinates,

$$\nabla_p^2 = \frac{\partial^2}{\partial x_p^2} + \frac{\partial^2}{\partial y_p^2} + \frac{\partial^2}{\partial z_p^2};$$

V_p is the potential energy of the pth electron and is a function of x_p, y_p, z_p only, and U_{pq} is the mutual potential energy of the pth and qth electrons and depends on both their coordinates. V_p would depend also on the spin in a magnetic field, but Dirac's form of the Schrödinger equation would in any case be required here. U_{pq} does inevitably depend on the spins of the two electrons concerned, but the interaction of the spins is small compared with the electrostatic interaction, and may be neglected even in a first-order perturbation theory. With the Franck–Condon principle already applied, all the particles are electrons, and all the m_p are m, the electronic mass.

If we now write

$$\mathcal{H} = -\frac{h^2}{8\pi^2 m} \sum \nabla_p^2 + \sum V_p, \tag{16.10.2}$$

$$\psi = \psi^1(x_1, y_1, z_1)\,\psi^2(x_2, y_2, z_2)...\psi^n(x_n, y_n, z_n)\,\eta_1^{\alpha_1}\eta_2^{\alpha_2}...\eta_n^{\alpha_n} \tag{16.10.3}$$

with every $\alpha = 1$ or 0, then the equation

$$\mathcal{H}\psi = W\psi \tag{16.10.4}$$

can be written

$$\sum_{p=1}^{n} \frac{1}{\psi^p}\left(-\frac{h^2}{8\pi^2 m}\nabla_p^2 + V_p\right)\psi^p = W. \tag{16.10.5}$$

Each term in this equation is independent of the rest, being a function of x_p, y_p, z_p only, and each term is thus a constant, W_p, the various terms being subject to the overriding condition

$$\sum W_p = W. \tag{16.10.6}$$

This means that each electron satisfies the equation it would satisfy if the other electrons were absent, the total energy being the sum of the several one-electron energies. Thus

$$\psi = \psi_h^1 \psi_j^2 ... \psi_k^n, \tag{16.10.7}$$

where $\psi_h,...,\psi_k,...$ are one-electron wave functions, is a solution of (16.10.4), the energy, by (16.10.6), being the sum of the separate energies of the electrons. The level is $n!$-fold degenerate, since permutation of the $1, 2,..., n$ in (16.10.7) gives rise to a new function with the same energy.

We now put $\mathscr{G} = \sum U_{pq}$, and apply, first static, then dynamic perturbation theory. Both $\mathscr{H}$ and $\mathscr{G}$ are invariant under π_n and therefore if the wave space is so split up as to separate the irreducible representations of π_n, we shall be a step farther towards solving the secular equation and determining the corrections to (16.10.6). The $n!$-dimensional space with $\mathscr{H}\psi = \sum W_p\psi$ displays the regular representation of π_n, and thus contains the symmetric and antisymmetric representations once each, the rest repeatedly. Two correct zeroth approximations are thus

$$\psi_h^{(1}\psi_j^{2}...\psi_k^{n)} \quad \text{and} \quad \psi_h^{[1}\psi_j^{2}...\psi_k^{n]}. \qquad (16.10.8\,\text{a, b})$$

and the rest (being repeated) would seem to need further investigation. But dynamic perturbation theory now allows us to state that $\mathscr{G}$ will never cause transitions from one representation to another, so that if the whole universe is at $t = 0$ in a state wholly conforming to one representation, then it will for ever remain so. There is now abundant experimental evidence that the universe is in fact describable by a wave function antisymmetric under the electron permutation group; we are saved further investigation and can restrict ourselves to the function (16.10.8 b).

We may ask whether it is necessary to appeal to experiment at this stage. It is usually done and probably is necessary. Most writers rule out the multi-dimensional representations of π_n on theoretical grounds. The complications of a universe in one of these representations would be considerable and very difficult to foresee. The simplest is in $n-1$ dimensions and it is evident that were it in operation the basic postulate of physics that a simple system can be considered in isolation would require radical examination. Yet it is difficult to suppose (considering how we have come to consider it as a possibility) that it would contain any inherent contradiction. If it were found to conflict with the postulate of isolability it is still open to argument—and to arguments independent of the present one, too—that postulate is the wrong word, observation being more accurate, in which case we are back at the appeal to experiment. In view of the experimental facts, the question is an academic one. So far as the symmetric representation is concerned, particles conforming to it are known—photons, for example, and α-particles. In the latter case, it is evident that if an *even* number of particles conforming to the antisymmetric representation are held together as a compound particle, the system will conform to the symmetric representation for permutations of complete compound particles; it follows that any argument for the necessity of the antisymmetric representation would thus be an argument for the compound nature of particles conforming to the symmetric representation.

The main effect of the requirement of antisymmetry is expressible in the statement that since

$$\psi_h^{[1}\psi_j^2...\psi_k^{n]} = \frac{1}{n!} \begin{vmatrix} \psi_h^1 & \psi_h^2 & \cdot & \cdot & \cdot & \psi_h^n \\ \psi_j^1 & \psi_j^2 & \cdot & \cdot & \cdot & \psi_j^n \\ \cdot & \cdot & \cdot & \cdot & \cdot & \cdot \\ \psi_k^1 & \psi_k^2 & \cdot & \cdot & \cdot & \psi_k^n \end{vmatrix} \qquad (16.10.9)$$

then $\qquad \psi_h^{[1}\psi_j^2...\psi_k^{n]} \neq 0 \quad$ implies $h, j,..., k$ all different

and thus no two electrons can occupy the same wave function. In interpreting this statement each ψ is to be of the type including the spin, of course, and the more familiar form is that not more than two electrons may occupy the same wave function. In either form it is known as the Pauli principle.

An important property of the antisymmetrized wave function is the following:

THEOREM 16.10.10. *Any set of wave functions which span the same subspace of wave space will give rise to the same antisymmetrized wave function.*

For consider the determinant in (16.10.9) as a matrix M, and each column of it as a vector. Then any replacement of ψ_h, ψ_j,..., ψ_k by linear combinations of these vectors may be effected by forming a product AM where A is a numerical $n \times n$ matrix. Since $\det AM = \det A \det M$, and $\det A$ is purely numerical, and therefore absorbed in any normalization process, the result is proved. A second important property is

THEOREM 16.10.11. *The antisymmetrized wave function derived from a complete degenerate set is invariant under all the symmetry operations of the system.*

For the subspace spanned by a degenerate set is invariant under such operations (§ 16.7). A third result which greatly simplifies our intuition of the situation is

THEOREM 16.10.12. *The electron density—or probability of finding one (unspecified) electron—at a point is equal to the sum of the densities—or probabilities—associated with the n electrons before symmetrization.*

The proof is a little more elaborate. To determine the probability of finding electron No. 1 at the point (ξ, η, ζ), we substitute these values for (x_1, y_1, z_1) and integrate over all the other $3n-3$ coordinates, in the probability function $*\psi\psi*$. As $\psi*$ after asymmetrization involves $n!$ terms, $*\psi\psi*$ will involve $(n!)^2$ terms. The multiple integral from each term can be expressed in the form of products of triple integrals, e.g.

$$\iint \cdots \int \bar\psi_1(\xi, \eta, \zeta)\,\psi_1(\xi, \eta, \zeta)\,\bar\psi_2(x_2, y_2, z_2)\,\psi_2(x_2, y_2, z_2)\ldots dx_2\,dy_2\,dz_2\,dx_3\ldots$$

$$= \bar\psi_1(\xi, \eta, \zeta)\,\psi_1(\xi, \eta, \zeta)\iiint \bar\psi_2(x_2, y_2, z_2)\psi_2(x_2, y_2, z_2)\,dx_2\,dy_2\,dz_2\iiint \ldots.$$

Now every integral of the form $\iiint \bar\psi_h^p\psi_k^p\,dx_p\,dy_p\,dz_p$ is zero unless $h = k$ and it is not difficult to see (though difficult to write out without undue verbosity) that there will always be one such factor except in certain terms where the $\bar\psi^1$ and ψ^1 factors carry the same suffix. (That is, all terms where $\bar\psi^1$ and ψ^1 carry different suffixes, and some in which they carry the same suffix, are zero.) The number of non-zero terms is such that the final expression is

$$\frac{1}{n}\{\bar\psi_h(\xi, \eta, \zeta)\psi_h(\xi, \eta, \zeta)+\bar\psi_j(\xi, \eta, \zeta)\psi_j(\xi, \eta, \zeta)+\ldots+\bar\psi_k(\xi, \eta, \zeta)\psi_k(\xi, \eta, \zeta)\}$$

provided that the separate wave functions are each normalized. The same result is naturally obtained for electrons Nos. 2, 3,..., n, and multiplying the above result by n the theorem is proved.

The second of the above theorems is important enough to illustrate by a simple example. Consider, therefore, an atomic p level, which is triply degenerate, the wave functions being $f(r)\cos\theta$, $f(r)\sin\theta\sin\phi$, and $f(r)\sin\theta\cos\phi$. By the third of the above theorems (which was proved independently of the second), we can ignore the Pauli principle and write for the charge density at any point

$$[f(r)\cos\theta]^2+[f(r)\sin\theta\sin\phi]^2+[f(r)\sin\theta\cos\phi]^2 = [f(r)]^2,$$

which is independent of direction and therefore totally symmetric under r_3 (and also, as it is positive, under o_3) the group under which the $\mathscr{H}$ of the atom problem is itself invariant. The same result would be found for higher levels (but the student who tries to verify this is warned to be sure he has his normalizing factors correct).

We have seen, then, that an n-electron system can be considered by perturbation theory, all the *interactions* making up the perturbation; in the unperturbed system (which is not physically realizable) each electron contributes to the wave function a factor which is a possible solution of the one-electron problem in the same field. There are two sources of degeneracy which make the seeking of correct zeroth approximations a problem, degeneracy in the one-electron problem, and permutation degeneracy. The latter we have dealt with; Pauli's law (surely a more appropriate word than *principle*) stating that the only wave functions actually found are those which conform to the antisymmetric representation of π_n. Degeneracy in the one-electron system is analysed by the symmetry (rotational symmetry) group; any one solution of the unperturbed problem defines a representation of this group in Hilbert space, and degenerate sets correspond to the irreducible representations contained in it. This, too, we have dealt with for one-electron systems; the remaining problem arises from the fact that the n-electron wave function which is the product of n one-electron wave functions may define a reducible representation even though its factors define irreducible ones. The wave space of the product function is, in fact, the Kronecker product space of the wave spaces of its factors, and the problem is the one of reducing Kronecker product representations.

Consider a two-electron system for simplicity, and let the one-electron functions $\psi_1, \ldots, \psi_k$ belong to W_k and $\phi_1, \ldots, \phi_{k'}$ belong to $W_{k'}$. Then all the two-electron functions

$$\psi_1\phi_1, \ \psi_2\phi_1, \ \ldots, \ \psi_k\phi_1, \ \psi_1\phi_2, \ \ldots, \ \psi_k\phi_{k'}$$

belong to the level $W_k + W_{k'}$. This level is at present kk'-fold degenerate. To a higher degree of approximation it may split, and the extent of inevitable degeneracy is determinable by reducing this kk'-dimensional representation of the symmetry group into its irreducible parts. For further simplicity let us suppose the system is an atom; then we have already the solution of the problem, for, by § 12.4,

$$\Gamma_r \times \Gamma_s = \Gamma_{r+s} \dotplus \Gamma_{r+s-2} \dotplus \ldots \dotplus \Gamma_{|r-s|}$$

whence, introducing the nomenclature for these irreducible representations, we have

Electrons in:		r	s	$\lvert r-s \rvert \ldots r+s$			Possible atomic states		
s	s	0	0	0			S		
s	p	0	1	1			P		
p	p	1	1	0	2		S	D	
s	d	0	2	0	2		S	D	
p	d	1	2	1	3		P	F	
d	d	2	2	0	2	4	S	D	G, etc.

We have followed spectroscopic convention by using capital letters on going over to the two-electronic representations. This is the result which was obtained on the old quantum theory by quantizing first the resolved parts along the Z-axis of the orbital angular momenta of the separate electrons and then taking the sum, the $s, p,...$ labels of the orbits referring to their orbital angular momenta before resolving and the $S, P,...$ to this sum. With lower symmetry types as in molecules the group-theoretic analysis is similar but simpler, as with finite groups the analysis is arithmetical, not algebraic. Care must be taken, however, to remember that in $\mathscr{E}$ and $\mathscr{F}$ levels the complex characters are to be used. Thus the following table gives the possible states of a two-electron system in a field of symmetry T; the entries are obtained by multiplying the characters of the representations for the separate electrons and analysing the result:

		1st electron		
	A	$\mathscr{E}_1$	$\mathscr{E}_2$	T
A	A	$\mathscr{E}_1$	$\mathscr{E}_2$	T
$\mathscr{E}_1$	$\mathscr{E}_1$	$\mathscr{E}_2$	A	T
$\mathscr{E}_2$	$\mathscr{E}_2$	A	$\mathscr{E}_1$	T
T	T	T	T	$A+\mathscr{E}_1+\mathscr{E}_2+2T$

(2nd electron labels the rows: A, $\mathscr{E}_1$, $\mathscr{E}_2$, T.)

With n-electron systems no new principles are introduced. One might have doubts about the associative nature of Kronecker multiplication, but fortunately there is none about the multiplication of the characters, which are numbers. The possible states, for example, of an atom containing three s and two p electrons, are obtained by trigonometric rearrangement of

$$\left(\frac{\sin \tfrac{1}{2}\theta}{\sin \tfrac{1}{2}\theta}\right)^3 \left(\frac{\sin(1+\tfrac{1}{2})\theta}{\sin \tfrac{1}{2}\theta}\right)^2.$$

But we shall not follow this up. It is not one of the triumphs of group theory to obtain so cumbrously what can be seen quite simply on the old picture of the atom, and as far as molecules are concerned excited states are too infrequently stable to be of very much importance. A notable exception is the class of molecules with conjugated double bond systems (§ 17.6).

Three matters remain to complete this account. The permutation and symmetry groups are independent and their operators commute. It therefore makes no difference to the final result whether we anti-symmetrize before or after the state of the complete system has been decided upon. (It may affect intermediate stages of the calculation, however: compare § 17.2 on the Heitler–London and Molecular Orbital approximations.) Secondly, one might inquire about the explicit forms of the wave functions. It is one of the interesting features of group theory that it allows so much to be determined without the need for this. Should explicit forms be required, however, the means for obtaining them are to hand. In the case of the two-electron atom we did, in § 12.4, obtain explicitly the Clebsch–Gordan reduction of the polynomial in four complex variables which separates out the representations of r_3. So far as π_n is concerned, only the antisymmetrical representation is required, and this is given in determinantal form. For other symmetry groups the route is that through the class algebra and the primitive idempotents. A glance at the Clebsch–Gordan series for two electrons will suggest that although the means may be at hand in principle, it is just as well that the theory allows many important results to be obtained in complicated cases without recourse to explicit wave functions.

Thirdly, there is the introduction of electron spin, which has been ignored above. The qualitative classification of states arising from spin degeneracy is also so straightforward on the old model that spectroscopists prefer to handle it that way. In our picture the states $\psi(x, y, z)$ and $\eta \, \psi(x, y, z)$ which conform to representations of the symmetry group are, by § 12.9, eigenstates of the spin. In an n-electron system, an orbital product approximation based on such orbitals will be

$$\eta_1^{\alpha_a} \, \eta_2^{\alpha_b} ... \eta_n^{\alpha_k} \, \psi_a(1)\psi_b(2)...\psi_k(n)$$

with every α equal to 1 or 0. (And although this is based on an approximation, the wave space which contains these vectors will also contain the true state vectors.) Since any coordinate change must be applied to every electron simultaneously, the η factors will contribute a factor $(-1)^{\Sigma \alpha}$ in an improper rotation, and the analysis of the product representation will depend only on whether $\Sigma \alpha$ is odd or even, not on the separate α's.

The wave space of the system is the Kronecker product of the n Hilbert spaces and the n spin two-spaces, or rather it is that subspace of this one which displays the antisymmetric representation of π_n (compare § 14.5). We can reach this subspace by combining the Hilbert spaces together, combining the spin spaces together, picking out the antisymmetric parts of each of these two separately, and then combining them. The *total* spin is given by the operator

$$\eta_1 I_2 I_3 ... I_n + I_1 \, \eta_2 I_3 ... I_n + ... + I_1 I_2 I_3 ... \eta_n$$

(Kronecker multiplication understood) in the total spin space, and the possible values of the total spin are the eigenvalues of this operator which belong to eigenvectors in the asymmetric part of the space.

If two electrons are in orbitals with the same ψ function, then their spins must be opposed. It is interesting to examine this case separately, and to begin with a slightly more general form of the wave function, namely,

$$\psi_a(x_1, y_1, z_1, \eta_1)\, \psi_b(x_2, y_2, z_2, \eta_2)\ldots\psi_k(x_n, y_n, z_n, \eta_n)$$

with every ψ of the form

$$\psi_i(x_j, y_j, z_j, \eta_j) = (\cos\theta_i + \eta_j \sin\theta_i)\,\phi_i(x_j, y_j, z_j).$$

Not more than two ϕ can be the same, and if $\phi_i = \phi_{i'}$, then the orthogonality requirement demands that $\theta_{i'} = \theta_i + \tfrac{1}{2}\pi$. The effect of the operator which antisymmetrizes these two electrons is to produce the function

$$\begin{vmatrix} \cos\theta_i + \eta_j \sin\theta_i\,\phi_i(j) & \cos\theta_i + \eta_{j'} \sin\theta_i\,\phi_i(j') \\ -\sin\theta_i + \eta_j \cos\theta_i\,\phi_i(j) & -\sin\theta_i + \eta_{j'} \cos\theta_i\,\phi_i(j') \end{vmatrix} = (\eta_j - \eta_{j'})\phi(j)\phi(j').$$

(This is interesting in itself; it shows that the two electrons cannot both be found in the real world nor both in the inverted world, and shows that 'having opposed spins' is equivalent to 'existing one in each world'.) The full antisymmetrizing operator can be expressed as a product which includes a series of binary alternating operators of this type and further as a product in which all such pairs are operated on before any other operations are performed, these operations being independent. The alternating operator from π_4, for example, can be factorized in the form

$$\{I + (1)(234) + (1)(243)\}\{I - (13)(24)\}\{I - (1)(2)(34)\}\{I - (12)(3)(4)\},$$

in which the two final factors are of the form we have been discussing. The first two if multiplied out give

$$I + (1)(234) + (1)(243) - (13)(24) - (143)(2) - (123)(4),$$

whence the completely asymmetrized orbital product, for four electrons in two orbitals, reduces to the relatively simple form

$$(\eta_1 - \eta_2)(\eta_3 - \eta_4)[\phi_a(1)\phi_a(2)\phi_b(3)\phi_b(4) - \phi_b(1)\phi_b(2)\phi_a(3)\phi_a(4)] +$$
$$+ (\eta_1 - \eta_3)(\eta_4 - \eta_2)[\phi_a(1)\phi_a(3)\phi_b(2)\phi_b(4) - \phi_b(1)\phi_b(3)\phi_a(2)\phi_a(4)] +$$
$$+ (\eta_1 - \eta_4)(\eta_2 - \eta_3)[\phi_a(1)\phi_a(4)\phi_b(2)\phi_b(3) - \phi_b(1)\phi_b(4)\phi_a(2)\phi_a(3)].$$

Further discussion of this subject, including selection rules incorporating spin, depends upon considerations of the magnitude and type of the potentials involved, upon which we do not propose to enter.

CHAPTER XVII

MOLECULAR STRUCTURE AND SPECTRA

NOTE: *The chemist who wishes to follow the methods developed in this chapter without committing himself to the heavier mathematics of previous chapters is advised to master the following sections. Those in brackets are required only for the detailed theory of the π-bond developed at the end of § 17.4, and those marked with an asterisk need only be read sufficiently closely to realize the significance of the results quoted from them.*

WHEREAS the force field in an atom has symmetry r_3, that in a diatomic molecule has the symmetry $C_{\infty v}$ if the nuclei are unlike or $D_{\infty h}$ if they are like. Quite a number of molecules have some small degree of symmetry, such as a single mirror plane, and a few, such as methane, show one of the more elaborate symmetries. But most molecules have no symmetry elements at all—they belong to the symmetry class $C_1(1)$. Nevertheless the concept of the valency bond seems in most cases to carry over from one molecule to another, and it is clear that a theory of molecular structure must compromise in some way between admitting the relative irrelevance of distant nuclei in determining what happens near a given nucleus, and, on the other hand, making allowance for the quantum principle that the true wave function of a system is anti-symmetric in *all* its electrons. The method we shall use is essentially a perturbation one; a field in a given small volume can often be expressed in terms of one with high symmetry plus a perturbation of lower symmetry. *Per contra*, such a field around a point not on an axis or plane of symmetry may have a lesser symmetry than the field as a whole. As an example of the former, consider chloracetic acid $CH_2Cl.COOH$. Neglecting nuclear spins, the field around each carbon atom is spherical to a first approximation, between them it is a $D_{\infty h}$ field to a first approximation, but the effects of distant nuclei destroy all symmetry of either sort if included. As an example of both, the field close to a nucleus in chlorine, Cl_2, is spherical to a first approximation, and to a second it is of type $C_{\infty v}$, which is less than the $D_{\infty h}$ of the complete molecule. In discussing the effects of the perturbations we shall use Table 16.9.2.

17.2. Diatomic molecules

The equation for a single electron in the presence of two nuclei, A and B, is

$$\left(\nabla^2 + \frac{Z_A e^2}{r_A} + \frac{Z_B e^2}{r_B}\right)\psi = W\psi, \qquad (17.2.1)$$

where Z_A and Z_B are the charges on the nuclei and r_A and r_B are the distances of a point from A and B respectively. It presents some intractable features from the point of view of perturbation theory, and requires another method for numerical solution, the variation method, which we shall outline shortly.

Meanwhile let us consider first a symmetrical molecule, with $A = B$. If the distance d between the nuclei is large, there will be a volume around A in which $Z_B e^2/r_B$ is small. We consider successive stages of approximation as follows. (1) A unperturbed. The allowable wave functions are those of the isolated atom, their types conforming to the representations of r_3. (2) A perturbed infinitesimally. At distances from A small compared with d, the perturbation will resemble a uniform electrostatic field; the degenerate atomic levels will split as the symmetry drops from r_3 to $C_{\infty v}$ according to Table 16.9.2, as in the Stark effect. We can do this because at any distance from A at which r_A/r_B is appreciable, ψ_k is so small that this part of space makes no appreciable contribution to $*\psi_k \mathscr{G}\psi_k*$, or at any rate this is so for the lower energy states in which we are interested. (3) As d decreases the perturbation becomes finite, but what is more important, at even low energy levels ψ_k is large in parts of space in which the effects of the two nuclei are comparable. We postpone discussing this to raise another issue. There will be another set of similar wave functions centred on B; every level will be twofold degenerate. This is to be expected since the system has a plane of symmetry.

The trouble about the perturbation method lies just here, that as we have derived the two members of each degenerate set they are not solutions of the same approximate equation, and there is no one term which we can identify with $\mathscr{G}$. We can get over this. It is only necessary to define $\mathscr{H}$ and $\mathscr{G}$ by different analytic expressions in the two halves of space, viz. $\mathscr{H} = \nabla^2 + Z_A e^2 / r_A$ in the half that contains A and $\nabla^2 + Z_B e^2 / r_B$ in the other half, and $\mathscr{G} = Z_B e^2 / r_B$ in the former half and $Z_A e^2 / r_A$ in the latter. Then so long as we remain at stage (2) of the approximation, and are content to regard any wave function as dropping effectively to zero before it reaches the mirror plane, we can apply the theory of § 16.8. The immediate conclusion is that the correct zeroth approximations are the functions

$$\psi_{Ak} + \psi_{Bk}, \qquad \psi_{Ak} - \psi_{Bk}, \qquad (17.2.2)$$

symmetric and antisymmetric respectively for reflection across the mirror plane and possessing the same type of symmetry for rotations about the axis of the molecule as their component parts already possess. In these expressions ψ_{Ak} is the kth wave function of the isolated A atom, etc. But since

$$(\psi_{Ak} + a_{k1}\psi_{A1} + a_{k2}\psi_{A2} + \ldots) \pm (\psi_{Bk} + a_{k1}\psi_{B1} + a_{k2}\psi_{B2} + \ldots)$$
$$= (\psi_{Ak} \pm \psi_{Bk}) + a_{k1}(\psi_{A1} \pm \psi_{B1}) + \ldots$$

we see that it makes no difference whether we regard the perturbed atomic wave functions and symmetrize them, or whether we symmetrize before applying perturbation theory corrections.

At stage (3) the perturbation method breaks down because it is no longer possible to regard isolated atom wave functions as solutions of the equation in which the potential field changes character at the mirror plane. But it is difficult to believe that the functions (17.2.2) are not still a good basis for some type of approximate treatment, and this is where the variation method begins to raise its head.

The principle of the variation method is to consider an arbitrary wave function which depends on several parameters, $\phi(a, b, \ldots; x, y, z)$. Such a function could, of course, be expanded in terms of the orthonormal eigenfunctions of the problem in hand were these already known. The coefficients would be functions of the parameters:

$$\phi(a, b, \ldots; x, y, z) = c_1(a, b, \ldots)\psi_1(x, y, z) + c_2(a, b, \ldots)\psi_2(x, y, z) + \ldots. \quad (17.2.3)$$

We make a note at once that if $\mathscr{H}$ is invariant under $\mathfrak{g}$ and ϕ belongs to an irreducible representation of $\mathfrak{g}$ then $c_k = 0$ for every ψ_k belonging

to other irreducible representations. If the eigenvalues are W_1, W_2,...,
with W_1 the smallest, then

$$*\phi\mathscr{H}\phi* = \bar{c}_1 c_1 W_1 + \bar{c}_2 c_2 W_2 + ... \qquad (17.2.4)$$
$$= W_1 + \bar{c}_2 c_2 (W_2 - W_1) + ...$$
$$> W_1.$$

Then any change in a, b,... which diminishes c_2, c_3,... also diminishes
$*\phi\mathscr{H}\phi*$. The converse is not necessarily true; a small diminution in $\bar{c}_n c_n$,
if $W_n - W_1$ is large, may cover up a large increase in $\bar{c}_2 c_2$ if $W_2 - W_1$ is small.
Nevertheless, if ϕ is suitably chosen, the values of a, b,... which make
$*\phi\mathscr{H}\phi*$ a minimum may well produce a good approximation to ψ_1; no
matter how badly ϕ is chosen they certainly give the best value for the
energy which can be obtained from functions of the form of ϕ. As to the
nature of the parameters, although they may be anything, two cases
stand out. The first is that any natural constant in an approximate
solution may be treated as a parameter for this purpose. Especially is
this true of nuclear charges in many-electron problems, for this has a
simple physical interpretation; the electrons which are mostly to be
found nearer to the nucleus than the one specifically in mind, 'screen'
the nucleus and reduce its effective charge. The second case is that in
which ϕ is made up as a linear combination of other functions, the
coefficients being the parameters. In this case the process of minimizing
(17.2.4) with respect to a, b,... leads to an equation exactly similar in
form to (16.8.11) or (16.8.14), though simpler in appearance than these,
as both Hamiltonian and eigenvalues are kept in one piece:

$$\begin{vmatrix} *\chi_1(\mathscr{H}-W_1)\chi_1* & *\chi_1(\mathscr{H}-W_1)\chi_2* & . & . & . \\ *\chi_2(\mathscr{H}-W_1)\chi_1* & *\chi_2(\mathscr{H}-W_1)\chi_2* & . & . & . \\ . & . & . & . & . & . & . & . \\ . & . & . & . & . & . & . & . \end{vmatrix} = 0,$$

where the χ are the functions from which the linear combination is to
be built up, and $\mathscr{H}$ is the *whole* Hamiltonian. The variation method may
be used to obtain the lowest wave function of each symmetry type in
this way. (It may also be used to obtain the next lowest if this is kept
orthogonal to the first, and so on.)

It is clear that even if the functions (17.2.2) are not a good basis for
a perturbation treatment, they are probably very well suited for variation treatment. Numerical work confirms this; the ground state of the
system H_2^+ is quite well described by $\psi_{A1s} + \psi_{B1s}$ without any further

terms. Naturally it is improved by further terms; the only ones it is necessary to include are those with σ_+ symmetry, of which the first is the $2p_z$ type (z-axis = molecular axis); this corresponds physically to allowing some polarization of each atom by the other nucleus. The results are also improved by varying the nuclear charge as it appears in the wave function, though the physical interpretation of this in a one-electron problem is not so obvious unless there is some sort of 'self-screening'.

It is possible to reduce d to zero. The system is then known as the 'united atom'. The system in which d is infinitesimal may be regarded as the united atom perturbed by a 'tripole'—

$$+m \cdots\cdots\cdots +n \text{ equals}\begin{cases} +(m+n) \\ \text{perturbed by} \\ \dfrac{m+n}{2} \cdots -(m+n)\cdots \dfrac{m+n}{2} \\ \text{and then by} \\ \dfrac{m-n}{2} \cdots\cdots\cdots -\dfrac{m-n}{2} \end{cases}$$

The field of the latter falls off so rapidly with distance that the perturbation will be small. In this case the levels of the united atom split as usual; s levels becoming first σ_+ and then σ levels, p_z levels becoming first σ_- and then σ levels, p_x and p_y levels remaining degenerate as π levels, etc. (Table 16.9.2 shows that p becomes $\sigma_-+\pi$ but no details; it is clear, however, that the correct zeroth approximations within the p level are as we have stated them.) The levels of the united atom being known accurately, this limit has proved useful in discussing the levels of a molecule semi-quantitatively.

Before discussing the transition more generally we may dispose of the awkward fact that the antisymmetrical functions would seem to become identically zero at $d = 0$. This is not so. When normalized the $1s$ functions, for example, are

$$\frac{1}{\sqrt{(2+2\Delta)}}\,(\psi_{A1s}+\psi_{B1s}) \quad \text{and} \quad \frac{1}{\sqrt{(2-2\Delta)}}\,(\psi_{A1s}-\psi_{B1s}),$$

where Δ is the integral $*\psi_{A1s}\psi_{B1s}*$, which, rather surprisingly, can be evaluated exactly, and is $e^{-d}(1+d+\tfrac{1}{3}d^2)$, which is unity at $d = 0$. Consequently, as the factor $\psi_{A1s}-\psi_{B1s}$ becomes zero, the normalizing coefficient becomes infinite, and it is necessary to apply the usual procedure for indeterminate forms. Similar considerations apply to other levels, so that what $\psi_{Ak}-\psi_{Bk}$ actually tends to is $d\psi_k/dz$. This is not a wave function of the united atom, of course; we have not included the perturbing terms. But from

$$\frac{df(r^2)\xi}{dz} \equiv 2f'(r^2)\,(z\xi) + f(r^2)\,\xi'$$

and a study of § 16.7, we see that because of the presence of the z in the first term on the right-hand side of this expression, the antisymmetric combination of two s levels will be a p level, of two p levels will contain a d level term (together with some s terms possibly, which are removed by the perturbing terms) and so on. At the same time the σ, π,... character of the wave functions is unaffected (since it depends only on the rotation about the z-axis) and we have:

Original terms	Symmetric combination	Antisymmetric combination
$s\sigma$	$s\sigma$	$p\sigma$
$p\sigma$	$p\sigma$	$d\sigma$
$p\pi$	$p\pi$	$d\pi$
$d\sigma$	$d\sigma$	$f\sigma$, etc.

An important feature is that since the lowest p level is $2p$, the antisymmetric combination of $1s$ levels can only be $2p$, and so on. This raising of the principal quantum number is called 'promotion'; it betrays the fact that the energy of the antisymmetric combination rises as the internuclear distance d is decreased, creating a repulsive force between the nuclei, whence the description 'anti-bonding' for such wave functions. The symmetric combination, on the other hand, gives rise to a decrease in energy which may be sufficient to overcome the repulsive force between the nuclei themselves if d is not too small, and such wave functions are 'bonding'. This also follows qualitatively from the fact that the latter, with finite d, locate the bulk of the charge between the nuclei in a region of low P.E., whereas the former locate it outside the region between the nuclei.

Turning now to the unsymmetrical molecule, we lose most of the basis of the argument. But we can use its results as a guide. The device of dividing the whole of space into two 'spheres of influence' still works and shows that when the distance d is large, the lower energy levels of the isolated atoms are still good approximations to those of the molecule. There is now no degeneracy between the two sets of solutions, but if two levels, one from each, are fairly close, then by § 16.8 (summary at the end of the section), they will be fairly well 'mixed up' as soon as $*\psi_{Ak}\,\mathscr{G}\psi_{Bk'}*$ is not infinitesimal. This will occur as soon as ψ_{Ak} and $\psi_{Bk'}$

overlap appreciably provided that they belong to the same representation of $\mathfrak{c}_\infty$. Under these circumstances the functions

$$c_1\psi_{Ak}+c_2\psi_{Bk'} \quad \text{and} \quad c_3\psi_{Ak}-c_4\psi_{Bk'}$$

can be constructed so as to be orthonormal (even though ψ_{Ak} and $\psi_{Bk'}$ are not), and the former can be made the subject of the variation method to determine c_2/c_1. Further discussion of this is of very academic interest as long as we are considering one-electron systems.

The simplest molecule of chemical interest, H_2, is a two-electron system, and at the outset we are confronted with a question of method. The molecule is symmetrical. Shall we (a) follow the lines of this section starting with d infinite but with two electrons, or (b) combine the method of § 16.10 with the results obtained in this section, simply putting our two electrons into the wave functions already found and then considering their interaction as a perturbation ? The former is the historic treatment of Heitler and London; the latter is the method of molecular orbitals (a term we are avoiding pending definition). In method (a), that of Heitler and London, the lowest energy state of the system at large d will obviously have one electron in the $1s$ wave function of each nucleus. Writing $f(1)$ for $f(x_1, y_1, z_1)$, the description of the atoms separately will be $\psi_{A1s}(1)$ and $\psi_{B1s}(2)$, and of the whole system will be the product $\psi_{A1s}(1)\psi_{B1s}(2)$. Applying the principle that the wave function of the molecule must conform to a symmetry type, we have, for the correct zeroth approximations

$$\psi_{A1s}(1)\psi_{B1s}(2)\pm\psi_{B1s}(1)\psi_{A1s}(2).$$

In method (b) the ground state is

$$\{\psi_{A1s}(1)+\psi_{B1s}(1)\}\{\psi_{A1s}(2)+\psi_{B1s}(2)\},$$

both electrons being permitted in the same wave function provided that they have opposite spins.

It is important to realize that the Heitler–London expression has been obtained by imposing symmetry conditions on the two-electron wave function, and not by exchanging the electrons; the latter has to be looked into later, and, when spins are included, both the symmetric and antisymmetric (to reflection) functions must be antisymmetric in an exchange of the electrons. As many writers have pointed out, the expression given by method (b) is the same as the Heitler–London (symmetrical) expression with the addition of the terms $\psi_{A1s}(1)\psi_{A1s}(2)$ and $\psi_{B1s}(1)\psi_{B1s}(2)$. These represent two-electron wave functions with both electrons on the same nucleus, and it is interesting to see how they have been omitted. If they are discussed by the method of § 16.10, and electronic interaction within the H^- is neglected, then they have the same energy as the other two states (compare equation (16.10.6)). This being so, they ought therefore to be included in the degenerate set from which the correct zeroth approximation, which would then be of the form

$$a\{\psi_{A1s}(1)\psi_{B1s}(2)+\psi_{B1s}(1)\psi_{A1s}(2)\}+b\{\psi_{A1s}(1)\psi_{A1s}(2)+\psi_{B1s}(1)\psi_{B1s}(2)\},$$

is constructed. But they are instinctively recognized as higher energy states, and as they have the right symmetry they will in any case contribute when perturbation terms are included, though not as much as they do in the zeroth approximation of method (b).

This is perhaps the moment to draw attention to what the student has probably realized already—that the contribution of group theory to our understanding of molecular structure is essentially qualitative. It is therefore beyond our province to discuss in any detail calculations which are justified by their numerical results, either with or, as in the variation method, without comparison with experiment. Group theory normally provides short cuts to the determination of the correct zeroth approximations and indicates the nature of correction terms. But we cannot remain entirely unaware of numerical results since it is often these which make the decision between equally legitimate alternative procedures. Actually the Heitler–London treatment gives better results than the molecular orbital method when applied to hydrogen, where, it must be admitted, the electron-interaction/electron-nuclear-action ratio is at its most disadvantageous. But very accurate treatments of the hydrogen molecule have been carried out. In that of James and Coolidge, a wave function was used of the form

$$\psi_0(c_0 + \sum c_i \phi_i),$$

where (a) ψ_0 was a very simple modification of the united atom approximate wave function $\psi_{1s}(1)\psi_{1s}(2)$, namely, one in which the distance from the nucleus is replaced by the mean distance from the nuclei, and the nuclear charges were suitably 'screened', and (b) the ϕ_i were functions which were usually homogeneous functions of the coordinates conforming to the symmetry requirements (they were pairs of monomials in confocal elliptic coordinates, but that does not affect the issue) but might involve the interelectronic distance $\{(x_1-x_2)^2+(y_1-y_2)^2+(z_1-z_2)^2\}^{\frac{1}{2}}$.

They found that terms which did include this distance were essential to accuracy.

This emphasis on electronic interaction may well cause us to reconsider § 16.10. Does not the presence of one electron, for example, seriously affect the symmetry of the field in which another moves? The numerical method known as the 'self-consistent field' in which the n-electron problem is reduced to n simultaneous one-electron problems by requiring that each one-electron wave function should satisfy a Schrödinger equation in which the potential due to the other electrons has been averaged, would certainly seem to suggest this. But the answer is, in the main, 'no!'; the argument of (16.10) is for the most part on a deeper level. The group-theoretic part depends only on the symmetry of the Hamiltonian, including the e^2/r_{ij} terms and asserts only the symmetry of the total wave function. In this connection we should remember that r_{ij} is introduced as a *scalar* and as such is invariant under all symmetry elements; however it may vary in position and direction its absolute magnitude is unchanged. As regards the rest of the conclusions, we are asking too much. Once terms such as James and Coolidge introduced are included in a wave function it becomes impossible to factorize, and it is impossible to identify any part of it as the wave function of one of the electrons, even if we are careful not to specify which! (Nor is discussion of instantaneous positions really reasonable in quantum mechanics.) In other words it is not true that the probability of finding *an* electron at P and another at Q simultaneously is equal to the product of the probabilities of finding one at P and one at Q independently; they are not independent events in the probability sense, since the probability of their simultaneous occurrence is enhanced if P is well removed from Q and diminished if P and Q are close. Nevertheless, if the interaction terms are multiplied by λ and λ is then varied from 1 down to 0, each wave function for the molecule as a whole tends to a factorizable form in this process, and this form can be used for a formal description and classification of the possible states. For numerical calculation it may well be that other types of functions are better.

17.3. Methods of molecular analysis

The situation we have been describing has been known to chemists for a long time as the covalent bond, and by them it has been recognized in complex molecules as well. Before turning to more complex molecules we shall consider in some detail F_2 and HCl.

The fluorine atom has nine electrons and is described briefly as $1s^2 2s^2 p^5$ when in the lowest energy state, the indices denoting the number of electrons in each type of wave function. A completely united atom would be $1s^2 2s^2 p^6 3s^2 p^6$ in its ground state, a considerable amount of promotion being required. This is a general conclusion, in accordance with the experience of chemists that to explain valency it is necessary to assume that the outermost electrons but not the inner ones interact. In these circumstances the equilibrium distance of the fluorine nuclei is such that the second stage of approximation considered in the previous section is adequate to the original $1s$ electrons. The lowest energy levels are thus the $\psi_{A1s} \pm \psi_{B1s}$ wave functions, perturbed to a degree which can be neglected, or, in other words, owing to the value of d, the promotion which is incipient in the antisymmetric combination has not gone far enough to raise its energy seriously. These two levels are precisely equivalent to the original $1s$ ones, and whichever way we consider it, four electrons can be accommodated. In describing the fluorine molecule, they are usually denoted by the letters KK, since they are the source of K X-radiation. In the second quantum group we have, in each atom, $2s$ and $2p_z$ showing σ symmetry, and $2p_x$ and $2p_y$ showing π symmetry. The typical molecular one-electron wave functions will thus be of three types. Choosing the p_z wave functions so that Ap_z reflects into Bp_z, not $-Bp_z$, the first two are

$$a\{\psi_{A2s} \pm \psi_{B2s}\} + b\{\psi_{A2p_z} \pm \psi_{B2p_z}\}$$

with symmetries σ_+ and σ_-, according as the upper or lower signs are taken, and the third is shown by either of the functions

$$\psi_{A2p_x} \pm \psi_{B2p_x}$$

together with a corresponding one based on $2p_y$, the pair showing π symmetry. (The pair with $+$ signs are $p\pi$ orbitals of the united atom and the pair with $-$ signs are $d\pi$.) The first type can be rewritten

$$\{a\,\psi_{A2s} + b\,\psi_{A2p_z}\} + \{a\,\psi_{B2s} + b\,\psi_{B2p_z}\}.$$

The first bracket in this expression is usually known as a hybridized wave function on atom A. Hybridization of this type was introduced by Pauling, and has been used very freely—too freely, perhaps, but of that more when we discuss tetrahedral molecules. A feature of the hybrid wave function is that it is not symmetrical about the plane through the nucleus perpendicular to the Z-axis, but is concentrated on one side—

and there is an orthogonal combination concentrated on the other side.

In the 2 or L levels of the separate atoms there are eight independent wave functions each accommodating two electrons because of spin. However we combine these to give correct zeroth approximations we must still have eight wave functions, and we have fourteen electrons to distribute among them. It is because perturbation effects lower the energy of some of these and raise the energy of others (leaving the total approximately the same if d is not too small), and because when there is a deficit of electrons it is the higher levels that are unoccupied, that we get that increased stability from propinquity which causes molecule formation. The eight levels in the present example are:

1.	$\psi_{A2s}+{}^*\psi_{A2p_z}+\psi_{B2s}+{}^*\psi_{B2p_z}$	$\sigma 2s$	$z\sigma$
2.	$\psi_{A2s}+{}^*\psi_{A2p_z}-\psi_{B2s}-{}^*\psi_{B2p_z}$	σ^*2s	$y\sigma$
3.	${}^*\psi_{A2s}-\psi_{A2p_z}+{}^*\psi_{B2s}-\psi_{B2p_z}$	$\sigma 2p$	$x\sigma$
4.	$\psi_{A2p_y}+\psi_{B2p_y}$	$\pi_y 2p$	$w\pi$
5.	$\psi_{A2p_x}+\psi_{B2p_x}$	$\pi_x 2p$	
6.	$\psi_{A2p_y}-\psi_{B2p_y}$	$\pi_y^* 2p$	$v\pi$
7.	$\psi_{A2p_x}-\psi_{B2p_x}$	$\pi_x^* 2p$	
8.	${}^*\psi_{A2s}-\psi_{A2p_z}-{}^*\psi_{B2s}+\psi_{B2p_z}$	σ^*2p	$u\sigma$

They are here given in the order which, as shown by molecular spectra, is usually from lowest to highest. On the right are spectroscopic symbols for the levels; in this notation the asterisk denotes an antibonding function (and the roman letter is somewhat misleading—see the table on p. 349). Wave functions prefixed by an asterisk in the linear combinations should, perhaps, be shown with a coefficient less than unity. Levels 4 and 5 are degenerate, also 6 and 7. It is interesting to take an electronic formula as understood by chemists, and number the electrons according to their levels, thus

but the picture must not be taken too seriously, even when it is understood, for example, that the pairs shown above and below the symbol are actually at right angles ('above, in the paper' and 'below, behind the paper').

(NOTE: Coulson (*Chem. Soc. Quart. Rev.* 1947, p. 149) states clearly that in a 'digonally prepared atom'—i.e. an atom with its wave functions appropriately arranged for a c_∞ perturbation—the ψ_{2s} and ψ_{2p_z} functions are *equally* mixed, but in discussing molecules (cf. his fig. 6, p. 156) he omits the terms asterisked in the above table—i.e. does not mix these functions at all; the latter is implied in the spectroscopic notation, and the former raises difficulties in identifying which is which of 2 and 3 above. I have assumed the truth to be somewhere between these two, since the former is certainly qualitatively true. But the doubt remains whether it is fair to write the electrons in 3 'in the bond'. Electrons in 4, 5, 6, and 7 undoubtedly are so nearly equivalent *in toto* to the $2p_x$ and $2p_y$ electrons in the isolated atoms that they can be written off as contributing nothing to the bond, but electrons in 1, 2, and 3 are four bonding and two antibonding, and it is probably unreasonable to ask whether the electrons in 1 counteract those in 2 and those in 3 form the bond, or vice versa. A point for chemists which we shall take up later is to avoid the assumption that the pairs of electrons, whether shared or unshared, are tetrahedrally arranged.)

The oxygen molecule, with twelve electrons to distribute in these eight wave functions, is a classic triumph of the molecular orbital approach. In both atoms and molecules the rule that electrons take the lowest free orbitals is supplemented, if there is a choice between degenerate levels, by Hund's rule that electrons take different levels with parallel spins rather than the same level with opposed spins. This choice occurs here; levels 1–5 are therefore completely filled, and one electron goes into each of 6 and 7, with parallel spins. This accounts for the paramagnetism of oxygen. In levels 4–7 there are now four bonding and two antibonding electrons, the situation in levels 1–3 being as before. Thus the 'double bond' in oxygen is half caused by the excess of bonding over antibonding electrons in the σ wave functions and half by the similar situation in the π functions. We therefore refer to this situation as one σ bond and one π bond. It should be noticed that the common description of a valency bond as the coming together of unpaired electrons on the atoms into one (molecular) level with paired spins, while true enough of most σ bonds, is emphatically saying too much if applied to the π bond of this molecule.

As typical unsymmetrical molecules we could take CO or HCl. In the former, the same functions as discussed above are available, in a qualitative sense—that is, symmetry requirements demand that functions 1–3 and 8 remain distinct from functions 4–7, but in the absence of the mirror plane we have greater liberty to prefix coefficients. These must be prefixed (a) so that the four functions in each symmetry type remain orthogonal to one another, and (b) in such a way that the largest coefficients in any function are prefixed to terms of originally comparable energy. Thus Coulson (loc. cit.) argues that since the O2s level is the lowest, O2p and C2s about equal, and C2p the highest, function 1 will be mainly O2s, function 2 compounded of O2p and C2s with like signs, function 3 will be mainly C2p, and function 4 (which he does not mention) compounded of O2p and C2s with unlike signs. The last is unoccupied. He then discusses spectroscopic data on the energy levels which suggests that the $w\pi$ electrons, especially when there are four of them present, are not as binding as we might have guessed, which accounts for some of the problems connected with carbon monoxide.

We refer to HCl only to mention that here the comparable energy levels are the 1 (K) level in H and the 3 (M) level in Cl. Thus the K and L levels in Cl are too deep to be affected appreciably, and we deal with linear combinations of $\psi_{\mathrm{H}1s}$ with any of the $\psi_{\mathrm{Cl}3}$ which has σ symmetry—viz. $\psi_{\mathrm{Cl}3s}$, $\psi_{\mathrm{Cl}3p_z}$, and $\psi_{\mathrm{Cl}3d\sigma}$, probably mainly the second of these, in which case the formal description of the ground state of HCl is

$$\mathrm{HCl}[KL(3s)^2(\sigma3p)^2(3p_x)^2(3p_y)^2],$$

$$\sigma3p = \psi_{\mathrm{H}1s} + c\,\psi_{\mathrm{Cl}3p_z};\ \text{others pure Cl functions.}$$

In concluding this part of the subject we should remember that whatever results we may obtain for our wave functions, they should be antisymmetrized in all the electrons after spin coordinates have been assigned In the case of factorizable approximations this can be done in determinant form as in (16.10.9). To a very large extent, however, this is unnecessary in view of Theorem 16.10.3, which says that we get the same charge distribution even if we neglect to do this. For this reason there is no harm, for most purposes, in still talking of the $F_A 1s$ electrons in F_2 (= $F_A F_B$), for example. The $F_A 1s$ wave function is not an eigenfunction of this system, and if we 'removed an $F_A 1s$ electron' by any means we should, by dynamic perturbation theory, find that after a time it was an $F_B 1s$ electron that was missing. The time required is directly related to the magnitude in the split of the energy level, and so

far as the electrons in the bond are concerned, where large energy changes
are involved, is so small that it would be meaningless to use this form
of description at all.

When we turn to more complicated molecules we find that chemists
have for nearly a century made great progress on the assumption that
the same type of binding that occurs in diatomic molecules occurs in all
molecules. The concept has developed, naturally. In 1916, Lewis put
forward the theory that every valency bond was a pair of shared electrons,
and although at first it was possible for Sidgwick to comment that what
chemists meant by an electron and what physicists meant could hardly
be recognized as the same object, the situation was gradually improved.
But the chemists have always felt free to interpret valency in terms of
chemical reactions, and rightly so, and in consequence there are many
features of valency, such as the tetrahedral distribution of the four
bonds of a carbon atom, which have arisen completely from the chemical
side.

In a molecule such as $\begin{smallmatrix} Cl \\ \diagdown \\ \diagup \\ I \end{smallmatrix}$ C$=$N—O—H, it is not difficult to see how

our present ideas are to be extended. The deeper levels of each atom are
all different, and in the space occupied by a bond the electrostatic field
is similar to that in a diatomic molecule. Thus those wave functions
which were found to be valid for diatomic molecules should still be valid
provided they are concentrated in the space in which the approximation
to the field holds good. But these were just those which made up the
bond; the wave functions which were concentrated outside that volume
were the antibonding ones in every case. And there is no degeneracy.
But such molecules are rare. In most molecules there is degeneracy and
often there is symmetry. As regards degeneracy, say, of the $1s$ functions
on the various carbon atoms of an organic compound, our remarks two
paragraphs back will hold, and we need not worry. The molecules where
different approaches need reconciliation are the highly symmetrical ones.
We shall illustrate the situation by a discussion of tetrahedral molecules
such as CH_4, CCl_4, etc., in the next section. We conclude this one with
a discussion of nomenclature, which is rendered rather necessary by the
somewhat bewildering way in which various methods of approximation
are used in succession.

The key processes are the approximate method of § 16.10 and the variation method. We recognize these if we make the following definitions:

A *state* is an exact solution to an n-electron problem.

An *orbital* is an exact solution to a one-electron problem.

A *screened orbital* is an orbital in which, in applying it to an n-electron problem, the nuclear charges are replaced by alternative quantities chosen to minimize the energy integral.

The adjectives *atomic* and *molecular* as applied to any of the above should need no particular definition.

An *orbital product* is a first approximation to a state obtained by multiplying together n orbitals.

An *asp*, or antisymmetrized product, is the result of antisymmetrizing an orbital product with respect to all the electrons. A *screened asp* is one in which the orbitals are screened. It is the closest approximation to a state which does not contain the inter-electronic distances explicitly.

A *variant* is an approximation to an orbital consisting of a linear combination of functions whose coefficients are chosen to minimize the energy integral. *Sensu strictu* it will be a linear combination of atomic orbitals approximating to a molecular orbital. We introduce this word diffidently in protest against the habit of calling such a function by the unpronounceable combination of initials *LCAO*. It can be used as an adjective, and normally a variant asp will be an asp in which the orbitals are not exact but are variants *sensu strictu*, whereas a variant state will be a direct approximation to a state such as that of James and Coolidge to H_2.

A *localized* orbital is a wave function which satisfies the one-electron problem approximately because it satisfies a simpler problem in which the potential field is the same at all points where the orbital is not vanishingly small (but may be different elsewhere). A localized biorbital (m-orbital) similarly satisfies a two (m) electron problem. A valency bond is a localized biorbital, as a rule.

17.4. Tetrahedral molecules

The principal aim of the discussion which follows is clarification of the situation which is produced by our varying methods of arriving at an approximate solution to the structure of a highly symmetrical molecule, and a number of the details of the discussion which have very little relevance to actual molecules are introduced in furtherance of this aim. Typical tetrahedral molecules are CH_4, CF_4, CCl_4, $SiCl_4$, etc. We shall refer to CF_4 in general, but introduce others as and when the argument requires.

We start with the nuclei in their places, and consider the molecular orbitals. It will help to imagine the equipotential surfaces drawn in, as their appearance is sufficient to indicate both actual and approximate types of symmetry. As the nuclear framework has the symmetry T_d ($\overline{4}3m$), five types of orbital are possible, A, D, E, U, and T. At a great distance from the nuclei the equipotential surfaces will be almost spherical and appropriate to a central charge equal to the sum of the nuclear charges. The orbitals will be approximately the high quantum number orbitals of the united atom, in degenerate sets of n^2 (excluding spin) describable as ns, np, nd,... (1, 3, 5,...-fold degenerate); Table 16.9.2 (column T_d with p and f derivatives barred) shows that more accurately they will be nsA, npU (3-fold), ndE (2-fold), ndU (3-fold), etc. Close in to the central atom the same will be true. The $1s$ orbital will be distorted from spherical symmetry into an A type orbital but will be recognizable as the $1s$ orbital. If the central atom is Si (but not if it is C) the next shell will also be recognizable as a shell—$2s$ and $2p$ types distorted into $2A$ and $2T$ types.

Around an F nucleus the $1s$ orbitals will again be recognizable but the distortion will be different. The major perturbation—that due to the central atom—will reduce the symmetry from r_3 to $C_{\infty v}$, and a smaller one, due to the other three fluorine atoms, will reduce it still further to C_{3v} ($3m$). But neither an F$1s$ orbital nor any distortion of it is a molecular orbital, since it does not conform to any representation of T_d. Labelling the four fluorine atoms F_1,..., F_4, the four orbitals $F_1 1s$,..., $F_4 1s$ constitute a representation of T_d. We write these four orbitals as components of a four-vector, and consider that as the symmetry operations of T_d permute these orbitals, they will act on this vector in the form of permutation matrices. (This would be an oversimplification in some cases—see p orbitals, below—but is valid here.) The character of a permutation matrix being the number of elements left unchanged, the character of this representation will be

$$
\begin{array}{ccccc}
I & 3C_2 & 8C_3 & 6m & 6S_4 \\
4 & 0 & 1 & 2 & 0 = A \dotplus U.
\end{array}
\qquad (17.4.1)
$$

The combination $\frac{1}{2}(F_1 1s + F_2 1s + F_3 1s + F_4 1s)$ shows the representation A, and any three combinations forming an orthonormal set with this one will constitute the U. One set is

$$
\begin{aligned}
A: \quad & \tfrac{1}{2}(F_1 1s + F_2 1s + F_3 1s + F_4 1s) \\
U: \quad & \left\{
\begin{array}{l}
\tfrac{1}{2}(F_1 1s + F_2 1s - F_3 1s - F_4 1s) \\
\tfrac{1}{2}(F_1 1s - F_2 1s + F_3 1s - F_4 1s) \\
\tfrac{1}{2}(F_1 1s - F_2 1s - F_3 1s + F_4 1s).
\end{array}
\right.
\end{aligned}
\qquad (17.4.2)
$$

These are therefore correct zeroth approximations to molecular orbitals. They are variants *sensu strictu* in which the coefficients have been determined by group-theoretic principles instead of by applying the variation method and solving the secular equation. The three U orbitals are strictly degenerate, and all four are so to a first approximation. If they are all filled they are exactly equivalent to the four atomic orbitals from which they have been built, but if an electron is removed it will be possible spectroscopically to say whether it came from the A or U orbitals, and impossible to say from which fluorine it came.

In CCl_4 the second quantum groups of the chlorine atoms contain, when isolated, four orbitals each, one s and three p, and will still be recognizable. In CBr_4 the third group will also be recognizable. Abstracting from Table 16.9.2 the sequence r_3, c_∞, c_3 already discussed, we can say that any orbital of the halogen atom (F, Cl, Br, etc.) which degenerates into an A type of c_3, will combine with corresponding orbitals of the other halogen atoms in a similar manner to the $1s$ orbitals as set out in (17.4.2). The π type, or any other type which degenerates into the $\mathscr{E}$ type of c_3, need further investigation. As this is somewhat elaborate and rather academic, we postpone it until the rest of the picture is complete.

Needless to say, if the central atom is Si or Sn, its 2, or its 2 and 3, quantum orbitals remain recognizable as such, but are distorted and possibly split into different levels, s orbitals becoming A, p becoming T, and d becoming $E + U$. The change of nomenclature of the s and p orbitals reflects the distortion, but there is no splitting; the d level splits into two.

But between the inner and outer regions of approximately spherical symmetry there are regions where the equipotential surfaces are not even approximately spherical. In one sense this does not matter. In quantitative perturbation theory it is bad to begin with too crude an approximation, but in group theoretic analysis the magnitude of the perturbation is irrelevant. Nevertheless, not all valid analyses are useful! In the present case, useful analysis of the intermediate regions commences with the approximation that the symmetry is $C_{\infty v}$ in the space immediately surrounding the line joining the C nucleus to any F nucleus, that is, that the circumstances of the C—F bond in CF_4 are not so different from those of the bond in a diatomic molecule, or in a molecule which shows no symmetry whatever. Both of these have been discussed in the previous section. The primary question here is that of the polyvalency of the central atom. Briefly, is it possible for four orbitals originally designed as isolated orbitals of four diatomic molecules to function as orbitals in a tetrahedral five-atom system of tetrahedral symmetry ?

Lennard-Jones has discussed this problem. As they do not conform separately to a representation of the symmetry group of the molecule they cannot separately be (even approximations to) molecular orbitals. But all four of them together are merely permuted by the group and thus form a representation of the group. The subsequent calculation is identical with that by means of which we discussed the F1s orbitals. The four bonds are equivalent to one A and three U molecular orbitals. (More precisely, if by 'bond' we mean a localized biorbital of the system, then the four bonds are equivalent to one A and three U molecular biorbitals to the same degree of approximation as is implied by the word 'localized', though that word can now hardly be used to express the approximation. If to 'bond' we give a Heitler–London interpretation, then a different but similar interpretation is possible.)

These may be thought of as distorted s and p orbitals of the central atom, but this is to ignore the contribution of the F orbitals to the bond. Pauling's treatment is classical here. He started with one $2s$ and three $2p$ orbitals of the C atom and formed from them the hybrids

$$\left.\begin{aligned}
\phi_1 &= \tfrac{1}{2}(s+p_x+p_y+p_z)\\
\phi_2 &= \tfrac{1}{2}(s+p_x-p_y-p_z)\\
\phi_3 &= \tfrac{1}{2}(s-p_x+p_y-p_z)\\
\phi_4 &= \tfrac{1}{2}(s-p_x-p_y+p_z)
\end{aligned}\right\}, \tag{17.4.3}$$

showed that they are directed tetrahedrally, and combined each separately with an orbital of the corresponding F atom (of σ symmetry) to obtain four bonds—i.e. to form four localized molecular variants,

$$\left.\begin{aligned}
V_1 &= \tfrac{1}{2}c^{\frac{1}{2}}(s+p_x+p_y+p_z)+(1-c)^{\frac{1}{2}}\mathrm{F}_1\,2\sigma\\
V_2 &= \tfrac{1}{2}c^{\frac{1}{2}}(s+p_x-p_y-p_z)+(1-c)^{\frac{1}{2}}\mathrm{F}_2\,2\sigma\\
V_3 &= \tfrac{1}{2}c^{\frac{1}{2}}(s-p_x+p_y-p_z)+(1-c)^{\frac{1}{2}}\mathrm{F}_3\,2\sigma\\
V_4 &= \tfrac{1}{2}c^{\frac{1}{2}}(s-p_x-p_y+p_z)+(1-c)^{\frac{1}{2}}\mathrm{F}_4\,2\sigma
\end{aligned}\right\}. \tag{17.4.4}$$

But we now see that the molecular variants are to be obtained by combining these with each other according to equation (17.4.2), giving

$$\begin{aligned}
A:\quad &c^{\frac{1}{2}}\mathrm{C}2s\ +(1-c)^{\frac{1}{2}}(\mathrm{F}_1\,2\sigma+\mathrm{F}_2\,2\sigma+\mathrm{F}_3\,2\sigma+\mathrm{F}_4\,2\sigma)\\
U:\quad &\left\{\begin{aligned}
c^{\frac{1}{2}}\mathrm{C}2p_x&+(1-c)^{\frac{1}{2}}(\mathrm{F}_1\,2\sigma+\mathrm{F}_2\,2\sigma-\mathrm{F}_3\,2\sigma-\mathrm{F}_4\,2\sigma)\\
c^{\frac{1}{2}}\mathrm{C}2p_y&+(1-c)^{\frac{1}{2}}(\mathrm{F}_1\,2\sigma-\mathrm{F}_2\,2\sigma+\mathrm{F}_3\,2\sigma-\mathrm{F}_4\,2\sigma)\\
c^{\frac{1}{2}}\mathrm{C}2p_z&+(1-c)^{\frac{1}{2}}(\mathrm{F}_1\,2\sigma-\mathrm{F}_2\,2\sigma-\mathrm{F}_3\,2\sigma+\mathrm{F}_4\,2\sigma)
\end{aligned}\right\}
\end{aligned} \tag{17.4.5}$$

as the molecular variants. (In these expressions we have restored the

C which was omitted for simplicity in (17.4.3) which dealt only with the carbon atom.)

Pauling's original hybridization of the s and p orbitals was criticized at the time as invalid in mixing orbitals of different symmetry types. It will be seen that this objection disappears in the final result, where the functions are variants constructed from one symmetry type only, and his method is thus justified heuristically. The generalization of his method opens the question whether it is possible in a given case to construct functions of the right type from atomic orbitals—apart from providing an affirmative answer by actually constructing such functions. The general answer which group theory provides to this question has been discussed by Kimball and we shall consider it in the next section.

We return to the problem of molecular variants constructed from π orbitals of the halogen atoms. As before we call the fluorine atoms

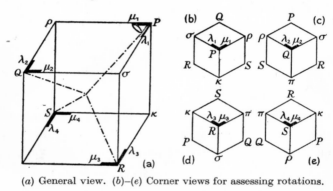

(a) General view. (b)–(e) Corner views for assessing rotations.

Fig. 29.

$F_1,..., F_4$ and we call the π orbitals $\lambda_1, \mu_1, \lambda_2,..., \mu_4$. A tricky problem at the outset is how to define these initially to our greatest advantage. They have positive and negative lobes on either side of the C—F bond, to which they are perpendicular. Since λ_i and μ_i are degenerate they may be chosen oblique—i.e. their lobes not at right angles and the functions not orthogonal—if it suits us, and since at this stage matrices with integral elements are more advantageous than orthogonal orbitals, we shall choose $\lambda_1,..., \mu_4$ as shown in Fig. 29, which represents the carbon atom as the centre of a cube, the fluorine atoms being just inside four of its corners, P, Q, R, S, the diagonally opposite corners $\pi, \kappa, \rho, \sigma$ being empty, and the valency bonds marked in chain line. To render the perspective clearer the orbitals themselves are not marked in, but the positive lobe of the orbital is understood to be the resolved part, perpendicular to the bond, of the appropriately labelled short thick line. (The lobe of μ_1 only is shown to clarify this.) The orbitals as thus defined are at $120°$ to each other, and the matrices of the rotation group c_3 are those referred to in § 9.6 but left to the student to derive. The only part of this which concerns us at the moment, however, is that if the cube is rotated about P so that R moves to Q, Q to S, and S to R, etc., λ_1, which is along $P\sigma$, is rotated into μ_1, along $P\rho$, whereas μ_1, rotated into something along $P\kappa$, is thus rotated into $-(\lambda_1+\mu_1)$, which we shall denote for short by s_1. (The expression 'directed along' refers to the conventional direction of the thick line in the diagram, not to the true direction of the lobe, but our statement that μ_1 becomes $-(\lambda_1+\mu_1)$ is only true of the component perpendicular to the valency bond.)

It is now a straightforward matter to tabulate the effect of each operator in T_d on each of these orbitals.

	P	Q	R	S	λ_1	μ_1	λ_2	μ_2	λ_3	μ_3	λ_4	μ_4
I	P	Q	R	S	λ_1	μ_1	λ_2	μ_2	λ_3	μ_3	λ_4	μ_4
	Q	P	S	R	λ_2	μ_2	λ_1	μ_1	λ_4	μ_4	λ_3	μ_3
$3C_2$	R	S	P	Q	λ_3	μ_3	λ_4	μ_4	λ_1	μ_1	λ_2	μ_2
	S	R	Q	P	λ_4	μ_4	λ_3	μ_3	λ_2	μ_2	λ_1	μ_1
	P	S	Q	R	μ_1	s_1	μ_4	s_4	μ_2	s_2	μ_3	s_3
	P	R	S	Q	s_1	λ_1	s_3	λ_3	s_4	λ_4	s_2	λ_2
	R	Q	S	P	μ_3	s_3	μ_2	s_2	μ_4	s_4	μ_1	s_1
$8C_3$	S	Q	P	R	s_4	λ_4	s_2	λ_2	s_1	λ_1	s_3	λ_3
	S	P	R	Q	μ_4	s_4	μ_1	s_1	μ_3	s_3	μ_2	s_2
	Q	S	R	P	s_2	λ_2	s_4	λ_4	s_3	λ_3	s_1	λ_1
	Q	R	P	S	μ_2	s_2	μ_3	s_3	μ_1	s_1	μ_4	s_4
	R	P	Q	S	s_3	λ_3	s_1	λ_1	s_2	λ_2	s_4	λ_4
	P	Q	S	R	μ_1	λ_1	μ_2	λ_2	μ_4	λ_4	μ_3	λ_3
	Q	P	R	S	μ_2	λ_2	μ_1	λ_1	μ_3	λ_3	μ_4	λ_4
$6m$	P	S	R	Q	s_1	μ_1	s_4	μ_4	s_3	μ_3	s_2	μ_2
	R	Q	P	S	s_3	μ_3	s_2	μ_2	s_1	μ_1	s_4	μ_4
	P	R	Q	S	λ_1	s_1	λ_3	s_3	λ_2	s_2	λ_4	s_4
	S	Q	R	P	λ_4	s_4	λ_2	s_2	λ_3	s_3	λ_1	s_1
	R	S	Q	P	μ_3	λ_3	μ_4	λ_4	μ_2	λ_2	μ_1	λ_1
	S	R	P	Q	μ_4	λ_4	μ_3	λ_3	μ_1	λ_1	μ_2	λ_2
$6S_4$	S	P	Q	R	s_4	μ_4	s_1	μ_1	s_2	μ_2	s_3	μ_3
	Q	R	S	P	s_2	μ_2	s_3	μ_3	s_4	μ_4	s_1	μ_1
	R	P	S	Q	λ_3	s_3	λ_1	s_1	λ_4	s_4	λ_2	s_2
	Q	S	P	R	λ_2	s_2	λ_4	s_4	λ_1	s_1	λ_3	s_3

This table can be translated into matrix form. Translating one from each class, the characters are found to be

$$I \quad 3C_2 \quad 8C_3 \quad 6m \quad 6S_4$$
$$8 \quad\quad 0 \quad\quad -1 \quad\quad 0 \quad\quad 0 = E \dotplus T \dotplus U.$$

This eightfold level, therefore, under the mutual interaction of the electrons, splits up into three—one twofold and two threefold levels. We proceed to find the correct zeroth approximations to these levels by a straightforward step by step application of the principles in Part I.

We first determine the matrices of the classes, which can be read off from the table on the previous page by summing each column over each class. Thus the third (λ_2) column entries in the class $6m$ sum to

$$\mu_2 + \mu_1 + s_4 + s_2 + \lambda_3 + \lambda_2 = \mu_1 + \lambda_3 - \lambda_4 - \mu_4,$$

and the coefficients in this expression (including zeros) give the third column of the matrix below for $6m$. The results are

$$I = \begin{bmatrix} 1 & 0 & 0 & 0 & 0 & 0 & 0 & 0 \\ 0 & 1 & 0 & 0 & 0 & 0 & 0 & 0 \\ 0 & 0 & 1 & 0 & 0 & 0 & 0 & 0 \\ 0 & 0 & 0 & 1 & 0 & 0 & 0 & 0 \\ 0 & 0 & 0 & 0 & 1 & 0 & 0 & 0 \\ 0 & 0 & 0 & 0 & 0 & 1 & 0 & 0 \\ 0 & 0 & 0 & 0 & 0 & 0 & 1 & 0 \\ 0 & 0 & 0 & 0 & 0 & 0 & 0 & 1 \end{bmatrix} \quad 3C_2 = \begin{bmatrix} 0 & 0 & 1 & 0 & 1 & 0 & 1 & 0 \\ 0 & 0 & 0 & 1 & 0 & 1 & 0 & 1 \\ 1 & 0 & 0 & 0 & 1 & 0 & 1 & 0 \\ 0 & 1 & 0 & 0 & 0 & 1 & 0 & 1 \\ 1 & 0 & 1 & 0 & 0 & 0 & 1 & 0 \\ 0 & 1 & 0 & 1 & 0 & 0 & 0 & 1 \\ 1 & 0 & 1 & 0 & 1 & 0 & 0 & 0 \\ 0 & 1 & 0 & 1 & 0 & 1 & 0 & 0 \end{bmatrix}$$

$$8C_3 = \begin{bmatrix} -1 & 0 & -1 & 0 & -1 & 0 & -1 & 0 \\ 0 & -1 & 0 & -1 & 0 & -1 & 0 & -1 \\ -1 & 0 & -1 & 0 & -1 & 0 & -1 & 0 \\ 0 & -1 & 0 & -1 & 0 & -1 & 0 & -1 \\ -1 & 0 & -1 & 0 & -1 & 0 & -1 & 0 \\ 0 & -1 & 0 & -1 & 0 & -1 & 0 & -1 \\ -1 & 0 & -1 & 0 & -1 & 0 & -1 & 0 \\ 0 & -1 & 0 & -1 & 0 & -1 & 0 & -1 \end{bmatrix} \quad 6m = -6S_4 = \begin{bmatrix} 0 & 0 & 0 & 1 & -1 & 0 & 1 & -1 \\ 0 & 0 & 1 & 0 & -1 & 1 & 0 & -1 \\ 0 & 1 & 0 & 0 & 1 & -1 & -1 & 0 \\ 1 & 0 & 0 & 0 & 0 & -1 & -1 & 1 \\ -1 & 0 & 1 & -1 & 0 & 0 & 0 & 1 \\ -1 & 1 & 0 & -1 & 0 & 0 & 1 & 0 \\ 1 & -1 & -1 & 0 & 0 & 1 & 0 & 0 \\ 0 & -1 & -1 & 1 & 1 & 0 & 0 & 0 \end{bmatrix}$$

From these we calculate the primitive idempotents by (5.5.2) and (5.5.4). Two of them,

$$I_{[4]} = \tfrac{1}{24}(I + 3C_2 + 8C_3 + 6m + 6S_4), \quad I_{[1^4]} = \tfrac{1}{24}(I + 3C_2 + 8C_3 - 6m - 6S_4),$$

are identically zero; this is because the corresponding irreducible representations, A and D, are not found in our eight-dimensional representation. $I_{[2^2]} = \tfrac{1}{12}(2I + 2 \cdot 3C_2 - 8C_3)$ is equal to minus one-quarter the matrix given above for $8C_3$, and the other two are

$$I_{[21^2]} = \tfrac{1}{8}(3I - 3C_2 - 6m + 6S_4)$$

$$= \tfrac{1}{8}\begin{bmatrix} 3 & 0 & -1 & -2 & 1 & 0 & -3 & 2 \\ 0 & 3 & -2 & -1 & 2 & -3 & 0 & 1 \\ -1 & -2 & 3 & 0 & -3 & 2 & 1 & 0 \\ -2 & -1 & 0 & 3 & 0 & 1 & 2 & -3 \\ 1 & 0 & -3 & 2 & 3 & 0 & -1 & -2 \\ 2 & -3 & 0 & 1 & 0 & 3 & -2 & -1 \\ -3 & 2 & 1 & 0 & -1 & -2 & 3 & 0 \\ 0 & 1 & 2 & -3 & -2 & -1 & 0 & 3 \end{bmatrix},$$

$$I_{[31]} = \tfrac{1}{8}(3I - 3C_2 + 6m - 6S_4)$$

$$= \tfrac{1}{8}\begin{bmatrix} 3 & 0 & -1 & 2 & -3 & 0 & 1 & -2 \\ 0 & 3 & 2 & -1 & -2 & 1 & 0 & -3 \\ -1 & 2 & 3 & 0 & 1 & -2 & -3 & 0 \\ 2 & -1 & 0 & 3 & 0 & -3 & -2 & 1 \\ -3 & 0 & 1 & -2 & 3 & 0 & -1 & 2 \\ -2 & 1 & 0 & -3 & 0 & 3 & 2 & -1 \\ 1 & -2 & -3 & 0 & -1 & 2 & 3 & 0 \\ 0 & -3 & -2 & 1 & 2 & -1 & 0 & 3 \end{bmatrix}$$

It will be noticed that these matrices are unsymmetrical. This is due to our employment of a non-orthogonal reference system. It carries with it the implication that we must pay heed to the distinction between contravariant (column) and covariant (row) vectors. The idempotents we have calculated, operating upon an arbitrary vector, project it on to the space in which the corresponding representations are displayed. This is true of the vectors $(0, 0, ..., 1, ..., 0, 0)$, whence every column of one of these matrices is a vector in the representation associated with it. The rows likewise pick out the representations in terms of the basic set reciprocal to the one defined by Fig. 29. Thus to obtain a p-dimensional representation which occurs once only we have only to pick out p independent columns from the corresponding idempotent. (The orthogonality of the vectors to those from another representation can be checked by forming the scalar produced with *covariant* vectors from the second representation.)

While this is a complete solution when $p = 1$, when $p > 1$ an element of choice remains, and it is advantageous to use this to display each representation in a form capable of easy physical interpretation. Two methods of doing this suggest themselves. (1) E is the representation of π_4 by the representation Γ_3 of its factor group π_3, in which, by suitable choice of axes, any given m can be given the matrix $\begin{bmatrix} 1 & 0 \\ 0 & -1 \end{bmatrix}$. Take any m therefore—say the first in the table on p. 363, and multiply its matrix as given in that table by $I_{[2^2]}$. The resulting matrix will have six eigenvectors, one with eigenvalue 1, one -1, and six 0. The latter are the vectors belonging to other representations; the two former will be comparatively readily given a physical interpretation in relation to the chosen m. As the only possible real eigenvalues of a rotation are ± 1 we cannot expect one single rotation to separate out a three-dimensional representation so easily. It is accordingly better to determine the unique eigenvector (with eigenvalue $+1$) of *each* of the $3C_2$. (These commute, so can be simultaneously diagonal, but even if they did not, it would only mean that our resulting orbitals would not be orthogonal.) (2) Alternatively, by inspection of the idempotents, we may combine the columns in such a way as to produce the requisite number of independent vectors which 'look nice'—i.e. have a maximum of symmetry and small numbers in their make-up. For example, from $I_{[21^2]}$, we can form

Columns: 1+2	1+3	2+3
3	2	-1
3	-2	1
-3	2	1
-3	-2	-1
1	-2	-3
-1	2	-3
-1	-2	3
1	2	3

and these can be given physical interpretation fairly readily—first interpreting $\lambda_i + \mu_i$ (this we have already done: it is $-s_i$) and $\lambda_i - \mu_i$, for which see Fig. 29.

The following choice is therefore somewhat arbitrary, but no choice would not be. The eight levels can be combined into correct zeroth approximations to molecular orbitals in the following way:

$$E_1 \quad \lambda_1 + \lambda_2 + \lambda_3 + \lambda_4$$
$$E_2 \quad \mu_1 + \mu_2 + \mu_3 + \mu_4$$
$$T_1 \quad 3(\lambda_1 + \mu_1) - 3(\lambda_2 + \mu_2) + (\lambda_3 - \mu_3) - (\lambda_4 - \mu_4)$$
$$T_2 \quad (\lambda_1 - \mu_1) - (\lambda_2 - \mu_2) + 3(\lambda_3 + \mu_3) - 3(\lambda_4 + \mu_4)$$
$$T_3 \quad (\lambda_1 - \mu_1) + (\lambda_2 - \mu_2) - (\lambda_3 - \mu_3) - (\lambda_4 - \mu_4)$$
$$U_1 \quad (\lambda_1 + \mu_1) + (\lambda_2 + \mu_2) - (\lambda_3 + \mu_3) - (\lambda_4 + \mu_4)$$
$$U_2 \quad (\lambda_1 + \mu_1) - (\lambda_2 + \mu_2) - (\lambda_3 - \mu_3) + (\lambda_4 - \mu_4)$$
$$U_3 \quad (\lambda_1 - \mu_1) - (\lambda_2 - \mu_2) - (\lambda_3 + \mu_3) + (\lambda_4 + \mu_4).$$

Other permissible choices mix the above E's, T's, and U's among themselves, but not among one another. (The expressions *within* each representation are not necessarily orthogonal.)

17.5. Covalency maxima and stereochemistry

The procedure for converting localized orbitals into molecular orbitals which we have ascribed to Lennard-Jones is very similar to one applied earlier by G. E. Kimball to the problems of stereochemistry and covalency maxima. In effect, it takes four orbitals to make a bond, two filled and two unfilled. The process can be illustrated thus, a vertical axis representing energy level:

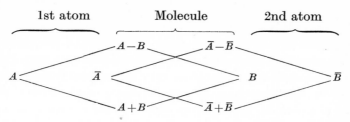

| | 1st atom | | Molecule | | 2nd atom | |

For this process to take place, A and B must have the same symmetry about the (geometrical) bond, and the bonding orbitals $A+B$ and $\bar{A}+\bar{B}$ must be filled, but the antibonding orbitals $A-B$ and $\bar{A}-\bar{B}$ must be empty. Our discussion of Pauling's hybridization process can be generalized; a set of bonds—i.e. a set of localized biorbitals—is equivalent to a certain set of molecular orbitals. In order to build these bonds the central atom must provide atomic orbitals which are exactly equivalent in symmetry. In a tetrahedral molecule the four bonds are equivalent to molecular orbitals $A+U$, and to form them the central atom must provide atomic orbitals of this symmetry, to build which, one s and three p orbitals suffice. In dealing with σ bonds the procedure is straightforward; we regard the bonds as permuted by the operations of the symmetry group, analyse the representation into its irreducible components, and refer to Table 16.9.2. As regards π bonds, permutation is an oversimplification, but, as illustrated in the previous section, the underlying principle is the same, and unless we want explicit forms for the bonds it is unnecessary to analyse as fully as we did there; each pair of π bonds contributes to the character

2	if unchanged by the operation,
$2 \cos \phi$	if merely rotated about the geometrical bond,
0	if permuted with another bond.

In view of the extension to Table 16.9.2 occasioned by our discussion of spin, it suffices, if this analysis shows that an orbital with symmetry P is required, if either P or $\bar{P}$ is found in the table.

Before embarking on the analyses themselves, it is necessary to remember that interaction between the electrons profoundly alters the order of the energy levels. Elementary theory, ignoring this interaction, shows all 1 levels as degenerate, all 2 levels, and so on, but owing to this interaction, if electrons are added one by one to an atom, they enter the orbitals in the order

$$1s \quad 2s \quad 2p \quad 3s \quad 3p \quad 4s \quad 3d \quad 4p \quad 5s \quad 4d \quad 5p \quad 6s \quad 4f \quad 5d \quad 6p \quad ...$$

i.e. each level in this sequence is the lowest free level if all the preceding ones have been filled. The degeneracy within any of the above levels effectively remains. This order, which is quite different from the order of levels in the one-electron problem, may be deduced from the periodic variation in the properties of the elements with atomic number known as the periodic law, or from spectroscopic evidence, and has in some cases been verified by calculation. In certain cases, particularly where there is a reversal of the order of the principal quantum numbers, adjacent levels in this list are not much separated, and valency bond formation, or a change in the distribution of nuclear charges, may suffice to invert them. The importance of this list arises from the fact that the requisite conditions for the mixing of orbitals are (1) symmetry requirements, and (2) approximate equality of energy. Our present calculations examine (1), and to satisfy (2) we must choose adjacent terms in the above sequence.

The molecule is held together by its σ bonds, so that for a molecule to be possible it is essential that the proposed arrangement of σ bonds is possible. Except in one case, which we deal with in the next section, the formation of π bonds is merely an additional luxury. The more π bonds are possible, the greater will be the stability of the molecule, since every bond means two electrons in a lower energy level than they would be able to occupy in the isolated atoms. This will affect heats of formation, and stability towards molecules of attacking reagents. If the calculation shows that some but not all of the molecular orbitals required for equivalence to a complete set of π bonds are available, and the number of electrons available permits of filling some of these, we shall have a situation which cannot be described in terms of double bond formulae, though the single bond formulae will be meaningful. These are the cases which the inorganic chemist has been accustomed to deal with by writing some of the bonds as double and others as single, while invoking 'resonance' to maintain symmetry. We deal with the corresponding situation in organic chemistry in the next section. But the two are hardly comparable, for the states between which resonance is assumed to occur are, in organic chemistry, almost always natural formulations. In particular, charges rarely appear except on four-covalent nitrogen atoms and other atoms for which parallel behaviour of an unequivocable nature can be found. Resonance states suggested for simple inorganic molecules often show wild movements of charge within the molecule, at least formally. It is to be hoped that one outcome of studies along the lines of this section will be the devising of a satisfactory notation for molecules in which there are filled π orbitals but too few of them for the alternative bond notation to present the situation satisfactorily.

The following results are mostly from Kimball's paper, adapted to our notation for representations and to our presentation of electron spin. A few examples will show their use.

TABLE 17.5.1: CONVERSION OF BONDS TO MOLECULAR ORBITALS

No. and arrangement of bonds		Symmetry	σ-Bonds		π-Bonds M.O.'s
			M.O.'s	A.O.'s	
a 2	linear	$D_{\infty h}$	$\sigma_+\ \sigma_-$	sp pd	π^2
b	angular	C_{2v}	AD_2	sp p^2 pd	ABD_1D_2
c 3	trigonal	D_{3h}	AE	sp^2 dp^2	BD_2EF
d	triangular pyramid	C_{3v}	AE	sp^2 p^3 dp^2	ABE^2
e	as b+one axial bond	C_{2v}	A^2D_2	sp^2 dp^2	$ABD_1^2D_2^2$
f 4	tetrahedral	T_d	AU	sp^3 fp^3	ETU
g	square (tetragonal)	D_{4h}	AC_1E	sp^2d p^2d^2 d^4	$B^2C_2^2E^2$
h	tetragonal pyramid	C_{4v}	AC_1E	sp^2d p^2d^2 p^3d	$ABC_1C_2E^2$
i	as d+one axial bond	C_{3v}	A^2E	sp^3 sp^2d dp^3	ABE^3
j 5	trigonal bipyramid	D_{3h}	A^2D_2E	sp^3d	$D_1D_2E^2F^2$
k	tetragonal pyramid	C_{4v}	A^2C_2E	sp^2d^2 p^2d^2f	$ABC_1C_2E^3$
l	pentagon	D_{5h}	AE_1E_2	sp^2d^2	$BDE_1E_2E_3E_4$
m	pentagonal pyramid	C_{5v}	AE_1E_2	sp^2d^2	$ABE_1^2E_2^2$
n 6	octahedral (cubic)	O_h	AET	sp^3d^2 sd^2f^2 p^3d^2g	T^2U^2
o	trigonal prism	D_{3h}	AD_2EF	sp^3d^2 p^3d^3	$ABD_1D_2E^2F^2$
p	trigonal antiprism	D_{3d}	ABE^2	sp^3d^2 p^3d^3	$A^2B^2E^4$
q	tetragonal bipyramid	D_{4h}	A^2BC_2E	sp^3d^2 p^3d^2g sp^2d^2f	$B^2C_1^2E^4$
r 7	ZrF_7^{-3}; as $n+$one bond on 3-fold axis	C_{3v}	A^3E^3	sp^3d^3	$A^2B^2E^5$
s	TaF_7^{-2}; as o side-centred	C_{2v}	$A^3BD_1^2D_2$	sp^3d^3	$A^3B^3D_1^4D_2^4$
t 8	cubic	O_h	$ACTU$	sp^3d^3f	$E^2T^2U^2$
u	tetragonal antiprism	S_{8v}	$AC_2E_1E_2E_3$	sp^3d^4	$ABC_1C_2E_1^2E_2^2E_3^2$
v	dodecahedral	S_{4v}	$A^2C_1^2E^2$	sp^3d^4 p^3d^5 sp^2d^4f	$A^2B^2C_1^2C_2^2E^4$
w	as o+bonds centering two rectangular faces	C_{2v}	$A^3BD_1^2D_2^2$	sp^3d^4	$A^4B^4D_1^4D_2^4$
x	as o+bonds centering ends	D_{3h}	$A^2D_2^2EF$	sp^3d^3f	$ABCDE^3F^3$
y	as p+bonds centering ends	D_{3d}	$A^2B^2E^2$	sp^3d^3f	$A^2B^2E^6$

Consider, then, the formation of four bonds. Four symmetry types are considered (f) tetrahedral, (i) a distortion of this with one bond odd and the other three symmetrically disposed with the first as the axis, (g) a square arrangement, and (h) a distortion of this in which the central atom is out of the plane of the four atoms surrounding it. These have symmetries (f) T_d, (i) C_{3v}, (g) D_{4h}, and (h) C_{4v}. The bonds in (f) have already been analysed, and shown to be equivalent to $A \dotplus U$. By analogy with spectroscopic practice this is contracted to AU; $2A \dotplus 3U$ would become A^2U^3. Consultation with Table 16.9.2 shows that this can be derived from an s and a complete p, or from an s and three d levels, or from the three p levels and one of the f levels, etc. These possibilities are entered in Table 17.5.1 as sp^3; sd^3; p^3f. (It is to be remembered that we look for a given symbol with or without a bar (in this case for *either* A *or* C, and either T or U) since Table 16.9.2 includes only s_g, p_u, d_g,.... It is important to consult Table 16.9.1 to discover what the equivalences of this sort are.) In the symmetry type (i), the U breaks down into AE, but the final analysis is the same. In (g) and (h), on the other hand, an orbital of the symmetry type C is required, which cannot be obtained from either s or p atomic orbitals, but is first available from d orbitals. Accordingly the analysis of these types leads to sp^2d.

Conventionally, the atom is now 'prepared' for bond formation by arranging one electron in each of the four orbitals sp^3 or sp^2d, the result being equivalent to one electron in each bond, in the sense that either A or $\bar{A}$ of the diagram with which we opened this section is filled and the other empty. With the other atom similarly containing an electron in either B or $\bar{B}$, the bond then forms by the two electrons going into $A + B$ and $\bar{A} + \bar{B}$. The details of this process need not be taken too literally. (And in some cases, known to the chemist as coordinate bond formation, A and $\bar{A}$ may be initially occupied and B and $\bar{B}$ empty or vice versa.) We notice, however, that in the sequence of energy levels given above, the first occurrence of s, p, and d levels in close succession is at $3p$ $4s$ $3d$ $4p$ with the $3p$–$4s$ gap wider than the others. Thus the most natural place to expect the square arrangement is when the configuration can be between

$$1s^22s^2p^63s^2p^64s3d^7 = 1s^22s^2p^63s^2p^6d^4(4s3d^3)$$

and $$1s^22s^2p^63s^2p^64s3d^94p^4 = 1s^22s^2p^63s^2p^6d^84p^2(4s3d4p^2),$$

i.e. when there are between twenty-six and thirty-two electrons. (The left-hand expressions above show the levels in energy order. The bracketed part in the right-hand expressions must be capable of being doubled, a corresponding empty set being necessary.) Since tetrahedral bonds can be formed with either sp^3 or sd^3, but d orbitals are necessary for square bonds, we see that the square arrangement cannot be expected with less than twenty-two electrons in any event, and if the tetrahedral arrangement is preferred, it cannot be expected before twenty-seven electrons. (The first right-hand expression above is the highest number of electrons for which $4s3d^3$ tetrahedral bonds are possible.) The chemical evidence is that the square configuration occurs readily only in nickel (30) and copper (31), and in corresponding elements in later periods, but can be forced in iron (28) and cobalt (29).

Systems AX_n with n large and odd are relatively rare—an empirical formula of this form generally turning out to be at least A_2X_{2n}—and interest therefore centres next in AX_6 and AX_8. It is clear that six bonds cannot be formed without the use of two d orbitals. AX_6 thus becomes possible under similar conditions to planar AX_4, viz. from twenty-four electrons onwards, two more electrons being required for the extra two bonds. This is at chromium. It actually appears as soon as the third quantum group begins to form, in compounds—hydrated sodium salts, for example—in which both electrons are contributed by the atom at the other end of the bond. The tables show that a set of atomic orbitals sp^3d^2 can suffice for any symmetry of the bonds. AX_8 seems to be possible at the same point in the table in two forms: (a) with the bonds to the corners of a tetragonal anti-prism (a figure with two square faces parallel and their corners alternating, and eight triangular faces—symmetry S_{8v} ($\bar{8}2 = \bar{8}2m$)), and (b) with six bonds to the corners of a triangular prism and two more to the centres of two of the rectangular faces; other possibilities, including the direction of the bonds to the corners of a cube, must wait until there are f orbitals available, that is, as or after the rare earths make their appearance, or earlier in so far as the electrons are contributed by coordination.

[*Note added in proof*. There are two symmetry classes in which the simple rules developed on pp. 324–31 are misleading. In S_{4v} and D_{3h} alternative sets of axes which were equivalent under the proper groups D_4 and D_6 are no longer equivalent owing to the fact that of two sets of elements which were equivalent under the proper group one, but not the other, has been multiplied by i. Consequently a change of suffix no longer implies a trivial reorientation of axes. The first of these two classes occurs in the ion $Mo(CN)_8^{-4}$, in which the arrangement of the CN groups is described as 'a dodecahedron with triangular faces and symmetry V_d (D_2^d).' (This is S_{4v}; an alternative description is that the bonds are directed towards the vertices of two interlinked trapezia in perpendicular planes.) Through overlooking this point when first drafting Table 17.5.1, I questioned Kimball's conclusions in this case (letter to *J. Chem. Phys.* **21** (1953), 2224), but his conclusion that sp^3d^4 is a possible build up for this structure is quite correct. I am indebted to G. Giacometti for drawing my attention to the error in that letter.]

In discussing this problem in general we have, naturally, considered the lowest set of orbitals from which bonds of the desired symmetry can be constructed. But in particular cases everything depends upon the number of electrons to be accommodated. In an atom with n electrons forming p bonds, normally $n-p$ electrons will be accommodated in pairs in the lowest $\frac{1}{2}(n-p)$ orbitals of the atom, and the next p orbitals suitable for the purpose will rearrange to form the bonds. Thus in SiX_4, since Si has fourteen electrons, the arrangement will be $1s^2 2s^2 p^6 (3sp^3)$, but in SX_4, since the S has sixteen electrons, the arrangement would be $1s^2 2s^2 p^6 3s^2 (3p^3 d)$ if sulphur formed any purely four-covalent compounds. (The evidence is all against this, SF_4 is probably non-existent, SCl_4 probably ionized, and in the sulphones two links are coordinate, reducing the effective S electrons to fourteen.) To cover such possibilities we have included alternative groups of orbitals in Table 17.5.1.

The table also includes information on π bonds—the reduction of a complete set of two π bonds per σ bond. To illustrate this, we shall analyse the situation in SF_6—one of the molecules considered briefly by Kimball in his paper. It is a seventy-electron system, twenty-two being in the inner shells $(S: 1s^2 2s^2 p^6 + 6F: 1s^2)$ and forty-eight claiming our interest here. But it is important to begin with the orbitals and not with the electrons. There are sixty-six atomic orbitals, which come to our notice as $S: 3s^2 p^6 d^{10} + 6F: 2s^2 p^6$, or, as we had better put it in this context,
$$S: 3s_g\, s_u\, p_g^3\, p_u^3\, d_g^5\, d_u^5 + 6F: 2s_g\, s_u\, p_g^3\, p_u^3.$$

The octahedral field modifies and partly splits the former in the fashion laid out in Table 16.9.2, and the latter are equivalent to molecular orbitals as laid out in Table 17.5.1, so that the above expression is an approximation to the true
$$S: A\bar{A}T^3\bar{T}^3 E^2\bar{E}^2 U^3\bar{U}^3 + F_6: A^2\bar{A}^2 T^{12}\bar{T}^{12} E^4\bar{E}^4 U^6\bar{U}^6,$$
where we have multiplied the indices of E by two and of T or U by three so that they now give numbers of orbitals and not numbers of degenerate sets. The derivation of the second term needs explaining. The effect of the S on the orbitals of each F is to convert them from $2s_g\, s_u\, p_g^3\, p_u^3$ to $2\sigma^2 \bar{\sigma}^2 \pi^2 \bar{\pi}^2$ by Table 16.9.2; then by Table 17.5.1

      each σ with the five similar ones on the other F atoms
          becomes AE^2T^3;
    each $\bar{\sigma}$ becomes $\bar{A}\bar{E}^2\bar{T}^3$;
    each pair of π becomes $T^6 U^6$; and
    each pair of $\bar{\pi}$ becomes $\bar{T}^6 \bar{U}^6$.

The bond forming process described at the start of this section is then put into operation, not between atom and atom, but between the central S and the whole F_6 complex. Thus the four orbitals $S:A$, $S:\bar{A}$, $F_6:A$, and $F_6:\bar{A}$ are rearranged into a bonding A, a bonding $\bar{A}$, an antibonding A, and an antibonding $\bar{A}$, the total number of orbitals never changing. We can write the result of this process:

$$SF_6:[A\bar{A}E^2\bar{E}^2T^3\bar{T}^3]^2 + SF_6:[U^3\bar{U}^3]^2 + F_6:A\bar{A}E^2\bar{E}^2T^9\bar{T}^9U^3\bar{U}^3.$$

The first of these terms represents the six σ bonds, the last what the chemist knows as the 'lone pair' electrons, and the second shows to what extent π bond formation is able to take place. The orbitals now sorted out, the forty-eight electrons are put into the lowest forty-eight, leaving eighteen unfilled. These will be exactly the eighteen anti-bonding orbitals.

Thus the number of electrons in π bonding orbitals is only one-half. of the number required to build a single set of π bonds (every bond double) but they are nevertheless a closed shell, U^3, and the electron distribution they produce therefore has the complete symmetry of the molecule. (The chemist writes three bonds single and three double and invokes 'resonance' to keep the symmetry.)

When the covalency maxima were first discussed, the very noticeable stability of SF_6 was held to show that 6 was the maximum covalency of S. It was held that SF_6X (with X = e.g. OH^-) was impossible, but a necessary intermediate in hydrolysis, whence the impossibility of hydrolysis. But analysis of SF_6X and SF_6X_2 on similar lines shows the impossibility of the latter in the more likely steric arrangements (f orbitals being required), but not of the former. The stability of SF_6 must be ascribed to (a) the energetic stabilization due to the π bonding, and (b) the fact that all the orbitals except the antibonding ones, and none of the latter, are filled.

The methods discussed here apply primarily to systems of high symmetry, but it is well to bear in mind the use of the orbitals of a symmetrical system as a variation function for closely related systems of lesser symmetry. If, for example, the functions (17.4.3) are varied thus:

$$\left. \begin{aligned} \phi_1 &= \tfrac{1}{2}\{c.s && +p_x+p_y+(1-c^2)^{\frac{1}{2}}.p_z\} \\ \phi_2 &= \tfrac{1}{2}\{(1-c^2)^{\frac{1}{2}}.s+p_x-p_y-c.p_z\} \\ \phi_3 &= \tfrac{1}{2}\{(1-c^2)^{\frac{1}{2}}.s-p_x+p_y-c.p_z\} \\ \phi_4 &= \tfrac{1}{2}\{c.s && -p_x-p_y+(1-c^2)^{\frac{1}{2}}.p_z\} \end{aligned} \right\},$$

the effect is to pull together those bonds (ϕ_1 and ϕ_4) which lie nearer to the positive lobe of the p_z, simultaneously prising outwards, as it were, the other two. This effect is known to organic chemists as the Thorpe–Ingold effect, in which the presence of two large substituents on one carbon atom in a ring (forcing their bonds apart) reduces the strain in a small ring (helps to force the ring bonds together). Such variations are subject to the condition that the four functions remain orthonormal, but to keep this so is elementary, as $*\phi_i\phi_j*$ can be expanded by elementary algebra, and $*ss* = *p_xp_x* = \ldots = 1;\ *sp_x* = \ldots = 0$.

17.6. Unsaturated compounds

When three bonds are formed at $120°$ to each other, the usual analysis shows that (a) the symmetry is D_6, and (b) the orbitals required are $A+F$. This is therefore possible of synthesis from s, p_x, and p_y, the p_z being useless for the purpose. The p_z orbitals can form the basis of a π bond, as we saw when discussing oxygen. The s, p_x, p_y hybrids are strongly directed, and the bonding orbitals that they form are concentrated between the nuclei concerned. Under these circumstances we have seen that they are well approximated to by 'localized orbitals'. But the p_z orbitals are out of the plane of the three bonds, equidistant (in a symmetrical situation) from the three neighbouring nuclei, and the approximation of localized orbitals is not a valid one.

Chemists have long recognized double bonds, but it was mistakenly thought for a very long time that they were two like bonds pulled from their natural inclination of $109° 28'$, and the reactivity of a double bond was at first attributed to the strain energy involved in this. But quite early on it was realized that this was not the whole story, and in particular that when single and double bonds alternated in a chain some of the properties of the molecule were properties more of the whole 'conjugated' chain than of any of the localized bonds considered severally. The Lewis–Kossel theory showed that in such a system an electric charge could be conducted readily from one end of such a chain to the other, and this went a long way towards a qualitative explanation of most of the elementary chemical facts concerning such systems. But it remained qualitative, and somewhat crudely so at that, especially where ring structures were concerned.

The outstanding ring system is found in benzene, C_6H_6, the molecule of which was recognized early on to be a ring of six CH groups, with equivalent bonds between them. Classical valency theory allows such a ring with alternate single and double bonds, somewhat strained, and with the CH bonds directed somewhat to the single bond side of the radius vector; thus with threefold and not sixfold symmetry. Kekulé postulated rapid interchange between the two such possible forms, in order to explain the sixfold symmetry (manifested at that time in the absence of chemical difference between the bonds—one did not, for example, find two compounds with substituents replacing the H atoms on adjacent carbon atoms, according as the bond between was single or double). Wave mechanics provided a simple explanation of this finding, and as this example is such a *locus classicus* it may be well to repeat what was said in § 17.3 (under ionized fluorine, F_2^+). When one of the Kekulé formulae is written down it is a shorthand notation for a certain possible distribution of electrons, ψ_1. There are forty-two electrons, so this function is a function of 126 variables. Never mind, we do not need to know what it is! The other Kekulé formula has exactly the same energy. Both are approximations to the solution of the problem obtained by neglecting certain small terms—to be precise by using the approximation of localized bonds. As there is this complete degeneracy, we have a perturbation problem with degeneracy to which the correct zeroth approximations will be, owing to the symmetry, $\psi_1 \pm \psi_2$. Thus although we need not specify ψ_1 and ψ_2 precisely, assuming them known we see that neither is a correct zeroth approximation to the true wave function of the forty-two electrons. As was said in § 17.3, (a) if the molecule is initially in either state ψ_1 or ψ_2, it will oscillate between them, but (b) the lowest energy state of the system is one of the states $\psi_1 \pm \psi_2$, and even if the molecule is in one of the former states any measurement of its energy will yield the result appropriate to one of the latter. Chemists describe this situation as one of resonance between the two Kekulé structures. The important thing to bear in mind is (c) that there is an 'if' in (a) above, and (d) that benzene *in its ground state* has the wave function $\psi_1 + \psi_2$, and not either of the Kekulé forms.

An unfortunate feature of this explanation is that it appears to work equally well for any $(CH)_{2n}$, whereas other molecules of this formula do not show this remarkable stability in their ring systems. The explanation given above has therefore to be supplemented by a consideration of the fact that whereas four σ bonds can be formed at 109° 28′ to each other, three σ bonds can be formed at 120° to each other, the p_z orbitals being free for π bond formation. Thus the ring with an internal angle of 120° is a specially favoured one; each C atom in it makes three unstrained

σ bonds, two in the ring and one to an H atom. What happens to the p_z orbitals is what we are about to consider.

The general principle, then, in dealing with unsaturated compounds is to assume the compound already built using single bonds, the inter-bond angle in any trivalent C atom being $120°$. The p_z orbitals of any such C atom are then studied separately.

A common method of treating the p_z orbitals is to use them as approximate solutions of the perturbation method, assuming that the only interactions worth including are those between neighbouring atoms. This interaction is considered, moreover, to have a certain constant value, β. Then the ik element in the secular determinant is zero if the atoms i and k are distant from each other, β if they are neighbours, and $\alpha - E$ if $i = k$, where α is the energy of an unperturbed p_z orbital and E the energy of the perturbed one. The factorization of this equation as a step in its solution is accomplished if the correct linear combinations as dictated by group theory are taken.

Consider benzene, again. If the C atoms are labelled $1,\ldots, 6$ around the ring, the secular equation is

$$\begin{vmatrix} \alpha-E & \beta & 0 & 0 & 0 & \beta \\ \beta & \alpha-E & \beta & 0 & 0 & 0 \\ 0 & \beta & \alpha-E & \beta & 0 & 0 \\ 0 & 0 & \beta & \alpha-E & \beta & 0 \\ 0 & 0 & 0 & \beta & \alpha-E & \beta \\ \beta & 0 & 0 & 0 & \beta & \alpha-E \end{vmatrix} = 0. \quad (17.6.1)$$

To factorize the equation, consider the permutations induced in the p_z orbitals by the symmetry operations. In this example—and in any plane molecule—the signs of these orbitals may be ignored and only the proper rotations (those of D_6) considered. The decomposition of the permutation representation is $A \dotplus D_1 \dotplus E \dotplus F$. We now form the four operators $\sum \chi_{iR} R$, summing over all symmetry elements R, χ_{iR} being the character of the class to which R belongs in the representation i. (We consider only those i which we know we shall want, so omit B and D_2.) With these we operate on as many of the p_z as may be necessary. If $i = A$ every p_z leads to $\sum p_z$ and if $i = D_1$, every p_z leads to $\pm(\sum \text{even } p_z - \sum \text{odd } p_z)$; these are therefore the one-dimensional representation combinations of the p_z. (Even and odd here refer to the number of the C atom.) With the two-dimensional representations it is necessary to operate on any two of the p_z. Operating on the first and second gives independent wave functions, and operating on the other four gives linear combinations of these. A suitable set of wave functions is thus

$$A: \quad p_{z1}+ \ p_{z2}+p_{z3}+ \ p_{z4}+ \ p_{z5}+p_{z6}$$

$$D_1: \quad p_{z1}- \ p_{z2}+p_{z3}- \ p_{z4}+ \ p_{z5}-p_{z6}$$

$$F: \quad \begin{cases} 2p_{z1}+ \ p_{z2}-p_{z3}-2p_{z4}- \ p_{z5}+p_{z6} \\ p_{z1}+2p_{z2}+p_{z3}- \ p_{z4}-2p_{z5}-p_{z6} \end{cases}$$

$$E: \quad \begin{cases} 2p_{z1}- \ p_{z2}-p_{z3}+2p_{z4}- \ p_{z5}-p_{z6} \\ p_{z1}-2p_{z2}+p_{z3}+ \ p_{z4}-2p_{z5}+p_{z6} \end{cases}$$

and if these are used as a new basis set, the equation will factorize. The mechanical rule is:

Form a new determinant in which the six functions above provide the six rows by reading (row 1 + row 2 + ...) for $(p_{z1}+p_{z2}+...)$. (This determinant usually has a somewhat terrifying appearance!) Then form a third determinant by the same sequence of operations on the columns.

The justification for this rule is contained in § 4.1, certain liberties being permissible because purely numerical factors can be ignored if they do no more than appear as numerical factors in the algebraic equation. The rule is equivalent to evaluating the product

$$
\begin{bmatrix}
1 & 1 & 1 & 1 & 1 & 1 \\
1 & -1 & 1 & -1 & 1 & -1 \\
2 & 1 & -1 & -2 & -1 & 1 \\
1 & 2 & 1 & -1 & -2 & -1 \\
2 & -1 & -1 & 2 & -1 & -1 \\
1 & -2 & 1 & 1 & -2 & 1
\end{bmatrix}
$$

$$
\begin{bmatrix}
\alpha-E & \beta & 0 & 0 & 0 & \beta \\
\beta & \alpha-E & \beta & 0 & 0 & 0 \\
0 & \beta & \alpha-E & \beta & 0 & 0 \\
0 & 0 & \beta & \alpha-E & \beta & 0 \\
0 & 0 & 0 & \beta & \alpha-E & \beta \\
\beta & 0 & 0 & 0 & \beta & \alpha-E
\end{bmatrix}
\begin{bmatrix}
1 & 1 & 2 & 1 & 2 & 1 \\
1 & -1 & 1 & 1 & -1 & -1 \\
1 & 1 & -1 & 1 & -1 & 1 \\
1 & -1 & -1 & -1 & 1 & 1 \\
1 & 1 & -1 & -2 & -1 & -2 \\
1 & -1 & 1 & -1 & -1 & 1
\end{bmatrix}
$$

and the result is

$$
\begin{bmatrix}
6(\alpha+2\beta-E) & 0 & 0 & 0 & 0 & 0 \\
0 & 6(\alpha-2\beta-E) & 0 & 0 & 0 & 0 \\
0 & 0 & 8(\alpha+\beta-E) & 5(\alpha+\beta-E) & 0 & 0 \\
0 & 0 & 5(\alpha+\beta-E) & 8(\alpha+\beta-E) & 0 & 0 \\
0 & 0 & 0 & 0 & 8(\alpha-\beta-E) & 5(\alpha-\beta-E) \\
0 & 0 & 0 & 0 & 5(\alpha-\beta-E) & 8(\alpha-\beta-E)
\end{bmatrix}.
$$

$$(17.6.2)$$

The unimportance of the neglected factors is now clear, and the roots are $\alpha+2\beta$, $\alpha-2\beta$, $\alpha+\beta$ (twice), and $\alpha-\beta$ (twice). Since in benzene there are six electrons to be accommodated in these orbitals, and they will accommodate themselves in the three lowest orbitals—to decide which these are one must know that β is negative—the energy of the benzene molecule due to these electrons is $6\alpha+8\beta$. This should be compared with the 6α of the corresponding electrons in the isolated atoms, and the $6\alpha+6\beta$ of the hypothetical structure represented by one Kekulé formula, in which the interaction is in pairs only. The 2β energy difference between benzene and a Kekulé structure is known as 'resonance energy'; it can be detected by comparing the heat of combustion of benzene with that of other compounds from which the heat of combustion of a Kekulé structure can be estimated. Theoretically, the value of β will not vary from compound to compound and thus, even if its theoretical computation is difficult, an experimental value obtained from some compounds can be applied in a theoretical discussion of others.

Since the group theoretic part of this calculation depends only on the symmetry, it will remain valid even if we include interaction of the 1–3 and 1–4 types. We find, denoting these by γ and δ, that the secular equation is

$$\begin{vmatrix} \alpha-E & \beta & \gamma & \delta & \gamma & \beta \\ \beta & \alpha-E & \beta & \gamma & \delta & \gamma \\ \gamma & \beta & \alpha-E & \beta & \gamma & \delta \\ \delta & \gamma & \beta & \alpha-E & \beta & \gamma \\ \gamma & \delta & \gamma & \beta & \alpha-E & \beta \\ \beta & \gamma & \delta & \gamma & \beta & \alpha-E \end{vmatrix} = 0,$$

and that the roots are separated by the same process, and are $(\alpha+2\gamma)\pm(2\beta+\delta)$ once each, and $(\alpha-\gamma)\pm(\beta-\delta)$ twice each.

The extension of this method to other molecules needs no elaboration. We have not assumed the nuclei to be C nuclei, though we have assumed them to be all alike. As far as the six-ring is concerned, carbon atoms have the virtue of demanding the use of all the bonding orbitals and no antibonding ones. If not all the atoms are alike, the symmetry will be less—e.g. the symmetry of pyrazine, with the 1 and 4 positions occupied by N nuclei, is only D_2. If calculations are to be carried out on such structures, two points are to be noted. First, that instead of α and β we shall have α_C, α_N, β_{CC}, β_{CN}, and possibly, though not in pyrazine, β_{NN}. Secondly, as we saw in considering diatomic molecules, any

satisfactory treatment of the more symmetrical system will provide
suggestive material for variation treatment in the less symmetrical
systems.

We conclude this discussion with a brief account of fluorene:

$$
\begin{array}{ccc}
\text{CH} & \text{CH}_2 & \text{CH} \\
\text{HC} \quad \text{C} & \text{C} & \text{CH} \\
\text{HC} \quad \text{C}_1 & \text{—C} & \text{CH,} \\
\text{CH} & & \text{CH}
\end{array}
$$

which brings up one new point and illustrates an old one. We number
the carbon atoms clockwise around the perimeter from the one marked
as C_1. C_7 is different from the rest in carrying two H atoms. Ignoring

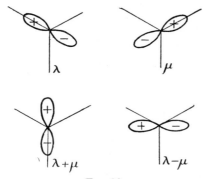

FIG. 30.

this for the moment, we can set up the secular equation. The symmetry
is only D_2 and only two of its representations occur in the permutation
representation; the thirteenth degree equation can only be factorized
into a sixth degree equation and a seventh degree equation in consequence. This is the old point illustrated—that our method is much less
powerful when the symmetry is small. The new point is what to do with
the CH_2 group. Under provocation one H can be removed; our straightforward treatment is then valid, and applies to the $C_{13}H_9^-$ ion which
occurs in metallic derivatives of fluorene, provided that the remaining
H moves into the plane. But we are interested in the hydrocarbon itself.
The modification from the ion in which the one hydrogen nucleus in the
plane is replaced by two, one above and one below, may be regarded as
a perturbation which conforms to the original symmetry, and which,
being a 'tripole' perturbation, is of quite local action. A satisfactory

modification of the procedure to deal with this would seem to be to replace the β by a β' in so far as C_7 is involved.

The picture of these rings which evolves is that of a plane arrangement of the nuclei held together by single bonds, and two 'haloes' of negative charge in parallel planes above and below the ring due to the π electrons. A recent X-ray study of a ferrous derivative of cyclopentadiene is interesting in this connexion. The ferrous ion is held between two $C_5H_5^-$ rings, staggered into an antiprism ($\bar{5}m$). Its relation to the π-bond rings is shown in Fig. 31. To analyse this situation by the usual method, a D_5 column must be constructed for Table 16.9.2. Full symmetry can

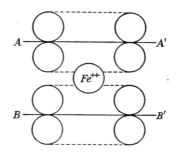

Fig. 31. AA', BB'-planes of cyclopentadiene rings. Unlabelled circles—sections of π-orbitals of these rings.

be maintained if the iron forms either (1) no bonds, (2) two bonds along the axis, or (3) ten bonds. The first case would amount to a purely ionic structure, stabilized by resonance between the rings as well as by the electrostatic forces. In the third case, the ten bonds analyse to

$$A \dotplus B \dotplus 2E_1 \dotplus 2E_2$$

and cannot be formed without using f electrons, which iron has not got. In the second, and most probable structure, the two bonds are equivalent to $A \dotplus B$, obtainable from a p_z and either an s or a $d\sigma$. The latter has the advantage in overlap with the π-ring-orbital, since the $p_z \pm d\sigma$, one for each bond, are wine-glass shaped, the 'rim' overlapping a π-ring-orbital and the 'stem' pointing towards the centre of the other ring. The result is hardly a conventional bond. The molecular orbitals are the symmetric and antisymmetric combinations of these, viz. the p_z hybridizing with the symmetrical combination of π-ring-orbitals and the $d\sigma$ hybridizing with the antisymmetrical combination.

But there is another way of examining the question whether the CH_2

can enter into the conjugated system, and that is to see whether there is any localized orbital sufficiently like a p_z orbital to behave as one. To be on the safe side, we should start from an analysis of the whole molecule, but in this we can ignore $1s$ levels on carbon atoms and electrons in them. The method is to add up all the atomic orbitals on one side and all known localized bonds on the other and to strike a balance, examining more closely what is left. With X as the rotation axis and Z perpendicular to the plane; *al* and *ar* (for *aliphatic* and *aromatic*) distinguishing the hydrogen atoms in the CH_2 from those in the six-rings, the analysis of the atomic orbitals can be set out thus:

Symmetry C_{2v}		I	m_y	C_x	m_z		A	B	D_1	D_2
Character table	A	1	1	1	1					
	B	1	-1	1	-1					
	D_1	1	-1	-1	1					
	D_2	1	1	-1	-1		A	B	D_1	D_2
A.O.'s *al* H$1s$		2	2	0	0	$=$	1	0	0	1
C$2s$		13	1	1	13		7	0	6	0
C$2p_x$		13	1	1	13		7	0	6	0
C$2p_y$		13	-1	-1	13		6	0	7	0
C$2p_z$		13	1	-1	-13		0	6	0	7
ar H$1s$		8	0	0	8		4	0	4	0
							25	6	23	8	$= 62$

(The number of electrons available is also sixty-two, but this is more or less of a coincidence; it always happens in uncharged hydrocarbons, but not in ions or hetero-compounds.) We now analyse those localized bonds we are fairly certain of, those obviously filled and those obviously unfilled. They are:

		I	m_y	C_x	m_z		A	B	D_1	D_2	
Full:	C—Cσ	15	1	1	15	$=$	8	0	7	0	
	ar C—Hσ	8	0	0	8		4	0	4	0	
	al C—Hσ	2	2	0	0		1	0	0	1	$(= 25)$
Empty:	C—Cσ*	15	-1	-1	15		7	0	8	0	
	ar C—Hσ*	8	0	0	8		4	0	4	0	
							24	0	23	1	$= 48$

We have included the *al* C—H since after all something must hold the H atoms to the molecule. (The one point here is whether there might be a μ bond to a hydrogen molecule—see § 17.9—but we shall ignore this possible approach.) We are left with fourteen available orbitals not used in making the obvious localized ones. At two electrons per orbit, we have to fill thirty-one orbitals, and twenty-five are already filled; which are the remaining six? They are to be chosen from one A, six B, and seven D_2, and they will be the six lowest from these fourteen.

Now were the present question nonsense, we should have two benzene rings and an aliphatic CH_2, and these fourteen would be the six $C—C\pi$, the six $C—C\pi^*$, and the two al $C—H\sigma^*$. One way of putting the present question might be to ask whether one of the two latter might not be as easily filled as the highest of the bonding π orbitals. That something like this happens almost follows from the chemical evidence, the 'activity' of the al H atoms implying some antibonding influence at work. But it is probably wrong to label these remaining fourteen orbitals so easily— as wrong as to label the double bonds in benzene. Let us therefore examine the symmetry implications more closely.

The conjugated system, being made up of π bonds, is built out of orbitals antisymmetric with respect to the plane of the molecule, that is, of B and D_2 orbitals, and the one remaining A orbital cannot be part of it. The two al $C—H\sigma^*$ bonds themselves (being in the median plane) constitute a representation of the symmetry group, and analyse to an A and a D_2, which are formed by combining them symmetrically and antisymmetrically, respectively. If the CH_2 can take part in conjugation, it will be through the latter orbital, an expression for which can easily be constructed. Confining our attention to the six orbitals $C2s$, $C2p_x$, $C2p_y$, $C2p_z$, H_a1s, H_b1s, these define a subspace of wave space and are approximately an orthogonal set of axes in it. We choose a new set of orthogonal vectors which represent correct zeroth approximations thus:

$H_a 1s$	$H_b 1s$	$C2s$	$C2p_x$	$C2p_y$	$C2p_z$	
0	0	$\frac{1}{2}$	$-\frac{1}{2}$	$\sqrt{\frac{1}{2}}$	0	orbitals which combine with those of other C atoms to form σ bonds in the five-ring.
0	0	$\frac{1}{2}$	$-\frac{1}{2}$	$-\sqrt{\frac{1}{2}}$	0	
$(1-k)^{\frac{1}{2}}$	0	$k^{\frac{1}{2}}/2$	$k^{\frac{1}{2}}/2$	0	$-k^{\frac{1}{2}}/\sqrt{2}$	$C—H_a\sigma$
0	$(1-k)^{\frac{1}{2}}$	$k^{\frac{1}{2}}/2$	$k^{\frac{1}{2}}/2$	0	$k^{\frac{1}{2}}/\sqrt{2}$	$C—H_b\sigma$
$-k^{\frac{1}{2}}$	0	$(1-k)^{\frac{1}{2}}/2$	$(1-k)^{\frac{1}{2}}/2$	0	$-(1-k)^{\frac{1}{2}}/\sqrt{2}$	$C—H_a\sigma^*$
0	$-k^{\frac{1}{2}}$	$(1-k)^{\frac{1}{2}}/2$	$(1-k)^{\frac{1}{2}}/2$	0	$(1-k)^{\frac{1}{2}}/\sqrt{2}$	$C—H_b\sigma^*$

Owing to the combined requirements of orthogonality and symmetry, only one arbitrary constant, k, is involved. The D_2 orbital is now obtained by combining the last two of these antisymmetrically, and is

$$\frac{k^{\frac{1}{2}}}{\sqrt{2}}(H_a1s—H_b1s)+(1-k)^{\frac{1}{2}}.\,C2p_z,$$

and it can be seen without recourse to plotting that as k increases from 0 to 1 (passing through its true value *en route*) that this orbital hardly changes its shape but moves outwards from the C atom to the H atoms.

Provided k is not too large, therefore, it would appear not to be disqualified from contributing to the conjugated system.

This general effect, in which the orbitals of a system which the chemist would call saturated mimic a genuine p_z orbital sufficiently to take some part in π-bonding in a conjugated system, is called 'hyper-conjugation'. There is considerable evidence of its occurrence to a slight degree (detectable by its effect on quantitative characteristics such as reaction rates and equilibria) in, one might almost say, the majority of organic compounds, but particularly where the carbon atom required to produce the p_z orbital is actually in a CH_3 group, or, as in fluorene, in a CH_2 group which is part of a conjugating ring system.

An alternative approach to the orbitals of conjugated systems, both linear and ring, has recently been advanced, in which the electrons are

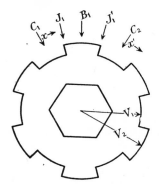

Fig. 32. Benzene: Dog-tooth potential field.
C_1–C_6 carbon planes; B_1–B_6 between planes;
J_1–J_6' junction planes.

regarded as constrained to the 'haloes' but otherwise are free. A second approximation introduces some potential field to take account of the nuclei. The simplest such field is a 'dog-tooth' or 'square-wave' field, having one potential, V_1, in the neighbourhood of the nuclei, and a higher one, V_2, between them, the change being abrupt. Calculations with such a field are greatly simplified if the two potentials have equal linear (or, in a ring, angular) ranges. The Schrödinger equation for the free particle applies at every point, and at the discontinuities it is necessary that both ψ and its first derivative are continuous. Let us consider a ring of n nuclei of this type; Fig. 32 shows $n = 6$ (benzene). Let d be the circumference of the ring, let $d/4n = l$, and let x be a linear distance along the ring measured from C_1, clockwise.

Now since the system has the symmetry D_n, its wave functions must conform to a representation of this group; most of these are two-dimensional, and we consider these first. By § 16.6, a degenerate pair of wave functions at C_1 must be

$$\psi_1 = A \sin \alpha_1 x, \qquad \psi_2 = A \cos \alpha_1 x,$$

where α_1 is written for

$$\left(\frac{8\pi^2 m}{h^2} (E - V_1)\right)^{\frac{1}{2}},$$

and no phase variable is introduced since this is merely to vary our choice of basic functions. If x' is measured from C_2, $x' = x - 4l$. Application of the transformation equations for the $(k+2)$th representation of $\mathfrak{d}_n$ shows that these wave functions must become

$$\psi_1' = A \cos \frac{2k\pi}{n} \sin \alpha_1 x' + A \sin \frac{2k\pi}{n} \cos \alpha_1 x' = A \sin\left(\alpha_1 x' + \frac{2k\pi}{n}\right),$$

$$\psi_2' = -A \sin \frac{2k\pi}{n} \sin \alpha_1 x' + A \cos \frac{2k\pi}{n} \cos \alpha_1 x' = A \cos\left(\alpha_1 x' + \frac{2k\pi}{n}\right)$$

$$(17.6.3)$$

at C_2, an example of the way in which group theory, in its simpler applications, is apt to provide a rigid proof of results which can be easily obtained by intelligent guess-work. Now let these wave functions at B_1 be

$$\psi_1'' = B \sin(\alpha_2 x'' + \mu), \qquad \psi_2'' = B \cos(\alpha_2 x'' + \mu),$$

where x'', measured from B, equals $x - 2l$. Then the conditions of continuity at the junctions can be shown to lead first to the equation

$$\mu = p\pi + \frac{k\pi}{n} = \frac{q\pi}{n} \qquad (p, q \text{ integers or zero}) \qquad (17.6.4)$$

and thence to

$$\frac{\alpha_1 + \alpha_2}{\alpha_1 - \alpha_2} = \frac{\sin[(\alpha_1 - \alpha_2)l + \mu]}{\sin[(\alpha_1 + \alpha_2)l - \mu]}. \qquad (17.6.5)$$

By choosing the zero of energy so that $V_1 = -V_2 = V$, and assuming that $E \gg V$, we can expand $(1 \pm V/E)^{\frac{1}{2}}$ by the binomial theorem and write

$$\alpha_1 + \alpha_2 \simeq \left(\frac{32\pi^2 m E}{h^2}\right)^{\frac{1}{2}}, \qquad (17.6.6)$$

$$\alpha_1 - \alpha_2 \simeq \left(\frac{8\pi^2 m}{h^2 E}\right)^{\frac{1}{2}} V. \qquad (17.6.7)$$

(17.6.5) now becomes an equation for E. Writing

$$(\alpha_1+\alpha_2)l = z = \left(\frac{32\pi^2 m l^2 E}{h^2}\right)^{\frac{1}{2}},$$

$$(\alpha_1-\alpha_2)l = \zeta = \left(\frac{8\pi^2 m l^2}{h^2 E}\right)^{\frac{1}{2}}V,$$

we have $\qquad z\sin(z-\mu) = \zeta\sin(\zeta+\mu),$ \hfill (17.6.8)

when $V = 0$ the right-hand side $= 0$, and

$$z = r\pi+\mu = \frac{s\pi}{n} \qquad (s \text{ integral or zero}),$$

whence $\qquad E = \dfrac{z^2 h^2}{32\pi^2 m l^2} = \dfrac{s^2 h^2}{32 n^2 m l^2} = \dfrac{s^2 h^2}{2 m d^2}.$ \hfill (17.6.9)

For small values of V this may be substituted in the right-hand side of (17.6.8) and by an iterative process a solution for E in powers of V may be obtained. In doing this μ is to be interpreted as $2\pi\times$ the non-integral part of s/n. It is interesting to compare (17.6.9) with (16.6.5), the corresponding expression for the particle in a box; the differences are first that here we can have $s = 0$, though whether this is compatible with $V \neq 0$ needs further study, secondly, that the factor in the denominator here is 2 against 8 in (16.6.5), and, thirdly, that all the levels here, except $s = 0$, are twofold degenerate. The separation produced by V is probably of academic interest only, as the square-wave field is so crude an approximation. The significant part of the above analysis is that the equations (17.6.3) in the form

$$\psi_1' = \psi_1 \cos\frac{2k\pi}{n} + \psi_2 \sin\frac{2k\pi}{n},$$

$$\psi_2' = -\psi_1 \sin\frac{2k\pi}{n} + \psi_2 \cos\frac{2k\pi}{n}$$

must hold whatever form of potential field is assumed, and would, for example, become the boundary conditions if it were proposed to investigate some other shape of field by numerical methods.

17.7. Spectra and selection rules

By the spectrum of a substance is meant the characteristic features of the light emitted or absorbed by the substance under suitable conditions. Frequently it consists of discrete 'lines' or frequencies, and there is good reason for thinking that when it does not do so it is always because either (1) the emitters are interfered with by their neighbours and in consequence vary so much from their true frequency that the lines are smudged into one another, or (2) because the transition causes the emitter to be unstable (predissociation spectra). In every type of spectrum except one each line represents the difference in energy between two states of the emitter, the frequency, ν, of the line being the energy difference divided by Planck's constant, h. (The exception is the Raman spectrum, where it is the difference between two frequencies that is proportional to the energy difference.) This simple rule covers rather an embarrassing diversity of mechanisms, but broadly speaking it may be said that the light (or, in emission, its possibility), constitutes a perturbing field, which, according to dynamical perturbation theory (§ 16.8), induces transitions from one state of the unperturbed system to another. As before, the contribution of group theory is to determine when $^*\psi_i \, \mathcal{G} \psi_j{}^* = 0$, and the transition probability therefore zero; this involves sufficient discussion of the mechanism in each case to determine the symmetry properties of $\mathcal{G}$.

Fortunately the experimental and theoretical classifications of spectra coincide very largely. We distinguish

X-ray spectra in which the substance is caused to emit X-rays by the action of a beam of electrons, a crystal, acting as a diffraction grating, being used to analyse the spectrum. The primary action of the beam is to knock electrons out of the deeper levels; these are then filled up by electrons falling in from the higher levels, the energy of falling being emitted as the X-rays. These deep levels are very much of the 'localizable' type and the spectrum is characteristic of the atomic species present, irrespective of how they are combined. We shall not consider them further.

Ultra-violet and visible spectra excited by an *electric discharge or flame temperature* form a continuous series. The experimental technique is simple in the visible, demands a photographic record in the ultra-violet, and a quartz prism in the more distant ultra-violet, but these distinctions are experimental only. The flame, the arc, and the spark represent varying degrees of excitation and an increasing number of lines. The excitation is from one electronic level to another and is almost inevitably accompanied by simultaneous changes of vibrational and possibly also rotational state, if the system is capable of them. This type of spectrum is thus relatively simple only for atoms. The thermal or electrical action excites the system to a high level (almost any one which is not too high for the exciting agent) and the simple perturbation rules determine *to* what levels it can then fall. As the upper levels are closer together than the lower ones an increase in the intensity of the exciting agent not only produces more intensity in the lines produced by a weaker excitation, but also adds lines of lower frequency.

Ultra-violet and visible absorption spectra are produced by the raising of a system to a higher electronic level by light which is of just the right frequency to do it. Only transitions from the ground state are possible since only systems in the ground state are present to absorb the light, unless the temperature is very high. Natural colour is due to a visible absorption spectrum, and requires the existence of an electronic excited state not very far above the ground state; on the whole this only occurs with long conjugated systems or with atoms with incompletely filled $3d$, $4d$,..., etc. levels—i.e. organic dyes and other coloured compounds, and compounds of the transition metals.

Near infra-red spectra require specially sensitive photographic film, and *far infra-red spectra* require the use of a rock-salt prism; again these are experimental distinctions. But the former spectra are produced by changes in vibrational state with or without rotational changes but without electronic changes, and the latter are produced by changes in rotational state only.

Raman spectra are obtained by observing the light transversely scattered by a substance through which a powerful beam of monochromatic light is passing. Much is scattered without change of wavelength, but some is scattered after losing energy to, or gaining it from, a normal mode of rotation or vibration.

It will thus be seen that the basis of all spectra is the series of all possible energy states of the system; allowing for changes in rotational, vibrational, and electronic states this is already a threefold infinity, and it is not the levels themselves but the differences between all possible pairs of levels which give rise to spectral lines. But the mechanism of the various types of spectra, and consequent difference in selection rules (i.e. different pairs i, j for which $*\psi_i \mathscr{G} \psi_j^* = 0$) is an important aid to sorting out the results. It is also fortunate, and the reason why the experimental and theoretical classifications do not cut across one another more, that rotational, vibrational, and electronic changes give rise to energy differences of three distinct orders of magnitude in general.

The light is usually considered to consist of its electric vector only, magnetic effects are smaller and may be neglected. If the direction of the electric vector is a persistent one, this and the direction of propagation of the light form the plane of polarization of the light; in 'unpolarized' light the plane is, over a period of time, indeterminate, because of random rotations about the direction of propagation. The separate molecules in a gaseous or liquid system are oriented at random, and therefore except in crystalline media polarization of the spectrum depends on either (1) polarization of the exciting light (if light is the excitant), or (2) the imposition of a direction-defining external field.

The condition for the appearance of a spectrum line corresponding to a transition from state i to state j has been stated in the form that $*\psi_i \mathscr{G} \psi_j^* \neq 0$. In many cases it is simplest to regard this as the product of $*\psi_i$ with $\mathscr{G} \psi_j^*$; the latter is then the product of two representations of the group, and can be analysed in the usual way, and unless ψ_i appears in this analysis we shall have $*\psi_i \mathscr{G} \psi_j* = 0$. Thus any ψ_j only combines with those states which appear in the analysis of $\mathscr{G} \psi_j$.

The simplest type of spectrum is that of an *isolated atom*. Its levels are mostly degenerate, but under applied electrostatic or magnetic fields they separate. The additional term in the energy of the system due to the electric field F of the light is Fw, where w is a coordinate vector. This means that the perturbation terms can be written in the form $F *\psi_i w \psi_j*$ provided, as is the case for all frequencies we consider, that F does not vary appreciably from point to point within the atom. (It will vary harmonically with time.)

Assuming that there is a static field applied to remove the degeneracy, two cases arise, w parallel to, and w perpendicular to this field. The symmetry, which in the isolated atom is $\mathfrak{o}_3$, will be reduced to $D_{\infty h}$ if the static field is an electrostatic one, and in this symmetry w belongs to the representation σ_- if it is parallel to the field but to the representation π if it is perpendicular to it. In the former case the equations

$$\chi_{\sigma_-} \chi_w = \chi_{\sigma_+}, \qquad \chi_{\sigma_+} \chi_w = \chi_{\sigma_-}, \qquad \chi_j \chi_w = \chi_j \quad \text{(all other } j\text{)}$$

show that transitions occur from σ_+ to σ_- and vice versa, and from π to π, δ to δ, and so on. In the latter case the equation

$$4 \cos m\phi \cos \phi = 2 \cos(m+1)\phi + 2\cos(m-1)\phi$$

shows that in this case $w\psi_m$ is orthogonal to all ψ except ψ_{m+1} and ψ_{m-1} (treating j numerically as in § 12.2), and thus transitions occur from σ to π, π to σ or δ, δ to π or ϕ, etc. But whereas lines corresponding to these transitions will be polarized at right angles to the field, the former transitions will produce lines polarized parallel to the field. No other lines will appear.

Considering now the isolated atom without the degeneracy-breaking field, w belongs to the representation p, and the equation

$$\Gamma_r \times \Gamma_s = \Gamma_{r+s} \dotplus \Gamma_{r+s-2} \dotplus \dots \dotplus \Gamma_{|r-s|} \quad \text{in } \mathfrak{u}_2$$

(§ 12.4), with $s = 2$ (for the p representation) shows that

$$\Gamma_j \times \Gamma_p = \Gamma_{j+1} \dotplus \Gamma_j \dotplus \Gamma_{j-1} \quad \text{in } \mathfrak{r}_3$$

(the representations of $\mathfrak{r}_3$ being those of $\mathfrak{u}_2$ with odd dimensionality, so that Γ_j of $\mathfrak{r}_3$ is Γ_r of $\mathfrak{u}_2$ if $r = 2j$); a similar rule therefore holds, that s states can undergo transition to s or p, p states to s, p, or d, d states to p, d, or f, etc. It should be observed, however, that this rule is meaningless in a cylindrical symmetry, and that unless the field used to break the degeneracy is very weak, it will itself give cause for this rule to be broken.

Extension of the character tables to include improper rotations now shows the additional rule that g and u states only undergo transitions into states of the opposite type. These rules are usually stated in terms of quantum numbers in the form $\Delta m = \pm 1$ or 0; $\Delta l = \pm 1$ or 0; $g \gtrless u$. The last of these rules implies that when $\Delta l = 0$ the spin of the electron must be reversed, but when $\Delta l = \pm 1$ it must not be. As the reversal of spin is a magnetic effect brought about by magnetic forces, and these forces are relatively weak, the lines corresponding to the former transitions may be expected to be weak in comparison with those due to the latter type.

The principles to be followed in determining the selection rules for the electronic spectra of molecules are fundamentally the same as those for atoms, but, of course, the appropriate symmetry group will have to be used in each case. The electronic spectra of most molecules are relatively uninteresting, however, as electronic excitation usually leads to electrons being lifted from bonding orbitals and thus to decomposition. Of much more interest are the infra-red and Raman spectra which are vibrational spectra.

Hitherto we have assumed the nuclei fixed and considered only the wave functions of the electrons. In Chapter X we discussed the vibrations in terms of classical mechanics. In a more radical quantum-mechanical treatment of molecules we must set up the Schrödinger equation for the system of both nuclei and electrons. By the Franck–Condon principle, already mentioned, the electrons, owing to their much lighter mass, adjust themselves to the instantaneous positions of the nuclei, and any corrections due to the fact that the nuclei are moving are too small to matter. An energy can thus be calculated for each nuclear configuration; it will be the electronic energy plus the mutual electrostatic energy of the nuclei. This provides the potential energy function which was used in § 10.2 for the classical treatment. The transformation to normal coordinates is unaffected by going over to quantum mechanics, but in each normal coordinate there is now a Schrödinger equation of the harmonic oscillator type to be solved, and the solution consists of a *nuclear* ψ function bearing the usual interpretation in terms of probabilities. The energy levels are of the form $(n+\frac{1}{2})h\nu$, where ν is the classical frequency, and the associated eigenfunctions are the Hermite orthogonal functions discussed in § 12.8. A complete function ϕ will be the product of such ψ-functions one in each normal mode. (These will have to be multiplied by electronic functions with coefficients which vary with time in such a way as to express the adjustment of the electronic functions to the instantaneous nuclear positions, but that does not concern us here.)

The function $*\phi_i \, \mathcal{G} \, \phi_j*$, whose non-vanishing is essential to the appearance of a line, can now be discussed. The perturbing potential $\mathcal{G}$ can be expanded in terms of the normal coordinates

$$\mathcal{G} = g_0 + \sum g_k \, Q_k + \sum g_{hk} \, Q_h \, Q_k + \cdots, \tag{A}$$

where the g are numerical coefficients. Inserting this into $*\phi_i \, \mathcal{G} \, \phi_j*$ and at the same time expressing the ϕ's as the product of ψ's, shows $*\phi_i \, \mathcal{G} \, \phi_j*$ as the sum of a series of terms of which

$$*\{\psi_{i'}(Q_1)\psi_{i''}(Q_2)...\}g_k \, Q_k\{\psi_{j'}(Q_1)\psi_{j''}(Q_2)...\}*$$

is one. The multiple integral expressed by this scalar product is expressible as the product of single integrals

$$*\psi_{i'}(Q_1)\psi_{j'}(Q_1)* \; *\psi_{i''}(Q_2)\psi_{j''}(Q_2)*...*\psi_{i^{(k)}}(Q_k)g_k \, Q_k \, \psi_{j^{(k)}}(Q_k)*...$$

all of which, except the kth, are unity if $i = j$ and zero if $i \neq j$. This term is therefore zero unless the transition is confined to the kth mode, and even then unless $g_k \neq 0$. This is typical of terms in the *first sum* in (A). The isolated *first term* of (A) gives rise to a term which is zero if there is any transition at all. Terms in the *second sum* are of two kinds. If $h \neq k$, they are operative for a simultaneous change in two modes. If $h = k$ they supplement the previous term for a transition in the kth mode. But these terms are in any case associated with second-order effects and give rise to weak lines in a spectrum. Thus the strong lines in a spectrum are normally associated only with transitions confined to one normal mode.

The mechanism of absorption or emission of a normal infra-red spectrum resembles that of electronic spectra, the perturbation being the potential energy of the electric moment vector of the molecule in the electric field of the light. In a given mode (we suppress the k from now on) the transition can occur provided $*\psi_i(Q) \, Q \, \psi_j(Q)* \neq 0$ and $g \neq 0$. The former condition leads to the requirement that $j = i \pm 1$, and the latter to the requirement that the mode be one which is of the same symmetry type as one of the translational modes of the molecule. For, as regards the former, by equation (12.8.7),

$$Q H_j(Q) = \tfrac{1}{2}H_{j+1}(Q)+n H_{j-1}(Q),$$

whence $Q\psi_j(Q)$ is orthogonal to all $\psi_i(Q)$ except those with $i = j\pm1$. As regards the latter, since the electric moment vector has the transformation properties of a vector, which are the same as those of a translation vector, it must belong to the same representation of the symmetry group as the translation vector, and therefore can only be made up of the normal coordinates which belong to this representation or to one of the representations into which it reduces if it is reducible.

The mechanism of Raman emission is different. Classically, in one coordinate, q, the electric field vector of the light, whose time variation must now be explicit, induces a proportionate dipole. If the field is $E_0 \sin 2\pi\nu_0 t$ and the polarizability is α, the dipole is $\alpha E_0 \sin 2\pi\nu_0 t$. But if there is a vibration in this coordinate of frequency ν, α may be changing with this frequency, and we must write

$$\left(\alpha_0+\left(\frac{\partial\alpha}{\partial q}\right)\sigma \cos\left(2\pi\nu t+\epsilon\right)\right)E_0\sin 2\pi\nu_0 t$$

$$= \alpha_0 E_0 \sin 2\pi\nu_0 t+\left(\frac{\partial\alpha}{\partial q}\right)\sigma\,\frac{E_0}{2}[\sin\{2\pi(\nu_0+\nu)t+\epsilon\}+\sin\{2\pi(\nu_0-\nu)t-\epsilon\}],$$

where σ is the amplitude of the vibration. The three terms of this expansion show that light will be scattered with the three frequencies ν_0, $\nu_0+\nu$, and $\nu_0-\nu$. The first is the original light and the second and third the Raman lines, the difference of whose frequencies from that of the original light gives the frequency of the molecular vibration. The emission therefore turns on the polarizability and its variation with coordinate changes. In the quantum-mechanical treatment we find that this creates a situation similar to that in infra-red theory, but with the *tensor* α_{xx}, α_{xy},..., α_{yz} replacing the electric moment *vector*. The condition that $g \neq 0$ is now that the normal mode shall belong to a representation of the symmetry group which is among those obtained by analysing this tensor, the character of whose transformation is $\pm 2 \cos\theta+4 \cos^2\theta$. (This analysis assumes that we are still dealing with fundamentals only.)

We may pause to apply these results to the ozone problem. The table in § 10.4 giving the D_{3h} analysis shows that of the two frequencies, only the degenerate one belongs to a representation to which any of the components of the translation vector belong. This frequency should therefore appear in infra-red spectra, but not the other. But the character

$$6 \quad 2 \quad 0 \quad 2 \quad 2 \quad 2$$

of the polarizability tensor will be found to analyse to $2\Gamma_1 \dotplus \Gamma_5 \dotplus \Gamma_6$, and therefore both frequencies will appear in the Raman spectrum. In the C_{2v} analysis, on the other hand, all three frequencies will be found to be active in both types of spectrum. In the $D_{\infty h}$ model we have, using the nomenclature of § 12.2 for the representations,

Representations	T and ω	α	Internal vibrations	Infra-red	Raman
1		2	1	inactive	active
1′	z		1	active	inactive
2	ω_z				
2′					
3	$x+iy$		1	active	inactive
3′	ω_{x+iy}	1			
4		1			

The distinctiveness of the spectra produced by the different models thus increases. As each vibrational change is accompanied by rotational changes which convert the line into a band, however, we can do with all the distinguishing criteria available.

Nor are overtones and combination lines absent, though they tend to be weaker than fundamentals. The proof that $i = j \pm 1$ in infra-red spectra can be adapted as follows:

$$H_{n+2}(Q) = 2QH_{n+1}(Q) - 2(n+1)H_n(Q)$$
$$= 2Q\{2QH_n(Q) - 2nH_{n-1}(Q)\} - 2(n+1)H_n(Q)$$
$$= 4Q^2 H_n(Q) - 2n\{H_n(Q) + 2(n-1)H_{n-2}(Q)\} - 2(n+1)H_n(Q),$$

whence

$$4Q^2 H_n(Q) = H_{n+2}(Q) + (4n+2)H_n(Q) + 4n(n-1)H_{n-2}(Q)$$

showing, by the same argument as before, that the term $*\psi_i(Q)\, Q^2\, \psi_j(Q)*$ in $*\phi_i\, \mathscr{G}\, \phi_j*$ leads only to transitions with $i = j \pm 2$. The frequency of the line so produced will be double (or approximately so if the harmonicity is imperfect) that of the fundamental; it is known as the first overtone. The terms from the second sum in (A) with $h \neq k$ give rise similarly to combination lines whose frequencies are the sum of those of two different fundamentals. The question of the appearance of either overtones or combination lines again turns on the non-vanishing of a g, and only those g are non-vanishing for which the analysis of the product of the characters of Q_h and Q_k includes, for infra-red spectra, a representation in common with a component of the translation vector, or, for Raman spectra, a representation in common with the tensor α. We leave it to the reader to make the application of this part of the technique to the analysis of ozone.

A few general principles can be demonstrated. Since the tensor on which the Raman effect is based transforms like $(x^2, y^2, z^2, xy, xz, yz)$, and this includes the invariant $x^2+y^2+z^2$, vibrations in the totally symmetrical (A) class are always Raman active. Their combinations with other modes behave like the other mode. First overtones are always Raman active, since the square of a character, by the orthogonality rules, always contains the totally symmetric representation once and once only.

17.8. The structure of ozone (ii)

We chose ozone for discussion in § 10.4 on account of its suitability as a problem in which structure and symmetry could be clearly related. In fact it has proved a relatively intractable problem on which the last word has yet to be said. There are two reasons for this. First there are the practical difficulties (a) of obtaining ozone in a pure state in a form concentrated enough to yield reliably informative spectra, and (b) that it is unstable towards exciting agents such as heat. These considerations practically restrict us to the absorption spectra, and we are thus deprived of some of the techniques we have described for identifying frequencies. Secondly, an accidental coincidence of frequencies has complicated the interpretation. Herzberg (1945) quotes and identifies the infra-red lines as in the following table, to which we have added a later interpretation due to Dewar:

Herzberg (obtuse-angled C_{2v})				Dewar (acute-angled C_{2v})	
$\left.\begin{array}{l}695 \\ 725\end{array}\right\}$ 710	doublet ? strong		$\nu_2(a_1)$	705	ν_3 bending of O_2-O
1043·4	doublet ? v. strong		$\nu_1(a_1)$	1043	ν_2 stretching of O_2-O
$\left.\begin{array}{l}1724 \\ 1740\end{array}\right\}$ 1740	doublet ? weak		$\nu_3(b_1)$	1740	$\nu_2+\nu_3$
2105	?	strong	$2\nu_1(3\nu_2)(A_1)$	2108	ν_1 stretching of $O=O$
2800	?	weak	$2\nu_1+\nu_2(A_1)$	2800	
3050	?	weak	$3\nu_1(A_1)$	3050	

(These 'lines' are band-heads, of course, and the query as to the doublet character is due to the difficulty of being certain of the absence of a weak 'Q-branch'.) The coincidence lies in the fact that $1740 \simeq 1043+710$ (Herzberg) or that $2108 \simeq 2.1043$ (Dewar). What is clear is that D_{3h}, which gives rise to *two* fundamentals, *one active only in overtones*, is an impossible basis for the interpretation, and that $D_{\infty h}$, which does not allow binary combinations of active bands, seems to be equally impossible.

Discrimination between the obtuse and acute angled isosceles models (the unsymmetrical model is quantum-mechanically unlikely) turns on quantitative considerations outside our scope. Herzberg rejected the identification which Dewar advocates—an inherently reasonable one, since it regards the three strongest lines as fundamentals—on the grounds that it leads to one impossibly large force-constant (twice that in O_2). Dewar meets this partly by a re-estimate of the constants but more by a revision of the electronic structure of which we give our own treatment below, and he further supports this interpretation of the acute-angled structure by an identification, in terms of his molecular orbitals, of the electronic absorption lines. 'The debate continues.'

Dewar's assumption is that after the formation of an O_2 molecule there will be a further readjustment of orbitals if an O approaches it along its median plane, and that this will lead to a stable configuration at a distance greater than that corresponding to an equilateral triangle. To investigate this we suppose B and C to be the atoms of the O_2, its axis the X-axis, and A to lie on the Z-axis, and we label the twelve two-quantum atomic orbitals $A_s,...,C_z$, all positive lobes being in the positive direction of the appropriate axis. These axes are conventionally correct for the whole system, which has C_{2v} symmetry, but not for the O_2 molecule. To avoid confusion we shall label the molecular orbitals of the O_2 according to the following scheme:

Axis as named here	Axis as named in O_2 theory	Nomenclature for O_2 orbitals
X	Z	ζ
Y	Y	η
Z	X	ξ

As the symmetry is C_{2v} we can analyse the twelve orbitals thus:

		A	B	D_1	D_2
$3s$	$2A+D_1$	A_s; $\frac{1}{2}\sqrt{2}(B_s+C_s)$		$\frac{1}{2}\sqrt{2}(B_s-C_s)$	
$3p_x$	$A+2D_1$	$\frac{1}{2}\sqrt{2}(B_x-C_x)$		A_x; $\frac{1}{2}\sqrt{2}(B_x+C_x)$	
$3p_y$	$B+2D_2$		$\frac{1}{2}\sqrt{2}(B_y-C_y)$		A_y; $\frac{1}{2}\sqrt{2}(B_y+C_y)$
$3p_z$	$2A+D_1$	A_z; $\frac{1}{2}\sqrt{2}(B_z+C_z)$		$\frac{1}{2}\sqrt{2}(B_z-C_z)$	

There is possibly further hybridization between orbitals in the same column. When A is a large distance from BC, the A orbitals and the combinations of y and z orbitals shown above will all be unperturbed, but the s and x orbitals of atoms B and C will be hybridized to the σ and σ^* orbitals of the O_2 as in the treatment of § 17.3. When A is close enough to make the configuration that of an equilateral triangle, the symmetry becomes D_{3h}. The analysis is

$3s$	$A+E$
$3y$	D_2+F
$3x+3z$	$A+B+2E$

with

D_{3h}	A	B	D_2	E	F
C_{2v}	A	D_2	B	$A+D_1$	$B+D_2$

(The inversion of B and D_2 which occurs here and which our notation is supposed to avoid, occurs because the Z-axis of a threefold symmetry is conventionally the threefold axis.) In these circumstances we can lay out the twelve orbitals in the following scheme:

D_{3h} \ C_{2v}	$5A$	B	$4D_1$	$2D_2$
$2A$	* *			
B			*	
D_2				*
$3E$	* * *		* * *	
F		*		*

We are still ignorant of the precise mode of hybridization between orbitals within each rectangle of this table, but the choice of the two basic orbitals in a two-dimensional representation is governed by the condition that they are the correct zeroth approximations for the less symmetrical state when A is not quite at the correct distance from BC, and furthermore, the six E orbitals must be chosen in three correct pairs. A set of orbitals satisfying these conditions is shown in Table 17.8.1.

It is immediately apparent that the orbital $\frac{1}{2}\sqrt{2}(B_y-C_y)$ of the original O_2 (a, π^*, orbital) is entirely unaffected by the approach of the O, but that the π-bonding orbital $\frac{1}{2}\sqrt{2}(B_y+C_y)$ hybridizes with the A_y orbital to form (1) a bonding orbital with the charge concentrated in the centre of the triangle, and (2) an anti-bonding orbital which becomes degenerate

TABLE 17.8.1

		5A			B		4D₁			2D₂		
	A_2	$\frac{1}{2}\sqrt{2}(B_x+C_x)$	$\frac{1}{2}\sqrt{2}(B_x-C_x)$	$\frac{1}{2}\sqrt{2}(B_3+C_3)$	A_3	$\frac{1}{2}\sqrt{2}(B_1-C_1)$	A_z	$\frac{1}{2}\sqrt{2}(B_x+C_x)$	$\frac{1}{2}\sqrt{2}(B_3-C_3)$	$\frac{1}{2}\sqrt{2}(B_2-C_2)$	A_y	$\frac{1}{2}\sqrt{2}(B_y+C_y)$
	$O\,2p_z$	$O_2\,\pi_\xi\,2p$	$O_2\,\sigma\,2s$ & $2p$		$O\,2s$	$O_2\,\pi^*_\eta\,2p$	$O\,2p_x$	$O_2\,\sigma^*\,2s$ & $\sigma^*\,2p$		$O_2\,\pi^*_\xi\,2p$	$O\,2p_y$	$O_2\,\pi_\eta\,2p$
2A { 1	$\sqrt{\frac{1}{4}}$	$-\sqrt{\frac{1}{8}}$	$\sqrt{\frac{3}{8}}$									
2				$\sqrt{\frac{3}{8}}$								
B 3					$\sqrt{\frac{1}{3}}$		$\sqrt{\frac{1}{2}}$	$-\sqrt{\frac{1}{8}}$		$\sqrt{\frac{3}{8}}$	$\sqrt{\frac{1}{3}}$	$\sqrt{\frac{1}{3}}$
D 4						1						
3E { 5,6		$-\sqrt{\frac{3}{8}}$	$-\sqrt{\frac{1}{4}}$						1			
7,8	$\sqrt{\frac{1}{4}}$	$\sqrt{\frac{3}{4}}$	$\sqrt{\frac{3}{8}}$	$-\sqrt{\frac{1}{8}}$	$\sqrt{\frac{3}{8}}$		$\sqrt{\frac{1}{2}}$	$\sqrt{\frac{1}{8}}$ $\sqrt{\frac{3}{4}}$		$-\sqrt{\frac{1}{4}}$ $\sqrt{\frac{3}{8}}$	$\sqrt{\frac{3}{8}}$	$-\sqrt{\frac{1}{3}}$
F { 9,10												
11,12												

with $\frac{1}{2}\sqrt{2}(B_y - C_y)$ as soon as the triangle becomes equilateral. If we write

$$\pi'_\eta\, 2p = \sqrt{\frac{\delta^2}{3}}\, A_y + \sqrt{\left(1 - \frac{\delta^2}{3}\right)}\, \pi_\eta\, 2p,$$

$$\pi'^*_\eta\, 2p = \sqrt{\left(1 - \frac{\delta^2}{3}\right)}\, A_y + \sqrt{\frac{\delta^2}{3}}\, \pi_\eta\, 2p$$

it will be a reasonable assumption, though no more, that δ increases monotonically from 0 to 1 as A approaches BC from infinity to the equilateral position. We have thus a three-dimensional subspace of wave space in which the basic orbitals are, according to circumstances,

In 3O	*In O$_2$+O*	*In O$_3$*
A_y	A_y	π'
B_y	$\frac{1}{2}\sqrt{2}(B_y + C_y)$	π'^*
C_y	$\frac{1}{2}\sqrt{2}(B_y - C_y)$	π^*

This is completely in agreement with Dewar's conclusions, and the notation for O_3 is his.

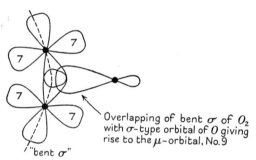

Overlapping of bent σ of O_2 with σ-type orbital of O giving rise to the μ-orbital, No. 9

"bent σ"

FIG. 33. Ozone.

The remaining orbitals are not quite so straightforward, and allow rather more latitude in interpretation. Pictorially, orbital No. 7 shows that the B_z and C_z orbitals which make up the O_2 'pivot on their nuclei as the O forces itself between them'. The $\frac{1}{2}\sqrt{2}(B_x - C_x)$, which is the chief contributor to the B—C σ-bond, rotates similarly, but it also hybridizes with the A_z orbital and is completely hybridized by the time the O reaches the equilateral position. The process is illustrated in Fig. 33, and can be described as a bending of the σ-bond, convex to the A atom, as a result of which it becomes, in the neighbourhood of the A atom, sufficiently like the p_z orbital of a single atom that, by a process analogous to the formation of a σ-bond, a new type of bond can be formed. Dewar calls this a μ-bond. μ-bonds analogous to π-bonds are also possible; the bond denoted by $\pi'_\eta\,2p$ above is of this type.

Adopting the hypothesis of 'monotonically varying coefficients' used above, we can develop a further part of Table 17.8.1 thus:

Orbital No.	A_z	$\frac{1}{2}\sqrt{2}(B_z+C_z)$	$\frac{1}{2}\sqrt{2}(B_x-C_x)$	$\frac{1}{2}\sqrt{2}(B_s+C_s)$	A_s	In O_2—O	In O_3
1				$\sqrt{(1-\frac{1}{3}\gamma^2)}$	$\sqrt{(\frac{1}{3}\gamma^2)}$	$2s\sigma$	
2	$\sqrt{(\frac{1}{2}\beta^2)}$	$-\sqrt{(1-\frac{1}{2}\beta^2)\frac{1}{4}\alpha^2}$	$-\sqrt{(1-\frac{1}{2}\beta^2)(1-\frac{1}{4}\alpha^2)}$			$2p\sigma$	$2p\sigma'$
5				$-\sqrt{(\frac{1}{3}\gamma^2)}$	$\sqrt{(1-\frac{1}{3}\gamma^2)}$	A_s	
7		$\sqrt{(1-\frac{1}{4}\alpha^2)}$	$-\sqrt{(\frac{1}{4}\alpha^2)}$			$2p\pi_\xi$	
9	$\sqrt{(1-\frac{1}{2}\beta^2)}$	$\sqrt{(\frac{1}{2}\beta^2)(\frac{1}{4}\alpha^2)}$	$\sqrt{(\frac{1}{2}\beta^2)(1-\frac{1}{4}\alpha^2)}$			A_z	$2p\sigma'^*$

It is here that our conclusions seem most at variance with Dewar's. We have assumed, possibly incorrectly, (1) that the major contributor to any D_{3h} orbital is the one into which it changes adiabatically as A recedes, and where this criterion fails, (2) that orbital No. 2 is of lower energy than orbital No. 9 and therefore, by the 'non-crossing rule', that it is adiabatically continuous with $\frac{1}{2}\sqrt{2}(B_x-C_x)$ which has a lower energy than A_x. If detailed calculations show either of these assumptions to be wrong, it merely means that other rule-of-thumb criteria must be found to continue the argument from the point at which group theory leaves us. It is also to be borne in mind (a) that $\frac{1}{2}\sqrt{2}(B_x-C_x)$ and $\frac{1}{2}\sqrt{2}(B_s+C_s)$ are certainly hybridized to some extent in O_2+O, a feature we have made no allowance for, since of several simple possibilities none is convincing, (b) that similar arguments should be applied to the four orbitals with D_1 symmetry, independently of the above since the degeneracy occurs only in the equilateral triangle model, and (c) that it should not be assumed that α, β, and γ tend from 0 to 1 at equal rates. The criterion in this last point is that orbitals which cease to overlap most rapidly as A recedes will also dehybridize most rapidly. On this ground Dewar assumes that in the acute-angled model of ozone A_x and $\frac{1}{2}\sqrt{2}(B_x+C_x)$ do not hybridize whereas A_z and $\frac{1}{2}\sqrt{2}(B_z+C_z)$ do.

There are eighteen electrons in the two-quantum orbits of ozone, and therefore nine of the twelve orbitals are filled. This involves filling and leaving unfilled bonding and antibonding orbitals respectively which are bonding or antibonding in the sense of binding the O to the O_2, and therefore lead to a stable aggregate of three oxygen atoms.

(NOTE: The significance of the foregoing discussion is considerably modified by the fact that the most recent spectroscopic work on ozone, by Pitzer, seems to support the obtuse-angled model. But it remains valid as an illustration of a particular method of attacking this type of problem, and the method could equally be applied to configurations between the *linear* and equilateral ones.

I am indebted to Professor Dewar for drawing my attention to Pitzer's work, and for the following comment 'I don't think our conclusions do differ much; our tables of symmetry orbitals agree, and the subsequent treatments differ only in the assumptions about the relative magnitudes of resonance integrals . . . which . . . must depend entirely on intuition in the absence of actual calculations and there's no reason why intuitions shouldn't differ !' Intuition is a tricky gift at the best of times, but at times indispensable, and then the more legs it has to stand on the better. The type of argument given here is simply one leg, of course. The 'hypothesis of monotonically increasing coefficients' is probably most safe with wave functions having the smallest number of nodal surfaces, and less safe with wave functions of higher order.)

17.9. Related problems in crystals

In this section we discuss briefly the adaptation to crystals of the theories of orbitals and spectra developed for molecules in the previous sections.

The spectra of crystals are discussed by Bhagavantam and Venkatarayudu. Nuclear displacements must be real, and the only real representations of the lattice translation group are those associating ± 1 with the basic lattice vectors. On the basis of an elaboration of this argument they deduce that the vibrations of an atom must be in phase with those of the corresponding atom in the *next cell but one*, though they may be in antiphase with those of the atom in the next cell, and thence that the complete analysis of the modes of vibration of a crystal can be accomplished by an analysis of the vibrations of a 2^3-fold unit cell. We refer the reader to their work for further discussion of this procedure and examples, as also for an introduction to the calculation of the characters for the analysis in the difficult case, which arises also in free molecules, when the form of the potential energy function is such that there is free rotation in certain of the normal modes.

The idea of 'crystal orbitals' is an attractive one but not as useful as appears at first sight. When there is one atom per cell, its orbitals will already have been analysed on the assumption that there is a slight perturbing field having the crystal symmetry (Bethe's analysis). The requirement that a crystal orbital conform to a representation of the symmetry group of the lattice is then fulfilled already except as regards the lattice translation group. The representations of this group are all one-dimensional and the effect of this requirement is that in the formation of variants by combination of atomic orbitals there shall be a regular phase difference in the coefficients of terms from successive atoms. If the orbitals are deep the result is no more interesting than was the combination of the KK orbitals in chlorine or oxygen.

More interesting is the case in which the electrons are free. In the central field problem this means that their kinetic energy is still positive at distances from the origin at which the potential field is sensibly uniform, and therefore the wave function at such distances is approximately periodic. In the crystal problem it is sufficient that their kinetic energy remains positive up to the maximum of the potential field between two neighbouring nuclei, where, because the potential is a maximum, it is again approximately uniform and the wave function approximately periodic. In these circumstances some form of crystal orbital theory is essential. Brillouin has applied the theory referred to at the end of § 9.8 to such wave functions. Taking the maximum of the potential field as zero and assuming that the wells around the nuclei are fairly localized, the wave function is periodic except near the nuclei, its wavelength being proportional to the square root of its energy (equation (16.6.1)). Each permissible orbital can then be represented by a vector in the reciprocal space, the square of its length giving its energy. If a vector is permissible, then corresponding vectors into more distant cells of the reciprocal space are also possible and represent higher levels. In crystals of high symmetry there is considerable degeneracy, and the splitting of degenerate levels into levels of higher and lower energy means that each original degenerate level becomes a 'banned' value for the energy, these banned values separating the reciprocal space into 'zones'. The lower levels in each zone are levels raised from the banned level below and the higher levels in a zone are lowered from the banned level above so that each zone contains what in molecular orbital language would be called antibonding and bonding levels, except that the first zone contains only bonding levels. A stable crystal thus forms when the number of electrons is just adequate to fill a zone. In this way the Hume-Rothery rules for the composition of alloys, which relate the average number of free electrons per atom to the preferred crystal structure, are explained.

In molecular crystals the molecule may not be in an environment showing the full symmetry of the crystal. In such a case repetition of the molecule *complete with its orbitals* will restore the crystal symmetry, and the orbitals can be combined to give cell orbitals before any building of crystal orbitals is attempted. A more interesting case would occur if the repetition is not exact—for example, in a crystal with atoms on a simple fourfold axis and only one of the p_x, p_y orbitals filled, the lowest crystal orbitals might conceivably be found to have a *screw* symmetry. Little has been done on these problems, but the forces which hold a crystal together must, when not electrostatic, have their origin in these effects.

(*Note added in proof*: Recently a certain amount of interest in the calculation of orbitals in crystals seems to have arisen; a few typical references have been added to the Bibliography, pp. 447–8.)

CHAPTER XVIII

EDDINGTON'S QUANTUM RELATIVITY

WE have seen how quantum mechanics can be developed from the starting-point of 'observation is interference', or, more fundamentally, perhaps, 'all numerical knowledge is the result of an operation performed by us on the universe'. In Chapter XVI this principle was only pushed as far as was necessary to provide a consistent mathematical physics which should be an improvement on the classical one in its correspondence with experiment. In his book *Fundamental Theory*, Eddington has pushed this principle much further; he starts by remarking that observation in the form of measurement is a relatively complex type of observation, and he works out the implications of this on the matrix operators which must represent it in our symbolism. It would appear that very little else is necessary in order to set up the whole structure of physics, but such a statement can only be judged at the end of the argument—not at the beginning.

It will be realized that in a line of reasoning which starts at the nature of measurement and develops to such results as the electron-proton mass ratio, there must be changes in the type of argument employed, and consequently some difficulty in following it as a single line, and that this difficulty can be avoided since the argument makes contact at several points with familiar results. For this reason Eddington adopts what in other contexts is known as the 'flash-back technique'; he starts by assuming certain results of relativity and quantum theory and discusses the relation between them; later he goes back to the more primitive group-theory on which he bases them, and only at the end does he give the real beginning of the story. Unfortunately the final chapters of *Fundamental Theory*, one on the nature of measurement and one a summary of the book, were never written. In lieu of the former we have in an appendix a reprint of an earlier paper (*Proc. Cambridge Phil. Soc.* **40** (1944), 37), which was to have been expanded.

Despite the advantages of the flash-back technique, it will be more convenient here to begin at the beginning—the Appendix to *Fundamental Theory*. In this Eddington states his aim—to calculate the number of protons and electrons in the universe. And he says:

Before calculating their number it would not be unreasonable to demand a definition of 'proton' and 'electron' . . . . But the present investigation is more ambitious. It seeks to determine N directly from the principles of measurement. The proposition is that, as soon as we become obsessed with the idea that the right way to find out about the universe is to measure things, we are committed to an analytical conception which divides the universe into $\frac{3}{2}.136.2^{256}$ particles. Naturally, in the course of counting the particles, we shall arrive at a mathematical specification of that which is being counted ... and identify them with (observational) protons and electrons.

The number $\frac{3}{2}.136.2^{256}$ he calls the *cosmic number*, and the argument he calls a prologue and an epilogue to physics. We reproduce the prologue in the next two sections and the epilogue in outline in § 18.12. The intervening sections are physics itself from an unusual view-point suggested by the cosmic number argument. It has been impossible to isolate completely the parts which are applications of group-theory from those which are not, and when it has been necessary to incorporate material irrelevant to the subject of this book, we have not hesitated to save space by replacing Eddington's arguments by shorter ones which are of less generality or even analogical in character. This apart we follow Eddington quite closely and it will save wearisome repetition if we say here that in the sequel, whenever the context does not prove the contrary, 'we' means 'following Eddington, we'.

18.2. The nature of measurement

The first question to be dealt with is the possibility of an observation, and this depends on the existence of what we are trying to observe. 'Mere observation' of something is equivalent to 'ascertaining its existence or non-existence', and precedes any question of detailed properties. In conformity with current probability theory we associate the number 1 with existence and 0 with non-existence, and we say that 'mere observation' is an operator J with two eigenvalues, 1 (meaning 'there'), and 0 (meaning 'not there'). The observation of the existence or otherwise of different objects A, B,... will be associated with different operators J_a, J_b,..., each of this type, and, unless the existences of the separate objects are interdependent, in different carrier spaces.

Measurement is much more complicated than observation. The simplest measurement, measurement of length, requires both ends of the object (which we may call A and B) and both ends of the measuring scale (which we may call C and D) to be there before it is possible. Their existences are completely independent of one another. Thus if we have a system on which the operations of J_a, J_b, J_c, and J_d all produce the answer 1, the operation $M = $ 'measurement possible?' will also yield the answer 1, but if *any* of the operators $J_a, ..., J_d$ yield the answer 0, then M will also yield the answer 0. M is thus an operator whose eigenvalues are the sixteen possible products of those of $J_a, ..., J_d$. It is therefore the 16×16 matrix which is the Kronecker product of the four 2×2 matrices which represent the J's.

There is a further requisite for measurement, which need not trouble us at this stage, namely, the existence of such regularity in the background as makes possible the *graduation* of the scale. If, on the other hand, we take the existence of the measuring rod completely for granted, then a 4×4 matrix will be sufficient. This simplification proves to be permissible in all those parts of the work which do *not* form part of the calculation of the cosmic number.

And here it will be as well to remind ourselves that a physical system always arises by our ignoring all of the universe except the part we are interested in, and that the more we ignore, the simpler we may expect the carrier space to be. Otherwise we are apt to get worried by the fact that at one time a two-dimensional vector seems adequate to represent the universe, and at another a sixteen-vector is necessary. The true carrier-space for the whole universe is immensely more complicated, but these simpler spaces are contained within it, or obtained by projection from it.

18.3. Measures and measurables

In an argument such as the present one, however, it is hardly possible to ignore any part of the universe, and we are confronted with the problem of how to consider, without approximation, a single measurement which does not ignore any part of the universe. There is one way in which this can be done. We can define the results of the measurement, and ask how many particles satisfy the conditions of our definition. The results of our measurement we may then call the measure, and since they are the properties of the particle—its only properties, since we are going to use the results of this process to define what we mean by a particle—the particle may be called a measurable. As an aid to thought we may suppose the results of a measurement to be three position and three momentum coordinates, with a time coordinate and possibly mass and some electrical properties, so that our question asks how many particle-points occupy a certain volume of phase space at a particular time and also fulfil certain mass and electrical specifications. But this should be merely an aid to thought, as we are not going to prejudge how many independent variables must be specified to complete the description of a particle.

Any measure is possible, since it is only a thought-process; if we are tempted to call a certain measure impossible, all we mean is that the number of particles occupying it is necessarily zero. But the number of particles in a measure must be a positive integer or zero. It simplifies the mathematics, however, and corresponds more with the fact that we normally consider *changes* in physics, if we alter our ground somewhat, and consider the excess of the number of particles over some large average number. The number of particles must then be a positive or negative integer. Counting the number of particles must then be an operator whose eigenvalues are all the positive and negative numbers up to some very large number which we may at this stage treat as infinite. The characteristic equation of this operator, which we shall call K, is therefore

$$K(K^2-1)(K^2-4)(K^2-9)... = 0$$

or, equivalently, dividing by the square of the factorial of the largest possible eigenvalue

$$K\left(1-\frac{K^2}{1}\right)\left(1-\frac{K^2}{4}\right)\left(1-\frac{K^2}{9}\right)... = \pi^{-1}\sin \pi K = 0,$$

where the second expression assumes that the number of factors is large enough to be treated as infinite.

Let K'_m be the eigensymbol of K with eigenvalue m (see § 7.7). Then K'_1 is the symbol which represents one excess particle, because when the question 'what occupies?' is asked of it, it answers 'one'. Now since, as we saw in Chapter XVI, systems are combined by multiplying their symbols, we have $K'_m = (K'_1)^m$. Now

$$\frac{d}{d\log K'_1}(K'_1)^m = m(K'_1)^m,$$

so that $$K = d/d\log K'_1,$$

which we can summarize to advantage by introducing a new symbol θ and writing

$$K = -i\frac{d}{d\theta}, \qquad K'_1 = e^{i\theta}.$$

By the first of these relations, θ is a coordinate conjugate with the 'momentum' K. θ is not necessarily a scalar; it is called 'phase'.

Using Taylor's theorem and the relations already established,

$$f(\theta+\pi)-f(\theta-\pi) = e^{\pi d/d\theta}f(\theta)-e^{-\pi d/d\theta}f(\theta)$$
$$= 2i\sin\pi K . f(\theta)$$
$$= 0.$$

This is a very remarkable relation, although, as we have said, θ is not necessarily a scalar. It shows that θ behaves as an angle.

We now have two pieces of information about measurables. First that they are (or contain) 16×16 matrices which for many purposes can be simplified to 4×4 matrices, and, secondly, that they are expressible in terms of θ which has the properties of a rotation. We shall further require that θ shall contain within itself two things, (1) the results of the measurement, and (2) the identity of the thing being measured. It is the latter which leads Eddington to his cosmic number.

18.4. The E-frame and sedenion algebra

In §§ 3.9 and 12.3 we saw that the algebra of 2×2 matrices can be expressed as a linear algebra in a number of ways, and that one of them, the quaternion system, is closely related to the rotation group in three dimensions. In § 13.10 we extended this to n dimensions and saw that when $n = 2k$ or $2k+1$, an algebra of 2^n elements generated by n elements, with a representation in 2^k dimensions, called the Clifford algebra, results. The essential feature of the relation of these algebras to the rotation groups lies in the fact that each generating element is a square root of $-I$, for it is this property which permits of a sufficient number of simultaneous independent 'Argand–de Moivre expressions'

$$(\cos\theta\, e_0+\sin\theta\, e_i)^n = \cos n\theta\, e_0+\sin n\theta\, e_i.$$

The algebra employed by Eddington differs in an apparently insignificant but in fact far-reaching feature from the Clifford algebras, namely, that instead of $e_0 = I$, he uses an element equal to iI. The significance of this is, as we shall see, that on replacing i by $-i$ a different algebra results. It will be advantageous to study the 4×4 matrices first, and to develop the algebra in a slightly different way from the approach of § 13.10.

We therefore take two sets of quaternion-like elements

$$\eta_1 = \begin{bmatrix} 1 & 0 \\ 0 & 1 \end{bmatrix}, \quad \eta_{02} = \begin{bmatrix} i & 0 \\ 0 & -i \end{bmatrix}, \quad \eta_{21} = \begin{bmatrix} 0 & -1 \\ 1 & 0 \end{bmatrix}, \quad \eta_{10} = \begin{bmatrix} 0 & -i \\ -i & 0 \end{bmatrix},$$

$$\zeta_1 = \begin{bmatrix} 1 & 0 \\ 0 & 1 \end{bmatrix}, \quad \zeta_{35} = \begin{bmatrix} i & 0 \\ 0 & -i \end{bmatrix}, \quad \zeta_{54} = \begin{bmatrix} 0 & 1 \\ -1 & 0 \end{bmatrix}, \quad \zeta_{43} = \begin{bmatrix} 0 & i \\ i & 0 \end{bmatrix}.$$

It will be noticed that one of them differs from the other in the sign of two of its elements; this, as well as the particular suffix notation employed, is designed to conform with Eddington's notation in the finished product. But the point is unimportant, as it is the algebras, not their particular representations (so long as they are in matrices of the correct size) which are important. We next combine these two sets by Kronecker multiplication into sixteen elements, multiplying by i when necessary to preserve the feature that the square of every element is $-I$. The resulting elements are called *E-symbols*. We number them as follows:

$$i(\eta_1 \times \zeta_1) = E_{16}, \qquad \eta_{pq} \times \zeta_1 = E_{pq}, \qquad \eta_1 \times \zeta_{pq} = E_{pq},$$

$$i(\eta_{pq} \times \zeta_{rs}) = E_{tu}, \quad \text{where } p, q, r, s, t, u \text{ is an even permutation}$$
$$\text{of } 0, 1, 2, 3, 4, 5.$$

Introducing the convention that $E_{qp} = -E_{pq}$, we have an algebra which can be verified (most easily by an application of (5.6.7)) to have the multiplication table:

$$E_{pq} E_{rs} = E_{16} E_{tu} \quad (= iE_{tu}),$$

$$E_{pq} E_{pq} = -I \quad (= iE_{16}),$$

$$E_{pq} E_{pr} = E_{qr}.$$

The student should carry out the Kronecker multiplications, and obtain the explicit 4×4 matrix forms for the E-symbols. He should thence verify that they do form a basis for an arbitrary complex 4×4 matrix, and that they are either real and antisymmetric or pure imaginary and symmetric, noting which are which for future reference.

We have thus found a particular solution to the problem of finding quantities with (*a*) four eigenvalues and (*b*) the properties of a rotation, since (1) the E-symbols form a basis for an arbitrary 4×4 matrix, and (2) every E_{pq} is a square root of $-I$. Obviously other solutions exist, since the original quaternion bases are not unique. We shall call any equivalent set of matrices an *E-frame*.

We distinguish certain sets of E-symbols by special names, viz.:

Cyclic triads E_{pq}, E_{qr}, E_{rp}, to each of which there is a *conjugate triad* E_{st}, E_{tu}, E_{us}. Within a triad the symbols anticommute ($AB = -BA$), but two symbols one from each triad commute.

Anti-triads E_{pq}, E_{rs}, E_{tu}, or, with E_{16} added, *anti-tetrads*. All members of an anti-tetrad commute with each other.

Pentads E_{pq}, E_{pr}, E_{ps}, E_{pt}, E_{pu}. All the symbols of a pentad anticommute with each other. Each symbol is a member of two pentads; it thus anticommutes with eight other symbols and commutes with eight (including itself and E_{16}). Any four members of a pentad constitute a *tetrad*.

A *generating set* is a set of E-symbols sufficient by inter-multiplication to generate the whole sixteen. Four are required, with E_{16} to define chirality (see next paragraph), and they may be either (1) two members from each of two conjugate triads (effectively the method we have used), or (2) four members of a tetrad (which, with I instead of E_{16}, is the method used in § 13.10 for generating the Clifford algebra).

In three dimensions we are familiar with the fact that reversing the direction of either one or three of the axes converts a right-handed frame into a left-handed one. In a right-handed frame $\eta_1 \eta_2 = \eta_3$ but in a left-handed one $\eta_1 \eta_2 = -\eta_3$, so that the algebras are different. We introduced the word 'chirality' in § 14.7; we shall also describe two right-handed systems (or two left-handed systems) as 'homochiral', whereas two systems of 'opposite handedness' will be described as 'antichiral'. In an E-frame, chirality depends on the sign of E_{16}; reversing it prefixes a minus sign to the two expressions in brackets in the multiplication table (corresponding to the change in sign in the three-dimensional case noted above), but the unbracketed forms are unaltered, so that the algebra itself does duty for both types of system, chirality only appearing when we substitute for E_{16}. It is here that the advantage of Eddington's modification of the Clifford unit element appears.

A frame antichiral to the one we have set up can therefore be obtained by picking out any generating set from it, and then using $-i$ instead of $+i$ for E_{16}. Of all the possibilities this opens, the one which proves most useful for future purposes is that based on the tetrad generating set E_{12}, E_{13}, E_{14}, E_{15}. Confining p, q, r, s to 2, 3, 4, 5, we have, for the remaining elements,

$$E_{pq} = E_{1p} E_{1q}, \qquad E_{0p} = -E_{16} E_{1q} E_{rs}, \qquad E_{01} = E_{0p} E_{1p},$$

so that as well as the four generating elements, the six elements E_{pq} are unaffected by the change in sign of E_{16}, while the five members of the pentad based on the suffix 0 have their sign changed. Now the only part of physics in which a sign in a formula depends on the chirality of our axes is electro-magnetism. We shall therefore anticipate, and call those E-symbols which change in sign 'electrical' and those which do not 'mechanical' (though this a slight over-simplification, as we shall see).

The double classification of E-symbols into real and imaginary, electrical and mechanical, is exceedingly important in the theory. It may be summarized in the following table:

	Imaginary symbols (10)	Real symbols(6)
Electrical symbols (6) .	E_{16} $E_{01} E_{02} E_{03}$	$E_{04} E_{05}$
Mechanical symbols (10) .	$E_{14} E_{24} E_{34}$ $E_{15} E_{25} E_{35}$	$E_{12} E_{13} E_{23}$ E_{45}

18.5. Rotations and reality conditions

If $E'_{ab} = RE_{ab} R^{-1}$, where R is any non-singular matrix, i.e. any non-singular element of the E-algebra (any non-singular linear combination of E-symbols), then the E' obey the same multiplication table as the E. E_{16} commutes with every matrix, and is thus transformed into itself; the new frame therefore has the same chirality as the old one. We already know this process as a change of coordinates, of course, and in this chapter we shall refer to it simply as a rotation. The simplest type of rotation is obtained from

$$R = \exp\left(\tfrac{1}{2}E_{pq}\theta\right) \quad = I \cos\tfrac{1}{2}\theta + E_{pq}\sin\tfrac{1}{2}\theta,$$
$$R^{-1} = \exp\left(-\tfrac{1}{2}E_{pq}\theta\right) = I \cos\tfrac{1}{2}\theta - E_{pq}\sin\tfrac{1}{2}\theta.$$

Since $RE_{ab} R^{-1} = E_{ab}$ if E_{pq} commutes with E_{ab} but equals $E_{ab} R^2$ if it anticommutes, we have, when p, q, r, s are all different,

$$E'_{rs} = E_{rs}, \qquad E'_{16} = E_{16}, \qquad E'_{pq} = E_{pq},$$
$$E'_{pr} = E_{pr}\cos\theta + E_{qr}\sin\theta,$$
$$E'_{qr} = E_{qr}\cos\theta - E_{pr}\sin\theta.$$

Thus, for example,

$R = \exp\tfrac{1}{2}E_{12}\theta$	rotates together	E_{13} and E_{23}	but leaves unaltered	$E_{03}, E_{04},$
		E_{14} and E_{24}		$E_{05}, E_{12},$
		E_{15} and E_{25}		$E_{34}, E_{35},$
		E_{01} and E_{02}		$E_{45}, E_{16}.$

The fourteen other possible $\exp\tfrac{1}{2}E_{pq}\theta$ (omitting E_{16}) link the E's in rotation in other ways, but pairs with no suffix in common (commuting pairs) cannot be so linked. It can be shown, however, that if E'_{ab} are any set of E-numbers (i.e. elements of the E-algebra) which satisfy the multiplication table in the previous section and have the same chirality as the E_{ab}, then there is a transformation $RE_{ab}\,R^{-1} = E'_{ab}$, but in general R will be more complicated in form than the simple exponentials considered here.

As was mentioned in § 16.2, imaginary numbers are a mathematical concept not met with in the laboratory, where all measurements are real numbers. If, therefore, a complex number has any meaning, it must have it by separation into real and imaginary parts and separate identification. The physical relation between the real and imaginary parts is that they have different dimensions but their squares have the same dimensions. It is difficult to give a clear-cut example, since in classical physics the matter is always obscured by the assignment of dimensions to quantities such as permittivity. But in relativity units, with $c = 1$ and $L = T$, electrostatic and electromagnetic units become the same, and we can define the permittivity and the permeability of free space as pure numbers. If we also make the constant of gravitation a pure number, then e^2/r and $-m^2/r$ are respectively the mutual energies of two charges and two masses; both expressions have the same dimensions (energy), but charge and mass are different. Significantly, the electrical and gravitational mutual energies of two like particles are of opposite sign. (This argument is not affected by the fact that in § 15.8 we did not propose to make the constant of gravitation a pure number—all that is actually necessary is that we deal with it and with the permittivity of free space in appropriately related ways.)

As we have seen fit to distinguish real and imaginary E-symbols, we shall have to define a physically real rotation as one which does not upset this distinction; if E_{pr} is real (imaginary), then

$$E'_{pr} = E_{pr}\cos\theta + E_{qr}\sin\theta$$

must also be real (imaginary).

We call two real or two imaginary quantities homothetic, whereas a real and an imaginary quantity are described as antithetic. For a physically real rotation, then, $\cos\theta$ must be real and $E_{qr}\sin\theta$ must be homothetic with E_{pr}. Reference to the multiplication table shows the latter condition to be equivalent to $E_{pq}\sin\theta$ being real, in which form the condition is seen to be independent of r. The reality of $E_{pq}\sin\theta$ implies in its turn that E_{pq} and θ are homothetic. Thus the rotations based on the real E_{pq} are circular; those based on the imaginary E_{pq} are hyperbolic (Lorentz).

If, in the same way, we wish to preserve the distinction between electrical and mechanical E-symbols, we find, quite simply, that rotations based on any E-symbol involving the suffix 0 are banned. But whereas the distinction between real and imaginary numbers is fundamental, that between mechanical and electrical quantities is perhaps less so, since conditions under which it breaks down are not so much unthinkable, as merely outside our normal experience.

This leads to an important development. Starting with an E-number with only one term, say $a_{12} E_{12}$, we can add further terms by applying rotations. This is the reverse process to that of reducing a vector to a single term by rotating the axes; it is starting with a single term and rotating the axes until no term is zero. If a_{12} is real, so that the whole term $a_{12} E_{12}$ is real, we find that if we restrict ourselves to physically real rotations, every complete new term is real. That is, every a_{pq} so introduced is homothetic with E_{pq}. Alternatively, if we start with a_{12} imaginary, every a_{pq} is antithetic to its E-symbol.

But this conclusion in its general form can only be reached by including the E_{0r} rotations. Without them we cannot extend a single term to include both electrical and mechanical terms, and starting with two terms we reach the less general conclusion that the electrical and mechanical parts separately are homothetic within themselves. But earlier in this section we have seen a reason for regarding charge and mass as antithetic. We therefore lay down the rule that in a physically significant E-number which combines electrical and mechanical terms, the electrical and the mechanical parts must be antithetic.

18.6. Anchoring the E-frame

It is time to get back to physics if we can. (The use of the word 'physical' in the previous section has been somewhat Pickwickian.) The method of doing this is to discover a parallelism in relation-structure between the mathematical quantities we have been handling and the quantities of experimental and theoretical physics. We can do this if we bear certain things in mind.

Primarily we must ask under what conditions we regard two or more numbers as parts of the same vector or tensor. When, for example, do we regard momentum density and energy density as parts of the same quantity? From the present point of view the answer is that as long as our coordinate changes are restricted to space rotations, these quantities appear different, but when we introduce Lorentz rotations they become components of the same tensor. Everything depends, then, on how big a rotation group is included under the expression 'an equivalent co-ordinate system'.

We therefore consider a series of increasingly large rotation groups, choosing them in such a way as to add the least satisfactory rotations last, that is, we begin with circular rotations, then add hyperbolic rotations, but leave to the end all rotations based on the suffix 0. This gives us the groups

(a) E_{12} with structure $\mathfrak{r}_2$

(b) $E_{12}\, E_{13}\, E_{23}$ $\mathfrak{r}_3$

(c) $E_{12}\, E_{13}\, E_{23}\, E_{14}\, E_{24}\, E_{34}$ Lorentz group

(d) all 10 E_{pq} with $p, q = 1, 2, 3, 4, 5$

(e) all 15 E_{pq} excluding E_{16}.

Then starting with a given E_{pq} and applying all the rotations of one of the above groups to it, we find which of the other E_{pq} must be counted with it as components of a single quantity. Omitting (a) as trivial, denoting a scalar by S, a vector by V, and an antisymmetric tensor by T, we find that the general E-number breaks down into scalars, vectors, and tensors in the following way:

Imaginary	Real	Group: Dimensions: (e) 6	(d) 5	(c) 4	(b) 3
Electrical E_{16}		S	S	S	S
$E_{01}\, E_{02}\, E_{03}$	E_{04}			V	V, S
	E_{05}		$\Big\} V$	S	S
		T			
Mechanical $E_{14}\, E_{24}\, E_{34}$	$E_{12}\, E_{13}\, E_{23}$		$\Big\} T$	T	V, T
$E_{15}\, E_{25}\, E_{35}$	E_{45}			V	V, S

The analysis between groups (c) and (b) is just the converse of the process discussed in § 15.5.

We are now in the position, say, of a man who has studied graphs, including curves of the second degree, and has also studied accelerated motion under gravity, and being already knowledgeable about both, realizes that it may serve his purpose and give him a still better understanding if he identifies, for the purpose of his arguments, certain physical quantities with certain of his coordinates and parameters in the mathematics, because the relation structure is the same. There is no need to regard this identification in any wider light. Eddington calls this process 'anchoring the coordinate system'.

A suitable anchoring of the E-frame is achieved as follows. In the four-dimensional scheme, (c), both $p_1 E_{15} + p_2 E_{25} + p_3 E_{35} + p_4 E_{45}$ and $p_1 E_{01} + p_2 E_{02} + p_3 E_{03} + p_4 E_{04}$ are vectors, but the E-symbols in the former are mechanical and those in the latter are electrical. We accordingly associate displacements and momenta with the former, the expression

$$ix_1 E_{15} + ix_2 E_{25} + ix_3 E_{35} + t E_{45} \tag{18.6.1}$$

representing a displacement vector in space-time, and the expression

$$ip_1 E_{15} + ip_2 E_{25} + ip_3 E_{35} + m E_{45} \tag{18.6.2}$$

a momentum vector whose fourth term is the mass (or energy) $m_0 \beta$. Although these two vectors are in the same direction they are distinguished by their dimensions (L and M respectively). The groups (b) and (c) are then the rotation and Lorentz groups of ordinary physics. The coefficient of E_{16} as an electrical scalar is naturally identified as electric charge. An antithetic $E_{15}, ..., E_{45}$ vector will then be $i = E_{16}$ times a displacement or momentum vector, and will be an appropriate form for electric moment (generalized to four dimensions). The product of two displacement vectors has the form

$$-i(x_1 \xi_1 + x_2 \xi_2 + x_3 \xi_3 - t\tau) E_{16} +$$
$$+ (x_1 \xi_2 - x_2 \xi_1) E_{12} + ... + i(x_1 \tau - \xi_1 t) E_{14} + ..., \tag{18.6.3}$$

showing the scalar product of the vectors associated with iE_{16}, and angular displacements in space and space-time (the latter being velocities, of course) associated with E_{12}, E_{13}, E_{23} and E_{14}, E_{24}, E_{34} respectively. If one of the vectors is a momentum vector the latter become angular momentum and a certain unnamed quantity, and the former is action.

Before proceeding any further we might naturally inquire whether there is any advantage to be gained from a five-dimensional anchorage. This would seem to imply that space-time-something is five-dimensional. It turns out that there is considerable advantage to be gained but that the process is not entirely straightforward. Whichever set of symbols $E_{01}, ..., E_{04}$ or $E_{14}, ..., E_{45}$ we try to expand, the natural fifth component is E_{05}, but whereas the combination $\sum p_r E_{0r}$ is an electrical and not a mechanical vector, the combination $\sum p_r E_{r5}$ is not a vector at all. The latter objection is not as serious a matter as it seems. Whichever trail we follow, a rotation involving the fifth dimension breaks down the distinction between linear and angular momenta, exhibiting them as components of one tensor, and thus corresponds to something outside our experience. The combination $\sum p_r E_{rs}$ could be a vector if we modified the five-dimensional rotation group to p, $q = 0$, 1, 2, 3, 4; this is to include rotations banned for violating the distinction between electrical and mechanical E-symbols, but it is quite on the cards that under those unknown conditions in which angular and linear momentum are indistinguishable in character, electrical and mechanical quantities might also appear as components of one quantity. Eddington gives reasons for supposing that these conditions may be realized in a space which is not electrically neutral; but space as a whole *is* neutral, and if we consider a part of space which is not, we usually consider the non-neutrality as a perturbation. Taking the universe as we find it, therefore, we stick to our original anchorage, and investigate the hypothesis of a fifth dimension, inaccessible, with symbol E_{05}. Our first problem here is to determine the symbolic association of certain quantities used in the definitions of tensor calculus.

A five-volume formed by unit vectors along each of the five axes in this space will be associated with the symbol $E_{05} E_{15} E_{25} E_{35} E_{45} = E_{16}$, and is thus symbolically a scalar. Tensorially, by § 14.7, it is a scalar-Δ-density. We omit mention of the reality or otherwise of the coefficient since we have not settled that of the coefficient of E_{05}.

A four-volume in space-time formed from the vectors $i\,dx_1\,E_{15},...,dt\,E_{45}$ will be, similarly but unambiguously as to reality, $E_{05}\,dx_1\,dx_2,...,dt$. As a geometrical quantity in space-time it is again a scalar-Δ-density, but as a quantity in the five-space it is a covariant vector-Δ-density, having, owing to the way it is formed, only one non-zero component and that in the E_{05} direction. It has this dual character because we do not rotate into the fifth dimension. Its character as a scalar is consistent with the fact that E_{05} is associated with a scalar under the group (c).

An ordinary volume in space has the symbol E_{04} by similar reasoning. This is the same as the product of the symbols of the other two axes $E_{05} E_{45}$. Its tensor character in the five-space is that of a second rank covariant tensor-Δ-density, and in space-time that of a covariant vector-Δ-density. To obtain the equivalent covariant vector we must multiply by the reciprocal of the $|R|$ of transformations in space-time, which, from the previous paragraph, has the symbol $(E_{05})^{-1} = E_{05}$ (ignoring sign, which is in any case conventional). The result, E_{45}, has the direction of the fourth axis of space-time, a reassuring conclusion.

Owing to the fact that the symbols E_{05}, E_{04}, and E_{45} are all square roots of $-I$, we shall find that multiplying by any one of them has the same effect symbolically (apart from sign) as dividing by it. This fact can be very confusing, but 'forewarned is forearmed'.

We now consider the expression

$$P = p_0 E_{05} + ip_1 E_{15} + ip_2 E_{25} + ip_3 E_{35} + p_4 E_{45} + ip_5 E_{16} \quad (18.6.4)$$

which is made up by adding the two mechanical scalars to the momentum vector in space-time, but is to be divided up variously according to our point of view. Then

$$\mathbf{P} = PE_{05} = -P(E_{05})^{-1}$$
$$= ip_0 E_{16} + ip_1 E_{01} + ip_2 E_{02} + ip_3 E_{03} + p_4 E_{04} - p_5 E_{05}. \quad (18.6.5)$$

Now in all the rotations we consider, the numerical value of $|R|$ is unity. Consequently, if P is a four-vector+two scalars, $\mathbf{P}$ is a four-vector-density+two scalar-densities, and conversely. Similarly,

$$\mathfrak{P} = PE_{45} = -P(E_{45})^{-1}$$
$$= -p_0 E_{04} - ip_1 E_{14} - ip_2 E_{24} - ip_3 E_{34} + ip_4 E_{16} - p_5 E_{45}, \quad (18.6.6)$$

so that if P is a three-vector+three scalars, then $\mathfrak{P}$ is a three-vector-density+three scalar-densities. The physical densities in space of the components included in P will be obtained by dividing P not by the volume $|R|$ but by the volume which in fact contains P, which may be numerically different but will be symbolically the same, and it is thus symbolically the same as $\mathfrak{P}$ but may have all the coefficients changed proportionately.

We shall need the full relations of the previous paragraphs in § 18.9. Meanwhile they allow us to take full advantage of the five-dimensional anchorage without the disadvantage of losing our mechanical vectors. By (18.6.5) we could abandon mechanical vectors, anchor our axes to $E_{01}, ..., E_{05}$ and find that all mechanical properties are tensor-densities. This might be the right way of anchoring the E-frame to describe a universe of protons only or of electrons only. But to describe the actual universe we keep our anchorage of the axes to $E_{15}, ..., E_{45}$, add E_{05} as an extra dimension into which rotation is impossible, abandon the group (d), and use (18.6.5) and (18.6.6) to identify the anchorage of those quantities associated with symbols involving the suffix 0 which we cannot identify by rotations.

Since E_{05} is, among other things, the symbol attached to the scalar unit of space-time volume, it carries the *scale of measurement*. We shall see later that this is most conveniently the E_{05} component of a momentum vector, not a displacement vector. In so far as it is perpendicular to the four axes of space time, it might be expected to contain the radius of space-curvature. It is one of Eddington's points that the uncertain scale of quantum theory and the radius of space-curvature in relativity theory are related; he opens his first chapter in a manner calculated to capture the imagination, by showing that if the standard deviation of the uncertainty of the position of the C.G. of the particles in a euclidean space is used as a natural unit of distance, then a metric usually associated with curved space is obtained, the radius of curvature being numerically the standard of length multiplied by twice the square root of the number of particles in the universe. Since the radius of space-curvature is unchanged in sign if the chirality of the axes is reversed, its symbol must be $E_{05}\,i$. Curved space is thus a statistical way of dealing with the fifth coordinate.

The following table shows each physical quantity attached to its correct symbol by the above or similar arguments. In reading it we note that vectors in space-time carry suffixes 1, 2, 3 with homothetic coefficients, and 4 with a coefficient antithetic to them, and that mechanically conjugate quantities always have the same symbol.

Symbol	Real coefficients	Imaginary coefficients
E_{16}	Electric charge	Energy (mass) density
E_{01}, E_{02}, E_{03}	Magnetic moment	Angular velocity; angular momentum density
E_{04}	Three-volume as five-space tensor	Magnetic energy
E_{05}	Volume of space-time; scale (momentum)	Magnetic pole-strength; radius of space-curvature
E_{15}, E_{25}, E_{35}	Electric moment; vector potential	Space displacement; momentum
E_{45}	Time displacement; energy; mass; volume; particle density	Charge density; electrostatic potential
E_{12}, E_{23}, E_{31}	Angular displacement; angular momentum	Magnetic force
E_{14}, E_{24}, E_{34}	Electric force	Momentum density; velocity; mechanical force

It is interesting to note here how naturally we have been led from the concept of measurement to a $3+1$ space-time. It is worth extra mention, perhaps, that time, which we cannot reverse, has been associated with real symbols, and space, in which reversal of the direction of an axis does not particularly affect our description of things, has been associated with imaginary quantities. For mathematically, $+1$ and -1 are different in their properties, whereas $+i$ and $-i$ are not.

18.7. The primary analysis

At this stage we should note that 4×4 matrices are inadequate in two distinct ways, rectification of either of which leads us to 16×16 matrices, and rectification of both of which leads us to 256×256 matrices. First there is the argument of § 18.2 that measurement involves the existence of a reference standard as well as that of the thing being measured. (Actually we commonly assume that a rod has a length of say, 3 metres, independently of the existence of any metre scale, and this is why we have got as far as we have with 4×4 matrices.) But there is a second reason. If the E-numbers, with this reservation, deal successfully with vectors by the procedure of the previous section, then the matter (or energy) tensor, discussed at the end of § 14.5, will need to be the outer product of two E-numbers $P**Q$, where P and Q are E-numbers. This is a quantity of 256 components, capable of representation by 16×16 matrices.

The neutrality of the universe restricts the number of these components which are significant, and we distinguish active, dormant, and dead components. If an E-number with the dimensions of momentum represents a system, in a neutral environment only the ten mechanical components (four linear and six angular in space-time on the one hand, or excluding E_{16} and those E-symbols with a suffix 0 on the other) are observable, and only these are active. But the electrical components are important, for in multiplying two momentum vectors together to give the energy tensor, two electrical components combine to give a mechanical one. For this reason they are described, not as dead, but as *dormant*. In a 16×16 matrix, therefore, $(10 \times 10) + (6 \times 6) = 136$ components are active; since we have no cause to go to tensors of higher rank the remaining 120 are *dead*. (These associations would be reversed in a universe of protons only or electrons only.) These numbers will become important after the next section.

If, returning to the argument of the first paragraph of this section, we are right in thinking that the symbol representing a measurable can be separated into two, one for the observable and one for the standard which converts observation into measurement, then we ought to start by the study of E-numbers which have one unit and three zero eigenvalues; they are idempotent and have a trace equal to unity. As a preliminary we note the following facts about the general E-number $P = \sum_r p_r E_r$; all except the fifth are obvious from the matrix notation and the multiplication table. We shall refer to these as (18.7.1) (a)–(f).

(a) The trace of P is $+4ip_{16}$.

(b) The trace of $E_s P$ is $-4p_s$.

(c) A Hermitian matrix in E-number form has all its p_{rs} imaginary.

(d) An E-number with all its p_{rs} real has eigenvalues which are pure imaginaries. In the present context, of course, such a matrix is as important as one with real eigenvalues.

(e) The determinant of P is

$$\sum p_r^4 + 2\sum(\pm p_r^2 p_s^2) + 8\sum p_{rt}p_{ru}p_{st}p_{su} + 8\sum(\pm p_{pq}p_{rs}p_{tu}),$$

where the sign is positive in the second term if the E-symbols anticommute and negative if they commute; positive or negative in the fourth term according as p, q, r, s, t, u is an even or odd permutation of 0, 1, 2, 3, 4, 5; equivalent combinations—i.e. consisting of the same factors in a different order—are counted only once.

(f) The characteristic equation of the E-number is obtained from the determinant by replacing p_{16} by $p_{16} + i\lambda$, and setting the result to zero.

It is easily verified that if

$$P = -\tfrac{1}{4}E_{16}(E_{16} + E_{ab} + E_{cd} + E_{ef})$$

then $P^2 = P$ if a, b, c, d, e, f is an even permutation of 0, 1, 2, 3, 4, 5, and $P^2 = -I$ if the permutation is odd, and that the trace is 1 in either case. Eddington shows that every idempotent vector of trace unity can be brought to this form by a rotation; we shall not reproduce the proof but the conclusion is easily seen to be reasonable. For a product of two four-vectors, $X**Y$, contains seven adjustable quantities, four in each factor less one because $(aX)**(a^{-1}X) = X**X$. The requirement that the trace is unity reduces the number to six. This is just the number of degrees of freedom of an arbitrarily directed four-frame, three constants being required to fix the direction of the first axis, two for the second, one for the third, the fourth being then completely determined except for sign. We have thus just enough disposable constants in the general rotation to reduce the idempotent matrix to this standard form.

Having anchored the E-frame, we are in a position to interpret the E-number representing a measurable. We choose the form

$$-\tfrac{1}{4}iE_{16} \pm \tfrac{1}{4}iE_{01} \pm \tfrac{1}{4}iE_{23} \pm \tfrac{1}{4}iE_{45} \tag{18.7.2}$$

because it is the only one (apart from cyclic permutations of 1, 2, 3) which fits the condition that the electric part of a physically significant E-number must be antithetic to the mechanical part. The number of minus signs must be even to preserve the even permutation of suffixes (since $E_{pq} = -E_{qp}$). Then reference to the dictionary shows that these measurables concern something with a mass density (iE_{16}), angular momentum density (iE_{01}), a magnetic force (iE_{23}), and a charge density (iE_{45}). The minus sign of the first need not worry us at the moment; the other signs show that if either the charge or the spin changes sign the magnetic effect does so too. The signs of the E_{01} and E_{23} components can be changed simultaneously by a space rotation, of course, so that this change does not represent anything new. We have thus two types of measurable, both have mass and spin, but they are oppositely charged. An unexpected result is that as well as having the same spin and (apart from sign) charge, they have the same mass.

Denoting the four E-numbers by $P_1,...,P_4$, it is easily checked that $P_a P_b = 0$; $P_a^2 = P$; $P_1+P_2+P_3+P_4 = I$. (These relations define what is known as a spectral set—compare also our comments on the primitive idempotents of an algebra in § 5.5 and Chapter XIII.) Thus as operators these four E-numbers will sort out anything representable by an operand into four exclusive and exhaustive parts. As they stand, they are applied to I, which, being $-iE_{16}$, represents something electrically neutral, not spinning, but possessing energy (or mass). This they sort out into four types of charged, spinning matter.

They also, as they stand, represent densities. To convert them to particles we must multiply by the volume containing one particle. This carries the symbol E_{45} and multiplication of the idempotent by E_{45} reproduces the same symbols, without the coefficient i, in a different order, and, of course, the 'dictionary' interprets them as before but without the word 'density'. Actually this is not the correct way to clear up this point, but we shall defer further consideration of it until the next section but one, meanwhile making one yet closer contact with experimental physics.

18.8. k-Factor theory

Now protons and electrons are charged particles with a spin, which seem to be bricks out of which matter may be built, but their masses are not equal. (Positrons and electrons do not form a basis for all matter, and neutrons have no charge, so in every case there is some difficulty in identification.)

Eddington claims that the currently accepted mass ratio of the proton and electron is due to a misunderstanding, circumstances having led us to partition their equal energies differently between their rest masses and their P.E. in the gravitational field of the rest of the universe. Although the exposure of this misunderstanding involves no group or matrix theory beyond the use of numbers we have already deduced, some reference to it is necessary if the subsequent developments of the theory are to be understood.

When an iceberg is put into the sea it causes a depression in the surface in which it sits. The sea surface rises simultaneously by an amount which can be taken as infinitesimal provided the area of the sea can be treated as extremely large. If the height of the iceberg would have been e on a solid surface, but owing to the depression its base is actually w, a negative quantity, above the surface of the sea, the effective resultant height of the iceberg above the level of the sea is h where, if ρ is the density of ice,

$$h = e + w,$$

$$w = -\rho e,$$

$$h = (1-\rho)e = -(\rho-1)e.$$

These formulae apply only to cylindrical icebergs, of course, and they break down if $\rho > 1$, but they serve as typical of a general situation. The quantities e, h, and w may be thought of as potential energies in the gravitational field; e is the P.E. of the iceberg placed on a rigid surface, h is its energy under the given circumstances, and w is the energy given to it by the water which it displaces. In the same way we must recognize that every object reacts on its surroundings. The total resultant energy H of a particle is the sum of E, its own energy, and W, the changes of energy it produces in surrounding particles:

$$H = E + W.$$

We consider a system of a large number, n, of identical particles, singling out the nth to talk about. The total particle energy of the system is $\sum_{1}^{n} E_r$. On removing the nth particle it is changed to $\sum_{1}^{n-1} E_r'$. The total change, $\sum_{1}^{n-1}(E_r - E_r')$, produced in these $n-1$ particles is by definition W_n. The loss of energy of the system when the nth particle is removed is

$$\sum_{1}^{n} E_r - \sum_{1}^{n-1} E_r' = E_n + W_n = H_n.$$

If we assume that the surroundings are unchanged by the presence or absence of the nth particle, we shall measure H_n and mistakenly call it E_n. Orthodox relativity and orthodox quantum theory are at opposite extremes in this. Relativity theory, in which all the effects due to a particle are interpreted as changes in the geometry of the surroundings, carries out all its calculations in terms of W, and becomes too complicated to handle almost as soon as the introduction of a second particle to talk about involves us in W_{n-1} and E''''s. Quantum theory assumes that the system under discussion exists independently of the rest of the universe, thus neglecting the W's with two important consequences. The first is that it is valid only so long as changes in W are of at least second order in $1/n$, and the second is that H_n *is* mistaken for E_n, and the proportionality factor analogous to ρ is overlooked. The former requirement can be restated in the form that our calculations in quantum theory may refer only to changes in a few unidentified members in a large assembly (which aptly describes most of our experiments in atomic physics); the proportionality factor is not so easily eliminated and must be calculated.

Let each system in the assembly, or, in our previous language, each particle in the system, be specified by k independent parameters, all quantum-relativistically (see § 15.8) of the same dimensions as the components of the energy-momentum tensor. Let each particle be plotted as a point in a common representation space. This may be of more than k dimensions, but if it is, the points will lie in a k-dimensional subspace (not necessarily flat). Divide this space into small volumes labelled 1, 2,..., r,..., and let the number of points in the rth volume be j_r. The total energy will be a function $H^0(j_1,...,j_r,...)$ of the occupation factors j. The result of removing a particle of type r is to diminish H^0 by $\partial H^0/\partial j_r$, and the apparent total energy of the system, obtained by summing the apparent energies of each particle in this way, is $\sum j_r\, \partial H^0/\partial j_r$. (Note that the particles are not removed in succession, but alternatively; each is replaced after measuring its energy so that each is the only one to be removed when its energy is being estimated.) In current practice we say that this quantity—the apparent average energy of a particle multiplied by the number of particles—is the energy of the particles E^0, and that the total energy is this, lessened by adding to it the negative energy W^0 of the *field* which the particles generate.

Let us now assume that the system can be made λ times larger in mass, volume, etc., without affecting its qualitative properties such as density.

(This means that it must be neither small enough to need quantum treatment nor large enough to need cosmological treatment; such a system is described as *scale-free*.) Then

E^0, W^0, H^0 will all be multiplied by λ, but

$\partial H^0/\partial j_r$ being the energy of a single particle, is unchanged.

If, however, we now take a fundamental unit λ times the old one,

E^0, W^0, H^0 will be restored to their former numerical values and

$\partial H^0/\partial j_r$ will be multiplied by $1/\lambda$,

but further, with the change of unit, the size of the small elements of volume of phase space will be changed. (The net picture after the double change will be of a macroscopically identical system based on smaller atoms.) Each volume element will be λ^k times what it was before, and the j_r will therefore be multiplied by λ^k. The two conclusions (1) that $\partial H^0/\partial j_r$ is multiplied by $1/\lambda$, and (2) that the j_r are multiplied by λ^k, together imply (3) that H^0 is a homogeneous function of degree $-1/k$ in the j_r, whence by Euler's theorem $E^0 = \sum j_r \, \partial H^0/\partial j_r = -(1/k) \, H^0$. Thus

$$H^0 = -kE^0, \qquad W^0 = -(k+1)E^0.$$

By assuming that the particle we are studying can be removed or replaced without effect on the rest of the assembly, therefore, our observed E, which is really an H mistakenly identified with an E, is $-k$ times too large. This conclusion applies to masses, of course, since they are relativistically equivalent to energies. It calls for several comments.

(1) The minus sign is surprising. Eddington accepts it as it stands, and says that in consequence we have done all our estimations of energy the wrong way round, adopting a negative unit. One result of this is that when reckoned positively, kinetic energy must be $-\frac{1}{2}mv^2 = \frac{1}{2}m(iv)^2$— a premonition of the appearance of i in the quantum expressions for momentum. This upside-down reckoning he calls 'the inversion of energy'. It is the justification for ignoring the minus sign of the mass term in the idempotent E-number in the previous section.

(2) The numerical value of k is obviously important. The difficulty is that it depends on the assumptions we make, as much as on the nature of what we are talking about. For example, the mass of an as yet unidentified particle is arbitrary, and represents a degree of freedom mathematically. But if we assume the particle to be identified as an electron, its mass may still be unknown—to be determined from the

experiment—but on the other hand it may be assumed to be known, and used as data, and in this case it does not represent a degree of freedom.

The k-factor situation may be summed up qualitatively by saying that 'the total energy of n particles is less than n times the energy of one (the one we observe, that is!)'. And this in its turn can be explained in two ways. One is that the P.E. of each particle is reduced by the presence of the others—an effect we call gravitation. The other is that the observed particle is always that of highest quantum number—an effect we call exclusion, or the Pauli principle. Eddington asserts that these are merely two aspects of the same effect. The reason why we can only observe the particle of highest quantum number—the 'top particle'—is that this is the only particle with degrees of freedom that allow it to be moved without upsetting the background of other—'mean'—particles, and the more degrees of freedom we claim for the particle, the greater the discrepancy between it and the mean particle.

The principle is, then, that the energy or mass of an observed ('top' or 'quantum') particle is numerically $1/k$ of the energy or mass of an unobserved ('mean' or 'relativity') particle, where k is the number of degrees of freedom of the particle.

(3) We have seen that a complex particle has 136 significant degrees of freedom, and if it can be replaced for other purposes by two separate particles with no internal strains, these have each 10 degrees of freedom. (A strained particle requires the energy tensor to describe it; a particle with no internal strain is adequately described by the momentum vector.) The two-particle theory (compare § 10.1) shows that a system of two particles of masses m and m' is expressible in terms of an external mass $M = m+m'$, and an internal mass $\mu = mm'/(m+m')$. k-factor theory affects these masses differently.

Let m_0 and $p^2/2m_0$ be the rest mass and kinetic energy found for a standard particle fully observed in all 136 degrees of freedom. The rest mass of a corresponding unobserved particle will be $-136m_0$. (The missing $-137m_0$—we use this somewhat perverse looking expression on account of the inversion of energy—has been lost by cancelling it against the gravitational P.E. which is not taken into account explicitly.) The same particle considered as a system of two unstrained particles, and therefore only observed in $10+10$ degrees of freedom, will be observed to have the mass $m+m' = M$, from which the rest mass of the unobserved particle must be $-10m-10m' = -10M$. (In this case the field energy is differently estimated as $-11M$.) Hence $M = 136m_0/10$. We now seek a similar relation for μ. The whole of the rest mass is accounted for in the foregoing calculation and there is no contribution to rest-mass energy from the internal mass μ. We therefore consider the term $p^2/2m_0$ of the fully observed particle which gives rise to a term $-136p^2/2m_0$ in the energy of the corresponding unobserved particle. There is a similar term $p^2/2\mu$ if we start from the system of two 10 d.f. particles. But for two reasons this differs from the previous case. (*a*) As μ does not contribute to rest masses it does not contribute to gravitational P.E. and therefore no *k*-factor is involved in passing to the unobserved particle. (*b*) It is a degree of freedom demanding quantum treatment, and therefore p is to be replaced by ip (compare (1) above). Hence

$$-136p^2/2m_0 = (ip)^2/2\mu, \quad \text{or} \quad m_0 = 136\mu.$$

The four equations

$$mm'/(m+m') = \mu = m_0/136,$$

$$m+m' = M = 136m_0/10$$

lead at once to the quadratic

$$10m^2 - 136mm_0 + m_0^2 = 0$$

for m and m', the ratio of whose roots is $1847 \cdot 60$.

This is so close to the proton electron mass ratio as to lead us to identify provisionally the simplest 'complex particle' with the combination of a proton and an electron—namely, a hydrogen atom. Nor is this identification unreasonable on the face of it. As our idempotent vector was to be the fundamental measurable we have hereby achieved one of the objects stated in the quotation from Eddington in § 18.1, namely, 'the mathematical specification of that which is being counted [and their identification] with (observational) protons and electrons'.

If, in splitting the hydrogen atom into proton and electron, we ask which part is which, we are introducing another degree of freedom, the 'permutation variate', which raises k to 137. This question does not arise in discussing the spectrum of hydrogen, but it does in discussing free electrons, though currently the mass of the electron is assumed to be the same in both cases. Thus the factor 136/137 occurs unsuspected in comparing spectroscopic and deflexion methods of determining the mass of the electron (and in other places too). Allowing for this gives a more accurate equation for the currently accepted proton-electron mass ratio, in which the third term of the above equation for m and m' is multiplied by $(137/136)^{5/6}$, and the ratio of its roots becomes $1836\cdot34$ (observed value $1836\cdot27\pm0\cdot19$).

18.9. Strain vectors and quantum theory

Availing ourselves of the latitude offered by the considerations of § 7.7, we have been considering E-numbers sometimes as 4×4 matrices obeying the laws of matrix multiplication, and at other times as sixteen-vectors which can be multiplied by a generalized quaternion (i.e. sedenion) algebra, and we have considered that one E-number can be the eigen-symbol of another. At this point it becomes advantageous to introduce the four-vectors of the four-space in which the 4×4 matrices are operators, and to write the idempotent E-number of trace unity as the product of two such vectors of unit length. By § 7.7 this product must be $\psi^{+\circ}\phi$ if the E-number is contravariant, and $\psi^{\circ+}\phi$ if it is covariant. (Compare also § 14.2.) The combinations $\psi^{++}\phi$ and $\psi^{\circ\circ}\phi$ are something new. In order to give these quantities names we may at this point introduce Eddington's nomenclature in general, without necessarily presupposing any implications which these names may carry until we have proved them. We therefore define:

A *wave vector*, ψ, is a four-vector.

A *space vector*, P, is equivalently (1) a sixteen vector, (2) a 4×4 matrix, and (3) a mixed second rank *wave tensor*. If contravariant as a vector it is the sum of terms like $\psi^{+\circ}\phi$ and if covariant it is the sum of terms like $\psi^{\circ+}\phi$.

A *strain vector*, S, is a quantity which, if covariant, transforms like $\psi^{\circ\circ}\phi$ and if contravariant like $\psi^{++}\phi$; i.e. it is a pure second-rank wave tensor.

A *space tensor* is a fourth-rank wave tensor; there are several types which need not be enumerated, and they transform like the product of two space or strain vectors.

As the idempotent measurable is a momentum vector, we shall assume that this factorization is only applied to momentum vectors unless it is explicitly stated to the contrary. Our immediate problem is to decide the nature of a strain vector.

One type of strain vector appears as a result of the following argument. The idempotent (measurable) in standard form has linear momentum components equal to zero, and is therefore at rest. This is naturally possible of achievement by suitable choice of coordinate system. But what of a particle in a system, when the axes will naturally be chosen to bring the C.G. of the *system* to rest? In a gas, for example, we think of the gas as at rest, with a given density and other properties specified in the coordinate system in which the gas is at rest, and we specify the component molecules in this system. Let a given particle be represented by the E-number P in standard form, and by P' in this coordinate system. Its contribution to the density of mass, momentum, etc., is $P'E_{45}$ per unit volume. But $P' = RPR^{-1}$, where R is a certain rotation from the group (d) of § 18.6. Now an examination of this group will show that $RE_{45}\tilde{R} = E_{45}$ for every R, since in every case either $\tilde{R} = R^{-1}$ and commutes with E_{45} or else $\tilde{R} = R$ and its E-symbol anticommutes. Hence if $S = PE_{45}$, then

$$S' = P'E_{45} = RPR^{-1}RE_{45}\tilde{R} = RPE_{45}\tilde{R} = RS\tilde{R},$$

so that S is a strain vector.

The same type of strain vector appears in another connexion. The hydrogen atom is a system of two particles, and in five-space the two-particle transformation will apply to all five coordinates. As we have pointed out in § 18.6, E_{15}, E_{25}, and E_{35} carry the space coordinates, E_{45} the time, and E_{05} the (uncertain) unit of measurement. The 'external particle', which is the whole system located at the C.G., is dealt with by classical mechanics; this makes no use of the scale, which is assumed constant and given, or, in other words, is averaged and treated as a scalar. The 'internal particle', whose coordinates are the relative position of proton and electron, requires quantum treatment, and therefore a scale variable, but as the relative position is always the difference between the *simultaneous* positions of the proton and electron as measured by an observer moving with the external particle, the 'relative time' is always zero. Thus classical mechanics reduces the five-space to E_{15}, E_{25}, E_{35}, E_{45}, but quantum mechanics reduces it to E_{05}, E_{15}, E_{25}, E_{35}; both reduce it to a four-space, but differently. To this we add the fact that although quantum mechanics observes particles, classical mechanics observes only large aggregates of particles, and thus effectively space densities. Moreover, in 'the primary analysis' which resolved 'matter' into four charged spinning parts, these parts appeared as densities, and although we proceeded to relate them to particles (protons and electrons) there was a discrepancy in doing so which cannot be left unchallenged.

The resolution of these difficulties involves rather desperate measures. We have to assume, in fact, that much of our previous work in anchoring the E-frame is only appropriate to classical applications and not, therefore, to protons and electrons, which are quantum particles. The process of dropping a dimension consists, in effect, in summing or integrating over all values of the dropped coordinate. In order not to upset our previous work, we now consider that the 'true' anchorage should have been the $E_{01}, ..., E_{05}$ axes anchorage after all, with 'true' vectors of the form **P** of (18.6.5). The dropping of E_{05} in classical mechanics converts this to $\mathbf{P}E_{05} = P$ which is the form we have used all along. But the dropping of E_{04} in quantum mechanics converts it to $\mathbf{P}E_{04} = \mathfrak{P} = PE_{45}$. The vectors used in quantum mechanics (and called vectors) are thus the strain vectors of the classical viewpoint.

We are not accustomed to allow for this in our nomenclature. A simple renumbering of our E-symbols does not alter the physics, and throws some light on the confusion thus created. We still call p_1, p_2, p_3 momentum, and the fourth axis time. A renumbering by the permutation $(4, 5, 0)$ restores these essentials and shows how, if we persist in this nomenclature, we shall name other properties; these false names are called by Eddington 'designation by analogy'. They may be summarized thus:

Classical		Strain vector	Quantum-analogical	
Name	Symbol	Symbol	Symbol	Name
Momentum	15 25 35	14 24 34	15 25 35	Momentum
Time; energy	45	i16	i16	
Scale; phase	05	04	45	Time; energy
	16	i45	i05	
	04	05	04	
	01 02 03	i23 i31 i12	i23 i31 i12	
	23 31 12	i01 i02 i03	i14 i24 i34	
	14 24 34	15 25 35	01 02 03	

The multiplication of the idempotent by E_{45} at the end of § 18.7 now appears in a different light. The idempotent is itself a particle, as it should be, and the reason for multiplying by E_{45} is not the one given in § 18.7; it is that such multiplication will always be necessary when interpreting quantum systems, based on three space dimensions+scale, in terms of words designed for use in classical systems based on three space dimensions+time. If this argument is correct, and we have in this way managed to mistake particle vectors for their three-dimensional densities (and vice versa, possibly, since $|E_{45}^2| = 1$), this is, Eddington suggests, the source of all our interpretative difficulties in quantum mechanics—fairly obviously so when we have recourse to electron-clouds and similar pictures, but equally so when our interpretations are more sophisticated.

We now consider further properties of the wave vectors, our object being ultimately to link them with the vectors of the same name which we introduced in Chapter XVI. With this end in view we consider (1) the operational form of the variables of a system, and (2) the effect of considering them to be functions of the space coordinates. It will be remembered that we are confining our interest to momentum vectors. Consider therefore

$$P = \psi^+{}^\circ\phi = \sum_\mu E_\mu p_\mu,$$

then we have

(a)
$$^\circ\phi\psi^+ = \text{trace } P = 4ip_{16},$$

(b)
$$^\circ\phi E_\nu \psi^+ = \sum_{\alpha=1}^{4} \sum_{\beta=1}^{4} \phi_\alpha (E_\nu)_{\alpha\beta} \psi_\beta$$

$$= \sum_{(\alpha,\beta)=1}^{16} (E_\nu)_{\alpha\beta}(\psi^+{}^\circ\phi)_{\beta\alpha}$$

$$= \sum_{\mu=1}^{16} (E_\nu P)_{\mu\mu}$$

$$= \text{trace } E_\nu P = p_\nu,$$

whence
$$^\circ\phi(4ip_{16} E_\nu)\psi^+/{}^\circ\phi\psi^+ = p_\nu,$$

so that $4ip_{16} E_\nu$ is the operational form (P_ν in the notation of § 16.3) of the momentum p_ν.

If the wave vector is a function of position, and is contravariant, let the functional form of it be, in two systems of coordinates

$$\psi^* = f(x_1, x_2, x_3, t), \qquad \psi^+ = f'(x_1', x_2', x_3', t').$$

Suppose the second system to be derived from the first by the infinitesimal rotation $e^{\frac{1}{2}E_{12}\,d\theta_{12}}$. Then

$$x_1' = x_1 - x_2\,d\theta_{12}, \qquad x_2' = x_2 + x_1\,d\theta_{12}, \qquad x_3' = x_3, \qquad t' = t,$$

whence, by Taylor's theorem,

$$f(x_1', x_2', x_3', t') = e^{\{x_1(\partial/\partial x_2) - x_2(\partial/\partial x_1)\}d\theta_{12}} f(x_1, x_2, x_3, t).$$

But as ψ is contravariant, we have

$$\psi^+ = R\psi^* = e^{\frac{1}{2}E_{12}\,d\theta_{12}}\psi^*,$$

that is,
$$f'(x_1', x_2', x_3', t') = e^{\frac{1}{2}E_{12}\,d\theta_{12}} f(x_1, x_2, x_3, t),$$

whence

$$f'(x_1', x_2', x_3', t') = e^{[\frac{1}{2}E_{12} - \{x_1(\partial/\partial x_2) - x_2(\partial/\partial x_1)\}]d\theta_{12}} f(x_1', x_2', x_3', t').$$

Alternatively, thinking of f as an operator which operates on the coordinate vector, we can omit the operand and write

$$f + = e^{[\frac{1}{2}E_{12} - \{x_1(\partial/\partial x_2) - x_2(\partial/\partial x_1)\}]d\theta_{12}} f * = e^{L_{12}d\theta_{12}} f *.$$

We have to apply here the same care which we took in § 16.3. If

$$O_{12}(d\theta) = O_{12}(\phi)$$

denotes the operation of rotating the operand (which is a description of the system in some form) through the angle $d\theta = \phi$ in the 12-plane, then according as the form of the description is numerical or in the form of the functional operator f, we have

$$O_{12}(\phi)\psi = e^{\frac{1}{2}E_{12}\phi}\psi, \qquad O_{12}(\phi)f = e^{L_{12}\phi}f.$$

Now

$$\frac{dO_{12}}{d\phi} = \frac{1}{2}E_{12} = \frac{i}{2p_{16}}P_{12}$$

when p_{12} is localized or uniform throughout space, from the first of these two relations; the argument obviously generalizes and we can write, in these circumstances,

$$P_{rs} = -2ip_{16}\frac{d}{d\phi}O_{rs}(\phi),$$

where r, s are any pair from 1, 2, 3, 4 in classical or quantum-analogical theory or from 1, 2, 3, 5 in true quantum theory. When the wave vector varies in space, the result of applying this operator to f is

$$P_{rs}f = -2ip_{16}\frac{d}{d\phi}O_{rs}(\phi)f = -2ip_{16}\frac{d}{d\phi}e^{L_{rs}\phi}f$$

$$= -2ip_{16}\left(\frac{1}{2}E_{rs} - \left(x_r\frac{\partial}{\partial x_s} - x_s\frac{\partial}{\partial x_r}\right)\right)f.$$

This corresponds (dropping the f) to the previous equation for a localized or constant vector together with the extra term in the inner bracket, which, as it depends upon differentials with respect to the coordinates, must be due in some way to the influence on the measurement at the point in question of the state of things elsewhere, i.e. to what we have described in § 18.8 as a field effect. Although it refers to angular momentum, it is immediately equivalent to our former (§ 16.4)

$$p_x = \frac{h}{2\pi i}\frac{d}{dx}$$

for linear momentum, provided we put

$$\frac{h}{2\pi i} = 2ip_{16} \quad \text{or} \quad p_{16} = -\frac{h}{4\pi}.$$

This equation provides the link between Planck's constant and the theory here developed. It is important to note that in the complete expression for the angular momentum, the term $\frac{1}{2}E_{rs}$ represents the angular momentum possessed by the particle when considered as a point and at rest—i.e. it is the spin of the electron or proton, while the differential operators represent the angular momentum inescapable from a distribution of the particle—i.e. they represent the orbital angular momentum.

Eddington's development from this point parallels the usual theory with certain differences in interpretation, but it is beyond the scope of this work to follow these up.

18.10. The double frame and wave tensors

(NOTE: The problem of presenting Eddington's argument in a reasonable space without over-condensation becomes much more acute at this point, and for the guidance of the student we give an analysis of this section.

Subsection 1: Presentation of results already obtained in a form more suitable for generalization.

Paras. 1–3   Elementary matters.

,,   4–7   Co- and contravariance of space and strain vectors and an appropriate notation.

,,   8–9   Reality conditions and the introduction of phase space.

Subsection 2: Generalization from momentum vectors to second-rank space tensors.

Paras. 10–14   General considerations.

,,   15–16   The interchange operator.

Subsection 3: Further developments.

Paras. 17–18   Relation of the tensors so derived to the R.C. tensor which also represents matter.

,,   19–20   Corresponding treatment of strain tensors.)

Before discussing tensors it may be well to summarize our results on vectors, starting from the more physical end. The three-dimensional momentum of a point-mass, p_1, p_2, p_3, is extended in relativity to four dimensions by including the mass, and in symbolic form is

$$ip_1 E_{15} + ip_2 E_{25} + ip_3 E_{35} + mE_{45}.$$

When angular momenta are included the number of terms reaches ten, every pair of suffixes from 1, 2, 3, 4, 5 being possible. The complete vector may also contain six electrical terms ($E_{0\mu}$, $\mu = 1,...,5$, and E_{16}), which, however, have no significance in a neutral environment.

The E-numbers can be given a matrix representation in 4×4 matrices. These can be such that (a) E-symbols based on suffixes from one only of the triads 1, 2, 3 and 4, 5, 0 are real and antisymmetrical, the rest being imaginary and symmetrical, and (b) the mechanical terms of the complete vector are then real and the electrical ones imaginary. Although representations which do not show these features are possible, we confine our attention to those which do—'true representations'. A complete momentum vector may thus be expressed in the alternative forms

$$P = \sum_{01}^{16} p_{ab} E_{ab} = [P_{\alpha\beta}].$$

It will be very important not to confuse, say, p_{23} and P_{23}; we shall reserve the earlier greek letters for suffixes of the latter type. If P is idempotent and factorizes into $\psi^{\dagger\dagger}\phi$, then $P_{\alpha\beta} = \psi_\alpha \phi_\beta = \phi_\beta \psi_\alpha$, but there is no such simple relation for p_{ab}.

Normally a rotation or change of coordinates in a 16×1 vector would be a 16×16 matrix. But with the E-number, P, in 4×4 matrix form, it can be rotated to RPR^{-1} where R is another E-number. The group $R = \exp(\tfrac{1}{2} E_{pq} \theta)$, with p, q from 1, 2, 3, 4 and $E_{pq}\theta$ real, is the familiar Lorentz group, and the 'trueness' of the matrix representation is preserved under this group.

The first new question to be considered is that of co- and contravariance. If $P^+ = RP^*R^{-1}$, then, by § 7.7,

$$P^\circ = \tilde{R}^{-1}P^*\tilde{R} = \begin{cases} R^{-1}P^*R & \text{if } E_{pq} \text{ is imaginary and the rotation} \\ & \quad \text{hyperbolic,} \\ RP^*R^{-1} & \text{if } E_{pq} \text{ is real and the rotation circular.} \end{cases}$$

This is 4×4 matrix language. For E-algebra language, since the momentum four-vector is subject to the metric of flat space-time in which raising or lowering an index simply changes the sign of spatial components leaving temporal ones unaffected, the change from P^+ to P° is one of altering the signs of the spatial components. To link the two we recall the result, also from § 7.7, that if $P = \sum \psi^+ {}^\circ\phi$ it is contravariant, whereas $\sum \phi^\circ {}^+\psi$, which will be $\tilde{P}$ or $\bar{\bar{P}}$ according as the orthogonal or unitary convention is in use, is covariant. Now $E_\mu = -\bar{\bar{E}}_\mu$, all μ, but transposing the E-symbols changes the sign of the real ones, including E_{45}, and leaves unaltered the imaginary ones, including E_{15}, E_{25}, E_{35}. As the latter is the reverse of the situation in special relativity, we see that if P is a simple contravariant momentum vector, its covariant form under the special relativity metric is $-P$. Our notation is a trifle intractable here; we can say, if we like, that if

$$P^+ = ip_1 E_{15} + ip_2 E_{25} + ip_3 E_{35} + p_4 E_{45},$$

then
$$P^\circ = -ip_1 \tilde{E}_{15} - ip_2 \tilde{E}_{25} - ip_3 \tilde{E}_{35} - p_4 \tilde{E}_{45}$$

$$= -ip_1 E_{15} - ip_2 E_{25} - ip_3 E_{35} + p_4 E_{45}$$

provided that we realize that in doing so we are, for our momentary convenience, equating a 16×1 vector to a 4×4 matrix! Even more compact but equally more misleading unless clearly understood is the form
$$P^\circ = -\tilde{P}^+.$$

The extension of this argument to the ten-vectors is valid, and its extension to the sixteen-vectors a natural sequel.

In order to avoid further difficulties with notation we shall, from now on, assume (i) that the wave vectors ψ, χ,... are always contravariant while ϕ, ω,... are always covariant, (ii) that contravariant vectors are defined in column form and covariant vectors in row form. Then the space vectors $\psi^{**}\phi = \psi^{\dagger\dagger}\phi$, $\psi^{**}\omega = \psi^{\dagger\dagger}\omega$, etc., are contravariant; $-\phi^{\dagger\dagger}\psi$ is the covariant form of the former, and $\phi^{**}\psi$ is another, but different, covariant space vector. Alternatively, if we show the co- or contravariance explicitly we shall assume the $\dagger$ convention, so that $\phi^{\circ+}\psi = \phi^{\dagger\dagger}\psi$; then $\phi^{**}\psi$, if required, will be $\bar{\phi}^{\circ+}\bar{\psi} = \phi^{\circ+}\psi$. The advantage of this procedure is that all taking of conjugates is then shown explicitly and we can enjoy the validity of commutation in relations such as

$$(\psi^+)_\alpha ({}^\circ\phi)_\beta = (\phi^\circ)_\beta ({}^+\psi)_\alpha.$$

The object carrying the above momentum vector is considered in isolation, against a reference system of axes defined only theoretically. But in practice our actual reference systems are derived from a background which usually consists of other particles considered, either individually or on an average, as stationary. This approach predetermines a given time axis and a given space perpendicular to it, though not coordinates within this space. The densities of momenta in this three-space are given by the strain vector $S = PE_{45}$ and if the object, say by collision, has its proper-time axis rotated relatively to the given time axis, then if S is contravariant,

$$S^+ = RS^\dagger \tilde{R} = \begin{cases} RS^\dagger R \text{ if } E_{pq} \text{ is imaginary and the rotation hyperbolic,} \\ RS^\dagger R^{-1} \text{ if } E_{pq} \text{ is real and the rotation circular,} \end{cases}$$

or, if it is covariant,

$$S^\circ = \tilde{R}^{-1}SR^{-1} = \begin{cases} R^{-1}SR^{-1} \text{ if } E_{pq} \text{ is imaginary and the rotation} \\ \qquad\qquad \text{hyperbolic} \\ RSR^{-1} \text{ if } E_{pq} \text{ is real and the rotation circular.} \end{cases}$$

It will be noticed that the rotations are identical for P^+, P°, S^+, and S° when the rotation is circular—only the hyperbolic rotations expose the difference. This is natural, since E_{45} does not define the orientation of the space coordinates.

The reality condition for a momentum vector, P, is 'mechanical part real, electrical part imaginary'. On conversion into the strain vector $S = PE_{45}$, the six electrical symbols $E_{01},..., E_{05}, E_{16}$ become the six real symbols $E_{23},..., E_{04}, E_{45}$. It follows first that the coefficients in S are all imaginary—a simplification in itself—secondly (by 18.7.1 (c)), that S is Hermitian, and thirdly (by Chapter III), that if S factorizes it does so in the form $\bar{\psi}^{\dagger\dagger}\psi = \psi^{**}\psi$ (i.e. $\psi = \phi$). With P in standard form, but not otherwise, $S = iP$, so that if P factorizes, S does so; the standard form of P being one in which linear momentum components have been eliminated, this means that the form $\psi^{**}\psi$ is appropriate for describing the internal structure of a H-atom at rest. That most writers regard the Schrödinger equation as separable between the external and internal coordinates and the form $\psi^{**}\psi$ as applicable irrespective of external motion is simply due to the fact that the treatment is non-relativistic and Lorentz β-factors ignored.

If we plot all ten mechanical components of a strain vector as real coordinates in a euclidean ten-space, we call this space *phase space*. Its internal transformations can be broken down into a series of rotations in planes defined by pairs of axes. Then

(a) if the E-symbols of the pair contain a common suffix—are $E_{\mu\sigma}$ and $E_{\nu\sigma}$, for example—the rotation is $RS^\dagger R^{-1}$ with $R = \frac{1}{2}\exp E_{\mu\nu}\theta$. $E_{\mu\sigma}$ and $E_{\nu\sigma}$ are both imaginary, $E_{\mu\nu}$ is real and antisymmetrical so that $RS^\dagger R^{-1} = RS^\dagger\tilde{R}$,

(b) if the E-symbols do not contain a common suffix—are $E_{\mu\sigma}$ and $E_{\lambda\rho}$, for example—no rotation $RS^\dagger R^{-1}$ will link them, as we have seen. But the 'pseudo-rotation' $RS^\dagger R$ does so correctly, with $R = \frac{1}{2}\exp E_{\nu\tau}\theta$, and since $E_{\nu\tau}$ is imaginary and symmetrical, $RS^\dagger R = RS^\dagger\tilde{R}$.

Thus every $RS^\dagger\tilde{R}$ corresponds to an internal rotation of the ten-dimensional phase space. But $RS^\dagger\tilde{R}$ is an ordinary transformation of the strain vector. Thus strain vectors have this important property, which is not shared by momentum vectors—that their mechanical parts form an invariant subspace under the *complete* rotation group (e) of § 18.6.

The same double approach, of matrix and E-number languages, applies to tensors. The tensor T_{rs} of relativity theory (revised definition of § 15.5, consisting of terms representing density, density of momentum, and

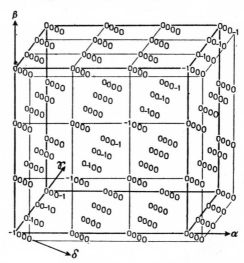

Fig. 34. The matrix $E_{16}F_{16}$.

pressure) is, if the quantum-relativistic units of § 15.8 are accepted, dimensionally the product of two momentum vectors. We assume that the extension of the momentum vector from four to ten and sixteen components remains valid, and we consider the outer product $T = P_1^{\dagger\dagger}P_2$ of two factorizable momentum vectors; the transformations we describe will apply equally well to sums of such tensors. The double approach now involves us, on the one hand, in fourth-rank wave tensors, with four greek suffixes, and, on the other, in a double E-algebra.

Taking the wave tensor approach first, we are no longer dealing with matrices but with 'double matrices' with 'rows, columns, piles, and tiers'. We have, if P_1 and P_2 are contravariant and factorizable,

$$T^{00} = P_1^{\dagger\dagger}P_2 = P_1^{++}P_2 = (\psi^{\dagger\dagger}\phi)^{\dagger\dagger}(\chi^{\dagger\dagger}\omega),$$

$$(T^{00})_{\alpha\beta\gamma\delta} = (P_1)_{\alpha\beta}(P_2)_{\gamma\delta} = \psi_\alpha\phi_\beta\chi_\gamma\omega_\delta.$$

(We write T^{00} instead of T^{rs} as the symbol for the whole tensor, and

$(T^{00})_{\alpha\beta\gamma\delta}$ for the element in the α row, β column, γ pile, and δ tier, which is the product of the α component of the first wave vector factor, the β component of the second, and so on. For the setting out of a double matrix, see Fig. 34.) In accordance with the considerations already stated concerning vectors, we shall have

$$T_0{}^0 = P_1{}^{+\circ}P_2 = -P_1^{\dagger\dagger}\tilde{P}_2 = -(\psi^{\dagger\dagger}\phi)^{\dagger\dagger}(\omega^{\dagger\dagger}\chi),$$

$$(T_0{}^0)_{\alpha\beta\gamma\delta} = -\psi_\alpha\,\phi_\beta\,\omega_\gamma\,\chi_\delta = -(T^{00})_{\alpha\beta\gamma\delta}.$$

Similarly,

$$(T^0{}_0)_{\alpha\beta\gamma\delta} = -(T^{00})_{\beta\alpha\gamma\delta}, \qquad (T_{00})_{\alpha\beta\gamma\delta} = (T^{00})_{\beta\alpha\delta\gamma}.$$

Thus raising and lowering indices is achieved by certain permutations of (greek) suffixes. There are twenty-four possible permutations, of course, but one-third of them are not space tensors but mixed strain tensors—e.g. $(\psi^{++}\chi)(\phi^{\circ}{}^{\circ}\omega)$ is one such. We can usefully tabulate the whole twenty-four according to (1) the order of the $^+$ and $^\circ$ signs, and (2) the order *within* the pairs (ψ, χ) and (ϕ, ω), thus:

TABLE 18.10.1

		$(\psi, \chi)(\phi, \omega)$		$(\chi, \psi)(\phi, \omega)$	$(\psi, \chi)(\omega, \phi)$	$(\chi, \psi)(\omega, \phi)$
Contravariant space tensor	+o+o	$T^{00} =$	$T^{00}_{\alpha\beta\gamma\delta}$	$T^{00}_{\gamma\beta\alpha\delta}$	$T^{00}_{\alpha\delta\gamma\beta}$	$T^{00}_{\gamma\delta\alpha\beta}$
Mixed space tensor	o++o	$T_0{}^0 =$	$T^{00}_{\beta\alpha\gamma\delta}$	$T^{00}_{\beta\gamma\alpha\delta}$	$T^{00}_{\delta\alpha\gamma\beta}$	$T^{00}_{\delta\gamma\alpha\beta}$
Mixed space tensor	+oo+	$T^0{}_0 =$	$T^{00}_{\alpha\beta\delta\gamma}$	$T^{00}_{\gamma\beta\delta\alpha}$	$T^{00}_{\alpha\delta\beta\gamma}$	$T^{00}_{\gamma\delta\beta\alpha}$
Covariant space tensor	o+o+	$T_{00} =$	$T^{00}_{\beta\alpha\delta\gamma}$	$T^{00}_{\beta\gamma\delta\alpha}$	$T^{00}_{\delta\alpha\beta\gamma}$	$T^{00}_{\delta\gamma\beta\alpha}$
Mixed strain tensor	++oo	$Z_0{}^0 =$	$T^{00}_{\alpha\gamma\beta\delta}$	$Z''_0 = T^{00}_{\gamma\alpha\beta\delta}$	$T^{00}_{\alpha\gamma\delta\beta}$	$T^{00}_{\gamma\alpha\delta\beta}$
Mixed strain tensor	oo++	$Z_0{}^0 =$	$T^{00}_{\beta\delta\alpha\gamma}$	$Z'_0 = T^{00}_{\beta\delta\gamma\alpha}$	$T^{00}_{\delta\beta\alpha\gamma}$	$T^{00}_{\delta\beta\gamma\alpha}$

The table gives (*a*) the term of T^{00} which is the $\alpha\beta\gamma\delta$ term of the new tensor, and (*b*) the symbol (if any) which is given by Eddington to the result.

From the E-algebra point of view, just as we proceeded from two quaternion algebras (of η-symbols and ζ-symbols) to sedenion algebra, and introduced new symbols, E-symbols, for the new basis elements, so to handle these tensors we pass from *two* sedenion algebras, one (of E-symbols) of which carries the first vector $\psi^{+\circ}\phi$, and the other (of 'F-symbols') of which carries the second vector $\chi^{+\circ}\omega$, to one '256-ion', or 'double-frame' algebra, with 256 EF-symbols (or, if we wish to emphasize the single character of the name, Ef-symbols), as basis elements. Note, however, that our purpose here is different from that in § 18.4, and we therefore allow each Ef^2_μ to remain as $+1$, no further i factors being introduced.

We assume the E_μ and the F_μ to have the same matrix representation, including the same chirality, and the same anchorage, so that a given transformation of physical axes corresponds to the same transformation in each. The Ef-frame is therefore suitable only for a pure space tensor. If

$$T^{00} = \sum_1^{256} t_\mu \, Ef_\mu = \sum_1^{16} \sum_1^{16} t^{pq} E_p \, F_q,$$

then

$$T_0^{\;0} = \sum t^{pq} \tilde{E}_p \, F_q, \qquad T^0_{\;0} = \sum t^{pq} E_p \, \tilde{F}_q, \qquad T_{00} = \sum t^{pq} \tilde{E}_p \, \tilde{F}_q.$$

The coefficients t^{pq} common to each of these will be numerically the same as the corresponding terms of the relativity energy tensor where these exist (p, $q = \mu 5$, $\nu 5$) but with an additional i or i^2 for momentum and pressure terms. The latter can be compensated by raising or lowering an index; t^{pq} as defined above is thus numerically and in sign equal to the corresponding term in the relativity *mixed* tensor $T_r^{\;s}$ for the one density and the nine pressure terms, equal to $\pm i$ times it for the six momentum terms, and has a further 240 terms (120 electrical and 120 mechanical) for which there are no counterparts. It is among the latter that the specifically atomic phenomena are to be sought.

An important link between the two approaches is the Ef-number $\Im = \frac{1}{4} \sum E_\mu F_\mu$ ($\mu = 1,...,16$), which is known as the interchange operator. For (with the same representation for the E- and F-algebras) it can be shown that

in $-T\Im$ the second and fourth (greek) suffixes are interchanged,

in $-\Im T$ the first and third (greek) suffixes are interchanged,

in $\Im T\Im$ both the above interchanges occur.

It can be verified that $\Im^2 = 1$, whence it is clear from the third of the above relations that

$$\Im(E_a \, F_b)\Im = \Im(E_a \, F_b)\Im^{-1} = E_b \, F_a,$$

so that this permutation is an interchange of the E- and F-frames and is also a change of coordinates. What is its interpretation? The two frames are all right as a mathematical dodge for obtaining the tensor, but what is their physical significance? When we write the momentum vector of a particle as $\sum p_a E_a$, instead of, say, $\sum p'_a E'_a$, where

$$E'_a = R E_a \, R^{-1},$$

the significance of the E-symbols is that we have already defined our reference frame. But the reference frame must be *physically* defined—

just as, for example, the reference frame in geography is not really an 'imaginary' set of lines but is defined partly by the rotation of the earth and partly by certain geographical landmarks such as the Greenwich observatory—and the physical definition of our reference frame could be, at the one extreme, another particle (one of the background particles), or at the other, the whole universe (the whole background—its C.G. as origin, etc.). The latter, being an average, has two outstanding advantages—first that its quantum uncertainties are all reduced by a factor $\sqrt{N}$, which we shall see to be of the order of 10^{39}, and, secondly, that the probability distribution of these uncertainties is necessarily Gaussian. The distinction between the E- and the F-frames thus implies that the frames used for the two vectors are thought of as different—different 'comparison particles' at the one extreme, but at the other—what? Possibly every physically significant Ef-number ought to be symmetrical between the two frames. But Eddington argues (even while accepting this suggestion for molar physics, where quantum theory does not enter) that even if the E- and F-frames may be the same frame, physically, they have to be distinguished because it is the frames that carry the label which 'we mentally chalk on the otherwise indistinguishable particles'. (The simplest particle with 256 (or 136 mechanical) degrees of freedom is usually considered as a combination of two particles.) Interchanging the frames is thus equivalent to interchanging ('becoming muddled about' if you like) the identity of the two particles—a characteristically quantum phenomenon. This interchange need not be complete; the rotation $e^{\frac{1}{2}\Im u}Te^{-\frac{1}{2}\Im u}$ with u real, is a physically real rotation in the sense of § 18.5, and corresponds to gradual interchange of the particles; it does not include complete interchange unless u is allowed to tend to infinity, since the rotation is hyperbolic. But as a degree of freedom of the system, similar to ignorable coordinates in general, it carries its quantum of momentum and contributes a term to the energy of the system which is usually recognized as the energy of Coulomb attraction.

The interchange operator factorizes

$$\Im = \tfrac{1}{2}(E_{23}F_{23}+E_{31}F_{31}+E_{12}F_{12}-1)\cdot\tfrac{1}{2}(E_{45}F_{45}+E_{50}F_{50}+E_{04}F_{04}-1),$$

the first factor being the operator already discussed in § 12.9.

Before considering strain tensors we must consider the Riemann–Christoffel tensor. Since we have abandoned curved *space*, regarding the 'curved metric' as distinctive only of *physical* measurement subject to the usual uncertainties (two equal centimetres, for example, being two portions of space containing equal numbers of the particles at the lattice points of the material of which our scale is made), it follows that the Riemann–Christoffel tensor must be given a *physical* and not a geometrical interpretation. Eddington starts from the second definition (at the end of § 15.6) of this tensor; if a vector is taken by parallel displacement round a closed path in a flat space it must end up parallel to its original direction, and if when compared with a physical reference frame it seems not to do so, this can only be because the physical frame has suffered recoil. Or, to put it another way, we say we adopt the mean of the whole universe as a reference, but when we single out a rotating body, for example, we perforce measure its angular momentum against the *rest* of the universe. But since action and reaction are equal and opposite, the recoil is as good as a direct measurement of the mechanical variables of the body. We thus reach the conclusion that the R.C. tensor should be the same thing as the energy tensor if properly interpreted. (This is an advance on the orthodox relativity theory, where this appears as a hypothesis, though an extremely well-grounded one.)

But these tensors would seem to be of different rank. (In Chapter XV we contracted the fourth-rank R.C. tensor before attempting to equate it, in any form, with the second-rank energy tensor.) However, a purely mechanical momentum vector consists of terms carrying the (roman) suffixes a,b attached to the symbol E_{ab}, where a, b run from 1 to 5; a tensor formed from two such vectors has four suffixes, therefore. Further, as $E_{ab} = -E_{ba}$, this tensor is antisymmetric in the members of each pair of suffixes. By the procedure of § 14.5 we can split this into two parts, symmetric and antisymmetric in the pairs as pairs, and we saw earlier in this section that a *molar* tensor may be expected to have the former symmetry already. These are just the symmetry properties of the R.C. tensor (which has a cyclic symmetry in addition to these). This means that in any of the forms R_{shkp}, R_{sh}^{kp}, R_{kp}^{sh}, or R^{shkp}, this tensor can be considered as a *second*-rank tensor in a suitable Ef-frame. This removes the difficulty in identifying these two tensors. But the whole concept of the R.C. tensor will be widened by the admission of the suffixes 0 and 5. These extensions have no geometrical significance, and have to be interpreted in terms of recoil. The most interesting of these extra terms are R_{45}^{45} and R_{05}^{05}, which are $-2/R_0^2$ (R_0 = radius of space curvature) and Λ, the 'cosmical constant' introduced in § 15.7. (It should be added that the condition of symmetry between the pairs is not universally applicable; when it is broken the situation links up with Weyl's extension of general relativity to include electromagnetic potentials, which also involves an unsymmetrical R.C. tensor.)

We turn now to the strains—the E- and Ef-numbers which represent something against, and therefore different from the background, and thus represent the *salient* features of the universe. In contrast to the vector situation, we have *two* methods of deriving a strain *tensor* from an energy tensor. Given $T = (\sum p_\mu E_\mu)(\sum p'_\mu E_\mu) = \sum t_\mu Ef_\mu$, we can convert each space vector into a strain vector giving, since E_μ and F_ν symbols commute, $Z_u = \sum t_\mu Ef_\mu E_{45} F_{45}$, or we can apply an appropriate permutation of the greek suffixes. Examination of Table 18.10.1 shows that (a) exchange of the second and fourth suffixes converts a mixed space tensor into a strain tensor, while (b) exchange of the second and third suffixes converts a pure space tensor into a strain tensor, leaving in each case the other type unchanged. Eddington calls these two transformed forms of the tensor the dual and the cross dual. The former transformation converts T into $Z_a = -T\mathfrak{I}$. The two strain tensors thus derived are not the same, and represent the system, according to Eddington, against different backgrounds. The former we have already discussed, and as $E_{45} F_{45}$, considered as a tensor itself, represents neutral stationary mass, and thus represents symbolically the background which defines the time axis for anchoring the frame, Eddington assumes that the latter strain tensor represents the space tensor T as a strain in a background composed of $-\mathfrak{I}$. But $-\mathfrak{I}$ is invariant under the Lorentz group, and is thus a background of (at most) radiation only (the velocity of which is invariant under Lorentz transformations). There are analogies to be drawn here (a) with the use of the Einstein (inertial) and de Sitter (empty) universes as backgrounds, (b) with the distinction between relativity, which is Lorentz invariant, and quantum theory, which defines a unique time axis, and (c) the anchoring of the coordinate system in matter or in the aether.

Eddington uses them all, and the process is too intricate to be summarized further. But it is a fascinating process, especially when he considers certain effects as that part of a tensor which refuses to melt into the appropriate background—like looking at a coloured pattern through a series of different coloured spectacles which vary in the parts of the pattern which they bring out and the parts they render invisible.

18.11. The cosmic number

Before concluding, we must return to the problem with which we opened. The number of protons and electrons in the universe enters physical theory in a number of ways. Thus, for example, just as a mathematically-minded ant crawling over the surface of one of the regular polyhedra could calculate, after observing *one* of the vertices, how many vertices there were, so, on the basis of general relativity, one should be able to calculate, from a knowledge of the kink in space-time which represents one hydrogen atom, how many of them there are altogether. The cosmic number also occurs in the relation quoted in § 18.6 between the natural scale of measurement and the radius of the universe. By assuming that if it were not for uncertainty the non-coulombian force between nuclear particles would be associated only with their coincidence, Eddington identifies the natural scale unit with the range constant of nuclear forces (to within a small numerical constant). Thirdly, a more elementary evaluation is possible by multiplying an estimate of the *mean* density of matter in the universe (by no means easy to arrive at) with an estimate of the total volume and dividing by the mass of a hydrogen atom. From these and other data (including the ratio of the electrical and gravitational forces between the proton and electron) this number is clearly of the general order of 10^{79}.

But the group-theoretical calculation is completely theoretical. We saw in §§ 18.3 and 18.7 that the simplest measurable is a particle with no internal strain and a comparison particle, and is a 16×16 matrix; the more general 'particle with internal strain' plus comparison particle giving rise to a 256×256 matrix. Measurement is an operation on a measurable, the results being the measure, but the measurable contains more than the measure—it contains the identity of the particle being measured. (This is independent of the Pauli principle. The coordinates of n electrons being $x_1, y_1, z_1, x_2, ..., z_n$, the coordinates of any one electron are three numbers, but these numbers are not usable information without the serial number of the electron as well; that the wave function changes sign on exchanging two electrons presupposes that 'exchange' of this sort has a meaning.)

Eddington's argument from this point is extremely obscure, but his result is clear enough and its numerical agreement with experiment too striking to ignore. Just as the general E-number is the sum of sixteen terms and can, by suitable choice of coordinate system, be reduced to the sum of four terms involving a commuting set of E-symbols, so the 256×256 matrix is the sum of 256^2 terms but can be reduced by suitable choice of coordinate system to the sum of 256 terms involving a commuting set of '$EFGH$-symbols'. With each of these, as well as the coefficients, a $+$ or $-$ sign can be associated, and these 2^{256} 'signatures' —Eddington calls them 'grid-numbers'—retain their distinctness throughout all relativity rotations. They thus fulfil the following requirements of an 'identity':

1. Invariance under all coordinate changes—the particle keeps its identity however we look at it.
2. Complete independence of the actual results—the particle keeps its identity wherever it is and whatever it is doing.
3. Discreteness—for a continuous variable, implying that identities could differ infinitesimally, would never do.

Even granting this, it is yet another jump to suppose that because we have 2^{256} labels we have 2^{256} objects to put them on. Eddington's own words here are 'Since there is one phase associated with each grid-number, an enumeration of the particles as distinguished in current theory by incoherent phase, should agree with our enumeration as distinguished by grid-numbers'. Finally, our estimates of this number from experimental data will differ from the simple 2^{256} by a k-factor of $\frac{3}{2} . 136$, so that the ultimate figure is $\frac{3}{2} . 136 . 2^{256}$, which is $2 \cdot 36216 \times 10^{79}$.

18.12. Conclusions

The review of Eddington's work contained in this chapter has been guided by the fact that its group-theoretic aspects are our primary interest. The k-factor theory lies outside this and has been kept to a minimum, in consequence of which insufficient stress has been laid on the numerical results of the theory, which are impressive. Assuming the values $c = 2 \cdot 99776 \times 10^{10}$ cm./sec., $R = 109677 \cdot 58$ cm.$^{-1}$, $F = 9753 \cdot 56$ e.m.u./gm. for the velocity of light, the Rydberg constant and the Faraday, instead of referring to the deposited standards of the centimetre, gramme, and second, he computes the masses of proton and electron, the electronic charge, Planck's constant, the nuclear range and energy constants, the constant of gravitation and the nebular recession constant, as well as others which these imply, and a number of nuclear mass defects, all of which (with the exception of one or two meson masses) agree remarkably with experimental results. Its success in explaining the qualitative features of the universe as we know it—

its three-space+one-time character, and so on, will already be apparent to the reader.

At the same time, there are jumps which can only be described as acts of faith. They vary from the very reasonable identification of the basic measurable with the hydrogen atom on the basis of the calculated internal-external particle mass ratio, to such assumptions as the way in which electrical-mechanical and real-imaginary bases are cross-linked, and the jumps in the calculation of the cosmic number. As regards the latter, Eddington himself says

> A logically complete demonstration, if it is possible, would be extremely prolix; and it is not the kind of problem I could myself attempt. But I shall try to show that at each stage the investigation is being driven by its own momentum—that the moves are forced . . . or at least there is so much pressure behind the moves that it is the result of the pressure that causes the universe to appear to us as it does.

And as regards the assignment of real and imaginary character to the basic vectors of the E-frame, more recent work by Milner has deepened the logical foundations of this, and other outstanding problems have been attacked by Kilmister.

An aspect which has received less consideration is the bearing of Eddington's theories on the building of a scientific philosophy. Nineteenth-century science ran on the momentum of its own success; despite the fact that the scientists themselves should have known it could not be true, it was unquestionably worth developing. It could not be true because it left no room for the scientist's own work, *everything* in it being deterministic and automatic. A universe which is required to contain thinking beings in it, must be one in which logic is possible, and therefore also mathematics and measurement. And therefore, it would appear, it must be a universe of three space dimensions and one time, appearing to those thinking beings to contain $\frac{3}{2}.136.2^{256}$ particles, and its physics must be of a certain kind. Since we know we are thinking beings it is satisfactory to find that the physics *is* of this kind. Eddington would have said, perhaps, that thinking beings would interpret *any* kind of universe in this way, the mind imposing the pattern on it. But no minds could impose anything on a Newtonian universe. This is not a scientific philosophy, but it is a much sounder basis for one than earlier science has been.

Of the nuclear physics I am not competent to judge. An eminent nuclear physicist has told me that *Fundamental Theory* is nonsense. He added that he had not read it. Rosenfeld's *Nuclear Forces* appeared at about the same time as *Fundamental Theory*. To an outsider it has the appearance of being both comprehensive and authoritative, but it consists of a series of well-developed theories, inconsistent with each other, and no one of which stands up particularly well to the test of comparison with experiment. There can have been few such confessions in the history of theoretical physics that a large and important branch of the subject is in such chaos. The extent of agreement with experiment in *Fundamental Theory* seems to be better than in any other *single* current theory.

It would seem that *Fundamental Theory* has suffered the fate of many comprehensive theories. One does not judge evolution mainly on its application to the spiders of North Africa, nor yet mainly on its application to the orchids of Western Australia, yet this is just what workers in these specialized fields are inclined to do. To the writer, the reception accorded to *Fundamental Theory* is reminiscent of that given to Newland's *Law of Octaves*. Here was the dawn of a new era in chemistry seen 'through a glass, darkly', and Newland's contemporaries seized on the 'darkliness' (of which there was plenty) and made it an excuse for refusing to see what, in a much more fully developed form, was to be a light illuminating the whole structure of inorganic chemistry. Today we condemn them, not for being dissatisfied with what was put before them, but because, when a light shone dimly, they called it darkness.

BIBLIOGRAPHY

EXCEPT as regards the sections on molecular orbitals, the works consulted have been on the whole texts and monographs, not original papers. Most of them are given in the list below, classified according to the subjects with which they deal, and a few references have been added which ought to have been consulted but unfortunately were not available at the time of writing. The latter are marked with an asterisk.

I. GENERAL

1. WEYL, *The Theory of Groups and Quantum Mechanics*. (English translation: Methuen, 1931.)
2. BHAGAVANTAM and VENKATARAYUDU, *Theory of Groups and its Application to Physical Problems*. (Andhra University, Waltair, India, 1948.)

   Both of these works deal with both the mathematics and the physics. The former is practically a bible, though the physics occasionally reveals its date. The latter is particularly of value for Raman and infra-red spectra and the tensor properties of crystals; its value in other directions is more dubious.

3. *WIGNER, *Gruppentheorie*. (Vieweg, Braunschweig, 1931.)
4. *VAN DER WAERDEN, *Gruppentheoretische Methoden in der Quantenmechanik*. (Springer, Berlin, 1932.)

II. MATRICES

5. AITKEN, *Determinants and Matrices*. (University Mathematical Texts.)
6. TURNBULL and AITKEN, *The Theory of Canonical Matrices*. (Blackie, 1948.)
7. FRAZER, DUNCAN, and COLLAR, *Elementary Matrices and their Engineering applications*. (Cambridge University Press, 1938.)

   None of these books deal with groups at all. The first two are mathematical and were the background for much of Chapter VII; the third is practical and numerical, and includes many of the applications of matrices in numerical form.

III. GROUP THEORY AND ALGEBRA

8. LEDERMANN, *Theory of Finite Groups*. (University Mathematical Texts.)
9. BAUMGARTNER, *Gruppentheorie*. (Sammlung Göschen No. 837, 1921.)

   These works deal with the structure of abstract finite groups but omit all reference to their representations.

10. LITTLEWOOD, *The Theory of Group Characters*. (Oxford University Press, 1952.)
11. MURNAGHAN, *The Theory of Group Representations*.

    Both of these works cover the same ground but with very different emphasis, Littlewood concentrating on finite groups and Murnaghan on the continuous ones. The latter should be consulted to supplement our meagre treatment of integration over the group manifold.

12. LITTLEWOOD, *The Skeleton Key of Mathematics*. (Hutchinson's University Library.)
13. VAN DER WAERDEN, *Moderne Algebra*. (Berlin.)
14. WEYL, *The Classical Groups*. (Princeton.)
15. CHEVALLY, *The Theory of Lie Groups*.

> The first of these is an elementary, though condensed, presentation of abstract algebra. The other three were consulted in writing parts of Chapter XII, but they really have little to do with any of the present applications of group theory, and are very difficult reading for the non-mathematician.

16. *SPEISER, *Theorie der Gruppe von endlicher Ordnung*. (Springer, Berlin, 1927.)

> Probably the best single, reasonably simple, account of finite groups.

17. RUTHERFORD, *Substitutional Analysis*. (Edinburgh University Press, 1948.)

> A study of the algebra of the symmetric groups.

IV. HILBERT SPACE AND ALLIED FIELDS

18. STONE, *Linear Transformations in Hilbert Space*. (American Mathematical Colloquium Publications.)
19. TITCHMARSH, *Eigenfunction Expansions*. (Oxford University Press.)

> The former is very abstract in presentation but is a source for answering questions on rigour. The latter involves analyses of situations of the type that occur in solving the Schrödinger equation. The electrical applications of the Laplace transform are dealt with in an elementary fashion in, for example:

20. TROPPER, *Electrical Circuit Theory*,

> and the mathematical side is dealt with more rigorously in:

21. *PALEY and WIENER, *Fourier Transformations in the Complex Domain*. (American Mathematical Colloquium Publications, vol. xix, 1934.)
22. TRANTER, *Integral Transforms in Mathematical Physics*. (Methuen Monographs, 1951.)
23. JAEGER, *The Laplace Transformation*. (Methuen Monographs.)

V. CRYSTALLOGRAPHY

24. LONSDALE, *Crystals and X-rays*. (G. Bell & Son, 1948.)
25. ZACHARIASEN, *The Theory of X-ray Diffraction in Crystals*. (Wiley, and Chapman & Hall, 1945.)
26. PHILLIPS, *Introduction to Crystallography*.
27. BRAGG, *The Crystalline State*. (Vol. i, Bell, 1934, and *Vol. ii.)

> None of these except the last covers the whole field. Zachariasen's is the only book in current use to present the space group theory and he does so in an obsolete and difficult mathematical form. Mrs. Lonsdale's is easier on the theory and fuller on experimental methods and on the reciprocal lattice. Only Phillips treats the various structures seriatim.

28. *International Tables for the Determination of Crystal Structure*. (Kynoch Press, vol. i, 1951.)

> The specialist's reference book on the space groups.

VI. FACTOR ANALYSIS

29. THOMSON, *Factorial Analysis of Human Ability.*
30. BURT, *The Vectors of the Mind.*
31. HOLZINGER and HARMAN, *Factor Analysis.* (University of Chicago Press.)
32. WEATHERBURN, *Mathematical Statistics.* (Cambridge University Press, 1949.)
33. RAO, *Advanced Statistical Methods in Biometric Research.* (Wiley.)

VII. TENSOR AND RELATIVITY THEORY

34. TOLMAN, *Relativity, Thermodynamics and Cosmology.* (Clarendon Press, 1934.)
35. HAAS, *Introduction to Theoretical Physics.* (Constable, 1929.)
36. SCHOUTEN, *Tensor Analysis for Physicists.* (Clarendon Press, 1951.)
37. EDDINGTON, *Mathematical Theory of Relativity.* (Cambridge University Press, 1923.)
38. McVITTIE, *Cosmological Theory.* (Methuen Monographs, 1937.)

The second of these is a leisurely elementary introduction to both subjects. The first is but one of many accounts of relativity but is probably the most useful reference work on the subject. The third will be found unreadable unless the reader is already well acquainted with the basic concepts and simpler applications of the subject, but it is an invaluable reference work on questions of rigour once orthonormal cartesians are left behind.

VIII. QUANTUM THEORY AND MOLECULAR STRUCTURE

39. DIRAC, *Principles of Quantum Mechanics.* (Clarendon Press, 1947.)
40. TEMPLE, *The General Principles of Quantum Theory.* (Methuen Monographs, 1933.)
41. PAULING and WILSON, *Introduction to Quantum Mechanics.* (McGraw-Hill, 1935.)
42. *v. NEUMANN, *Mathematische Grundlagen der Quantenmechanik.* (Springer, Berlin, 1932.)
43. CORSON, *Perturbation Methods in the Quantum Mechanics of n-electron Systems.* (Blackie, 1951).

The first two of these were consulted in the discussion of the foundation equations of quantum theory, and the first and third for the standard treatment of perturbation theory, etc. These subjects are also treated in Corson, which is the most recent of these works, and which also includes some more specifically group-theoretic treatment. Pauling and Wilson also deal with the earlier work on molecular structure, and their treatment was supplemented from the following original papers.

44. BETHE, *Ann. der Physik*, (5) **3** (1929), 133.
45. MULLIKEN, *Phys. Rev.* **43** (1933), 279.
46. VAN VLECK, *J. Chem. Phys.* **1** (1933), 177.
47. KIMBALL, ibid. **8** (1940), 188.

48. LENNARD JONES, *Proc. Roy. Soc.* A **198** (1949), 1.
49. ROOTHAAN, *Rev. Mod. Phys.* **23** (1951), 69.

> NOTE: Many of the above papers are No. 1 in a series. But in most cases the subsequent papers go on to quantitative calculations which come outside the strictly group-theoretic purview. Of historical interest in this connexion are:

50. SIDGWICK, *The Electronic Theory of Valency.* (Oxford University Press, 1929);
51. SIDGWICK, *The Covalent Link in Chemistry.* (Cornell University Press, 1933);
52. PAULING, *The Nature of the Chemical Bond.* (Cornell University Press and Oxford University Press, 1940);

> and for the existence and stability of given compounds, especially when details of molecular structure are in question, see

53. SIDGWICK, *The Chemical Elements and their Compounds.* (Two Volumes, Clarendon Press, 1950.)

IX. SPECTROSCOPY

54. JOHNSON, *Atomic Spectra.* (Methuen Monographs, 1950);
55. JOHNSON, *Introduction to Molecular Spectra.* (Methuen, 1949);
56. *HERZBERG, *Molecular Spectra and Molecular Structure, I, Diatomic Molecules.* (Prentice Hall, 1939);
57. HERZBERG, *Infra-red and Raman Spectra.* (Vol. ii of former work.) (Van Nostrand, 1945);

> and a number of the papers listed in the previous section and some of their sequels.

X. FUNDAMENTAL THEORY

58. *EDDINGTON, *The Relativity Theory of Protons and Electrons.*
59. EDDINGTON, *Fundamental Theory.* (Cambridge University Press, 1948.)
60. MILNER, *Proc. Roy. Soc.* A **214** (1952), 292 and 312.
61. KILMISTER, ibid. A **199** (1949), 517; A **207** (1951), 402; and A **212** (1952), 559.

XI. ITEMS ADDED IN PROOF

17a. DAVID and KENDALL, *Biometrika*, **36** (1949), 431–49; **38** (1951), 435–62; and **40** (1953), 427–46.

> Tables of the decomposition of products of symmetrical functions up to weight 12.

19a. CARSLAW and JAEGER, *Operational Methods in Applied Mathematics* (Oxford University Press, 2nd edn. 1947).
19b. COOKE, *Infinite Matrices and Sequence Spaces.* (Macmillan, 1950.)
         Linear Operators. (Macmillan, 1953.)
20a. GOLDMAN, *Transformation Calculus and Electrical Transients.* (Prentice Hall, Inc., or Constable, 1949.)
20b. BERG, *Heaviside's Operational Calculus.* (McGraw-Hill, 1936.)
28a. BRILLOUIN, *Wave Propagation in Periodic Structures.* (Dover Publications, Inc., 2nd edn. 1953.)
38a. HUNTLEY, *Dimensional Analysis.* (Macdonald, 1952.)

Recent papers on 'crystal orbitals' include the following, from which other references may be obtained.

53 a. KOHN and ROSTOCKER, *Phys. Rev.* **94** (1954), 1111.

SLATER and KOSTER, ibid., 1498.

HALL, *Proc. Phys. Soc.* A **66** (1953), 1162.

INDEX

PRINTED IN
GREAT BRITAIN
AT THE
UNIVERSITY PRESS
OXFORD
BY
CHARLES BATEY
PRINTER
TO THE
UNIVERSITY